SEMIOTEXT(E) INTERVENTION SERIES

© 2015 by Jennifer Doyle

Published by Semiotext(e)
PO BOX 629, South Pasadena, CA 91031
www.semiotexte.com

Design: Hedi El Kholti

ISBN: 978-1-58435-169-6
Distributed by The MIT Press, Cambridge, Mass.
and London, England
Printed in the United States of America

Jennifer Doyle

Campus Sex

Campus Security

semiotext(e)
intervention
series □ 19

Contents

Prologue

Headlines conjure the university as a place where idealism is cultivated and destroyed. Students head off to college and become fodder for the campus scandal. They are raped, enslaved to student loans and beaten by the police. A cloud of outrage and anxiety hangs over the campus.

This book is about campus security as a structure of feeling. It is about the campus's soft underbelly.

In 2010, after more than a decade of working as a faculty member at a large public university, I came to know campus security intimately, as an apparatus and as a structure of feeling. I filed a complaint against a student via our campus Title IX office (which administers, among other things, complaints of sexual harassment). I did so at the request of my university's administration, to whom I'd appealed for help as this student had initiated an intense campaign of harassment and stalking. A few months later I would file a secondary complaint, regarding the way the first was handled. Over the nearly two years it took to administer my "case," I had direct experience with how the administrative structures ostensibly designed to protect the integrity of a campus produce the campus as a conflict zone.

This essay is not about that student, that crisis, or even what I went through. It is, rather, an attempt to share what I learned.

I share here, as a point of entry into this essay, one detail from my case that emblematizes how university security logics operate. When the student's behavior moved into the neighborhood of threat, my campus hired a security consultant to meet with my landlord, in order to "harden" my apartment. These men dreamed up a walled compound in the name of my safety. This security consultant also met with the chair of my department, and presented her with instructions preparing my colleagues for the possibility that the student harassing me might show up at our office with a gun. When I talked to the campus Risk Management Officer, my landlord, and the various men working on the case, I could feel the pleasure they took from these "solutions" and their surprise that I would refuse them. They meant well enough, but the swell of good feeling produced in the name of my security was hardly in my interest.

It was hard, then, to explain to the administrators handling my case that I did not want ramparts built around me. Not only because being so confined is a terrible way to live; the walls dreaméd up by university administrators and their consultants had the aspect of the madness that was the engine of the problem. My situation would become even stranger when, in a university hearing, my scholarship (which is feminist, queer, and about sexual politics) was treated by faculty as evidence of sexual impropriety. Writing about *Moby Dick* and *Jude the Obscure*, a syllabus from a queer theory class, and essays on abortion and promiscuity supported the committee's conclusion that I was not, in fact, being harassed. A mortified administrator told me that the hearing was the longest student disciplinary hearing on record at my campus. It was long because on some level, the committee dined on the misery of my situation as the sensational story of a "feminist accused of harassment."

My relationship to the campus was permanently altered by this experience. I have tried here to describe what you see and feel, as a campus citizen, when you've been through that kind of administrative trauma.

As I sifted through the long wake of my own ordeal, students across the state of California were being beaten by the police and threatened with criminal prosecution for their expressions of dissent.

Seated, nonviolent protesters at U.C. Davis were soaked with PepperSpray. The police dragged non-violent protesters at U.C. Berkeley by their hair, and rammed batons into their sides. Students at U.C. Irvine, speaking out against Israel's occupation of Palestine, were prosecuted in criminal court. We rarely talk about these abuses of power and authority as connected to the shape of sexism on college campuses, but we must.

In January 2012, a student of mine showed up to class with a bleeding gash, a wound delivered to the shin by police who pushed a demonstration against rising tuition into an assault. I had been at that demonstration earlier in the day, I stood next to this student for at least an hour before we were separated by the flow of the crowd. That evening, I would learn that a long-time faculty member was arrested at that demonstration, and charged with assault with a deadly weapon—the deadly weapon in question was the sign he had been holding. We had walked to the demonstration together, and I'd stood behind him for the better part of the afternoon. The campus press office did not identify him as faculty—instead, in the news, he was described as "an older man" from outside the campus community. Not only had he been thrown to the ground and arrested—his status as a member of the campus community was disavowed, as if his decade of teaching experience could be erased. We've had years of this.[1]

In 2013 I wrote and published a pamphlet about campus security: but "Campus Security" addressed only half of the problem.

The university has lost its collective mind. The madness of the apparatus is one reason the campus administration handled my own case so badly: it was incapable of recognizing the psychosis at the heart of the situation. A student's experience of their own vulnerability translated into a campaign of harassment—how is that not the character of the university's experience of its own precarity? Its sense of impending doom, to which it responds with a militarization of all of its processes.

Boundaries are being violated: walls need to be shored up. A pervasive sense of vulnerability yields a constant state of crisis—the building of one set of walls, and then another.

I write this essay not to break through these walls, but rather to describe them, to describe their shape. To describe what it feels like to live with them.

This essay is about the administration of harassment complaints, and the practice of administration as itself a form of harassment. It is an attempt to share, in my writing, what the university, as an organism, *feels*.

This portrait is fragmented. I hold Title IX and the discourse of campus rape to one side, and stories about the brutality of campus policing to another. I shuffle awkwardly back and forth between them. I resist letting the problem of the administration of sexual harassment flow seamlessly into the story of police violence. This is my way of drawing out the connections between these stories, while also resisting the system that enlists one in the service of the other.

Stories of campus sexual assault and stories about police violence on college campuses have different shapes. We have remarkable access to the details of police violence, when that violence happens on the campus of a public university. The stories of specific beatings, specific disasters, are accessible through an archive of investigative reports. The rape victim, in contrast, is an anonymized figure, a rumor and an abstraction. Where the person beaten by campus police appears in the news with a name and a face, the rape victim is rendered into an anywoman who might as well be every woman.

One figure whispers to the other, through cracks in the campus wall.

Campus Sex, Campus Security

Let us begin with the image of a man at work. The image of a campus scandal.

A police officer waters demonstrators with a jet of pepper spray.

A policeman and his pepper spray; students with their hoods up, stunned and slumped forward; a crowd of people watching. Recording.

On November 18, 2011, during the season of the Occupy Movement, the University of California Police Department at UC Davis assembled its troops to break up a camp recently established by students protesting endless increases in college tuition. A psychology student at Davis took this photograph of Sergeant John C. Pike at work. She was close enough to get pepper spray on her jeans. She posted the image on Facebook. It had explanatory power: it migrated to Reddit and went viral.

Photo credit: Louise Macabitas

The image speaks of the co-existence of professionalism and incompetence. Something is wrong. Everything is normal.

The students were not violent; they were not breaking any rule. They had merely gathered on their campus—a campus is, by definition, a place where people gather. Why were the police there? Why did the police use force? And why *this* force? Who is responsible?

Every aspect of this incident would be reviewed in at least two separate investigations: a confidential internal investigation produced by the police department, and a public external investigation produced by Kroll Securities, which was hired by the University of California Office of the President after photographs and video of this incident drew national attention.

Kroll Security's report on "the pepper spray incident" tells us that campus police had been sent there by the university's Chancellor, Linda Katehi. In an interview with Kroll investigators, Katehi explained that the administration was worried about "non-affiliates" on campus. Non-affiliates from Oakland.

> We were worried at the time about that [non-affiliates] because the issues from Oakland were in the news and the use of drugs and sex and other things, and you know here we have

very young students . . . we were worried especially about having very young girls and other students with older people who come from the outside without any knowledge of their record . . . if anything happens to any student *while we're in violation* of policy, it's a very tough thing to overcome.[2]

On the surface of her testimony, the Chancellor worries that Occupy Davis might turn into Occupy Oakland. A metonymic chain of associations accumulates (Oakland [black people], drugs, sex, young girls, older people, outsiders, violation) to bring the Chancellor to her fear: "older people from outside" interacting with "very young girls."

The administration's paranoid rape fantasy mirrors the geometry of the university community itself—what is a campus but older people, working with younger people?

The fear that "anything" might "happen" is haunted by another worry: the possibility that the campus itself is always already "in violation" ("if anything happens to any student while we're in violation"), that violation is in fact embedded into the campus, as a part of its structure. The administration worries about that which makes rape imaginable.

The administration's fear of being "in violation" repeats across Kroll's report, as the explanation for a series of bad decisions. For example: the administration insisted that the police be deployed to take down a student encampment in the middle of the day, instead of in the middle of the night—which is when police generally prefer to do such things:

> The idea of non-students being on the campus in tents led the Leadership Team to fears of criminal activity in general and potential sexual assault specifically.[3]

If the administration worried about sexual assault, it was through the lens of its sense of responsibility to its conditions of possibility.

This worry wraps itself around the worry about what happens to "very young girls" on a college campus: The Chancellor was worried about being "in violation" of Title IX, federal legislation that bans sex discrimination in all educational institutions receiving federal funding. Anxiety about the university's legal exposure, especially where sex is concerned (in all senses of that word "sex"), registers on every campus as a background hum.

"If anything happens to any student"—this diffuse anxiety spreads across the entire student body, as an object of concern. Students mirror it back: "if anything happens to us!" It perfectly expresses the institution's conservative nature as an administrative organism, its fear of and fascination with that which "happens."

> The Chancellor was concerned that Friday night was a "party night" and that the encampment might "become a place for fun [and] the use of alcohol and drugs and everything."[4]

Eventually this photograph and the reports that index the image are slipped into a file. The scandal of the incident dissolves over time, replaced by new headlines. The file is dropped into a cabinet, with other files. An infinite, expanding library. Photos, video archived on Youtube. Independent investigations and reports. White papers and memos. PowerPoint presentations, with their recommendations for change. Something went wrong, something shouldn't have happened. A filing cabinet of embarrassments and outrages. Anything and everything.

Let us begin again, then, with the story of a violated girl. A different campus scandal. A different kind of investigation.

Rolling Stone's November 2014 article, "A Rape on Campus," grabbed national headlines—how could it not? Its opening paragraphs seduce the reader with the story of a fraternity gang rape:

> "Want to go upstairs, where it's quieter?" Drew shouted into her ear, and Jackie's heart quickened. She took his hand as he threaded them out of the crowded room and up a staircase.[5]

The victim is eager and naïve. She is a "good girl." ("She'd congratulated herself on her choice of a tasteful red dress with a high neckline.") The writing is pornographic ("as the last man sank into her").

The titillating details are offered to the reader as sensational evidence of the epidemic of campus rape. Kirby Dick's 2015 documentary on the subject is thus titled *Hunting Ground*—to remind us that, after all, the campus is where rapists go to school.

Sabrina Rubin Erdely, the author of "A Rape on Campus," had been hunting for rape victims, in order to animate her report on university responses to harassment accusations. She had heard tell of this particular violation—a fraternity gang rape—from a campus activist at the University of Virginia. Erdely interviewed this victim-with-a-good-story, as well as activists working on the issue of sexual assault on campus. But the writer did not interview any of the accused, or witnesses. And her editors did not notice. This lapse in due diligence led to the story's second life, as evidence of another scandal: the victim lied. A plot twist, special to the special victims of *Law & Order*.[6]

Rolling Stone ignored basic protocols of journalism in its reporting of explosive accusations against not only the fraternity named in the story, but against a distinguished university which, as it happens, was, at the time, under investigation by the federal government for Title IX violations.[7]

A few weeks after *Rolling Stone* published "A Rape on Campus," journalists working at *The Washington Post* uncovered just enough information to suggest that the lead victim—the woman through whose eyes the entire story is reported—had concocted the gang rape story. Other writers deduced that this might have been an attempt to win sympathy and affection of a male friend who had rejected her romantic advances. Perhaps she produced herself as a victim in order to make herself appealing. Perhaps she narrated herself as violated in order to give her life a story.

The victim, in other words, is indeed a vulnerable person—desperate, delusional, perhaps the victim of a different kind of assault—the story of which she could not put into words. The violated girl, the lying girl, the vulnerable girl—the reviled girl. The object of anger and contempt.

The story of false accusation replaced the story of fraternity gang rape. The magazine staff shrugged, *whatever*. So what if the victim is crazy? Who cares if the story centered on a fantasy? Who cares, really, about what women say. For that matter, who cares about what women write? For *Rolling Stone*'s editorial staff, the story of sexual violence and sexual coercion is a good story, but not a *real* story. Popular misogyny and popular feminism: a snake eating its tale.

Rolling Stone editors apologized and handed the problem to the Columbia University's School of Journalism. Faculty investigated the story, and then wrote a report that indexed failures at every level of the story's production (investigation, writing, editing and fact-checking).[8] This report was discussed for a few days by the national media, and then filed away.

Title IX, a 1972 amendment to the Higher Education Act (HEA), governs how a college campus in the United States responds to accusations of sexual discrimination, harassment, and assault.[9] Title IX is civil anti-discrimination law designed to bar sex/gender discrimination in education. Insofar as sexual assault is a gendered form of violence, insofar as an assault on a college campus may create a hostile environment for a victim, insofar as a university depends on federal funding, it has an obligation to the state to work towards a rape and harassment-free community.

Within this framework, where an accusation of sexual assault is concerned, a university's obligation is not to determine if a crime has happened. It is to determine if someone's rights have been or are likely to be violated.

Like the Higher Education Act that it amends, Title IX is meant to make more things possible for more people. But the social mobility that it enables is shadowed by a negative sense of possibility.

Title IX shapes the university's experience of its own vulnerability. A university that obeys the letter of the law is "compliant"; a university that does not is "non-compliant." The non-compliant university is "in violation," and vulnerable to fines and lawsuits.[10]

Title IX's importance to a university's sense of security provides the infrastructure for the Davis Chancellor's worry that something might "happen" to the "very young girl" while the campus was "in violation." Rape discourse on the college campus has shifted dramatically: "In the 1980s and 1990s," Rachel Hall observes, "the paternalistic myth of women's vulnerability donned the neoliberal cloak of risk management."[11] Nowhere is this more in evidence than in the presentation of the college campus as a dangerous place for the "very young girl." That endangered girl is everywhere in this story, and nowhere. She is real and she is imagined.

Title IX is the administrative structure through which the university knows what exposure feels like, what vulnerability *is*.

It is the sex of bureaucracy.

If the 2011–2012 school year was the year of the Occupy Movement for student activists, it was, for universities across the United States, the year of risk management. The previous spring, just as schools were moving into the summer, the Department of Education sent a "Dear Colleague" letter to administrators across the nation. The letter maps out the department's thinking regarding the enforcement of Title IX (which was, by then, nearly forty years old). It advocates for new standards in campus adjudication of complaints about assault and harassment, and it associates a discrimination-free campus with a campus that "feels safe." In mapping a campus's federal obligations, it also maps the requirements for a federal complaint. This letter is the reason campus rape is in the news.

The letter opens with a straightforward summary of the basic principals of Title IX:

Dear Colleague:

Education has long been recognized as the great equalizer in America. The U.S. Department of Education and its Office for Civil Rights (OCR) believe that providing all students with an educational environment free from discrimination is extremely important. The sexual harassment of students, including sexual violence, interferes with students' right to receive an education free from discrimination and, in the case of sexual violence, is a crime.

Title IX of the Education Amendments of 1972 (Title IX), 20 U.S.C. §§ 1681 *et seq.*, and its implementing regulations, 34 C.F.R. Part 106, prohibit discrimination on the basis of sex in education programs or activities operated by recipients of Federal financial assistance. Sexual harassment of students, which includes acts of sexual violence, is a form of sex discrimination prohibited by Title IX.

The letter goes on to describe the college campus as in crisis:

The statistics on sexual violence are both deeply troubling and a call to action for the nation. A report prepared for the National Institute of Justice found that about 1 in 5 women are victims of completed or attempted sexual assault while in college. The report also found[12] that approximately 6.1 percent of males were victims of completed or attempted sexual assault during college. According to data collected under the Jeanne Clery Disclosure of Campus Security and Campus Crime Statistics Act (Clery Act), 20 U.S.C. § 1092(f), in 2009, college campuses reported nearly 3,300 forcible sex offenses as defined by the Clery Act. This problem is not limited to college. During the 2007–2008 school year, there were 800 reported incidents of rape and attempted rape and 3,800 reported incidents of other sexual batteries at public high schools. Additionally, the likelihood that a woman with intellectual disabilities will be sexually assaulted is estimated to be significantly higher than the general population. The Department is deeply concerned about this problem and is committed to ensuring that all students feel safe in their school, so that they have the opportunity to benefit fully from the school's programs and activities.[13]

It is hard to overstate the impact of this nineteen-page document. From the citation of the alarming (but also disputed) statistics on the frequency of sexual assault to the naming of "feeling safe" as a benchmark for measuring equity and feeling "unsafe" as a sign of violation, the letter describes the college campus as in a state of sexual emergency. In the following months, universities were put on notice regarding their responsibilities to potential and actual victims: the Assistant Secretary for the Office of Civil Rights in the Department of Education, addressing worried school administrators, explained: "There is no safe harbor. If you satisfy the law, then you have safe harbor. If you don't, you don't. We're not considering a middle ground."[14]

The campus is defined as a safe place; the campus is defined as in danger. The campus is a pure space, and so each instance of sexual violence appears as an absolute outrage, a betrayal and an affirmation of rape's ubiquity. The campus promises safety, security. To see that promise through, it must police and expel. It must establish a procedure and manage its risk.

The Davis Chancellor's decision to call out the troops on November 18, 2011 was shaped by the affective economy of a security culture in which a sense of injury and exposure revolves around sexual possibility—a possibility with the organizing force of a black hole. It is an unknowable thing because no one wants to know, really, any of this "anything."

The unknowing young girl. The young girl, and the unknown. The unknowable and the uncontrollable must be expelled.

The university administrator surfs a wave of institutional insecurity.

The process of administering sexual assault complaints on a college campus rolls along a Mobius strip. One thing (a crime) flips into another (a violation) and back again. The criminal and the civil converge, usually in the form of a hearing that mimics the rituals of a court. Secret committees and secret reports. Sanctions and appeals. It is a staple scene in episodes of *Law & Order*: a violated student testifies in court—tears streaming down her face as she complains about the failure of campus justice. "And then my rapist *graduated*," she (the character is almost always a woman) stammers, as if *this* were the worst thing, as if his degree was the real crime. The jury nods in agreement. (The sex offender should not go to school!)

But of course, most cases of sexual assault never make it to any court. Most victims of sexual coercion never file a complaint of any kind. (There are so very many kinds of coercion.)

Most people, including most university Deans, Chancellors, and Presidents, do not know what a Title IX complaint *is*.

On a college campus, Title IX investigations, student conduct committees and expulsion hearings promise to administer and redistribute injury for the minority that does come forward with a complaint. These investigations and reports attempt to absorb and contain all that sex, and sexual disaster, lets loose into the world. And as is the way of sex and power, when they are drawn together into administrative procedures and processes, the relationship between the two becomes more distorted, more disorienting and tortured. And the victim is the engine of this administrative trouble. *She* (again, always *she*) is a walking *situation*. This is her appeal: at risk, she is risk itself.

That 'she' causes trouble b/c she raises awareness of trouble ?

Once she makes a complaint, this risk is now escalated, and played out in a new dimension: it is often *retaliation* that is the university's real trouble. File a complaint and you may find yourself managing not only the original harassment—you might be removed from your classes, forced to move from your dorm, pushed to drop out by the cruelty of your peers. This, legally, is the zone of the retaliation complaint.

Retaliation, for the university, is a beast: it is often far easier for a victim to demonstrate a case of retaliation than the original complaint. A Title IX complaint, when poorly administered, will take on a mind-numbing fractal complexity—it will grow, and replicate itself in complaints about complaints. Each of its details will take on the aspect of the entire system.

The *idea* of Title IX has intense rhetorical effects: it gives body to an affective economy. The campus adopts a psychic identification with the scene violation, in which the university might be, like the paranoid psychotic who threatens because he feels threatened, both "in violation" but also *violated*—the criminal who projects criminal intention everywhere. The campus is the scene of violation. A fantasy space.

The campus. The co-ed. The rapist. The raped.

In the psychic space of the campus they become each other. One conjures the other, as a risk. The campus becomes, within the contemporary discourse of rape, the place where rape happens.

Thus the shape of the Chancellor's worry, which displaces the imagined victim's violation with an injury to the campus itself: "if anything happens to any student while we're in violation of policy, it's a very tough thing to overcome." Not for the "young girl" in question, but for the university itself. And yet the university, always already "in violation," is, here, the violator. The university might be violated, in other words, because it is always already violating.

The campus, the public feels, is asking for it. And so we elect another generation of publicly educated legislators who starve the university of public funding. A disciplinary action.

Administrators deploy force in the breaking up of a peaceful student demonstration against rising tuition and plummeting state investment. They do so in the name of sexual security; they do so with the aim of managing the possibility that an overnight camp-out might lead to contact between "affiliates" and "non-affiliates," to penetration of the inside by the outside, to an accusation and lawsuit in which the defendant is not the rapist, but the university.

Campus sex (as the condition of possibility for campus rape) haunts campus security discourse.[15] The tents at UC Davis must be removed, thinks the administrator. We must make the campus safe, in case anything should happen. They must be removed before the sun goes down.

Victims of sexual assault, harassment and intimate partner violence are encouraged to report. A minority file complaints and try to see the process through: doing so takes material and emotional resources. Few will tell you that this process provides resolution. There is no policy adequate to these crises. Victims report because they need help; a campus receives reports because it is bound by law to do so. This asymmetry warps their interaction.

The filing of a complaint often leads to the filing of more complaints—counter-complaints and complaints about the complaint process.

One finds oneself filing complaints with the hope that the complaint will force the campus to hire more investigators, more administrators. More boots on the ground. Complaint prevention officers, compliance review managers, a Vice Provost for Administrative Solutions.

The administrative processes that mushroom around a case infuses one's daily routine with the assaultive. One writes long emails, memos, and letters recounting, over and over again, what happened. One inventories one's pain, outlines one's confusion and frustration, usually in a context in which one does not know if one has been heard, acknowledged, believed.

One gets used to not being heard. One either clams up, or speaks like a hysteric—a repulsive verbal diarrhea spreads over every conversation. One has trouble finishing sentences. They go on, they are interrupted. They break off.

I see this in others; I see this in myself. Students, staff, faculty—sucked into the vortex of an administrative engine.

People turn to these processes looking for some form of relief. But few of these processes are designed to do so. Even in the best-case assault scenarios (which are worst-case scenarios, in which power differentials are clear; in which assaults are physically violent; in which the injury to the victim is visible), available mechanisms (criminal, civil) are brutal, if not, as they say, "re-traumatizing."[16]

We forget the limit of Title IX: it is not concerned with justice; it is concerned with equity. Have you been violated? Or was it your rights?

Sharon Marcus observes that victims of sexual violence are encouraged to "identify with a state that does not elaborate our subjectivity but denies it."[17] Perhaps this is why so many women faculty who are harassed-but-not-fired end up working in administration—taking on the project of faculty welfare, high-level administrative work (but rarely the kind of labor associated with leadership). We become handmaidens, of a sort, to the very system we hate.

Our encounters with these processes introduce us to another level of betrayal—one hard-wired and systemic, one in which we are betrayed by our own affective investment in an ideological apparatus like "school" or "the justice system."[18]

"In the criminal justice system," feminists observe, "charges are brought in the name of the state."[19] The criminal process is not victim-centered. It is notoriously flawed where gender-based crime is concerned. Police, judges, prosecutors and juries are often (almost always) biased. Studies on the benefits of pursuing criminal complaints are mixed: for those who take their cases to court, it can take longer to heal. At the heart of an assault is a moment of coercion in which one's desire to be left alone is not only ignored—it is actively re-written as not what you "really" wanted. That same discourse regarding what you may or may not have wanted is mobilized by the defense. One ends up repeating "no" in a hostile context, in which that "no" is emptied of any signifying power. Again, and by the system.

People victimized by assault will find themselves obliterated by the idea of the "rape victim."

The rape victim is a figure, an abstraction. The victim is #evidence; exhibit A.

The details of a rape itself—to consider such things at all within these contexts is to bathe in the sexual ignorance of the majority.

Juries routinely fail to convict: the public is, generally, sex-phobic and inclined to see any sex act through the lens of their own anxious relationship to being sexual.

And yet neighborhoods are packed with *sex offenders* whose sentences are life sentences, whose portraits are available on public rolls until their bodies are put into the ground.

In spite of the headlines, in other words, things are not better off campus.[20]

A not atypical case: Two men assault a woman in a parking lot. The three were friends and co-workers. They ran into each other at a bar. She asked them for a ride home, as she was too drunk to drive. Instead of looking after her, they raped her. A security camera recorded the assault: the video shows that she could neither sit up on her own nor hold her head up. When the men were finished with her, they left her on the ground. It was the dead of winter, just above freezing.[21] A jury failed to convict. Why?

Most people cannot imagine a consensual three-way. They imagine it as something that only prostitutes and pornographers do. The amateur?

Only when blind drunk. A woman who is that drunk consents by the fact of her drunkenness, and by the fact of the event having happened at all.

Her body is moved around: she does not resist. She seems to cooperate. Is she incapacitated? Who can tell from a grainy security camera's recording?

In the minds of the sexual majority, people who do such things do them in the dark, for money, or in parking lots because they are "damaged." They leave each other for dead, because they are all already versions of the undead.

The victim reports the rape; she makes people think about things they don't want to know (about themselves). She is responsible for the jury's predicament. This is why she, eventually, is the one put on trial.

The young girl, humiliated and in tears on the stand—it is not the verdict we want. We want that sad spectacle. More punishment, for her. These stories have their own libidinal economy.

The case of a woman raped by friends and left on the winter's ground was decided in a criminal court, where standards protect the rights of the accused and processes are organized to prevent people with any connections to the case from serving on the jury. These cases are hard, even when administered with care and consideration. And the accused's most basic civil liberties are at stake: it *should* be hard to put people in jail.

On a college campus, charges of sexual assault and harassment are investigated and adjudicated by people who administer the university's compliance. The accuser and the accused, and all of the people making decisions—to investigate or not, to forward a complaint to a committee for adjudication or disciplinary action—work for the same "company" and are in hierarchical relationships with one another.

On a campus, once a "violation" is logged, we arrive at a conflict between the accused and the school. The accused's behavior is in conflict with policy. This, however, is usually administered as a conflict between the victim and the assailant, as if (for example) a rape resulted from a failure to negotiate. People treat the relationship between the accuser and the accused as a conflict that might be mediated. The adversarial geometry of demand

and refusal that shapes the administrative process replicates the structures of relational violence that likely produced the original complaint.[22]

Title IX is meant to address a toxic, abusive set of actions as they unfold within a sexist social structure. Each crisis, as it is administered, is individuated. And yet each crisis vibrates with the largest and deepest of existing structural flaws.

A woman violated by a man becomes a woman at war with the world.

The woman and the man who violates her are moving parts within the paranoid narrative of a world that cannot imagine itself as not at war.

Each of these "wars" evidences the campus's vulnerability. Each situation is a cellular expression of the organism's disease. Each singular case is proof that sexism is real, and systemic. Once each case is resolved, an uneasy truce is struck.

The "ideal" victim is incapacitated by youth and/or substance (our "very young girl"). She has no responsibility, no desire.

"In a world where women are commodities," Angela Carter explains, "a woman who refuses to sell herself will have the thing she refuses to sell taken away from her by force. The piety, the gentleness, the honesty, the sensitivity, all the qualities she has learned to admire in herself, are invitations to violence; all her life, she has been groomed for the slaughterhouse."[23] Mythologies of childhood (as an asexual space; the child as neuter) meet sexist ideologies (women as passive sexual beings; her desire is a perversion and a crime waiting to happen).

The moment the victim becomes visible as a sexual subject, the moment the complexity of sexual intimacy comes into view—this is when her number comes up. *Desire* is, within this narrative, assaultive. The desire for her, the fact of her desire.

Within the discourse of rape, one cannot be a sexual subject and also innocent. And so one cannot acknowledge a victim's discourse regarding her own injury; ideally she won't remember anything because she was unconscious.

She, her—I repeat: she is, within this discourse, always female.

Her own discourse is dangerous: her story about her own injury is a problem. Within the system the victim is a wound, but a bloodless one. The victim cannot know the truth of the situation. The problem is that of sexual difference: her wound must be covered up. The wound itself must have no capacity to feel, it must be disavowed as itself a source of knowledge. She should not speak it. The hearing is confidential; the investigation requires that she keep quiet.

The alignment of the *very young girl*'s injury with the university's responsibility is that "tough thing to overcome." The institutional aim is to ensure that the burden of her injury is hers and hers alone. Ideally she will fold up; she will absorb it and move on.

What would it mean for a *campus* to actually account for its own sexual culture?

One in 5 women students will be raped or subjected to an attempted rape, we are warned. The public and the campus community are appalled by that figure, which was spun out from a National Institute for Justice study that surveyed women attending two universities. Another study came up with 1 in 4. One journalist observes of these numbers:

> The one-fifth to one-quarter assertion would mean that young American college women are raped at a rate similar to women in Congo, where rape has been used as a weapon of war.[24]

What, this journalist asks, makes the American public so ready to believe that the college campus is a conflict zone of this order? What makes us buy into the notion that the campus, as a place, is nearly as dangerous as some of the most dangerous places in the world? Those otherworldly conflict zones haunt the first-world imagination. In our minds, we wall off the campus as if it were a middle-class home in Johannesburg.

The fact remains, however, that American women who do not go to college are more vulnerable than those who do.

> Women without a high school diploma are sexually victimized at a rate 53 percent greater than women with a high school diploma or some college, and more than 400 percent greater than those with a bachelor's degree or more.[25]

Healthcare, birth control and abortion are easier for students to access than they are for members of the national public. But it is also the case that going to college isn't what it used to be. The ways in which the campus is being walled off *does* bear some resemblance to the day-to-day security practices of that *other* post-Apartheid state.

It's an inversion. A worm-hole. The campus is a "hunting ground" and a private zone that must be protected from the "non-affiliate," from public invasion.

Since the Department of Education sent out its "Dear Colleague" letter in 2011, students across the United States have organized groups against sexual assault.

As anti-violence/anti-rape activists advocate for a better disciplinary process, they shadow an apparatus set on putting more people in prison.[26] ("And then my rapist graduated," *instead of going to jail.*) The victim does not want to see her rapist out and about. And who can blame her for that?

The world called for is one of more and better procedures, one that absorbs the criminal justice system more directly, more efficiently, into the administration of life in the name of sexual security.

The term "sexual sovereignty" now appears in risk management literature, and somehow this registers to us as progress.[27] It is a bureaucratic progression.

The management of sexuality has been sewn into the campus. Sex has its own administrative unit.

"By creating the imaginary element that is 'sex,'" Foucault writes, "the deployment of sexuality established one of its most essential internal operating principles: the desire for sex—the desire to have it, to have access to it, to discover it, to liberate it, to articulate it in discourse, to formulate it in truth." Sex appears as its own thing, but also an entitlement, as a property, and a right—as if sex were something that one could *take* from someone else. That sense of property and entitlement might be particularized within a heterosexual economy of artificial scarcity (which imagines women as withholding) to produce a socially sanctioned anger at women who refuse to "give it up." This *sex*ism is not only the logic of patriarchy; it is, also, the discourse of sex itself.

> It is this desirability of sex that attaches each one of us to the injunction to know it, to reveal its law and its power; it is this desirability that makes us think we are affirming the rights of our sex against all power, when in fact we are fastened to the deployment of sexuality that has lifted up from deep within us a sort of mirage in which we think we see ourselves reflected—the dark shimmer of sex.[28]

For all of this association with "rights" and "power," sex is the site of our struggle.

Non-consensual sex within the context of a sexist and sex phobic culture can feel like the concrete expression of a psychic given. A promise, fulfilled. It is humbling. (You thought you were above this happening to *you*?)[29]

Within a sex phobic culture, sex is violation—it is that thing through which we know what violation is. We are each like a campus in this regard.

It is difficult to think of sexual violence outside the ideologies of sex and power through which we know and experience it. The gendered logics of rape exert a tidal pull on our conversation about sexual subjection: the discussion drifts towards the eternal struggle between men and women that women are destined by nature to lose, and towards a demand to the state, to the campus, that it look after us and our "goods," like a good father.

Forms of violation that do not follow these rules do not work as examples of "rape culture." These are the *bad examples*.

Sexual coercion between women, systemic sexual violence towards trans and gender non-conforming people, the victimization of men: if these things are barely thinkable within the dominant discourse on rape, it is evidence of the dissociation of the discourse of rape from the practice of sexual violence except where an individual rape bodies forth a "natural" logic in the "relationship between the sexes."[30]

Public conversation about sex, power and education never begins from those stories, except to mark certain ways of being in the world as always already dangerous. That's the lesson.

Two black gay men, both professors at Tier 1 research universities, were murdered eighteen months apart (July 2008 and December 2009) by men they knew—younger men, furthermore, of different ethnicities than the men that they murdered.[31] Lindon Barrett and Don Belton were prominent figures in their fields, and their fields were closely related (Lindon was a literary critic, Don was a writer. They both worked in English Departments at large public universities). If you knew one of these men, you likely knew them both. It's a small world.

Even those of us who knew these men hardly speak at work of how they died.

Is this because their deaths are not taken to represent anything more than the terrible "risks" that gay men take—especially men of color, for whom the public reserves a special order of judgment?

A colleague used the word "naive" to describe one victim's openness to the world. "He could be naive, in who he opened his house to."

Men are not supposed to be naive.

A black man, vulnerable as he is to violence walking around on the street—is not his home a safe place, a place that he must guard and protect from a racist, homophobic world? Is he not obliged by race and gender to be withholding? To curtail his interest in the world? To reassure the policeman that he is harmless, to stay inside and keep his doors closed?

By inviting younger men into his home, he makes himself vulnerable. He drops the guard he is supposed to maintain. He opens himself up.

Making oneself vulnerable: Is that not what we do in friendship, and in desire?

A campus administration asks itself how a university community can reduce the risk, the possibility of sexual violence. It does the opposite of what we do in friendship and in desire.

A broad cultural practice particularizes rape as the problem of each individual woman, the "risk" of her membership to the gender of vulnerability. One must avoid being raped, one must use the "gift" of one's fear, be careful, don't drink too much. Don't walk home alone. Be wary of the strange man; be wary of your partner. Men are dangerous, being a woman is risky. Men are awful. Women are pathetic. One's body is always already under siege, in violation.

One is taught not to resist. To be compliant. Play dead. Within the discourse of rape, the "woman" is always already dead (whatever one's gender, within this discourse of rape, to be raped is to be made into a woman).[32] The *Rolling Stone* article was framed by a black margin laced with the spray-pattern of a bloody crime scene—a graphic illustration of the ideological production of rape as murder.

The brutality of an actual rape hypostatizes one's psychic position as always already violated. The discourse of rape is a ready-made narrative through which we process nearly all experiences of sexual injury. A distorted mirror image of desire's operation: its intrusive nature, its alienating effects.

A fantasy of sexual violation/sexual trauma lies at the root of identity itself.[33] Which is, of course, why so much interpersonal and institutional violence is sexual. It is also why the narratives of paranoia and psychotic delusion are, often, so intensely gendered and sexualized.

What would it mean to de-traumatize the discourse of rape? What would it mean to reconcile the language of trauma that surrounds rape (as a "fate worse than death") against the ordinariness of peoples' experiences with sexual coercion?

The idea is not that we normalize sexual coercion, but that we refuse the cultural logic that equates a state of constant fear and hyper-vigilance with sexual awareness. Rachel Hall argues,

> The depressing and disappointing ordinariness of rape need not support a public imaginary

wherein rape's commonness is used to encourage women to live in fear of its virtual possibility. Admitting rape's ordinariness, we must hold ourselves back from the dramatic pull of treatments of rape as virtual [and as everywhere] and women as virtually [always] vulnerable.[34]

Especially for people just starting out in their lives as sexual adults, rape threatens to quash whatever glimmer of possibility one might have felt around desire, openness, and the possibilities of sexual generosity. If "rape becomes a particularly awful crime in direct proportion to the sacralization of women's sex as precious and innocent (read: without agency)," it arrives on campus before most students have had a chance to understand the practice of one's sexuality as an aspect of one's lived, social experience.[35] Students seek out this understanding of sexual practice, they seek it out in community, from each other. But they have no idea, really, what they are doing—they are, after all, *learning*.

Perhaps this is why the story of campus sex is so atomic.

Sexual promiscuity brings its own forms of intelligence; too few people get to know the truth of this. Sexual experience gained/encountered within a dynamic and diverse sexual community and supported by a network of non-judgmental friendship—this is the bedrock of sexual wisdom.

The possibilities of sexual experience draw people to a college campus as a social space—even as most students are only dimly aware of what "experience" it is they are seeking.

In the fall of 2010, Tyler Clementi and Dharun Ravi moved out of their parental homes in the New Jersey suburbs and into a dorm room at Rutgers University. Ravi was an outgoing guy; Clementi, on the face of things, more classically, a nerd.

But Clementi had recently come out as gay. He was now at a large public university—he could be himself—he could figure out what that meant. He was making use of gay social media apps, and hooking up as much as he could. He was, like most every sexually active college student, figuring out how to have a sex life in a communal living situation.

His roommate was just as new to college life.

Ravi seemed to like Clementi. He was making friends at the dorm, and, in the way of the juvenile, thought it was interesting—funny and weird—that he had a sexually active, gay roommate. He played that card with his friends: three weeks into the semester, he left his computer's camera on, hoping to capture one of his roommate's hook-ups. He and a friend, a woman, watched the stream together for a few seconds, for a laugh. Ravi tried to set Clementi up again, and failed.

Clementi found out. He was humiliated. He felt betrayed, confused. Weren't they friends? He reported the incident; he asked for a new roommate. And a few days later he committed suicide.

Tyler Clementi (a young white gay man) became a cause: his story was that of the victim, bullied by the homophobe (a young man of color). It was all anyone talked about that year. Bullying, queer suicide.[36] "It gets better!" chant a chorus of Youtube videos, as if there were a future for Clementi if only he could listen. The New Jersey State legislature passed the "Anti-Bullying Bill of Rights" which now governs most interpersonal conflict on the state's school campuses.[37] Ravi was blamed for Clementi's suicide; he was prosecuted and jailed for the privacy violation.

The actual reason for Clementi's suicide, however, has remained a mystery.[38] Although he was clearly upset by the situation, there was no indication that he was that desperate. Had something else happened to him? Why did he come apart so quickly?

For people not used to living under explicit surveillance, finding oneself stripped of a sense of privacy is profoundly disturbing. The experience of exposure doubles on itself. One comes to grips with how much work a sense of privacy does to maintain a specific kind of self-hood—and also with how much that work had depended on a fiction. It is a shift, a heightening of one's understanding. That sense of privacy gives us our shape—our psychic skin.[39] The sense of an inside and an outside—it is a foundational fiction. Even a movement in that boundary (me/not me) can be traumatic—but its sudden evaporation?

This fundamental boundary is already the site of much stress for new college students, most having just left their families, most sharing a bedroom with a complete stranger. This was, of course, exactly the boundary that Ravi was playing with. He wanted to watch his roommate hookup—*why* he wanted to watch that, with friends, is not something that can be explained by either the word "bullying" or even the word "homophobia." It has something to do with the sociality of sex, and the sexuality of friendships.

Tyler Clementi, the sexed subject—the white gay man—becomes understood only through this story about the invasion of his privacy. Dharun Ravi is, here, cast as the raced subject—the invading non-affiliate.

Clementi was putting himself out there, virtually and in the world. He was bringing men into his bedroom. Clementi's bedroom was Ravi's, too.

Here, demoralized by the ease with which Ravi emerged in national discourse as an explanation for Clementi's suicide (as if their ethnic and sexual differences were all one needed to know), I draw your attention back to the question of campus security, as it is figured by the body of the brown man who appears out of place.

We are unable to determine why Tabatabainejad was screaming.[40]

That sentence can be found in "A Bad Night at Powell Library," a document produced by the "Police Assessment Committee" at the University of California, Los Angeles after Mostafa Tabatabainejad, a student, was Tased in the campus library by UCPD on November 14, 2006.

The handful of Youtube videos created by

witnesses are very disturbing—these videos all begin in the same way, as students activate the cameras on their phones because they hear blood curdling screams. They search the study hall with their camera-phones—we see their books, half-written essays on their computer screens, other students looking around to see what is happening—the situation, however, becomes clear as they approach the scene of the confrontation. A student is screaming because he is being Tased by a police officer.

Tabatabainejad had been studying for exams at UCLA's Powell Library. A student working for the UCPD as a "Community Services Officer" made a pass through the room in which Tabatabainejad was working, to check IDs.

Such checks are not routine at public universities—the grounds of a public university are just that, public. ID checks are controversial on every campus, as men of color are selected for the college edition of "stop and frisk." So if I say they are not routine for the campus, I mean they are not uniformly routine: ID checks are all-too-common for black and brown students, staff and faculty.

That night, the ID check began with Tabatabainejad, who took exception to being singled out.[41] He refused to show his ID, and asked that this surveillance begin with others in the room in order to demonstrate that he hadn't, indeed, been identified out as someone who looked like he didn't belong at UCLA.

The Community Services Officer ignored his request and gave Tabatabainejad an ultimatum. Show the ID or leave. Tabatabainejad refused to do either. The UCPD were called in. As the police arrived, Tabatabainejad put on his backpack and walked towards the exit—by this point, the library wasn't a place of study, but the scene of harassment. He must have decided to cut his losses and leave. As he attempted to do so, the police confronted him. They announced the inevitable and the obvious. He had to leave. Reminded of the principle of the thing, he stopped and asked, Why? There was no good answer. A policeman grabbed his arm and Tabatabainejad went limp. If they insisted on ejecting the student, they would have to drag him out: he would not help them.

In 2006, the UCPD policy allowed the use of the Taser as a "pain compliance device against passive resisters."[42] UCPD policy still allows the use of PepperBalls and PepperSpray to force "compliance." The UCPD officer applied the Taser against Tabatabainejad's body and shocked him. After being brought to the ground, after screaming in pain and anger, he caught his breath and observed matter-of-factly: "I got Tased for no reason." It is surreal. It is hard to imagine that rational sentence coming from the same body that had just been screaming. And would, in fact, scream again.

The police Tased him because, in their words, when they touched Tabatabainejad he "tightened up his body" and "us[ed] his body weight to pull downwards." Witnesses described the same action as "laying down on the floor."[43]

When the police yelled "stand up or we will Tase you again," what was the student supposed to do? Why should he cooperate with his ejection from the library? Were they arresting him? Why didn't they just drag him away? Why was it so important that he actively comply?

The UCPD officer used his Taser on Tabatabainejad again. He screamed and sobbed. He begged them to stop. According to UCLA's investigative report, Tabatabainejad was Tased at least three times, for 2–5 minutes with each application of the device.

If the committee could not determine why Tabatabainejad was screaming, it was because he screamed through intervals in the application of the Taser. This was, for the Police Assessment Committee, a point of confusion. A momentary distraction from the greater question as to why he was Tased at all. A gap in the committee's focus.

The literature concludes:

The evidence available to us negates any suggestion that Tabatabainejad was physically fighting with the officers. A student witness in fact reported that Tabatabainejad "was not fighting [the officers] but was verbally screaming." Neither Officer 1 nor Officer 2 mention Tabatabainejad either inflicting or attempting to inflict physical harm on the officers. The officers' command to "stop fighting us" likely refers to Tabatabainejad continuing to bear his weight to the ground. In a small portion of audio of the incident captured by Officer 1's audio equipment, Tabatabainejad says, "I'm passively resisting… I'm exercising my…civil rights."[44]

Why, the compliant public ask, didn't he just show his ID? "Was it worth it?" the police asked him, once they'd put him in a squad car. "All this could have been avoided if you just showed your ID." The student replied: "Of course it could have been avoided…It's the principle of the thing. It's the god damn principle."[45]

Was it worth it?

Is there not a note of sadistic pleasure in that question? Is it too much to suggest that this officer enjoyed putting his boot on the student's neck? Am I going too far?

"In a world characterized by mass individualism," Paul Virilio writes, "my body becomes the final rampart."[46] Campus security, campus sex. We need the sexual subject to secure the campus.

Within a queer and feminist community, sexual violence is a betrayal of the social contract. Everywhere else it is an affirmation of the social contract.

Monique Wittig: "the category of sex is the product of heterosexual society that turns half of the population into sexual beings, for sex is a category that women cannot be outside of." She continues, rather scandalously: "One might consider that every woman, married or not, has a period of forced sexual service, a sexual service which we may compare to the military one, and which can vary between a day, a year, or twenty-five years or more."[47] The campus sex scandal bears out the truth of this.[48]

Some of us bristle at the mainstreaming of the phrase "rape culture": while the term can be useful (to name places where sexual violence is explicit, frequent, rewarded), it can also distance sexual violence from the force of the ordinary. Fraternity gang rapes orient our thinking, rather than the miserable parade of marriage announcements and children's birthday parties—the formations of the happy households as islands of calm in a sea of crisis.

Some of us are caught on the outside of those household walls, absorbed by the silence that swallows up the disaster of a colleague's murder.

"Rape culture," used too liberally, reinforces the structure of a normative sexual culture. What if the threat and fear of rape were exactly what kept that power structure in place? What does it mean to not be afraid of rape? What does it mean to fear, instead, a culture of sexual complicity (of which rape is a part, as is state-mandated pregnancy/reproduction)?

The critic of heterosexual structures will position rape on a continuum of these other coercive structures.

It is, largely, the routine disavowal and reproduction of forms of sexual coercion that is our undoing. It is the dailiness of sexual coercion that gets us; the ordinary suppression of the non-compliant. For, of course, it is within that world of the respectable that we don't tell the story of our "actual" rape.

Who *hasn't* been the victim of sexual coercion?

What if our experiences of coercion and assault were "war stories," swapped as a form of camaraderie? What would it require of the world, for sexual violence to *mean less*? What part of it would be gradated? Would it be less sexual? Less violent? Less absolute? Or more?

In the straight world, sexual coercion—emotionally, physically, economically enforced—positions the sexual subject as a child. That victim is a weakling, a fool, a naïf. (Like the "girl" who gets "knocked up." The man who cruises the park is naive if he is murdered; otherwise he is a predator.) One's openness—a willingness to walk down the street at night alone, to not be afraid, to trust, to take a "risk," to accept a drink from a stranger, to get high in a crowd, to fuck people you don't know —these are "mistakes," failures. One's victimization manifests an embarrassing ignorance of the "fact" that men (always men) are awful (always awful). But it also affirms your place in the world. It is the injury that makes sense of you. That *right* to be free from harm, from injury—it will be violated! It has already been violated. You exist!

Meanwhile, male students attend orientation seminars and are told not to rape. Their default position is that of being "in violation." Tired of being told what not to do, the campus feminist, working in student affairs, insists that men need instruction. And they do; we do.

In college, men will get more instruction on this question (how not to be a rapist) than they will regarding unwanted pregnancy, abortion access and HIV transmission. They are certainly not invited to explore the contours of their own sexual happiness and the workings of their own bodies; they are taught, instead, to avoid "getting into trouble."

On November 9, 2011, the students at Penn State University took to the streets of State College, Pennsylvania and rioted. The campus's football coach, a living saint for the town nicknamed "Happy Valley," had been fired.

In 1998, the mother of an 11-year-old boy contacted the campus police. Jerry Sandusky, an assistant coach at Penn State's football program and the founder of an outreach program for at-risk youth, had showered with this boy after an informal practice session on the university's campus. Sandusky had lifted and squeezed the woman's son in a way that made the boy very uncomfortable. When he came home, the boy acted so strangely that his mother called a range of authorities. The investigation of her complaint, however, seemed to go nowhere.

The university police department's report on the 1998 case was not stored as a complaint. It was labeled "Administrative Information" and filed away.[49] Administrators talked over the situation amongst themselves. They used abstract language and approached it as a managerial problem. Clearly, everyone agreed, the man should not be showering with these boys *on campus*. ^(its administrational on a campus)

Soon after this "administrative information" was put in a drawer, Sandusky took early retirement from Penn State. The football program's head coach, Joe Paterno, was famous in American sports for his longevity, success and for the sincerity of his commitment to Penn State's program. The various reports surveying Penn State's relationship to Sandusky show that Paterno was concerned about Sandusky's welfare. The two had worked together for years. On his retirement, Sandusky maintained a strong relationship with the university through his outreach program, The Second Mile. He was also given an unusual compensation package that brought him to the same financial level that he would have earned had he not retired early. He was awarded Emeritus status; this was also unusual, as it was not appropriate to his position. That status gave him full access to the university's training facilities for the rest of his life. ^(???)

Sandusky would be seen again showering on Penn State's campus with a boy in 2000, by janitors who felt they would lose their jobs if they came forward. He was seen in the showers with a boy yet again, in 2001: this time the witness, who would later describe himself as an abuse survivor, reported that what he saw was "sexual" and "way over the line."[50] This man reported what he saw only to his father and to his immediate superior, Head Coach Joe Paterno. Again, nothing seemed to happen. The story began to circulate, however, as a whispered rumor. Sandusky maintained a relationship to Penn State through his Emeritus status; he maintained his leadership role in the outreach program, and he continued to abuse pre-pubescent boys.

More than a decade would pass between the 1998 report and the day that Sandusky was arrested. In 2010, another mother and her son went to their local police, and *pushed*. Sandusky had been abusing this woman's son for years. That case broke open as rumors of the 2001 shower incident reached investigators working for the Pennsylvania Attorney General. They were now interested in the link between Sandusky and Penn State. Did administrators at Penn State, they wondered, *know*? Was Penn State not in compliance with Title IX and the Clery Act (which requires the tracking and reporting of complaints of sexual assault)? Was the campus in violation?

Sandusky was arrested. In short order, Penn State's Board of Trustees fired the university's President, its Athletic Director, its Senior Vice President and, most controversially, Joe Paterno.

Penn State became synonymous with campus disaster: the scandal was, at the time, widely identified as "the worst in sports history."

The university's Board of Trustees quickly commissioned an independent investigation. The authors of the 267-page, $8.2 million "Freeh Report" do not mince words:

> The most saddening find by the Special Investigative Counsel is the total and consistent disregard by the most senior leaders at Penn State for the safety and welfare of Sandusky's victims. As the Grand Jury similarly noted in its presentment, there was no "attempt to investigate, to identify Victim 2 [one of the boys seen in the shower], or to protect that child or any others from similar conduct except as related to preventing its re-occurrence on university property."[51]

The (controversial) report concludes that administrators at Penn State were aware that a senior member of the coaching staff of its football team had been accused of sexually assaulting boys, and that concern for the school's reputation—as well as concern for the abuser's dignity—eclipsed concern for this man's victims. The most senior leaders, the report concludes, showed a shocking lack of empathy and no concern for the victims' safety. They actively avoided learning the names of victims. Instead, they scrambled to protect the campus.

Joe Paterno represented and embodied Penn State: he had coached the university's football team since 1966. A distinguished professorship was named after his family, as was the university library.[52]

He was not just fired; his name was taken off of buildings. A statue honoring him was taken down. Although he was only one in a group of figures who turned away from what they surely knew (and disavowed, in the classic, psychoanalytic sense of the word), and although he was not the abuser, Paterno's fall from grace gave the story its public façade in the same way that his loyalty had given the campus its singular identity.

He died of lung cancer months after he was stripped of his coaching position. His family would eventually file a defamation suit against the authors of the Freeh Report.

In "Happy Valley," as Penn State's community is known, affection for Paterno is profoundly Oedipal. On November 9, 2011, students took to the streets when they learned that "JoePa" had been put to the curb.[53]

> Just before midnight, the police lost control of the crowd. Chanting, "Tip the van," the students

toppled the news vehicle and then brought down a nearby lamppost. When the police opened up with pepper spray, some in the crowd responded by hurling rocks, cans of soda and flares. They also tore down street signs, tipped over trashcans and newspaper vending boxes and shattered car windows.[54]

Even knowing what the patriarch had done—what he had refused to do—the students took to the streets in outrage. It seemed unfair to them that the shame should fall on his shoulders. They were angry. Gesturing to University of California students protesting tuition hikes on that same day at UC Berkeley, pundits called the Penn State students spoiled brats. Some complained that none of the Penn State students were arrested. But this was not true: local authorities threw the book at as many students as they could identify, if only because the students had managed to make an awful situation even worse.[55]

Other schools envy the intensity of student attachment to Penn State. University executives want former students to look back on their education with uncritical nostalgia, with the same set of feelings they might have for their first pair of expensive, brand-named sneakers. The hope is that nostalgia for "the college experience" will fund public education, just as the football program at

Penn State brings tens of millions of dollars to Happy Valley every year.

It is easy to sneer at rioting Penn State students. White and entitled, Penn State students are deeply invested in a specific patriarchal mythology. Students did not decry the defilement of children, but raged at the shame that settled on their house. Because they could not blame the father, they blamed the world.

In the fallout at Penn State, it is not the victims who center the discourse of injury: it is the campus itself. Penn State paid an incomprehensible fine to the National Collegiate Athletic Association; the football coach's wins were erased from the record. In its struggle to come to terms with the magnitude of what had happened, one might say the university turned against itself—at least in its staging of a theater of compensation. It has paid victims millions; it has spent millions investigating itself. And it is now defending itself against lawsuits from the accused.

The macho posturing that rallies around the idea of protecting innocent children comes from the last people one would actually trust to know what it means to support a robust, dynamic, equitable sexual culture.

Few of the people leading public discussion of these stories have any expertise in sexual politics, in the role of sexual violence and sexual coercion within intensely gender-segregated spaces like football. Where we find radical segregation—the complete banishment of sexual difference from a community—we will find sexual violence. We will find sexual violence at the center of that world, just as surely as we find it on its borders.

[handwritten margin note: Synonymous w/ the university + the outside?]

In the decade administrators avoided knowing what Sandusky was doing, they attended training seminars on sexual harassment, Title IX, and their obligations to report and address abuse. They were required to do so because Penn State had settled a federal complaint filed by a woman basketball player: for twenty years, Rene Portland reigned as one of the country's most openly homophobic college coaches—her "no sex, no drugs, no lesbians" policy was infamous, and had been nationally reported. None of the campus leaders at Penn State made an effort to address and change her discriminatory practices. An 18-year-old basketball player was kicked off the team, accused of being gay. She filed a Title IX complaint, and took the case to its limit—forcing policy change, Portland's retirement, and mandatory training for staff. None of the senior administrators, however, made the connection: what they were supposed to have learned in the wake of that complaint should have led them to take action—but it did not.

A few years after Sandusky was sent to jail, high school football players in New Jersey were called out for attacking teammates in a hazing ritual—punching, kicking younger players and using their fingers to penetrate boys through their football pants.[56] (The team's motto? "Character and Commitment.")

The men administering the consequences of the Penn State scandal have direct experience with the proximity of sexual play to the "rough and tumble" play that defines boyhood masculinity. The proximity of "rough and tumble" play to sexual assault—what would it mean to recognize that? Or to feel the proximity of those coming-of-age rites to the homosocial practice of intense misogyny?

In 2015, a new scandal: a Penn State fraternity (Kappa Delta Rho) created a secret Facebook page through which members shared photographs of their Animal House SVU antics, including pictures of (unconscious or sleeping) naked women. A member defended the practice to local media as "satire," the university's president asserted that it was time to "review" the fraternity system on the campus, and the district attorney's office contemplated prosecuting the fraternity using a newly passed law prohibiting "revenge porn."[57] The language is revealing: stripping women down serves the larger social purpose of revealing their essential worthlessness. It is punishment for our crime—that of withholding some form of the happiness to which men feel themselves entitled. We sometimes focus so much on this problem, we forget what men can do to each other.

These football coaches, fraternity members and college presidents do not know how to put all that into words. They do not know how to narrate the *centrality* of sexual-coercion-by-men to their formation as men, or what it means to affirm that non-consensual sex forms the bedrock of their masculinity. They do not know how to reconcile their hatred of women with their desire for intimacy with men, and with their certainty that they are not gay. They know even less what it means to resist the architecture of this whole scenario. Seeking out sex (with anyone) within a consensual context is just on the other side of reason. And so they drink themselves into oblivion.

For the students and for the "senior leaders" at Penn State, was it too hard to reconcile the picture of masculine power acted out in the football stadium with the stories of masculine vulnerability that made headlines? Or was it too easy?

Penn State, like most universities, is run by a community of men who cannot use the word "sodomize" or "rape" in a conversation. The idea of sex sexualizes. To allow these words to enter into the conversation is to violate the social contract that makes conversation between these men possible. Always already there, is an agreement not to talk *like that.*

The cultish emotional landscape that Sandusky mined for his pleasure is the same that makes thinking about his shame absolutely unbearable. His shame is contagious.[58]

The boys who know exactly what these locker room "rituals" are about, however, the boys who can put it in a sentence, are marked out as the queers.

The Penn State reports revolve around cowed staff and frightened leaders: administrators fearing not for the welfare of the children to whom Sandusky had easy access, but for the reputation of the university. The story is haunted by the anxiety of men who are afraid of disturbing the homo-social latticework of power and authority that gives them a sense of security. These reports—they describe a soft, fleshy world shellacked with a hard, mean shell of arrogance. These reports are, in fact, its literature.

Men use their arrogance to have sex with who they see fit (women or boys) and not care until their sense of power and security is stripped away

On May 23, 2014, Elliot Rodger, a former student at a local community college in Santa Barbara, went on a rampage. He murdered his two roommates and a friend of theirs who had spent the night. He then left the apartment to go on a hunt. He shot people on the street in Isla Vista, a neighborhood on the edge of the University of California's oceanside campus. He shot people in front of a sorority and a convenience store. He killed men and women, and he shot himself.

As the story broke, the public binged on his insanity: a 100,000-word manifesto and a Youtube video broadcasting his worldview. In those texts, the killer unfurls his hatred for the world. Women, of course, *are* the world in his narrative—women embody his sense of alienation and despair. Women are "sex," that thing which he deserves but cannot have. Women are the place from which he is exiled.

The public dives into the psychotic's text because it has the explanatory force of madness. The public amplifies that text's force—his madness gains mass.

And so, in this disaster's wake, popular discourse was taken over by a pseudo-anti-sexism, as sexism was blamed for producing the murderer.

People with the Isla Vista killer's suite of disorders will tap into the hate and fear that circulates through the ideological grid. Sexist thinking gave this killer's persecution complex a shape. It legitimized his God-like ego, his sense of absolute power. Of course his narrative is sexist. Supremacist logics are paranoid/psychotic/schizoid logics.

"Sexism," however, does not illuminate the shooter's crisis, or the conditions of possibility for his violence. The movement of a person's tilt into violence cannot be captured by that word. What to do with the coincidence (the happening-in-the-same-time-and-place) of the crazy and the real? With the singular (the "shooter") and the systemic ("sexism")?

The violent turn is usually accompanied by a suicidal not-caring about what might happen to others, or to oneself. Or by a complete delusion, in which one has no sense of what violence *is*, which is its own form of violence. An abstracted relationship to the flesh and the world—in which nothing has meaning. In madness, certain forms of violence lose their brutality.

The problem of campus security is often reduced to that of the shooter scenario. The campus, again, is imagined as a hunting ground. Campus police instruct us on what to do if a crazed gunman is on the loose. (Hide! Text your colleagues your previously-agreed-upon code word!)

The "shooter scenario" is more than a man with a gun. It is the projection of the death-drive onto the object of a campaign of harassment. It is a disaster scenario. A dark fantasy. A person might dream of that cataclysm, but an awareness, a certain grip on the sane—a desire to live, a desire to stay out of jail—might keep them from acting that fantasy out. When that awareness falls apart—when that sense of a modest future of not-murder/not-suicide fades—that is one place where murder happens.

The shape of this particular shooter scenario is too familiar: the community college student, the drop out, the quiet young man plotting to destroy his world.

Sexism circulates as an explanation and as a fertilizer and as a foundation for all kinds of misery. It explains everything and nothing.

The killer kills, anger at women gives a crazy shape to that killing. But she is only an alibi. This is another way that the victim is "murdered."

Statistically, men are more likely to act out these murder/suicide fantasies—one of patriarchy's signatures is its naturalization of a man's impulse to harm and destroy. And women attacked by men constitute a vast majority of certain kinds of violence—violence against women. (Women are not usually killed, in other words, by other women.) In disordered thinking, the consequences of harassing and threatening women feels less serious—easier to get away with. Worse, however: ideologically, women *are* sex—her body and being appears as a kind of pure discourse, as meaning and value itself. The body holding the promise of meaning and value is a target. She is a campus. She is the law. In his madness, the shooter will start with his ex-girlfriend, and then turn his gun on the police. A natural flow.

What made the people murdered by the Isla Vista shooter vulnerable to his violence? Sexism is a part of that story, but there are other things that escape that word. One might meditate on sex and its relation to power; one might consider this historical moment as one in which things feel pointless, when life within the US feels desperate—like living in the belly of an egomaniacal, outraged and embittered monster. What makes the world so chaotic, what makes the college campus and the female student such compelling targets for psychotic violence?

What makes someone want to burn down not only their life, but the world? To shoot up a sorority or deli, to drive his car into a crowd, to murder men while they sleep. To mainline the worst of everything?

Hate/fear/desire drives a fantasy of mutual destruction—the object of hate/fear/desire (the person who is the object of attachment but also rage) is absorbed into a suicidal mission. Is that not also the state's relationship to the public? How to explain prisons, our fucked up immigration policy, the mass disinvestment in public education? How else to understand the ease with which the police identify with, are hailed by the madman's scenario?

Sexism is such a powerful narrative structure—it gave the Isla Vista shooter his "reason." I repeat: master narratives are always sexist and racist, self-serving and, at their core, crazy. Our turn to sexism to explain his madness is only slightly less insane.

Sexism gave a sense of legitimacy to that shooter's psychotic narrative. And yet he didn't only murder women; he started off by murdering his male roommates and one of their friends. He did not only blame women for his unhappiness; he blamed the men around him, too. He started off his murder spree by killing the people closest to him—and these men were murdered with a knife. He murdered two women, and four men.

Most of his victims were men of color, like him.

That this killer—a man—said he was angry at women and drove to a sorority seems to give this story some kind of shape. But does it, really? The knife, the gun—the act of violence—what meaning it bestows on the world is itself a brutality.

In the spring of 2014, a profoundly distressed young man took all the pain and all the misery of his experience and loaded it into a gun. He enacted a murderous fantasy in the name of desire.

We return to the University of California, PepperSpray cop, and the events of November 18, 2011. We return to the landscape of the Chancellor's concern: the "dark shimmer" of sexuality, figured in the paperwork as the lurking presence of the outsider from Oakland.

> We were worried at the time about that [nonaffiliates] because the issues from Oakland were in the news…

For the Californian, in 2011, "the issues from Oakland" invited a specific chain of association. That fall, Oakland demonstrators took over a square opposite City Hall and renamed it Oscar Grant Plaza, in memory of the black man shot and killed by a Bay Area Rapid Transit officer on New Year's Day in 2009. (That policeman's defense: he meant to use his Taser, but grabbed his gun by mistake.) Occupy Oakland was subject to one militarized police assault after another. Police violence is one of Occupy Oakland's defining themes (as both a subject of protest, and as the story of the way that protest was suppressed).

According to Kroll's report on the events leading up to Sergeant Pike's decision to use PepperSpray on peaceful, seated protestors, the campus police were keyed into the nature of their deployment as management's blunt instrument. The police anticipated conflict. They were mystified by the Chancellor's sense of urgency. In the investigative literature, police department leadership described the administration as "not getting it."[59] The Lieutenants could not understand why one would take down tents in the middle of the day. (Such things are usually done in the middle of the night.) They were confused: were they taking down tents or breaking up a protest?[60] The police worried about their own safety. They wanted to wear riot gear, to "go in" fully protected against the angry mob they imagined would greet them. The Captain worried that her Lieutenants were too nervous—that their nervousness would bring on a disaster. She told them "'I just don't want another Berkeley.'"[61] She didn't want them looking like "an army."[62] Meaning, she didn't want her police department to be caught, like Berkeley's, in the middle of a firestorm of controversy about the use of military tactics to suppress campus dissent.

Earlier that month, on November 9, the same day that Penn State's students were busy making headlines as spoiled brats, UCPD officers attempting to dismantle the Occupy Berkeley Camp pulled demonstrators by their hair and struck them with the end of their batons. The crowd captured the violence of their policing with their smart phones. By November 18, the day of the pepper spray incident, Berkeley's administration had already commissioned a review of their November 9 incident. The Berkeley UCPD had been mobilized to dismantle the Occupy Berkeley Camp, it should be said, because that campus's administration was also worried about Berkeley turning into Oakland—meaning, a center for community organization.[63]

They might have worried about their policing turning into Oakland's. The controversy about the UCPD's behavior at Berkeley echoed that caused by the Oakland Police Department which gathered hundreds of police officers from 15 local law enforcement agencies (including the UCPD) to lead a 4:50 am "violent and chaotic" raid on the Occupy Oakland Camp on October 25.[64] By November 18, the day of the pepper spray incident, Berkeley's November 9th police action was the subject of an internal review. Oakland's

October 25th action would yield a series of (successful) lawsuits against the city.

In asking that her officers not go in like an army, the Davis UCPD captain hoped to avoid the administrative ritual of the production and reading of the Independent Investigation and the Internal Report. Who wants to be a character in the literature of responsibility?

The Davis administration was too preoccupied with its campus rape scenario to listen to the police. At a strategy meeting held just a few hours before the pepper spray incident, Katehi worried "I absolutely do not want those students staying overnight on a Friday where there could be a party or something could happen to them." At this point in the conversation Lieutenant Pike, the man who would later be caught holding the pepper spray, made the very reasonable suggestion that "Student Affairs should talk to them rather than bringing in the PD at this point." He was talked over and ignored.

> Pike "looked like he almost got disgusted with the conversation" and left the room for a brief period of time.[65]

The administration was worried about a rape. The policeman was worried about a riot.

Before they left for the quad Officer Pike seemed nervous "and stated this is a bad idea."[66]

The police headed out to the quad and asked the demonstrators to break down some tents. Students seemed to obey at first, but they only moved their camp to another part of the quad. The police arrested a few people. Protestors asked what law had been broken, and the police—whose confusion on this point is well-documented—offered no explanation. Using the Occupy movement's human microphone as a technique for self-management, the crowd eventually sat down in a loose circle around the police. Most of the seated students turned their backs to the cops, who stood in a confused huddle. As the police sorted themselves out, the crowd chanted a request that the police release the arrested: "if you let them go, we'll let you leave." The crowd seemed surprised by the fact that the police appeared to have been hailed by their chanting. Video of the footage shows the police stalled, uncertain of themselves. The crowd also seems confused. Their mood seemed to drift between anger, conciliation and a certain geniality.

Several "mic checks" followed as the officers remained inside the encircled crowd. First, someone announced that "*If someone has lost a beanie* [phonetic], *I have it*," several in the crowd laughed and a woman answered, "*It's Enosh's, he was arrested*," and the crowd cheered. Lieutenant Pike is seen holding his radio and looking over the crowd toward the south end of the Quad.[67]

The encounter has the shape of a confrontation but little of its affect. They revised their demand, turning it into a request that the police do what they were already doing: take their prisoners and go. Just go and leave us alone, they said. "You can go!"

Police do not participate in conversation, however, even a conversation that recognizes their presence and affirms that what is happening is happening. Or perhaps especially when a crowd affirms that what is happening is happening. There is no conversing with the inevitable.

Lieutenant John Pike stepped forward. He warned the students sitting across the sidewalk that if they did not move out of the way, they would be subject to the use of force. The lieutenant moved down the line, explaining this promise of force to individual students, appearing to extract their consent by, again, affirming their understanding of the inevitable.

A transcript records the conversation's surrealism:

Pike: [Walks up to student. Speaks directly to him for about 8 seconds. Nearly inaudible on video.]

Student: You're going to shoot me? You're going to shoot me for sitting here? Hey officer, is that what you said?

Pike: Yes.

Student: Officer, is that … [garbled audio]

Unidentified Male Protester: He just said yes.

Unidentified Female Protester: Shoot you. He's going to shoot you.

Student: Alright. Just making sure. Just making sure.

Pike: [pats student on the back] I'm telling you right now.

Student: You're shooting us for sitting here?

Pike: [garbled]… That pepper spray gun… [garbled] [pats student on the back again and starts walking back to the rest of the police]

Student: No, that's fine. That's fine. You're shooting us for sitting here.[68]

At about this point, the crowd started chanting, "Don't shoot students." The crowd then quickly revised this to "don't shoot your children." Rather than threaten the police, the students amplified their vulnerability.

If students were focused on the possibility of being shot, it might have been because their eyes were focused on the PepperBall Launchers that some officers held in their hands ready to use, and which were periodically directed at the students. The

PepperBall Launcher, which looks like a machine gun, shoots plastic balls filled with oleoresin capisicum in powdered form. The balls burst on impact. When they hit the body it hurts and it stings. Guidelines for their use are confusing: they are not meant to be pointed at vulnerable parts of the body (what part of the body is not vulnerable?), but they are intended for direct use against the non-compliant. At close range you will hurt the person at whom you fire. UC Police are instructed to use them to "contaminate" an area with pepper powder, but only if that area isn't populated with people. Its use must, of course, be safe. Which is to say that the use of PepperBall Launchers to disperse crowds is dangerous and the policy on their use is contradictory.

"PepperBalls…combine the kinetic impact of a projectile with the sensory discomfort of pepper spray." That observation appears frequently in case literature related to a civil lawsuit filed against the Regents of the University of California regarding the use of PepperBall Launchers (one might call them guns) by, as it happens, the UCPD at UC Davis. The court was compelled to make this observation in explaining why it did not accept the University of California's defense of a 2005 incident in which police fired PepperBalls at people attending—what else?—a party.

Timothy C. Nelson was waiting in an entryway with friends, trying to figure out what he was supposed to do—the police, called in to break up a large and noisy party at a Davis apartment complex, had surrounded them in full riot gear, ordering people to disperse—but where? To disperse, they would have needed to walk towards the police who were holding what looked like guns—but were, in fact, "less lethal weapons." The police fired at the crowd. Nelson, then a sophomore attending UC Davis on an athletic scholarship, was shot in the eye. The damage to his vision is permanent. Nelson lost his athletic scholarship thanks to that injury and fought for his day in court. University lawyers fought to keep that from happening.[69]

On the afternoon of the 18th of November 2011, some of the UCPD officers held batons in their hands; others held those troublesome PepperBall Launchers. When they found themselves surrounded by students shouting "don't shoot students" and demanding that they just "go," Timothy C. Nelson's case had already been in the courts for years.

Lieutenant Pike carried not a PepperBall Launcher, but another item from the "less lethal" toolbox, a can of First Defense MK-9.[70]

While Pike carefully explained to students that they would be subjected to force, other police officers, approaching the scene from outside the circle, began clearing the sidewalk without incident. Pike was so engrossed in his work he didn't seem to notice that students left with the police who escorted them out, presumably to arrest them. When he finished making his threats, he stepped back. In an oddly theatrical gesture, he held his can of First Defense MK-9 aloft so that the crowd could see it. He brought the can back down to hip-level, he stepped toward and then over the demonstrators so that he could spray them in the face.[71] People screamed. He sprayed more. Another police officer sprayed. The screaming got louder. Some students were dragged away. Some crawled.

With the students incapacitated and the crowd both stunned and also worked up, the police must have considered their goal met. The path was cleared.

The crowd gathered itself again. They shouted, "you can go, you can go" to the police, who backed away in a strange clump—they looked so stupid, their authority somehow had been completely dismantled and yet it didn't matter. They did what they did, and then they left.

The video archive on this event is deep. Students held their phones up, snapped photographs, recorded and uploaded video to Youtube. People poured over their recordings, annotating and indexing the pepper spray incident from as many angles as they could access. As the events unfold on the computer screen, you can hear the crowd's astonishment break open into anger and settle into a collective nausea. There was something particularly direct and brutally abstract about this encounter between campus police and the student body.

"The images are extremely disturbing," Holmes said. "Obviously we will be looking into the incident and appropriate measures will be taken. We will have to go through an investigation."[72]

There was a time when a University of California degree was free. That the University of California should not charge tuition is written into its 1868 founding document, as is the requirement that "it shall be the duty of the Regents, according to population, to so apportion the representation of students, when necessary, that all portions of the State shall enjoy equal privileges therein."[73]

Ronald Reagan brought an end to free tuition in 1970. California voters tried to bring an end to "all portions" enjoying "equal privileges" when they voted for Proposition 206, the California Civil Rights Initiative, which is exactly the opposite of what the proposition's title suggests: it banned the use of affirmative action in college admissions and whitened the student population across the most resourced campuses.

In 1990–1991, mandatory charges for a resident

undergraduate at the University of California totaled $1,624.[74] Four years at that rate cost $6,496. But of course tuition went up every year for the person who started their studies at a UC campus in the fall of 1990. By the time they finished in the spring of 1994, they paid $10,176 in tuition and mandatory fees.

In 2011, in a complete betrayal of the university's founding principles, for the first time in its history, the tuition paid by University of California students exceeded the state's contribution to the University of California's budget. For 2011–12, one year of tuition cost $13,181. In 2011–12, one year of tuition cost more than a four-year degree earned by the student enrolling in 1990. One year now costs more than four then. For the student of the 1990s, the cost of those four years was considered an outrage.

$52,724 for a four-year degree at any university is an obscenity. (Of course, students graduating today will have paid a good deal more than *that*.) At a public university this is not tuition; it is a crime. None of these numbers, it must be said, includes the cost of room and board. If you graduated from a public university in 1990, you could just about find your tuition: between family contributions (if they were to be had), grants, summer jobs, part-time employment during the year, living at home—a person could pay their way through school. It wasn't easy, especially as the University of California has no part-time degree program. But it was possible to get a college degree without taking on student loans; and if you were forced to do the latter, that loan would not have been disabling as long as you could find some sort of employment. The class of '94 may have been the last for whom a college education was just about affordable. Today, a four-year public university education is well beyond the reach of most of the U.S. population. It is not possible without aid—grants and loans.

University of California faculty can't afford to give their kids the education they give to their students.

The assumption is that students will mortgage their adult life. If it is true that angry demonstrations have become part of the routine of campus life, it is also true that the actual nature of our situation is hard to grasp. Who can understand what it means to acquire $60,000, $90,000, $120,000 of unsecured debt before you are 21? Who can understand the amount of wealth it takes in order to be free from that burden?

Who can understand the scale of that wealth, while also grasping the de-professionalization of the work of teaching? Welcome to the new campus, with its over-enrolled classes taught by part-time, adjunct teachers who receive poverty wages and no benefits. Governed by an army of bureaucrats.

I sit in a meeting of the Executive Council of my university and learn that the administration wants students who are richer, and better educated. How do we get *better* students? How do we get students who need less from us?

How indeed, from a world in which our students are so poor?

The conversation is generated by a growing crisis at college campuses: more and more incoming students do not have the remedial math skills they need to pursue majors in the sciences. A long-term consequence of national education policy, itself a reflection of a suicidal public's hatred of the future. Sure seems that way now

The narrative arc at campus demonstrations has a certain shape: We gather and we chant at the administration through a line of armed and armored police officers. The administration looks back at us, mute and with blank expression. Or, as was the case at UC Davis on that day, we chant at the police who are deployed as avatars for the university itself—a university which defines itself as a vulnerable space that must be protected from risk, which is to say, from the public. A "young girl" at risk of being violated by "non-affiliates." The university has transmogrified, from that "vulnerable resource" to the walls that surround it. We encounter the university not as a classroom, but as a moving wall, a shield, a security apparatus.

We gather, we surround, we ask, we are surrounded. The police do something incomprehensible. They fire PebberBalls into—at—the crowd. They shoot at us whether we are at a party or a protest. Or because we might make our event into both.

They spray us, in our faces. They throw us to the ground, drive a baton into our sides, whack our hands with their sticks and break our fingers,[75] they drag our friends, our teachers, our students to jail. By their hair.[76] And we scream.

On May 20th, 2014, as she crossed a street at the edge of campus, Arizona State University Assistant Professor Ersula Ore was stopped for jaywalking by Stewart Ferrin, then an officer with the Arizona State University Police Department.

Within minutes she was straddled against the car, thrown to the ground, and handcuffed. In that process, her dress became wedged up over her hips. In the grainy black and white video recording of the arrest, we can see another man lean in, reaching towards her body. He is not the arresting officer, but a civilian employee riding with Ferrin. Perhaps he was trying to adjust her dress; Dr. Ore felt hands on her body, and kicked. She was arrested and charged with assault. Two months later, Ore—an untenured scholar who was, by then, a national headline ("ASU Professor Slammed to the Ground by Police, Gets Arrested for Assaulting an Officer"[77])—pleaded guilty to resisting arrest, a misdemeanor; the assault charges were dropped.

An incident that the university tried to frame as "routine" becomes alarming exactly for its banality.

Dr. Ore's arrest was recorded by the police car's dashboard camera and widely circulated through the media. She seems bewildered at first, and then flat-out alarmed by what is happening. In the background, as her miserable encounter with the campus police unfolds, you can see other pedestrians. Two people wearing backpacks walk along and then cross the street. They appear to be jaywalkers, too.

Do you know this is a street? Officer Ferrin asks Dr. Ore this, as one would a child. The professor, who happens to be a rhetorician, politely questions the decision to single her out, as well as the policeman's aggressive, hostile tone. Sure, she was jaywalking, and of course that's not what one is supposed to do—but why make such a big deal out of it, she asked.

She does not sound happy in the recording, but she is far more respectful to him than he is to her. The police officer interrupts her over and over again, first asking for her ID and then promising violence and arrest. "Let me see your ID or you will be arrested." Soon after, he promises: "I am going to slam you against the car."

Incredulous, the professor replies: "Are you serious?"

As the exchange gets more absurd, alarming and humiliating, she repeats the question. He grabs her hands so that he can handcuff her, although she has posed no threat. "You have no reason to be touching me," she says, stating the obvious. He slams her against the car and straddles her. The video is harrowing. "Get your leg off of me," she says. She calms her voice: "You have me straddled across this car." The intention, clearly, is to explain that the physical situation is harassing. Gripping one of her arms, he swings her around and throws her to the ground.

At this point, she screams. You can see Ferrin's colleague move toward her as she is held to the ground—for what purpose, we do not know.

In the weeks immediately following her arrest, Dr. Ore's story was secreted away. ASUPD's internal review process cleared Officer Ferrin of misconduct; ASU administration issued a statement asserting that, in their view, there was nothing improper in the arrest.

It was a month before her arrest made headlines—it took concerted pressure from diverse sources to recover the story from an administrative hole. Were it not for Arizona's Critical Ethnic Studies collective (which issued a statement of concern in late June, and also called for an investigation of ASUPD's internal review process), the release of a 911 recording from a bystander who was alarmed by the ASUPD's use of force ("there's a police officer getting way too aggressive with a young lady on the street"), and a local television station's release of the dashcam recording of the incident, Ore's arrest would not have made headlines.[78]

In the following months ASU would revise its story. A June 2014 press release explains that the university has invited the FBI to review the arrest; the arresting officer has been placed on leave pending this review. Additionally, according to that press release, "university police are conducting a review of whether the officer involved could have avoided the confrontation." They hired an independent investigator. At the beginning of July 2014, the department announced that its Chief and Assistant Chief were taking early retirement, stepping down to move on to other opportunities. Once the independent investigative report was filed, the police department sent Ferrin an 18-page termination letter indexing all that he had done wrong: He had no reason to stop Ore, his demand for an ID was inappropriate, and his "rigid" response to the non-compliant (he had previously harassed another pedestrian, who also questioned the demand for an ID) was also unwarranted. The report picks apart every single element of her arrest.

There is no law in Arizona requiring citizens (note that word *citizen*) to carry ID, or to produce that ID on demand. Nevertheless, ASU police officers had fallen into the habit of demanding ID as a means for asserting their authority over the campus.

There is, however, in Arizona, a law that *requires* police to demand proof of legal residency status from people they detain or arrest, if they have a "reasonable suspicion" that the person is in the country unlawfully. The ACLU describes the effects of this law (Arizona SB 1020):

> Under this law, people who look "foreign" are more likely to be stopped for minor infractions—having a broken taillight, jaywalking or having an overgrown lawn—and then asked for their papers if police believe, just by looking at them, that they could be in the country unlawfully.[79]

SB 1020 is the legal expression of a xenophobic state of mind; the paranoid escalation from "contact" to violence in police interaction with the black pedestrian is surely one of SB 1020's administrative effects. A domestic shadow of anti-immigration policy.

At the start of February 2015, as more video of the incident went public, Ferrin resigned.[80]

ASU is more beleaguered, as a campus, than most. It is not a good sign that the best policing news for ASU that academic year (2013–2014) was the arrest of nearly 1400 people over three weekends in August 2013. The university's academic year began with "Operation Safe and Sober," a collaboration between the university and Tempe's police departments. The area around campus is notorious for partying and all that goes with a culture of binge drinking—noise complaints, underage drinking, drunk driving, fights, and sexual assaults. As students moved back into town at the end of the summer, the neighborhood was saturated with patrols. In September, a young man was shot and killed in this neighborhood by Tempe police. The police claim he was threatening them with a box cutter; witnesses, however, report that the man was unarmed.

ASUPD officers focused on bicyclists and pedestrians, issuing warnings for traffic violations not unlike that which led to Ore's arrest.[81]

The ASUPD and police departments at surrounding community college departments received 79 fully automatic M16 assault rifles through a notorious Department of Defense program that funnels military weapons to local police departments.

From "Operation Safe and Sober" ASU entered into a steady stream of bad news. To cite only a few incidents: In December 2013, Tempe police discovered that an ASU student was running an ecstasy lab out of his campus apartment. In January 2014, a fraternity was suspended for sponsoring an "MLK Black Party," which mixed racial minstrelsy and underage drinking. At the end of March that year, an inebriated 18-year-old student fell to her death from a balcony. Earlier that night, she had attended what one might call an all-you-can-drink party thrown by a fraternity so notorious that its charter had been revoked, and the fraternity kicked off campus.[82]

In May, ASU appeared on a list of universities under investigation by the Office of Civil Rights for possible violations of its handling of sexual harassment complaints. A student organization (Sun Devils Against Sexual Assault) has been collating instances of rape and sexual harassment at ASU. These range from sexual coercion within fraternity hazing practices, sexual assault associated with the campus party culture, and harassment of students by faculty within the campus's honors college.[83]

Increasingly, we know our local university as a walled-in compound, as a "safe space" that no one can actually afford to enter. And yet the campus appears in the headlines as a space of violence and harassment, a space defined by rape culture and besieged by federal complaints.

The story cycle of campus life is defined by shame and anger. As a character, the student is a source of constant embarrassment. Students take on too much debt, drink too much, and go looking for trouble. The professor is a figure of national resentment: Teachers don't work hard enough; they are entitled and demanding. It seems that we can't pay them too little. Too often, teachers and students make the headlines as monsters or as spectacular victims—evidence of a system gone off the rails.

Quietly, the university staff disappears from the story, with their jobs.

Throughout the 2013–2014 academic year that concluded with Ore's arrest, an anonymous group of ASUPD employees (current and former) published "The Integrity Report," an intensely detailed blog describing abuses of power and authority within the university's police department, as well as the university administration's deliberate negligence regarding major problems in staffing levels, training and in supervision.[84]

A July 2, 2014 post flags two cases for a promised FBI review: one incident involves the use of a Taser on a suspect in handcuffs; another describes a sergeant with an "entire history of issues with race." This man, the bloggers explain (addressing themselves to the FBI), "was most likely the supervisor on nights for the case [Ore's arrest] you are investigating." A constant in nearly nine months of posts: police officers frustrated by a meaningless internal review process—the same review process that was used, at first, to sweep Ore's arrest under a rug.

"Let me see your ID or I will arrest you," is not an invitation to conversation. It is, technically, a form of detention. "Show me your papers." Meaning: "You have no choice but to accept my authority. You will comply or you will be arrested." The state of Arizona has made this demand for papers into the foundation of its alarming relationship to the people who live there.

A scholar specializing in the discourses of race and power, Dr. Ore would know far too much about this subject to consider herself safe in the hands of any police officer who approached her with the level of hostility and contempt on display in the dashcam recording. In the video that went viral, we see her resist the policeman's address of her as stupid and criminal. She asks that the policeman speak to her with respect. She is non-compliant, given the terms of the exchange—does that mean, however, that she should have been thrown to the ground and arrested?

In May 2013, ASUP officers patrolling a parking lot pulled up to ASU student Faith Maxson's car and asked her for ID. As she wasn't accused of doing anything wrong, Maxson refused.

The 18-year-old was dragged out of her parked car and pulled onto the pavement. She was tied up, held face-down on the ground and searched. A judge ruled against the ASUPD in Maxon's case, finding that the request for her ID was inappropriate, and that Maxson was within her rights to refuse.

In a video recording of that incident, we can hear Faith Maxson praying as the policemen ran their hands over her body. She prays to god, asking him to help her get through it.

In the video of *her* arrest, Dr. Ore can be heard asserting her position within the university: "I'm a professor." She identifies herself as a member of the community: students, staff and faculty hang on to the notion that we work together. Many of us work at universities because are invested in the relationship between collective knowledge production and positive social change—whether we are teachers or campus cops, we tend to understand ourselves as part of a "good thing"—the work of education. Our sense of the campus as a safe space, the principle of the thing, is routinely deployed against us.

On November 18, 2011, like Tabatabainajad, the seated UC Davis students were "passively resisting." They, too, were exercising their civil rights and insisting on "the principle of the thing." When Lieutenant Pike saturated them with PepperSpray they slumped over. They didn't seem to do much else. At the moment the violence happened, it was like that violence wasn't happening.

A few people began to crawl away. A scrum of police officers formed over a couple of student bodies—were they pulling the students' arms away from their faces so that they could be sprayed more? Were they trying to pry the students apart from each other? What was the point of all this, if the police could step over and around the students? What was the principle of this thing?

The moment was captured by protestors, by people walking across the grounds, people hanging out with their friends. It was filmed by the Chief of Police, who "during the most turbulent minutes of this operation" stood back, "filming the police actions with her cell phone."[85] As chaotic and as strange as the event was, it is a miracle that it produced such an economical image in Macabitas's snapshot.

Lieutenant Pike is at work. He is a man watering his lawn. Routine maintenance. In his head, he is somewhere else. Perhaps he was thinking about the meeting in which his question was ignored, the stupidity of it all.

The disinterest of his posture is mirrored by the submissiveness of his targets. The image of their encounter is an allegory. It is not the image of an encounter between subjects. It is a diagram; an encounter with a mode of relation. It is an allegory for administration.

The aggressor and the aggressed, neither expresses a thought or feeling. It is not "an attack" but "an incident." "The pepper spray incident." A rule was administered; a rule was enforced—but was its enforcement administered properly?

He is our allegorical cop—the subject of formal and informal sermons, the agreed-upon example of authority gone wrong. The image made him a figure for total complicity with the system. Depending on one's point of view, he was following orders or he was *just* following orders.

It is a typical campus scandal. Whose rights were violated? What policy was ignored? There must be an investigation.

> Our overriding conclusion can be stated briefly and explicitly. The pepper spraying incident that took place on November 18, 2011 should and could have been prevented.[86]

Independent investigations of campus disasters never fail to make this kind of observation. Internal investigations, however, tend to conclude that things were inevitable.[87] Things just happen.

Can something be both avoidable and inevitable?

"Corporate social responsibility," Stefano Harney and Fred Moten observe, "is sincere." This administrative literature—reports and investigations, white papers and memos, complaints and resolutions—is remarkable for its lack of irony.

It is the administration of harassment, the harassment of administration. Each administrative digest of "an incident" fracks an encounter between subjects to convert an outrage into a policy. Anger is turned into violence; violence is turned into administrative process. University resources—time, energy, thought and compassion—are absorbed by a managerial world averse to the interpersonal, lateral and dynamic work of education. The latter is full of risk. The classroom is the university's soft flesh.

These reports appear before us as governance, as "a kind of exploratory drilling with a responsibility bit."[88] The purpose of this literature is to discern the governable from the ungovernable; that which can be disciplined from that which cannot learn. That which can be captured from that which escapes. Independent and internal investigative reports, consulting firms and their diagnostic reports—these organs squeeze life into policy; "the vitality of life" is the problem that provokes policy into being, and it is also that which can never be "responsible."[89] It is that for which an administration is responsible, but also that which it must expel, render into an intrusive "non-affiliate."[90]

Sex itself. The brown man from Oakland. The very young girl.

The campus is defined by its effort to identify and expel the outsider—by this war against itself. Variations on the expulsion hearing.

Students are mined for their debt capacity, and then discarded; the desire for social mobility is used to sell students the same loans that also keep their teachers on the economic margins. The workers that normally give the campus, as a place, its local character—the office managers, the student advisors and the groundskeepers—are outsourced and de-skilled. In this zone of exclusion, black and brown people are treated as always already unruly and non-compliant, as intrusions from the outside ("show me your ID").

"You have to break relationships and replace them with processes." An unidentified man, a consultant, is filmed explaining this to University of California administrators in Frederick Wiseman's documentary *At Berkeley* (2013). Wiseman's four-hour portrait of the University of California campus includes extensive footage from a 2010 administrative workshop discussing the implementation of recommendations that Berkeley's leadership solicited from a private consulting firm (Bain & Company) in the form of a three million dollar report on *Operational Excellence*.[91]

"You cannot optimize relationships," the unnamed man says, so you must break them. You cannot control relationships, but "you own the process." It is not obvious, given the tone of the meeting and the abstraction of the language through which that meeting is conducted, that they are talking about firing people. (In the language of university administration, firing, quitting and dying are all described as "separation.") The topic of that 2010 workshop was the institution of structural changes in the workplace—such as the centralization of lower-level administrative labor so that the woman who has, say, handled payroll and expenses for a department, who knows the department's PhD students by name, will be fired and replaced with someone working at a centralized call center not *at Berkeley*, but two hundred miles away in the California desert. This new university employee—removed from the campus, working in a low-wage gulag—will never know with or for whom she labors. There will be no students at her workplace. Unless the students work there themselves.

The financing for the 200-million-dollar payroll centralization project has been spread out over twenty years. It will be outmoded by the time it is implemented. Everywhere we encounter the same thing. It is a fractal logic in which the micro of individual student indebtedness is mirrored in the macro financing of the processes that deepen our alienation from the campus as a workplace.[92]

Can we see the image of that alienation in the image of Officer Pike at work? In the image of a professor being frisked? A student, hogtied and searched? A young woman, violated?

These images contain within them the problem of the nature of our workplace, but also the shadows of Oscar Grant, Trayvon Martin, Michael Brown (each one, an echo of another brutal shot).

This is a bad translation: the encounter with authority gone amok is recast on campus as a confrontation between The Spoiled Brat and the Fat Policeman. Isn't this how the country sees the student? Rich and lazy. "Privileged" because school is a scandalous luxury. Or that student is poor, naive and foolish.

An indentured servant, anchored to poverty like the Lithuanian workers of Upton Sinclair's novel *The Jungle*. Too embarrassed to question the terms of their mortgage, they sign the papers to spare the awkwardness of revealing their illiteracy or suggesting the banker is a crook, even though, in their guts, they know that is just what he is.

Michael Brown was days away from attending a for-profit school—a technical college that is only technically a college, a college that is already in court fighting outraged students mired in pointless debt.[93]

The students are an embarrassment. Teaching and learning, the immaterial labor that defines the university, must be exiled from the picture. And so our students submit their papers via plagiarism-detection platforms called TurnItIn and SafeAssign. These programs "read" for us, they tell us who the cheaters are so we know our classrooms are secure.

Bastions of privilege (Stanford, Princeton) refuse to treat students as if every single one of them was dishonest. The rest of us are encouraged to go with the flow. Instead of teaching students how to confront and work-through the natural confusion and anxiety produced by the fact that one's words *always* came from somewhere else (from the "outside"), we defer that work to an algorithm. We swap out teaching for securitization—for the internalization within every student of that same sense of being always-already-in-violation that defines the campus.

It is just as well. Our classes are too large to address the social intimacy of thought and expression with any responsibility. And so offending students, the plagiarists, miraculously identified like so many needles in so many haystacks, are palmed off on an understaffed "integrity" office, and the professor gets to indulge the minor thrill of the policeman working his beat.

Or, more likely, given the statistics, this administrative problem is first intercepted by an adjunct teacher paid less than $24,000 a year. If that teacher cares (and a great many do), this cheater will bear the brunt of her rage not at the student lie—but at the mass extinction of the possibility of teaching and learning.

The university's collective betrayal of the work of teaching is a humiliation—and so we have the culture of the bully: the stupid aggression provoked uniquely by a certain kind of shame—the shame of the noble patriarch who had devoted his life to the campus. The disavowal of one's privilege, the refusal of one's sense of injury and one's capacity to hurt. The determination not to know the truth (that it is we who have ruined things) is manifested as an intense paranoia: every student is a liar; every lie must be found. Why not just soak the whole campus with PepperSpray?

Seated, heads tucked behind their arms—is this not the posture of today's student? Brace position.

Is this what we mean when people talk about "campus rape culture"? The students resist. "We are children!" the students yell, mirroring the opinion of their Chancellors. The whole student body becomes the "violated young girl," that cipher of responsibility. And a whole world turns on her, and then shames her for provoking their violence.

The standing, shouting, angry protesters of the 1960s—the ones for whom an education was nearly free—we imagine that they disappeared but they have not. It is their iconicity that has waned. The outraged crowd does not represent the university campus. Nor do images of the police beating us. It is not the professor dragged by her hair, or knocked off a wall. It is not the professor in handcuffs. It isn't the student blinded by police indifference. The student whose fingers are broken. Nor is it the student who knows something is wrong, and will shout that outrage even as he is tortured in the library. Who has the time to hold all these people in mind? Who can see them behind the ramparts?

The image of non-violent protest means less, as the non-violent action is reframed as non-compliance.

These awful encounters between students, between university staff and students, between the university public and campus cops, between the security apparatus and the idea of the "very young girl," between the madman and the campus, between the idea of the very young girl and the actual people who must navigate a world designed to protect her from them—this is the campus the public sees, this is the campus the public *wants*, just as it wants another episode of *Law & Order*.

The student body becomes both the "girl" and the "non-affiliate" who threatens her—the black or brown man with his hoodie raised, the guy who went out for a walk and was murdered in an act of "self defense." We are frozen in our steps: hands up! Don't shoot the students!

NOTES

1. I teach at the University of California, Riverside: on July 19, 2012, The Regents of the University of California (the system's governing body) met at my campus. Their meetings always provoke a protest at the host campus: rumors are that Riverside was chosen for this particular meeting (when the whole UC administration was particularly embattled) on the assumption that our campus was more peaceable, more remote, and, perhaps, less iconic. Protesters came from University of California, California State and Community College campuses across the region and surrounded the building at the Regent's meeting. While I was in the crowd, I stood behind Ken Ehrlich (who had taught at UCR for a decade and whose arrest I mention), and next to undergraduate students enrolled in my classes. I left as, I thought, the protest was breaking up: behind the building, however, the police assaulted demonstrators with batons and with plastic pellets fired from a "launcher" that looks like an AK-47. (I discuss the use of the Pepperball Launcher below, in relation to a 2005 incident at UC Davis.) One of the students that had been standing near me came to our class that afternoon with an open wound on his shin. That this student came to class with that wound, barely 30 minutes after they were assaulted, speaks volumes about the degree to which hyper-vigilance and violence have become part of the routine of campus policing.

2. The Reynoso Task Force, "UC Davis November 18, 2011 'Pepper Spray Incident' Task Force Report" (March 2012), 8. Referred to below at *RTF* (Davis, 2011).

3. *RTF*, 114.

4. *RTF*, 21. Also: "According to Chancellor Katehi, she had observed that 'there are a lot of kids who go out to private parties very late … as you go to Saturday. And we thought … we did not want this to become a place where people come for fun. We worried about the use of alcohol and drugs and everything.' Chancellor Katehi 'was adamant that she didn't want them to stay one more night' and 'was worried, since it was a Friday night that it would become a party and impossible for us to do what was asked of us…remove the tents,' according to a document attached to an email sent by Chief Spicuzza." *RTF*, 52.

5. Sabrina Rubin Erdely, "A Rape on Campus," *Rolling Stone*, 19 November 2014. http://www.rollingstone.com/culture/features/a-rape-on-campus-20141119.

6. For an overview of the structure of the rape narrative, and the troubled status of truth and women's writing/speaking about rape, see Frances Ferguson, "Rape and the Rise of the Novel," *Representations* 20 (1987), 88–112. The *Rolling Stone* story would become the basis for an episode of *Law & Order: SVU* (S16/E18): "A Devastating Story," in which the "real" problem is not the irresponsible journalist but a feminist studies professor who pressures a student to exaggerate when she discloses her rape to university officials.

7. As of the fall of 2014, UVA had never expelled a student for having committed to sexual assault. Fraternity gang rape is, in fact, part of the University of Virginia's history. Liz Seccuro's *Crash Into Me: A Survivor's Search for Justice* (Bloomsbury, 2011) is an influential account of a university's total failure of a female student who was raped by three men. She was assaulted at Phi Kappa Psi, the University of Virginia fraternity named in the *Rolling Stone* article.

8. Sheila Coronel, Steve Coll, Derek Kravitz, "*Rolling Stone* and UVA: The Columbia University Graduate School of Journalism Report," *Rolling Stone*, April 5, 2015.

9. The Higher Education Act reaches deep into every aspect of university life. Since 1965 it has authorized (for example) Pell

Grants, Perkins and PLUS loans; the Jacob Javits fellowship program; teacher-training programs; federal work-study programs; federal assistance for HBCUs; support for diversification in STEM fields; grants to combat violence against women on college campuses (in 1998, recently renewed)—almost every project instrumental to the opening up of higher education to the public falls under the domain of the Higher Education Act. HEA is periodically renewed and amended by congress; it was its renewal in 1972 that occasioned the passage of Title IX. Sexual assault/harassment cases may trigger engagement with other forms of legislation—including the Civil Rights Act.

10. The campus is infected by the fear of being in violation; and yet the Federal government has never actually dropped the axe it holds over the campus's head. No university has ever been punished by the withdrawal of federal funding. When universities pay, it is to settle individual lawsuits.

11. Rachel Hall, "'It Can Happen to You': Rape Prevention in the Age of Risk Management" in *Hypathia* 19:3 (2004), 1–19, 1.

12. It is important, when reviewing statistics on the frequency of rape on college campuses, to bear in mind that by some measures, 80% of rape attempts are made against women who are under the age of 25. Women attending college may not be at risk because they are attending college, in other words, but because they are young. In 2013–2014, there was much debate from within professional communities regarding popularly cited sexual assault rates, including those invoked in this memo. The 2011 Dear Colleague letter reports that 1 in 5 women students in the United States report being victims of rape or attempted rape—that figure is now widely viewed as misleading (see below). Futhermore, as high (and controversial) as these statistics are, they are not as high as they are for people in the military, or for the incarcerated (those rates are not disputed). In 2014, the Department of Justice published more conservative figures regarding how many college-aged women are victimized by sexual assault: 6.1 per 1000. This is slightly *lower* than for non-students of the same age. The popular declaration that "1 in 5 college students will be raped" is a misapplication of the study

cited in the "Dear Colleague" memo. That report (based on on-line surveys of nearly 7,000 students at two large, public universities) found that approximately 1 in 5 women students identified themselves as victims of a "completed sexual assault," and 1 in 7 identified themselves as victims of a "completed rape." There is, in other words, some confusion in popular discourse regarding the difference between "assault" and "rape." (See Cristopher Krebs et al., "The Campus Sexual Assault Study: Final Report," RTI International for the US Department of Justice [2007].) This goes to one of the challenges of such surveys: some people do not identify their experiences of sexual coercion with the language of rape, sexual assault, and crime—when asked if they have raped, interviewees have a tendency to under-report, because the definition of rape is so ideological, even for victims. How people answer questions about sexual violence and assault, and how people interpret those responses is, in other words, intensely variable (and is itself the subject of research). A 2015 Washington Post-Kaiser Family Foundation study attempted to address this in its survey of 1,000 undergraduate students. This study found that nearly 25% of women and 7% of men in college report having been subjected to an "unwanted sexual incident." This study (which included follow-up interviews with a range of students) did not compare its sample with non-students. See Nick Anderson and Scott Clement, "1 in 5 College Women Say They Were Violated," 20 May 2015. Available data seems to be clear on the following point: people not in college are more vulnerable than those who are. See Sofi Sinozich and Lynn Langton, "Special Report: Rape and Sexual Assault Victimization Among College-Age Females, 1995–2013," U.S. Department of Justice: Bureau of Justice Statistics, December 2014. This is not to minimize the problem of sexual assault—but to ask why the rates of sexual assault on college campuses are the site of so much outrage, if women not in college are, in fact, at even greater risk.

13. April 4, 2011, "Dear Colleague" letter.

14. Jake New, "Major Sexual Assault Settlement," *Inside Higher Education* 21 July, 2014, web: http://www.insidehighered.com/

news/2014/07/18/u-connecticut-pay-13-million-settle-sexual-assault-lawsuit#ixzz3818IBK2e.

15. In the problem of campus security we encounter a first world, microcosmic cousin of processes described by Paul Amar (2013) in *The Security Archipelago: Human-Security States, Sexuality Politics and the End of Neo-Liberalism* (Duke University Press, 2013). Amar's work addresses "the sexualizing and moralizing discourses of cultural rescue and trafficking prevention that human-security regimes use to justify their actions" across the Global South (Amar, 15). Security states mobilize in the name of the vulnerable, and enact a "humanization (or, in these times, 'humanitarianization') of military and police security apparatuses." Amar argues that the subjects identified by the state (or, more nearly, by what Amar describes as the "parastatal") as vulnerable "should be more accurately analyzed as human-security products emerging in particular gender, racial, and transnational forms in and around military and police operations and parastatal security projects." Might not the campus itself, and the violated student that it protects, be one such "product"?

16. "Some but not all studies reveal that trial participation predicted negative outcomes. Rape victims whose cases were tried in court scored higher on measures of distress than those whose cases were not prosecuted." Mary P. Koss, Karen J. Bachar, C. Quince Hopkins and Carolyn Carlson, "Expanding a Community's Justice response to Sex Crimes Through Advocacy, Prosecutorial and Public Health Collaborations: Introducing the RESTORE Program" in *Journal of Interpersonal Violence* 19 (2004), 1435–1463, 1141.

17. Sharon Marcus, "Fighting Bodies/Fighting Words: A Theory and Politics of Rape Prevention" in Judith Butler ed., *Feminists Theorize the Political* (New York: Routledge, 2002), 364.

18. See Carly Parnitzke Smith and Jennifer J. Freyd, "Institutional Betrayal" in *American Psychologist* 69:4 (2014), 575–587.

19. Mary P. Koss et al. (2004), 1439.

20. See Callie Marie Pennington and Lynn A. Addington, "Violence Against College Women: A Review to Identify Limitations in Defining the Problem and Inform Future Research," *Trauma Violence Abuse* (July 2014) 15:3, 159–169. The authors of this study use the National Crime Victimization Survey to review rates of sexual assault for women between the ages of 18–24, and find that women who are not in college are 1.7 times more likely to be subjected to violence than are women students. This study is discussed briefly by Emily Yoffe in "The College Rape Overcorrection," *Slate*, 7 December, 2014.

21. I discuss a case like this in my sportswriting. See Jennifer Doyle, "What Happens When a Teammate Rapes a Teammate," *Deadspin* (7 November, 2013). Web. http://deadspin.com/what-happens-when-teammates-rape-a-teammate-1460111117 Originally published as "The Rape of a Teammate" on *The Sport Spectacle*, 6 November 2013. http://thesportspectacle.com/2013/11/06/rape-of-a-teammate.

22. This is one reason restorative and community-based models for justice refuse adversarial structures. See Mary P. Koss et al. (2004) and Sarah Deer's "Towards an Indigenous Jurisprudence of Rape" in *Kansas Journal of Law and Public Policy* (2004) for an overview of sexual violence and tribal justice models within Native American communities: Deer reviews restorative practices that are also decolonizing. The models she describes there (centered on healing victim and community) have interesting resonances for the campus community, perhaps in part because of the strong identification that members of that community have with the university itself.

23. Angela Carter, *The Sadeian Woman and the Ideology of Pornography* (New York: Pantheon Books, 1978), p. 55.

24. See Emily Yoffe, "The College Rape Overcorrection," *Slate*, 7 December, 2014. Yoffe exaggerates (almost every mass media citation of statistics regarding sexual violence is exaggerated): In the DRC, rates of sexual violence are roughly twice that cited by the 2011 Dear Colleague letter. Closer are statistics generated by surveys of South African women; in South Africa, violent sexual

assault is widely recognized as of epidemic proportion. See, for example, "A look behind the statistics of South Africa's rape epidemic," *Humanitarian News and Analysis*/The Office of the UN Coordination for Human Affairs, 1 November, 2013:

> "Rape is one of the most under-reported crimes in South Africa," noted the NGO coalition Shukumisa. It points to research, conducted in Gauteng in 2010, that found one-quarter of women questioned in the study "had been raped in the course of their lifetimes, while almost one in 12 women had been raped in 2009. But only one in 13 women raped by a non-partner reported the matter to the police, while only one in 25 of the women raped by their partners reported this to the police."

Are American women college students as vulnerable to rape as are women living in Gauteng? The affective climate surrounding conversation about rape is super-saturated: it is at times impossible to forward critical comparison, review, analysis of statistics—to question the "1 in 4" statistic is to somehow ask the public to take *rape less seriously*. This illogic is not altogether different from the editorial failures that led to the publication of a story pivoting on a false rape allegation in *Rolling Stone*. The discourse of sex/rape marks the whole subject off, as beyond the scope of analysis.

25. Callie Marie Rennison, "Privilege, Among Rape Victims," *The New York Times*, 21 December, 2014, A27. See also Callie Marie Rennison and Lynn A. Addington, "Violence Against College Women: A Review to Identify Limitations in Defining the Problem and Inform Future Research" in *Trauma, Abuse & Violence* 15:3 (2014), 159–169.

26. For a critique of the alignment of anti-rape movements with a culture of incarceration, see, for example, Dean Spade, *Normal Life: Administrative Violence, Critical Trans Politics, and the Limits of the Law* (Brooklyn: South End Press, 2011); Beth E. Richie, "A Black Feminist Reflection on the Antiviolence Movement," *Signs: Journal of Women in Culture and Society* 25:4 (2000).

27. Katie Koestner and Brett Sokolow, The National Council of Higher Education Risk Management Group, "Eliminating Force from Campus Sexual Misconduct Policies: The Rise of the Consent Construct" (n.d.), http://ncherm.org/pdfs/elimforce.pdf:

> The onus of giving consent is taken away from the object of the sexual initiator, instead requiring that the initiator gain that consent from the object of the sexual attention before any permissible sexual activity may take place. This re-emergence of consent-based doctrine recognizes and ratifies a simple principle of the common law—our personal sovereignty.

Also, Brett Sokolow, "NCHERM's 2005 Whitepaper: The Typology of Campus Sexual Misconduct Complaints" http://ncherm.org/pdfs/2005NC3.pdf:

> Consent was the way the law updated proof standards. It shifted the burden from the victim to resist, and placed the responsibility for obtaining sexual permission on the aggressor, or initiator of the sexual activity. The core of consent is the right of the victim to be unmolested until she gives clear permission for sexual activity to take place—what I call sexual sovereignty. Silence, in and of itself, cannot function as consent. With all due respect to Johnny Cochran, and his famous "If it doesn't fit, you must acquit," defense in the O.J. Simpson case, I have my own pithy version for sex: "If there's no consent, you must relent."

The term has special importance to the struggle against colonial forms of violence, and so it is odd to see it appear in white papers written by a risk management firm. It is used in the recovery of colonial histories of systemic rape, forced pregnancy/ sterility, and punitive gender policing. It is a way of naming gendered forms of violence as integral to genocidal practice. It is also used by feminist scholars working within communities of color, advocating for gender equity and sexual empowerment as an integral part of an anti-racist politics. Within queer scholarship, the term appears in a conversation about what it means to maintain a sense of agency as sexual subjects while also acknowledging that our bodies are not miniature states (or, at least, that this is not what our bodies *ought* to be); that being (not just being sexual, but *being*) is a form of undoing, unmaking boundaries and borders. Much feminist and queer scholarship contests the association of the sexual with the discourse of "rights" as it appears within liberal/neoliberal discourse; on the college campus, however, those "rights" morph into something else: a need for security. See, for examples of feminist/queer work with the term, Andrea Smith, *Conquest* (South End Press, 2005); Jasbir Puar, *Terrorist Assemblages: Homonationalism in Queer Times* (Duke University Press, 2007); Elizabeth Povinelli, *Economies of Abandonment: Social Enduring and Belonging in Late Liberalism* (Duke University Press, 2011).

28. Michel Foucault, *The History of Sexuality, Volume 1: An Introduction* (New York, Vintage, 1980), 156–157.

29. Rachel Hall observes: "rape is positioned as a prediscursive flow of violence that precedes not only the victims of rape but the rapists themselves. Rape seems, therefore, not only omnipotent but also inevitable." (Hall, 8)

30. See Kelley Anne Malinen, "Thinking Woman-to-Woman Rape: A Critique of Marcus's 'Theory and Politics of Rape Prevention'" in *Sexuality & Culture* (2013) 17: 360–376.

31. UC Riverside professor Lindon Barrett was murdered on July 13, 2008 by a 22-year-old man who would later die in jail; Indiana University professor Don Belton was murdered in December 2009 by a 25-year-old man who would attempt (unsuccessfully) to use a "gay panic" defense at his trial.

32. See Sharon Marcus, "Fighting Words." Feminist self-defense workshops seek to re-educate people regarding gender, embodied experiences of violence and the capacity to be violent. Phillip M. Norrell and Shelley H. Bradford offer a useful literature review of studies exploring the effectiveness of self-defense training in both prevention and recovery programs in their article, "Finding the Beauty in the Beast: Resistance as a Rape Prevention Strategy" in *National Social Science Journal* 40:2 (2013), 74–87.

33. See J. Laplanche and J.B. Pontalis, "Fantasy and the Origins of Sexuality," *International Journal of Psychoanalysis*, 49:1 (1968), 1–18.

34. See Rachel Hall, "'It Can Happen to You': Rape Prevention in the Age of Risk Management" in *Hypathia* 19:3 (2004), 1–19, 10–11.

35. Rachel Hall, 14. "In its most universal and aesthetic treatments," Hall laments, "rape is portrayed as the tragic and timeless violent dance between the sexes" (10).

36. Jasbir Puar addresses the politics of race, sexuality and mediation in the story of Clementi's suicide in "Ecologies of Sex, Sensation, and Slow Death," *Periscope/Social Text* 22 November, 2011:

> Missing from the debate about Clementi's suicide is a discussion about the proclivities of young people to see the "choice" of internet surveillance as a mandatory regulatory part not only of their subject formations, but of their daily bodily habits and affective tendencies. For these youth "cyberstalking" is an integral part of what it means to become a neoliberal (sexual) subject. Think of the ubiquity of sexting, and applications like Grinder, Manhunt, and of productions like DIY porn, and cellphone mass circulation of images, technologies that create simultaneous sensations of exposure (the whole world is watching) and alienation (no one understands). These bodily technological practices constitute new relations between public and private that we have yet to really acknowledge, much less comprehend. Legal discourse itself is clear that "invasion of privacy" remains uncharted territory for jurisprudence in relation to the internet. But more significantly […] the use of these technologies impel new affective tendencies of bodies, new forms of attention, intention, distraction, practice and repetition. What might easily be overdetermined as the difference between "gay" and "straight" could otherwise be thought of more generously through the quotidian and banal activities of self sexual elaboration through internet technologies—emergent habituations, corporeal comportment,

and an array of diverse switchpoints of bodily capacity. (http://socialtextjournal.org/periscope_article/ecologies_of_sex_sensation_and_slow_death/)

37. Assembly Bill No. 3466, submitted November 15, 2010 and passed on November 22, 2010, strengthens the enforcement of anti-bullying laws passed in 2002.

38. See Ian Parker, "The Story of a Suicide," *The New Yorker*, 6 February 2012.

39. I take the term "psychic skin" from Didier Anzieu et al., *Psychic Envelopes* (London: H. Karnac Books, 1990).

40. Police Assessment Resource Center, "A Bad Night at Powell Library: The Events of November 14, 2006" (August 2007), 38.

41. "Statement of Mostafa Tabatabainejad" (2007), hosted on the website for the firm that handled his case, Schonbrun, DeSinone, Seplow, Harris & Hoffman LLP. http://www.sdshh-law.com/tabatabainejad.html.

42. "A Bad Night at Powell Library," 1.

43. "A Bad Night at Powell Library," 21. Perhaps he was "using his body weight to pull downward" in the same way that a UCPD officer "guided" UC Berkeley Integrative Biology Professor Robert Dudley to the ground on November 20, 2009 before arresting him at a demonstration outside of Wheeler Hall:

> to get a better view of what was happening, [Professor Dudley] jumped up on the retaining wall that bordered the Wheeler lawn in that area. As he stabilized his perch on the edge of the planer box, he tore the yellow police tape that was cordoning off the west Wheeler lawn.
>
> An officer responded immediately and, without prior verbal warning, grabbed the professor from behind, twisting him around, and "guiding" him to the ground, where the professor came to rest, face down.
>
> U.C. Berkeley Police Report Review Board, "November 20, 2009: Review, Reflection & Recommendations—A

report by the Police Review Board, University of California, Berkeley" (June 14, 2010), 48.

44. "A Bad Night at Powell Library," 29.

45. "A Bad Night at Powell Library," 41.

46. Paul Virilio, *The Administration of Fear* (Los Angeles: Semiotext(e), 2012), 53.

47. Monique Wittig, "The Category of Sex," in *The Straight Mind and Other Essays*, 7.

48. My two internal Title IX complaints (filed at UCR in 2010), as well as an EEOC complaint (filed in 2011) are included in my employment record. They are listed as "University Service."

49. "[Penn State University Police Department Detective Roy] Schreffler said he delayed pulling an incident number for the Sandusky investigation because it was his normal procedure for drug investigations and he was not initially sure what type of investigation he had. Schreffler did not know why the report ultimately was opened as an 'Administrative Information' file but said he may have been the one who decided on the label. All pages of the police report are labeled 'Administrative Information.'" Free, Sporkin & Sullivan, "Report of the Special Investigative Counsel Regarding the Actions of the Pennsylvania State University Related to the Child Sexual Abuse Committed by Gerald A. Sandusky," 12 July 2012, 48–49. Referred to here as "Freeh."

50. See, for example: Don Van Natta Jr., "The Whistleblower's Last Stand," *ESPN: The Magazine*, 4 March 2014.

51. "Freeh," 14.

52. At the time, the professorship was held by Michael Berube. Berube resigned and posted an eloquent letter describing his ambivalence about having to do so. See: Michael Bérubé, "Why I Resigned the Paterno Chair," 15 October 2012, *The Chronicle of Higher Education*.

53. A few November 10 headlines: "Joe Paterno Fired, Penn State Students Riot" (ABC News); "Why Penn State Students Rioted—They Deify Joe Paterno" (Christian Science Monitor); "Thousands of Students Riot Over Firing of Child Rapist's Protector" (Gawker).

54. Nate Schweber, "Penn State Students Clash With Police in Unrest After Announcement," *New York Times*, 10 November 2011.

55. Dave Zirin, "Penn State and Berkeley: A Tale of Two Protests," *The Nation*, 10 November 2011. Zirin refers to a November 9 protest at UC Berkeley. That protest—which was violently suppressed by UCPD—would later figure into decision-making by police and by administration at UC Davis. Zirin writes that no students were arrested. Local news reported, however, that at Penn State "dozens of students were criminally charged" and over the summer of 2012, guilty pleas "piled up" as students struggled to avoid long jail sentences. One student, at Penn State on an ROTC scholarship, was kicked out of that program and is now forced to pay back $34,000 of scholarship money. See Michael Rubinkaum, "PSU Riot Ends Aspiring Army Officer's Dream," *NBC Philadelphia*, 27 August 2012.

56. See, for example, Kate Zernike, "Players in Sayerville Football Hazing and Abuse Case Will Be Tried as Juveniles," *New York Times*, 10 Nov, 2014.

57. Holly Otterbein, "Member of Penn State's Kappa Delta Rho Defends Fraternity," *Philly.com* 18 March 2015: "It's like, yeah, girls pass out or fall asleep all the time and somebody takes a Snapchat or a picture and, like, it's not that it's funny. But it's just satire." Revenge porn is the unauthorized distribution of intimate photography produced within the context of a romantic relationship. The Pennsylvania law was introduced as Senate Bill 1167, and was passed in 2014. "Revenge porn" is also its own pornographic genre and is sometimes produced (consensually within scripted scenarios) for commercial purposes.

58. In 1998, as part of a police investigation that would ultimately go nowhere, Sandusky was confronted by the mother of a boy that he had abused. He denied having "sexual feelings" but

also said: "'I understand. I was wrong. I wish I could get forgiveness. I know I won't get it from you. I wish I was dead.'" Freeh Report, 45. The investigative literature reveals that among senior administrators collective concern for Sandusky's feelings far outweighed concern for victims and even the university itself.

59. *RTF* (Davis, 2011), Appendix A: Kroll Securities "Report to the Office of the President, University of California, UC Davis Incident, November 18, 2011," 65.

60. The Kroll Security report documents confusion amongst the police regarding their objective that afternoon:

> UCDPD officers provided Kroll investigators with a wide range of explanations regarding the mission of the operation. At one extreme was the explanation provided by Officer H who said "what I got out of that briefing was ... our mission was to remove the occupants from the Quad, that set up tents and were camping out" and Officer D who said that "our mission was to eliminate the Quad area of the tents and the occupiers that were there." At the other extreme was Officer L who stated, "We weren't to disperse the students. We weren't to limit or prohibit the amount of protesting that was happening. We were just there to take down the tents." Officer C, Officer K, Officer G, Officer D, and Officer I also understood that the operation's goal was to remove just the tents.
> RTF (Davis 2011), Appendix A, 71.

61. "...the discussion ended with Chief Spicuzza stating, 'All right, I get it ... I just don't want another Berkeley.'" RTF (Davis 2011), Appendix A, 65.

62. "While the officers were staged on Shields Avenue West, the Chief called them on her cell phone and said, 'I don't want to come in here like an army. Could you change that?' And they apparently told her, 'no.'" RTF (Davis 2011), Appendix A, 74.

63. "The events in other cities, particularly those in Oakland, caused [Berkeley] campus leadership considerable worry that an encampment on campus would quickly grow to large propor-

tions, much as Oakland's had quickly grown to dozens of tents…Moreover, they feared that Berkeley's campus would attract 'non-affiliates' from Occupy Oakland, whom they deemed more radical." Committee of the U.C. Berkeley Police Review Board, "Report on November 9, 2011" (May 29, 2012), 12.

64. For local reporting on this raid see Kristen J. Bender et al., "Ousted protesters marching back to Frank Ogawa Plaza," October 25, 2011, *San Jose Mercury News*; Mattai Kuruvila et al., "Police tear gas Occupy Oakland protesters," October 25, 2011, *SF Gate*. See also occupyoakland.org for sustained reporting on that raid and others. In July 2013, the Oakland Police Department paid out 1.17 million dollars to settle twelve complaints produced by the October 25 attack. The largest settlements went to Suzi Spangenberg, who suffered permanent hearing loss after police threw two CS Blast (noise) grenades at her feet (she was imploring them not to use violence), and Scott Campbell, who was shot on the inner thigh with a shotgun firing lead-filled beanbags. "Scott […] inadvertently captured his own shooting on video." He was filming the police's front line, he was clearly obeying their orders (to step back), the crowd was not advancing on police. Campbell asked the police several times "is this OK," to be sure he was standing where they wanted him. The police did not respond although it is clear from video that he could be heard. He was fired on without any warning, and police congratulated the shooter with "nice shot." That settlement was paired with another. The class action suit Spalding v. City of Oakland, CV11–2867 TEH, was filed on behalf of 150 demonstrators illegally arrested while protesting the murder of Oscar Grant. For information on both cases, including access to video, see "NLG Obtains $1.17M, OPD Reforms for Occupy Oakland Protesters and Journalists" on the website for The National Lawyers Guild: San Francisco Bay Area Chapter. http://www.nlgsf.org/news/nlg-obtains-117m-opd-reforms-occupy-oakland-protesters-and-journalists. One cannot overstate the importance of Oscar Grant and, more recently, Trayvon Martin's murders to black and brown college students. The increasing need for students to theatricalize, perform "non-violence" in a situation in which every demonstration of dissent

is read as a direct threat mirrors the instruction that young men of color receive regarding the importance of responding to police authority with total docility and compliance—even then such displays may never be enough to dismantle the racist ideology which reads the mere fact of their presence as a problem that must be solved. On public campuses in California, the students participating in these demonstrations are from a similar demographic to that cited in fear about "non-affiliates from Oakland," a demographic one might define as "the policed." "Oakland" is where our students live, it is where they are from, and it is where they are going.

65. *RTF* (Davis 2011), Appendix A, 62.

66. *RTF* (Davis 2011), Appendix A, 66.

67. *RTF* (Davis 2011), Appendix A, 97.

68. November 18, 2011 UCPD Respond to Occupy UC Davis, Daviswiki.org. Accessed October 15, 2013. daviswiki.org /November_18%2C_2011_UC_Davis_Police_Response_to_O ccupy_UC_Davis.

69. Nelson v. City of Davis et al., 10–16258, US Court of Appeals for the Ninth Circuit (1/7/2012), 968. A detailed account of what one might call the PepperBall Incident:

> The students testified in their depositions that they stood in the breezeway awaiting instructions from the police. At various times they called out to the police, asking the officers to inform them what they wanted the students to do, and repeatedly raised their hands to show their willingness to comply. The students were disturbed by the presence of the police in full riot gear, and some of Nelson's female companions began to cry...When the partygoers failed to disperse, Wilson ordered his team to "disperse them," at which point Barragan, Chang and Garcia shot pepperballs towards Nelson's group from a distance estimated by various parties to have been 45 to 150 feet away. A pepperball launched from one of the officers' guns struck Nelson in the eye. He immediately collapsed on the ground and fell into

the bushes where he writhed in pain for ten to fifteen minutes. Although unable to see, Nelson heard the officers proceed past where he lay, but none of them provided assistance. 7969

These were the "less lethal" weapons used against our students, at a closer range than at Davis, in a more crowded environment.

70. MK–9 is manufactured by First Defense, which specializes in "less lethal" instruments of force. First Defense and other companies providing the UCPD with their armor and weapons are owned by a corporation named after a favorite colonial pastime—The Safariland Group.

71. "Lt. Pike's actions and body language include stepping over the seated protesters to get to their faces, a move that would not generally be undertaken with a hostile crowd." *RTF* (Davis 2011), 19.

72. UC Berkeley spokesperson Claire Holmes, quoted by Jennifer Gollan in "UC Berkeley Pledges to Investigate Police Response to Occupy Cal Protest," *The Bay Citizen*. 11 November, 2011. Web.

73. "An Act to Create and Organize the University of California," California State Assembly Bill No. 583, introduced March 5, 1868. Section 14.

74. University of California Office of the President/Budget and Capital Resources, "UC Mandatory Student Charge Levels." Accessed October 16, 2013. http://budget.ucop.edu/fees/documents/history_fees.pdf.

75. You can watch UCPD officers shoving their batons into the torso of demonstrators on November 20, 2009 at the Wheeler Hall occupation and demonstration at Berkeley on Youtube. See "UC Berkeley Protests at Wheeler Hall, Part 2 Cops Attacking Students," uploaded by justinslee on Nov 20, 2009: http://youtu.be/H1PuiY4Go8Y; UC Berkeley PhD student Zhivka Valiavicharska's finger was broken when her hand was struck by a UCPD officer's baton. She had lightly rested it on a metal barricade. The UCPD claimed she was shaking the barricade.

Video clearly showing that she was telling the truth can also be seen on Youtube: "UC Berkeley Protests at Wheeler Hall, Pt. 1," uploaded by justinslee Nov. 20, 2009: http://youtu.be/d6q0ebKT-QU. See also Nanette Asimov, "UC Cop Cleared in '09 Broken Finger Case," *SF Gate*, Feb 14, 2010.

76. At Occupy Cal on November 9, 2011 UCPD officers pulled protestors to the ground by their hair, although these protesters had, in fact, offered themselves up for peaceful arrest, placing their hands in front of them in order that they might be cuffed. See "Police brutalize professors and students at Occupy Cal on Nov 9," uploaded by NationalBAMN on Nov. 10, 2011: http://youtube/kNHXuf6qJas.

77. Tyler Kinkade, "ASU Professor Slammed to the Ground by Police, Gets Arrested for Assaulting an Officer," The Huffington Post, 29 June 2014.

78. See "Statement of Concern from Arizona Critical Ethnic Studies" (25 June, 2014): http://azethnicstudies.com/archives/565; "National Outpouring of Support for Investigation of ASUPD" (3 July, 2014): http://azethnicstudies.com/archives/610; the initial release of raw video from the arrest on local television station's website, "Raw video: ASU professor arrested after struggle with the police" (27 June, 2014): http://www.azfamily.com/video/raw/Raw-video-ASU-professor-arrested-after-struggle-with-police-265002461.html.

79. "FAQs about the Arizona Racial Profiling Law," *ACLU.org* (17 May, 2010).

80. See ASU June 30 press release: https://asunews.asu.edu/20140630-ersula-ore; Ray Stern, "Officer Stewart Ferrin Resigns; ASU Reversed Findings of Second Incident," *Phoenix New Times* (17 Feb 2015); see also Anne Ryman's "ASU officer resigns over incident with professor" for the *Arizona Republic* (17 Feb 2015)—Ryman links to the ASU PD January 7 letter to Stewart Ferrin, which reviews the investigation's findings.

81. On "Safe and Sober" and policing pedestrians, see Mark Remillard, "Tempe Police begin back-to-school operation," *The*

State Press (21 August, 2013): http://www.statepress.com/2013/08/21/tempe-police-begin-back-to-school-operation/.

On 1367 arrests, see Matthew Hendley, "ASU Semester Still Going Strong: 510 Arrests by Alcohol Task Force in Third Weekend," *Phoenix New Times* (4 September, 2013): http://blogs.phoenixnewtimes.com/valleyfever/2013/09/asu_semester_still_going_stron.php; On the shooting of Austin Del Castillo, see Matthew Hendley, "Tempe Police Didn't Have to Shoot Austin Del Castillo, His Friends Say," *Phoenix New Times* (24 September, 2013): http://blogs.phoenixnewtimes.com/valleyfever/2013/09/tempe_police_didnt_have_to_sho.php.

82. Greg Argos, "ASU fraternity suspended after 'offensive' MLK party," CBS5AZ/kpho.com (20 January, 2014): http://www.kpho.com/story/24502600/asu-fraternity-suspended-after-offensive-mlk-party; Jim Walsh, "Tempe police: ASU student in fatal fall was at banned frat's party," 12 News & *The Arizona Republic* (3 April, 2014): http://www.azcentral.com/story/news/local/tempe/2014/04/03/tempe-police-asu-student-in-fatal-fall-was-at-banned-frats-party-abrk/7262599/.

83. See Sun Devils Against Sexual Assault: http://sundevilsagainstsexualassault.wordpress.com/.

84. The blog authored by ASUPD officers (current and former): https://network23.org/theintegrityreport/.

85. *RTF* (Davis 2011) 20.

86. *RTF* (Davis 2011), 5.

87. An internal investigation—conducted independently from the Kroll investigation—cleared Pike, creating no doubt an administrative problem as it was unthinkable that he would not be fired. See Sam Stanton, "UC Davis Chief Overruled Panel to Fire Pepper-Spray Officer," *Sacramento Bee* (August 2, 2012). It should be said, the Kroll Report does not isolate Pike as the incident's "cause." If anything, it supports Pike's observation that it was the campus administration that should have asked students to break down their camp; that it was wrong to ask the UCPD to enforce Student Conduct policy.

88. Stefano Harney and Fred Moten, *The Undercommons: Fugitive Planning & Black Study* (New York: Minor Compositions, 2013), 54.

89. These reports index a literature of governance; the aim of each document is to map responsibility with the aim of effecting "better" (more) policy. What we see, in the UC administration as a system, is an entropic escalation of managerial discourse and process all aimed at negating the possibility of injury. Rather than work from a recognition that a campus is a space of shared vulnerability, this discourse produces the campus as the promise of a harmless space; a space in which one is protected from even the possibility of injury. This is not a public, but an anti-public. This discourse turns the university workplace into an inversion of the meatpacking plant as it strips the immaterial labor of education from the body. The body becomes a fearful remain—a site and an instrument of injury. As Harney and Moten write, "The invitation to governmentality is made by way of transfer of responsibility, and immaterial labor is distinguished from the vitality of life, from its vessel, by the taking up of responsibility, and life is now distinguished by its overt irresponsibility" (*The Undercommons: Fugitive Planning & Black Study*, 54). Every one of these stories concludes with a body being beaten, a body whose story can only be narrated according to its irresponsibility— which, here, means either the "irresponsibility" of a student who refuses to show his ID on "fucking principle" (and so incurs an avoidable conflict) or the "irresponsibility" of the student who is the embodiment of innocence, "your child," "a young girl."

90. On January 19, 2012, a long-time UC Riverside lecturer, the artist Ken Ehrlich, was on the front line of the demonstration at our campus. He was part of a "book barricade" formed by demonstrators holding placards painted to look like their favorite titles. (His choice that day was Cornelius Castoriadas's collection of essays, *Figures of the Thinkable*.) We had trapped the University of California Regents in the student union—the Regents were meeting to decide on more cuts, more tuition hikes. The police broke up our demonstration by firing PepperBalls at the crowd and hitting some of our students. Ehrlich was thrown to the ground, arrested and charged with

felony assault with a weapon—by which they meant his placard. In the university's press release about the incident, Ehrlich, who has worked for the Art Department for over a decade, was identified by UC Riverside's press office as a non-affiliate, "an older man from Corona." The Riverside District Attorney eventually dropped the charges against Ehrlich. (For reporting on the initial event, see Mark Muckenfuss et al., "Protesters and arrests at UC regents meeting," January 19, 2012, *The Press Enterprise*.) The failure to recognize Ehrlich is hard to believe, given his authorship of markyudof.com, a satirical website declaring the resignation of the University of California President at that time, Mark Yudof. For that satirical gem, Ehrlich and the faculty whose server hosted the site were investigated by the University of California for misuse of university property. Those charges were also dropped. A Youtube video of the January 19 event: "Cops shoot protester at UC Riverside," uploaded by RT America on January 19, 2012. http://youtu.be/pT9VOYR7cMo. Mark Yudof retired from his position in 2013, and has been replaced by the former head of Homeland Security, Janet Napolitano.

91. Chris Newfield has written extensively about managerial ethics and university administration at the University of California. In September 2010, he responded to Bain & Company's three million dollar report, "Achieving Operational Excellence at the University of California, Berkeley" (May 2010). Newfield argues that the information collected in Bain's report suggests that the university administration ought to move to a "flatter" and "more participatory model," to reflect and in fact amplify the "*bottom-up, semi-autonomous, modular, and decentralized* architecture" of the campus. Bain & Company (and the University of California), however, treat the interpersonal nature of university work as a liability—assuming (against all evidence to the contrary) that intensely centralized hierarchies and abstracted work processes are the foundation of innovation and efficiency. "In other words," Newfield explains,

> local, horizontal, cross-functional relationships will be gutted, and replaced by vertical single-function reports. Those who think this siloing and verticalization will increase efficiency are

about thirty years behind in their reading of the management literature, which abounds with tales of the effectiveness of cross-functional teams and horizontal collaborations based on local needs. Similarly, Bain-OE promulgates the dumb idea that 'generalist' supervisors are a problem (52, 76), although in fact they are the indispensible coordinators in any distributed, necessarily non-standardized innovation system. The first victims of this OE regression towards something that looks even more like a 1950s multidivisional corporation will be staff, and the second victims will be the faculty members who have built up local staff collaborations over time on which, in reality, their productivity depends. But the goal is not to enhance faculty productivity, but to optimize the pan-university. The big losers will be individual academic departments—their staff and faculty alike. Staff will be pulled away from frontline operational reports and into the authority field of the central office controlling their specific function.

See Chris Newfield, "Bain's Blow to Berkeley," September 14, 2010, Remaking the University (http://utotherescue.blogspot.co.uk/2010/09/bains-blow-to-berkeley.html#more). The Bain report is available at: http://oe.berkeley.edu/phase1/full.pdf. Frederick Wiseman's documentary *At Berkeley* includes extensive footage shot at a UC Berkeley workshop on "Operational Excellence."

92. See Chris Newfield, "Confronting Our Permanent Public University Austerity," Remaking the University (http://utotherescue.blogspot.fr/2014/07/confronting-our-permanent-public.html) 17 July 2014.

93. Michael Brown was enrolled at Vatterott College. In 2010, the former director of the school was found guilty of "conspiracy to fraudulantly obtain nearly $362,000 in federal student loans for ineligible students by providing false general equivalency diplomas (GEDs) and falsifying financial forms." See April 23rd 2010 news release from the U.S. Department of Education, "Former Vatterott Director Sentenced for Financial AID Fraud" (23 April 2010). http://www2.ed.gov/about/offices/list/oig/invtreports/mo042010.html. The same college later lost a civil suit filed by a student who

was awarded two million dollars in damages. See David Halberin, "What College Was Michael Brown About to Attend?," *Huffington Post*, 26 August 2014. See http://www.huffingtonpost.com/david-halperin/what-college-was-michael_b_5719731.html. If the statistics on the percentage of students who come forward after having been sexually assaulted are low, the numbers of students who file complaints after they have been defrauded by for-profit schools are even lower.

semiotext(e) intervention series

geek GIRLS don't DATE DUKES

GINA LAMM

sourcebooks
casablanca

Published by Sourcebooks Casablanca, an imprint of Sourcebooks, Inc.
P.O. Box 4410, Naperville, Illinois 60567-4410
(630) 961-3900
Fax: (630) 961-2168
www.sourcebooks.com

Printed and bound in the United States of America.
VP 10 9 8 7 6 5 4 3 2 1

To my sister. We used to want to kill each other, and now we're best friends. Nana was right. I love you, Heather!

One

"EXCUSE ME, YOU'RE STEPPING ALL OVER MY farthingale." Leah tugged her hoop underskirt free of the clueless knight's boots. Having the most spectacular garb at the Renaissance Faire was becoming more of a burden than a bragging right.

He staggered away from her and blundered into a tree, his homemade metallic armor clanking. Leah smothered her laugh at the sight. "Somebody should pop the lid off that tin can with legs, and if he doesn't watch out, I'll do it for him."

Ella, Leah's good friend and Ren-Faire buddy, snickered behind her hand. "Go easy on the guy. He didn't make the eye slits in his helm big enough."

Irritation wrinkled Leah's forehead as she watched him apologize to the tree and turn to walk the other way. "Made his codpiece too big if you want my opinion," Leah muttered as she brushed the dirt from the gold brocade hem of her handmade Anjou gown. "If he was packing that much, he'd never be able to sit on a horse."

Ella's snort brought a smile to Leah's face. She was kind of glad she hadn't called in sick like she'd planned.

This outing was just what she needed to get her mind off her best friend's upcoming wedding. Jamie's joy only reinforced Leah's own shit-tastic love life. Ella had encouraged her to stop moping and get back to having fun, and Leah was determined to give it a shot.

As Ella and Leah made their way through the Faire, Leah dipped her head and mumbled "Good morrow" to a passing fairy. Why did people insist on doing that? It was a Renaissance Faire, not a nearly nude fairy-for-all. It really burned her when people took one of her favorite events and turned it into another excuse to wear booty shorts, bikini tops, and clearance Halloween wire-and-sparkly-mesh wings.

"Ooh, a henna artist." Ella pointed to a silk tent strung beneath a large oak. "And bonus, no line! Want to get inked?"

Leah smiled. "I really need to get going, or I'll be late for the coronation. Why don't you go ahead? I'll catch up with you after, I promise."

"Okay," Ella said, tilting her head. "If you're sure."

Leah nodded. With a parting wave, she wound her way through the crowd as gracefully as her hooped skirt would allow.

Once alone, Leah's mood turned south. She slumped against a tree by a palm reader's cart, cradling her head in her hands. What was wrong with her? Jamie's wedding was in just a few days, and if Leah couldn't get herself together enough to be there for her best friend, she'd always regret it. Her own loneliness could shove it until Jamie's happy day was done. Besides, she wasn't really losing her best friend, so she needed to buck the hell up.

The cheerful chatter of the Faire goers surrounded

her—normally a wonderful, happy sound. Today, instead of scanning her fellow attendees' garb for historical accuracy and nifty ideas, all Leah could do was feel sorry for herself. Ella was right. She had to stop acting like she was losing her best friend. Shoving herself upright, Leah glared at the green canopy of leaves above her.

"Screw this," she said, adjusting her skirts and straightening her French hood. "I've got a coronation to attend." Leah strode toward the parade ground, nearly mowing someone down in the process.

"I do beg your pardon," Leah said as she bowed her head and bobbed a curtsy to the man. "I didst not see…" She trailed off as she got a look at his face. "Kevin? What are you doing here?" *Seriously?* She gripped the sides of her skirt so hard the fabric rasped in protest.

"Leah. I hoped you'd be here." Kevin's self-conscious smile didn't reach his eyes. He smoothed his clearly expensive jeans over his too-lean hips. "I need to ask you something."

"Sorry, I don't have time to talk. Her Majesty is expecting me to help with the coronation." Leah resumed walking, hoping like hell he'd get the hint and not follow. Their particular personal history wasn't one she wanted to relive.

No such luck. He trotted to keep up with her, weaving through the crowd. "You've got half an hour before that starts. I checked the schedule. Listen, Leah, I've been thinking."

"About Teresa, hopefully. She *is* the one you're going to marry." Leah fought the angry blush climbing her neckline. How could she have been stupid enough to believe that Kevin loved her? She quickened her step, wishing she could leave him, and the past he reminded her of, behind.

"You know I didn't mean for that to happen the way it did. I still care about you, Leah. I always wanted to stay friends with you, and Teresa wants that too. She actually wanted me to ask you to possibly, I don't know—beabridesmaidorsomething."

The rushed words sent a white-hot knife of hurt and anger through her chest. She stopped so fast that Kevin nearly knocked her down. Whirling, she gaped at him.

"You have *got* to be kidding me. A bridesmaid? She called me a slut the first time she met me! And she met me on the night that I'd thought…" The words swelled in her throat, and she fought to get them free. "I'd thought…"

"You thought I was going to propose to you." Kevin scuffed the toe of his leather loafer in the dirt. "I know. I didn't want to hurt you. It was just…I don't know."

"Hard to tell me you've been in love with Teresa for five years? Hard to tell me you'd been engaged the whole time you were stringing me along?" She dashed the angry tears away, hating that he could see how much she still hurt over the whole sorry situation, six months later. "Sorry, Kevin. I can't help you."

"Come on, Leah, it wasn't like that. You know how my parents are. Teresa is an attorney—she's great at what she does. Her family has known mine forever. They're from DC too, and they all move in the same circles. I like you, you know that."

"But an elementary school drama teacher who just happens to enjoy fantasy more than fund-raising events was more than your ancient and revered family name could take. It's fine, Kevin. I get it." Her voice was ragged and her chest tight, but she stood her ground. She wasn't going to apologize. She'd tried to be the kind of girl he wanted, but that particular mask hadn't fit. It was just as well. His mother had hated her with a passion, and no matter how hard Leah tried, she could never live up to that impossible standard. It had been much easier to cling to Jamie than to try to fight for Kevin anymore. Of course, now she didn't have her best friend either.

He took her hand, gently rubbing a tiny circle over her knuckles. "I still care about you. A lot. And I know it's shitty of me to ask this. But listen, Teresa's cousin Wendy had to back out of the wedding. Her doctor put her on bed rest until the baby comes. You can wear Wendy's dress for the ceremony and be in the pictures. And you don't have to worry about anything because the photographer said he can Photoshop Wendy's face in afterward."

She'd have laughed if it wasn't so pathetically painful. Jerking her hand away, she stared at him—his fancy clothes, hair perfectly gelled into that tousled look, his complete discomfort at standing on a dirt path in the middle of the woods—all of it. Even though she'd wanted him desperately at the time, she could see now that she'd been a total idiot to think he could have made her happy. Didn't stop it from hurting like hell, though.

"There is no way that I'll be in your wedding. You and that attorney bitch really deserve each other."

She walked away without looking back, her aching heart turning to lead in her chest. What a stinking mess her life had become, and it was nobody's fault but her own. She'd been so busy chasing the dream of a happily-ever-after that she'd completely lost sight of who and what she wanted.

The coronation, normally one of Leah's favorite events, seemed to drag on forever today. She performed her bit perfectly—*like a trained monkey in a circus*, she thought, her dark thoughts belying the bright smile on her face. She didn't miss a step, and her solo performance got the largest applause. Once the final song was completed and the parade through the fairgrounds done, Leah yanked off her hood and went straight to the gates. Her sanctuary was only a few miles away. She had to go see the one man in the world who could make her feel better about everything.

"Leah, there you are," Ella called to her from a pottery vendor's stall. She grinned as she approached. "You were beautiful in the coronation ceremony."

Leah gave as sincere a smile as she was capable of, considering the roiling mass of snarled emotions inside her. "Thanks." She scuffed the toe of her slipper in the dirt.

"Hey," Ella said, her voice soft and knowing. "What's up?"

Leah shook her head. "Don't worry about me. I'm fine." Leah turned away abruptly and cleared her throat. Between the pain of Kevin's request and Ella's gentle probing, she couldn't take much more today. Cursing herself inwardly for the lie, she said it anyway. "I wish I could stay longer, but Pawpaw needs some help at the shop this afternoon."

Ella crossed her arms over her middle, framing her green-corseted chest. "You going to keep lying to my face? Because we can play that game if you want."

Leah begged Ella with eyes already filling with tears. "Don't make me talk about it, please."

Ella lowered her brows but nodded. "Okay."

"Thanks for hanging out with me today. I do appreciate it."

Ella grabbed Leah's arm. "Anytime, Leah. I mean it. Call me."

The knowing look in Ella's eyes made Leah feel even worse somehow. She agreed anyway.

"I will." Leah pulled free and walked away. She hoped she was fast enough to keep Ella from seeing the stupid tears that flowed down her cheeks.

Two

THE BRONZE BELL STRUNG OVER THE DOOR OF RAMSEY'S Antiques had long ago lost its clapper, but it still managed to clang violently whenever Leah pushed through the door. Pawpaw said that it never sang that loud for anyone but his granddaughter.

"Pawpaw?" Leah dropped her French hood atop the glass counter at the front of the store. Scanning the empty sales floor, she drew in a deep breath, tasting the familiar scent of ancient leather, dust, and pipe tobacco. "You around?"

His voice sounded far away. "In the back, Leelee. What are you doing here so soon? I thought you were at the Faire today."

Leah rounded the corner and collapsed on the stool behind the counter. The hoops of her farthingale flopped upward, nearly whacking her in the face. With a frustrated groan, she stood and smacked them down again. "I was. I ran into Kevin, so I left after the coronation."

"Kevin?" Her grandfather pushed through the swinging door to the stockroom and set an antique vase beside the register. "What in the hell was he doing at the Renaissance festival? I thought he hated 'em."

"He does." Leah leaned on the counter, cupping her chin in her hands. "He came to see me."

Pawpaw's already lined face wrinkled further with temper. He crossed his arms over his barrel-like chest, his nostrils flaring. "What did he want with you?"

"To ask me to be Teresa's bridesmaid." Her stupid eyes were watering again. She sniffed and trained her gaze at the silver spoons nestled inside the glass case below her elbows. "This is complete and utter crap. I wasn't good enough for him to love, but I'm good enough to be her stupid bridesmaid?" She dashed the tears away. "Sorry, I don't mean to dump my problems on you."

"Leelee." Her grandfather pulled her upright. "Look at me, girl. Come on." He wiped the tears from her cheeks with his callused thumbs, demanding her attention with eyes that were so blue it was eerie—the same eyes that Leah saw in the mirror every day, only his were crowned by wiry salt-and-pepper brows instead of neatly groomed blond ones. Her grandfather, the gold standard for men everywhere. She just wished she could find someone as honorable and protective as he was. "That boy wasn't ever good enough for you."

Leah barked a bitter laugh as she averted her gaze. "Apparently he was *too* good for me. I'm not Washington caliber."

"I'm not talking about money and power and all that hooey. Leelee, you were a bright child, and you've grown into an even brighter woman. It's going to take a fine man to be able to make you happy. And Kevin wasn't it. Don't shed another tear over that good-for-nothin'." He pressed his lips to her forehead, chasing some of the chill from her heart.

She smiled shakily, drawing in a deep, cleansing breath. "Thank you, Pawpaw."

He folded her into his arms and she rested her head on his shoulder, just as she had a thousand times before. He smelled sweet, of his favorite pipe tobacco and aftershave. His broad hands were warm on her upper back, and she sighed against his familiar faded plaid shirt. Pawpaw was right. He'd always been right.

"Promise me somethin'."

She looked up at him.

He continued with a half smile, "Promise me you'll find somebody you can count on. A man who knows what it means to work for a living. A man who won't let you run over him but will listen to every word you say."

"I've got a grandfather like that," Leah said with a laugh. "There can't be another man like you."

He smiled, but his voice was serious. "Leelee, listen to me. A good, strong, honest man. You find him, and you marry him. I want to know you've got somebody to come home to, so when I'm dead and gone, I know you'll be taken care of."

She pulled free of his arms and shook her head vehemently. "Why would you say that? You're healthy as a horse."

He shook his head. "I'm not guaranteed tomorrow, and I want to know you won't be alone."

"I can take care of myself, you know." She tried to focus on the insinuation of her helplessness instead of the *dead and gone* statement. She refused to even consider a world without Pawpaw. And besides, she was an independent woman. While a romance would be wonderful, she didn't need it to survive.

"I'm not talking about money or protection or anything like that, and you know it, girl." He stared her down. "I mean a partner like I had with your grandma, someone to share life's burdens with. You haven't had it easy, and with Jamie gettin' married, you'll be more alone than is good for you."

Leah stared at the carpet. She couldn't look Pawpaw in the face. While the rest of the world saw the laughing, adventurous woman she'd chosen to be, she knew that he saw the lonely child she'd been when he and her grandmother had taken her in. He knew her too well. How could any man hope to do a better job of taking care of her than the man who'd raised her when her own mother hadn't cared enough to do the job herself?

Her grandfather sighed. "If you're going to stay around here this afternoon, you'd better change outta that getup. I could use some of your help staging the new silver I just bought. You've always been better at that than me."

He patted her on the back and nodded toward the office at the back of the store.

"Yes, sir." She caught the hood that he tossed at her and made her way through the back room. Maybe an afternoon of manual labor would keep the ugly memories of Kevin and her worries about the future at bay. Her throat tightened at the thought of Pawpaw's words. Why would he be so worried about her getting married? What had he meant, dead and gone?

It took most of the afternoon before she could breathe normally again.

❧

Leah stoically stared at Jamie's TV, determined to ignore the pitiful whining of one claiming-to-be-starved greyhound. He'd had a bowl and a half of food only an hour ago, the rotten liar. He pawed at the foot she'd propped on the coffee table, his high-pitched cries fighting with the TV for her attention.

She'd volunteered to house and dog sit for the happy honeymooners, but Baron seemed determined to pester her to death. Instead of teaching a week at summer theatre camp, she was moping around Jamie's house with a pile of movies, a boatload of snack food, and a greyhound that refused to get full.

"You are too generous to trifle with me. If your feelings are what they were last April, please tell me so at once. My affections and wishes are unchanged." Mr. Darcy's eyes melted Leah from the TV screen, that beautiful deep voice rumbling through her bruised heart. "But one word from you will silence me on this subject forever."

Leah mouthed the reply with Elizabeth Bennet. "I am ashamed to remember what I said then. My feelings are so different. In fact, they are quite the opposite."

Baron whined again and pawed at Leah's hand, shaking the tortilla chip free. He snatched up the forbidden snack and trotted happily to his bed beside a large mirrored bureau. Crumpling the chip bag closed, Leah tossed it on the side table atop her MacBook and lost herself in her favorite movie for a few more minutes.

She sniffed and wiped away her tears at the sight of Mr. Darcy kissing his new bride as they rode away in the carriage. Why wasn't life really like that? Modern guys—well, the ones she'd dated anyway—wouldn't know chivalry if it bit them on the ass.

The power button clicked beneath her finger and the TV went silent. Baron yawned and stretched, then trotted toward the kitchen, leaving Leah alone with nothing but her contemplation and half a bag of chips. A warm tugging began in her chest, a feeling she couldn't place at all. She glanced over at the bureau.

Jamie had traveled through that mirror. It was some kind of time portal, Leah knew. It stood silently—tall, gleaming, with an almost otherworldly allure. Her Converses hit the floor with a soft thump, and before she knew what was happening, she stepped toward the antique bureau.

The mirror's gilt edge gleamed at her, beckoning her onward. She couldn't keep herself from reaching toward the glass, and she couldn't stop her fingers from dipping into the mirror as if it were the cool waters of a pond.

Her mouth fell open in wonder. She pushed farther, relishing the tingling feeling that ran through her fingers and palm. This was insane. She should be scared. Lord knew what time period this mirror might dump her in. She should be screaming for help. But she wasn't, and she didn't. She smiled and pushed her arm through up to the elbow.

Excitement thrummed through her. Jamie had met her true love—an earl!—after a trip through the mirror. Leah bit her lip as the pulling grew stronger. Her shoulder was nearly through now.

A soft whine interrupted her, and reality cracked her on the skull. What the hell was she doing?

"Oh shit," Leah said, yanking backward. "Baron, wait! I can't...I'm stuck, I'm—"

Something pushed her from the other side of the glass,

and Leah popped free. She staggered backward, landing on the couch with a thump.

"Oh good heavens, Baron, do get out of the way, or I shall tread on you."

Leah bolted upright with a screech. Scrambling over the edge of the couch, she darted for the baseball bat she knew Jamie kept in the coat closet. Her heart thumped wildly as she brandished the Louisville Slugger at the intruder.

"Who are you? How'd you get in here?"

The bat clattered to the floor when Leah's brain finally clicked with what she was seeing. A short, rotund woman was climbing out of the bureau mirror—out of the mirror Leah had just tried to dive through. *Whoops.*

"What the hell?" Leah's knees gave way with shock. She clutched the edge of the sofa for stability as the woman's feet hit the floor and she straightened her skirts. What was going on here?

"Language, dear," the little woman admonished her with a motherly smile. She was dressed in a dark gown made of rough wool. Her grayish hair was done in a severe pulled-back style, not a wisp out of place. Her round face held laugh lines at the corners of her eyes, giving her a pleasant expression. Her simple dress and hairstyle were appropriate for a high-ranking servant of the nineteenth century. Only one person Leah had ever heard of fit the description.

"Are you—" Leah stopped, swallowing the knot of confusion that swelled in her throat.

"Pardon. I am Mrs. Knightsbridge." The woman bobbed a curtsy. "Whom do I have the pleasure of addressing?"

Leah's heart pounded so hard she was sure it would

leap straight out of her chest. "Leah. Leah Ramsey. I'm Jamie's friend."

"Oh, my dear Miss Ramsey. Miss Jamie told me so much about you." The little lady patted Baron on the head as he lapped her hand. "What a pleasure this is at last. I would dearly love to see Miss Jamie, and his lordship, of course. Are they at home?"

"I'm sorry," Leah said, shuffling from foot to foot. For all her theatre history and costume knowledge, she was a little light on time-traveling-visitor etiquette. "They got married two days ago. They're on their honeymoon."

Mrs. Knightsbridge clucked her tongue and sighed. "Oh goodness, what a bother. I have arrived too late for the nuptials. These time shifts are becoming so unreliable." She shook her head. "There is no hope for it. I shall have to go back and attempt to time my arrival more appropriately." The little woman stepped toward the bureau again.

"No, Mrs. Knightsbridge, wait!" Leah jumped forward and grabbed the woman by the elbow. "Please, just a minute."

"Yes?"

Leah swallowed hard. The words came of their own volition, and she couldn't stop their complete rush. "I need to ask you something."

Mrs. Knightsbridge arched a brow in a knowing manner but waited for Leah to continue.

"It's my grandfather. I'm worried about him. He started talking yesterday about dying." Leah ran her nails along her jeans, the rough edge of her thumbnail picking at the cotton. "I know you've got powers. Jamie told me. Is something going to happen to him? Is he sick and not telling me?"

"Why ask me, dear?" Mrs. Knightsbridge laid a hand atop Leah's.

"Because I know you see things. The scrying. That's how you found Jamie, right? Can't you tell if something's wrong with Pawpaw?"

Mrs. Knightsbridge shook her head, and Leah's hopes slipped through the floor.

"I do not have what I require for that, my dear. But"—she smiled conspiratorially—"I can assist you in the same manner I assisted Miss Jamie."

Her hopes leaped through the floorboards and lodged straight in her chest, making her heartbeat a ragged thump. "Really? You can send me to another time and place?"

"Of course," the housekeeper said.

Leah jammed her hands in her pockets to keep them steady. She was almost vibrating, she was so excited. Go back in time? To when the gentlemen knew how to treat a lady, to when class was something everyone aspired to? She could find someone there, someone who appreciated her. Someone her grandfather would approve of. Someone who wouldn't dick her over like Kevin had. And with time travel, she could be back before anyone knew she'd gone.

She grinned. "Let's do it."

Besides, who wouldn't jump at the chance to visit Regency England? *Not this girl.*

Three

THE SCUFF SIMPLY REFUSED TO BUDGE FROM THE DUKE'S favorite Hessians. Avery Russell sighed and resumed polishing the expensive leather boots. His Grace would be quite put out if these weren't presentable in time for the next morning's calls.

"Russell, are you about? I must speak with you."

Avery didn't look up from his work at the butler's supercilious tone. "I am here, Mr. Smythe."

The butler stepped into the dressing room and shut the door behind him. "Mrs. Harper has dismissed Fannie, the underhousemaid. Until a suitable replacement can be found, you shall attend to the sweeping up and tidying of His Grace's chambers."

Avery refused to raise his gaze from the boot. He bit his bottom lip to keep in the retort that first sprang to mind. Smythe could take that sweeping and shove it up his— "Are there not more than enough maids to attend to that? I have many other duties." In any other household, a valet would never be found doing the maid's work. But ever since Avery had come into the duke's household, Smythe had tried him to no end.

"The maids cannot be spared from their responsibilities," Smythe replied. "Mrs. Harper has divided the rest of Fannie's work amongst them. You shall attend to this, or I shall see to it that you are dismissed from His Grace's service."

The threat in Smythe's tone was clear. Avery set his jaw and swallowed his response. He had to mind his place. This position was much less hazardous to his well-being than his previous employment had been. The Duke of Granville had pressed the bounds of propriety in even hiring Avery for such a high position, and the rest of the servants knew it. Smythe was the biggest voice of dissent. Avery adjusted the boot before finally glancing up. "So be it."

Smythe nodded, looking down his nose at Avery, his forehead wrinkled—whether in frustration or in sheer dislike, Avery couldn't say. He'd simply have to continue doing his best to please the duke and hope that the servants fell into line. But after nearly a year as the duke's valet without change, his hopes were fading.

"I shall leave you to it then. Have a care with the grates, Russell. Though you have but come to service lately, your actions reflect upon this whole house. I will not allow our reputation to be blemished."

Without another word, Smythe turned and left the room. Avery resisted the impulse to curse beneath his breath. It would serve no purpose, none at all.

The door opened again. "Russell, His Grace's new bureau has arrived. Though I should like to direct the placement of it myself, a matter has arisen in the kitchens that must be dealt with. You shall have to do." Smythe disappeared again and was quickly replaced by the grunts and groans of the men as they strained under the furniture's weight.

Frustration tightening his jaw, Avery left the boots and entered the bedchamber with quick strides. If the workmen left a smudge on any of His Grace's things, Smythe would be sure to blame Avery. *Damn and blast*. Perhaps he should have remained in the boxing mills after all.

"Mind the doorway, lads," Avery said as he lifted the corner of the bureau that was drifting dangerously close to the polished floors. "Steady. Place it just here."

All four men blew heavy breaths of relief as their burden descended to the corner of the Aubusson carpet in the duke's massive bedchamber. Avery straightened his simple black waistcoat as he stood.

"Well done. Please, make your way down to the kitchens. I am sure that Cook can spare you a cup of tea."

With muttering thanks and doffing caps, the workmen departed, closing the chamber door behind them.

Avery eyed the bureau. A fine Chippendale piece, it had previously belonged to the Earl of Dunnington. After apparently boarding a ship for the colonies, his lordship would have no further need for his fine furnishings. Avery ran a hand along the polished wood, yearning filling his chest. If he had the coin that had purchased this fine bureau, he could support her for a year or more. His hand fell away, then curled into a fist. *Useless*. He turned away with a sigh to resume his duties in the dressing chamber.

Settling back on the stool with the scuffed Hessian, Avery tried to focus on the boot instead of his lot. Many others had lives much worse than his. He'd do well to mind his business and not waste time dreaming.

A solid thump from the bedchamber interrupted his musings. *What the devil?* Setting the Hessian aside, Avery turned, warning prickling through him. Was someone in the room? Had the duke come back early? Usually His Grace wasn't due back from his club until well past the evening hours.

"Your Grace?" Avery called, his deep voice echoing back to him in the dressing chamber. He stood and entered the adjoining bedroom. "May I be of service?"

The sight that greeted his eyes was nothing less than extraordinary. Skirts, voluminous black skirts, hung from the mirror, and delicate booted feet kicked wildly beneath the fabric. The rest of the form, if indeed there was one, was completely obscured by Avery's reflection in the bureau's mirror.

"Bloody hell," Avery breathed, unable to credit what he saw.

She continued to wriggle free, sliding farther and farther down the bureau's slanted front. A trim waist exited the mirror, followed quickly by a lean back, flailing arms, and a tumble of yellow curls. She would have fallen to the floor had Avery not stepped forward and caught her just in time.

"What the devil is this?" Avery set her on her feet and quickly stepped away. "Explain yourself, madam."

"Oh my gosh, you're perfect." She laughed, her face as shiningly pleasant as her tousled hair. Her accent was flat, smooth, and slow, like honey dripping onto a scone. "Sorry, I know this is sudden. Hello, I'm Leah Ramsey."

Avery shook off the whisper of interest that flicked in his brain. *Remember your place, my lad, and do not be taken in by a pretty face.* "The name means nothing to me, miss.

What are you doing in these bedchambers?" He kept his countenance grim. It was no wonder the men had struggled so with the bureau. She must have been hidden away inside it.

Her conspiratorial smile struck him dumb. "It's going to sound weird, but I'll tell you." She gripped his arm and leaned against him to whisper in his ear, "I traveled through time to find my true love, and I'm pretty sure, Your Grace, that it's got to be you."

The ease with which the overly familiar gesture came was no less startling than the intimate press of her body on his. He stepped backward as if burned, staring at her in shock.

A devil with an angel's face is sent to torment me.

Leah's heart fluttered with excitement. He was absolutely perfect—everything a duke should be. Well, except for the silvery scars on his knuckles and slight crookedness of his nose. And maybe the height. Shouldn't dukes clear six feet? He couldn't be more than an extremely well-muscled five foot ten. And his outfit was plainer than she'd imagined for such a high-ranking aristocrat. But his broad shoulders and slim hips more than made up for any height deficiency. At five foot seven herself, anything taller than her was tall enough.

She'd made a big faux pas right off the bat, though. Drawing in a shaky breath, Leah smiled apologetically. She hoped that slack-jawed look on his face was more intrigued interest than shocked disgust. *Tough call.* "Sorry, I was just excited. I mean, look at this place. Look at you. I can't believe I'm actually here!"

His silence didn't inspire much confidence. He stood there, scowling at her like Mr. Darcy in a room full of commoners. She had to play it cool. Drying her suddenly damp palms on her skirt, she breathed deeply. "Let me explain. Mrs. Knightsbridge—she's Micah, er, the Earl of Dunnington's housekeeper—well, she's got some pretty incredible talents. I asked her for help with my grandfather, but she sent me here instead. She said my true love was in this house, and she sent me here to meet you. *Oh*." Cheeks burning, she suddenly remembered the rank of the man standing there. You couldn't just run up to a freaking *duke* and make best friends. She sank into a low curtsy and whispered, "Your Grace."

A firm grip surrounded her arm, flooding her with warmth. Gosh, he was strong. He pulled her upright, but the seriousness in his eyes stopped her smile in its tracks. "Miss, you are mistaken. I am not your true love." His deep, raspy voice sent a tingle down her spine as he let go of her arm.

Her brain paused in mid-whirl. This was a stranger. A complete and utter stranger, and she'd just popped through the mirror and into his arms like she belonged there. No wonder he was treating her like she was crazy. If she was *when* she thought she was, this was a huge breach of etiquette. But she couldn't quite dismiss the idea that she had the right guy. She shivered. Lord, if he was this gorgeous while he was pissed, how incredible would he look when he was happy and laughing?

"Listen, Your Grace, I'm really sorry. I know this is strange and sudden and completely crazy. Just give me a chance, okay?" And then she winked at him in a bold attempt to lighten the mood.

Instead of the delighted laugh she'd been hoping for, she got a cold stare in return. "Miss, I am not in a position to give you anything. I am Avery Russell, the Duke of Granville's valet. And you are trespassing."

The same strong hands that had caught her before she could fall to the ground pointed her toward the door.

"Wait," she cried, grabbing at his arm. "I'm telling the truth!"

"A liar and a Bedlamite," he growled as he pried her fingers from his. "You hid inside that bureau and crept out like a thief. I'll listen to no more of this."

"Please," she begged, searching his still-grim features for some sign of compassion. "You've got to believe me."

"Why?" He scowled down at her like he was a priest and she'd just spat in the communion wine.

Why? She stopped struggling. In an instant, the fight leaked out of her, leaving her muscles weak and useless. This had been the worst idea she'd ever had, and for Leah, that was saying something. She'd thought that the musical version of *Attack of the Killer Tomatoes* she'd staged would hold that trophy for the rest of her life.

"I…I don't know." Leah looked at the carpet beneath her feet. "You don't have any reason to believe me." She swallowed hard, trying her damnedest to get the lump in her throat out of the way so she could breathe.

He sighed. She didn't look at him, fear and uncertainty keeping her eyes glued downward. This wasn't how she'd expected things to go. Truth be told, she'd been picturing a fairy tale. Love at first sight happened, didn't it?

But Avery Russell wasn't the duke. So all she had to do was get to the real Duke of Granville. He'd fall in love with her, and everything would be fine. She took a deep breath.

"Mr. Russell, I'm sorry. I know I've been acting like a lunatic. Can I have a minute to explain? I promise, if you don't believe me, I'll get out of here without another word." How she'd manage that she didn't have a freaking clue, but she *had* to get him to listen.

His expression softened but barely. He nodded. "You have one minute."

Great. And crap. What the hell could she say? Her brain buzzed, ideas flitting like deranged bumblebees, each one crazier than the last. She had to come up with something, anything. This was too important to screw up. The truth hadn't worked so well. Maybe she should get a little bit more creative.

"Okay, listen to me. I'm from two hundred years in the future. My grandfather is a trained assassin. I'm his scout. We've discovered that there's a threat to the duke's life, and his only hope is for me to marry him and take him back to the future with me."

He released her then but only to cover the bark of laughter that had escaped him at her ridiculous answer. Despite the gravity of the situation, she couldn't help but smile at herself. That hadn't been her best effort. Maybe she'd been watching too much *Doctor Who* lately.

Avery shook his head. "Your tales become more and more outrageous, Miss Ramsey."

"Well, you wouldn't believe the truth. I just wanted an adventure, and Mrs. Knightsbridge said my destiny was in this house. Would you turn down the chance to find your perfect love?"

He snorted in derision. "Love is a child's fairy tale.

And you must be more of a child than you seem to believe in such nonsense."

Hot shame burned her cheeks. She crossed her arms in self-defense at his mocking tone. "So you don't think the duke could be my true love? Even though Mrs. Knightsbridge has a hundred percent success rate?"

"It is impossible." He shook his head. "As I said, you must be a foolish girl."

Leah swallowed hard at the ridiculous knot in her throat. What did this stranger's opinion matter? This was a once in a lifetime adventure, and she'd be damned if a stuffy valet would stand in her way. Mrs. Knightsbridge said her true love was here, and she owed it to her grandfather to find the best husband she possibly could. She gathered her courage and stared Avery straight in the eye. She hadn't backed down from a challenge in her life, and she wasn't about to start now.

"I am not a child, and I am not a fool. I know exactly what I'm doing, thank you very much." With a confidence born of many years of acting classes, Leah smoothed her dress down her hips, willing them to twist slightly, enough to get his attention. "And if you don't believe in love, that's your problem." Turning with a dramatic swish of her skirts, she strode to the other end of the massive chamber like a queen, making sure to twitch her ass. Tossing a look over her shoulder, she smiled when she saw the lustful fury brewing in his eyes. Teasing him shouldn't make her this happy, but damn it, the stuffy jerk deserved it.

"Well, Miss Ramsey, who am I to stand in the way of true love?" The last words were said in a mocking tone so bitter that they made Leah wince. "If you should like to remain here, I will not stop you. You may look to Smythe for that honor."

With a bow that was more mocking than respectful, the valet turned on his heel and left the room.

Leah sank down on the bed, rubbing her forehead. Why didn't she feel triumphant? Hurdle number one had been cleared. So what was with the nervous bubble in her gut?

Swallowing her anxiety, she stood and took a deep, calming breath. Time to get her game face on and go round two with Mr. Smythe. *This isn't going to be easy, but then again*, Leah thought as she exited the massive bedchamber, *nothing worth doing usually is.*

The corridor was wide enough to put a couple of pool tables end-to-end and still have room to play them both. Gilt-framed portraits spanned the huge hall that was lined with expensive furnishings, showpieces, and closed doors. Picking up a small vase from a marquetry table, Leah examined it in the critical way her Pawpaw had drilled into her since she was tiny.

"Holy cow," she whispered to herself, and quickly put the ancient porcelain down. That piece could easily buy and sell a pretty nice Lexus a couple times over. Rubbing her suddenly sweaty palms against her borrowed costume skirt, Leah backed up to the wall to get another look at her surroundings. She was really beginning to worry that she was out of her league. And for a girl like Leah, who'd never met a challenge she didn't want to fling herself face-first into, that was really saying something.

Four

"THOUGHTLESS, FOOLISH CHIT," AVERY SNARLED BENEATH his breath as he resumed his polishing. With all the fury he felt at the beautiful girl who'd waltzed into the room as if she belonged there, he rubbed at the scuff mark. That such a complete stranger had roused this much ire, and if he was honest, interest, made his blood bubble into an angry froth.

It was several moments later when the red fog of frustration left his brain that he looked down at the Hessian. Blinking in surprise, he realized he'd mangled it. The boot's toe pointed toward the floor. A costly pair of His Grace's boots had been ruined because Avery had not kept his wits about him. He'd allowed her to divert his focus, a lapse in vigilance that could have had unforgivable consequences.

Letting the boot drop to the floor, Avery looked up at the beamed ceiling. Drawing air deeply into his chest, he blew it out through pursed lips, concentrating on slowing the too-rapid thumping of his heart. The prayers that his pious father had beat into him at a young age ran through his head as Avery searched for a semblance of calm.

"Mr. Russell?"

The sweet, feminine voice with its altogether odd accent ran roughshod over his attempt at peace. His pulse surged, and he fought to maintain his focus on the wooden beams above his head.

"Mr. Russell, I'm really sorry about before. I was wondering if you could help me."

He didn't respond. *Breathe in, hold it in…*

"Oh, are you praying? I didn't mean to interrupt. I'll wait until you're done." She sat on the narrow bench beside him, her soft thigh pressing innocently against his knee. From the corner of his eye, he watched her bow her head and lace her delicate fingers together in her lap. Her long eyelashes fluttered closed.

She looked the very picture of piety, but it was impossible not to notice the way her breasts swelled above the neckline of her dress with each breath. The way her body bled heat into his. The way she smelled of sweet, exotic spices. All thoughts of calm and prayer forgotten, Avery leaned closer, trying to draw another breath of her into his lungs.

Her eyes popped open, and he jerked backward in surprise. "Oh good, you're done." She smiled, a genuine expression that made her brilliant blue eyes sparkle with inner fire. "I didn't mean to interrupt you, but I think we got off on the wrong foot earlier."

He stared at her without a word. What more was there to be said?

"It was totally my fault. I really hope you can forgive me." She looked down at her lap, and Avery fought the bolt of protectiveness that struck him when her smile faltered. "It's just that I was so excited about being here and thinking I was meeting my perfect guy. I didn't think about how it would affect you, especially considering I screwed up."

Avery tried to swallow, but his throat was suddenly parched. His voice, when it came, was dry and cracked. "I took no offense. But you must realize how ludicrous this appears." He wished he could bite the words back—her opinion was a commodity he hadn't realized he valued—but once said, it was too late.

She picked at an imaginary thread on her skirt. He wished he could reach out and rub a finger across the fair skin of her wrist. A bitter laugh echoed in his head at the impossible thought. Despite how he was drawn to her, she was a beautiful stranger to him, nothing more.

"It was wrong, and I'm sorry. And I shouldn't even ask, but you're the only person I know here." When she looked up at him, her eyes were as blue and guileless as a midsummer sky. "I need your help if you can forgive me."

Before he could voice the protest that lay heavy on his lips, her small hand covered his scarred one. His heart stuttered in his chest as he fought to breathe, to keep his head, to not jerk away. She couldn't know that hers was the first hand to touch him so gently since his mother had passed away all those years ago. But he knew, and her touch shook him to the core.

⤜⧸⤏

Leah wasn't sure why Avery reacted so strongly when she touched his hand. The wary guardedness in his eyes intensified, and the tension lining his shoulders and spine increased. It was almost as if he needed to pull away but simply couldn't. As gently as she could, she broke the contact. Did he have some kind of social anxiety or something?

Shaking off the concern, she tried to focus. Like it or not, at the moment, she needed his help. *Nothing to it but to do it.* Opting for honesty, she launched straight into her idea.

"I know this doesn't seem like it's possible, but I'm from the twenty-first century, from what you'd probably call the colonies."

She tucked a stray hair behind her ear, scanning his features for disbelief. But, just her luck, Avery Russell had a poker face to end all poker faces. He was like a gorgeous statue with a slight bump in his nose. "It's magic," she said, and then immediately wanted to smack herself in the forehead. As if *that* would make it better.

"Of course." His tone was dryer than South Texas in July.

She rolled her eyes and stood, needing to put some distance between them. "There's no need to be sarcastic. I wouldn't have believed it either if it didn't actually happen to me—and my best friend, who's now married to the Earl of Dunnington, by the way." She hoped the name might mean something to him.

When he didn't respond, her smile faltered, but she held her pose. Fine, she'd lay it all out there on the table—either he'd help her or not.

"So listen, here's my problem. I can't meet the duke without some kind of introduction. You and I both know I'll need some help in order to meet him, let alone convince him we belong together." She sat back down beside him and leaned close to lower her voice to its most convincing level. "You're my only hope, Avery

Russell." She hoped her sincerity was clear in her face. There wasn't much else she could think of to say.

The only clue that he wasn't as composed as a sack of concrete was the slight flaring of his nostrils. It was almost like he smelled her perfume and liked it. Well, he could sniff her all damn day if he'd just agree to help her. And actually, there were a lot of things that could be worse than staying close enough to Avery to let him smell her perfume. The man really was magnetic, despite his attitude. Her gaze flicked to his full lips before she could stop it.

"It is madness, foolishness, and the worst sort of nonsense." He sighed and looked down at his hand, the one she'd touched only moments before. "But it is not for me to judge you. If your course is firmly set, then I shall do my best to aid you."

"Oh, Avery, thanks. You're the best." She flung her arms around his neck. His muscles trembled, and the slightly coarse fabric of his coat scratched at her cheek. She breathed in shoe polish and strong soap. But Leah didn't care. She'd made her first friend, albeit a handsome and reluctant one, and he was going to help her get her true love. How much better could today get?

～⁂～

"And this is where you'll sleep."

The door swung open and Mrs. Harper gestured into the dim attic room. Leah closed her eyes, made a wish, and walked toward the open door to face her fate.

A haughty sniff came from her unwilling tour guide. The housekeeper, Mrs. Harper, resembled a disapproving Q-tip more than anyone Leah had ever met. Her tiny, stick-thin frame was crowned by a bushy cloud of stark-white hair, but a duchess herself could be no more stuck-up than Mrs. Harper was.

The grand tour for the new underhousemaid had culminated with this, the reveal of Leah's temporary living quarters. She tried to contain her dismay as she looked around the tiny room, crammed with two beds and other people's belongings.

"You'll share this bed with Henrietta," Mrs. Harper said. "Teresa and Sara sleep in the other. You'll have one drawer for your things." She gestured to a simple wooden bureau in the corner. "Your uniforms are already inside. Dress—mind you take care—and be down for supper at the hour."

Mrs. Harper shut the door without another word, leaving Leah alone in the rapidly darkening attic room. She dropped the empty, beaten leather bag that Avery had produced to lend authenticity to her role as applicant for housemaid onto the floor beside her and crossed to the single, tiny window. After pulling it open, she ducked her head out to look at the city of London below.

She bit her lip, excitement thrumming through her veins. Carriages rolled down the cobbled streets, beautiful horses tossing their heads as Londoners called greetings to one another. Lamp boys scurried along, propping small ladders against the posts and touching their lit wicks to the lamp heads. A baker's boy ran past, his arms loaded with golden-brown loaves. It was picturesque, beautiful, everything she'd imagined.

Her happy sigh echoed through the room. Who'd have thought that she'd be living such a dream?

"From the country, are you?"

Leah nearly swallowed her own tongue in shock at the high-pitched voice behind her. She whirled and smiled.

"Hello. Who are you?"

The girl didn't answer at first, just tilted her head quizzically, causing her too-big mobcap to flop over one eye. She shoved it back with a motion that was clearly of longstanding habit.

"I'm Henrietta. You must be the new maid. Mrs. Harper sent me up to help you get settled." The girl gave a small smile, revealing crooked front teeth.

Faint discomfort nestled at the back of Leah's spine. This girl looked only a few years older than Leah's drama students at Concord Magnet Elementary School. She couldn't be more than twelve, thirteen years old, and she worked here? Reminding herself that child labor laws were still a work in progress, Leah nodded.

"Nice to meet you, Henrietta. Or do you go by Henry?"

"What a daft question. I am a girl, so I am Henrietta. They said you was a sight dim, and weren't they right and all." The polite smile was gone, and in its place was a look of dislike that was more suited to Mrs. Harper's drawn cheeks than Henrietta's apple-shaped ones.

Well well well, thought Leah as she drew herself up to her full height. *The little match girl is more of a little spitfire.* "Well, Henrietta, why don't you show me around?" Leah kept tight eye contact with the little demon, daring her to challenge further.

Aha, she thought as Henrietta looked away and marched to the bureau. *Round one to Ramsey.*

"Your uniforms is here, caps and aprons there. Hair tucked all beneath your cap. You'll be scolded if it's not

done to Mrs. Harper's liking. Oh"—the girl turned—
"and one more thing."

She might as well have a blinking neon sign on her
cute little forehead that read "I'm about to try to screw
you over." Leah crossed her arms and waited.

"Mrs. Harper said to tell you that supper has been
delayed. You're to remain here until quarter past the hour."

Leah inwardly shook her head. Poor kid. She had
talent but no control. Overplaying a part was worse than
underplaying it. "Hold it right there."

Henrietta had been about to turn the doorknob to
make her escape, but Leah's "freeze or you're dead meat"
voice had been fairly well honed over the years. The girl
turned slowly, a wary look in her wide brown eyes.

"If supper is delayed, then you can help me settle in."
Leah plopped down on the bed and patted the faded
covers beside her. "Sit down with me."

Henrietta's look of repugnance would have been funny
if it wasn't so damn depressing. Leah began wishing she'd
stuck closer to Avery. Clearly the female staff wouldn't be
giving her as warm a welcome as he had.

Leah sighed and rubbed at the temple that was beginning a steady throb. What a damn depressing thought.

Five

It had been easier than Avery had thought to convince Mrs. Dearborn, the cook, to pretend Leah was her relation from the colonies. An older woman with a softer heart than anyone else in the house, Cook had been Avery's only confidante. Despite their cordial acquaintance, he'd expected much more of a fight from her when he suggested the plan. But once Avery had explained that Leah would be out on the street if she couldn't provide a reference, Cook had agreed to the charade and bustled Leah away to meet Mrs. Harper and apply for Fannie's recently vacated position.

As Leah waved a cheerful farewell from the kitchen doorway, an odd twinge took up residence in Avery's chest. Turning, he'd thumped at his ribs, trying to dislodge the feeling as he'd exited the main house and walked out toward the stables. It hadn't worked. The buoyant, almost excited sensation cast an unfamiliar lightness to his walk.

Her tale was difficult to believe, but she had appeared sincere. Was it possible that she had come from nearly two hundred years in the future? The gravel crunched beneath his feet as he considered the notion.

When he was just a boy in the village of Chelmsford, their neighbor, Mrs. Comstock, had dabbled in the Old Ways. Though his clergyman father forbade him to speak with the old woman, he knew from her that strange things were possible. He'd seen her making potions and curing folk in ways that no normal person could, so it stood to reason that this stranger's outlandish claim could prove true.

His father was dead, and he was no longer a boy. Would he heed the warnings he'd been given as a child, or discover more about this beautiful stranger? Whether she'd come from the future or no, she stirred an interest within him that she should not. And he could not afford any distractions.

Once he'd reached the stables and tossed the hounds some scraps he'd gotten from Cook, he rounded to the back of the buildings into the lean-to shed he used for training. As he reached for the leather door strap, he could have sworn that his lips were stretched oddly, in what almost felt like a smile. Shaking his head, he tried to clear his thoughts of yellow hair and summer-sky eyes as he entered the shed. It was damn near impossible. She haunted him like a wraith.

The scents of dust, hay, and sweat hung heavy in the air, a reminder of the sole purpose of this room. Imagining the way she'd felt for that brief moment pressed against him, he methodically stripped to the waist. Streams of late-afternoon light reached through gaps in the slat wall, lying in wicked angles across the straw-dusted floor. Dust motes floated in the air as Avery carefully hung his valet's waistcoat, shirt, and jacket on iron hooks by the door. A rip, another, and then he wrapped thin linen strips around his knuckles, knotting them securely. Stretching his rib cage with a heavy breath, Avery turned and faced his opponent—a canvas bag filled with sand, hung with thick ropes from a ceiling beam. Settling his weight squarely on the balls of his feet, Avery's fists tingling and ready, he pulled back for his first swing.

The ghost of an impish smile with twinkling eyes winked at him, and he missed the bag completely. Overbalanced, he staggered forward, nearly plowing directly into his former employer's tall form.

"Oy, Russell, you'll never win another tourney with a pitiful showing like that."

Avery righted himself quickly, bringing his fist upward in defense. "Prachett. What are you doing here?"

Thomas Prachett laughed, moving closer to Avery. His heavy boots thudded on the straw-strewn floor. "I've need of my best man, is all. I told you I hadn't finished with you."

Avery circled, maintaining the distance between them. His nerves fired with alarm as he stared down his past in the form of a tall, thin, and cruel man. Prachett had loaned him funds when he'd had nothing, but Avery had paid sorely for that loan. Only the duke's mercy had rescued him from an early death in the boxing mills at the hands of one of Prachett's victims—or the man himself. "I've repaid my debt to you. You can have nothing else from me."

"Your debt is satisfied only when I say it is. That pittance you've returned to me, yes, but where is my interest? A man must have his pride." With a swift move, Prachett lifted the crop he'd been holding and brought it down across Avery's bicep.

A hiss of pain escaped Avery, but he ignored it. "Your damnable pride is naught to do with me." He swung at Prachett's face, but the stinging pain in his arm cost him focus. Prachett dodged the less-than-perfect blow as drops of blood rained onto the straw.

"Oh, but it is, lad. Without you, Emersen has moved up the ranks. He cannot be beaten. Except, perhaps…" Prachett trailed off as he moved closer. "By you. The Houndstooth tourney is soon, and you must enter. You'll lose there, and the wagers will turn against you. By the time you face this new threat, I'll have secured my fortune in the betting books."

Avery snarled as his anger overtook him. "Never again. I have left that life behind."

Prachett snapped his fingers, and three men burst into the room. Avery fought like a wounded bear, striking and kicking and struggling against his captors, but there were too many. When they'd restrained him, pressing his body into the straw beneath the bag, Prachett leaned down and blew his foul breath across Avery's face.

"If you will not do this for me, you may consider your time on this earth over and done. I will not tolerate another failure. I will not be shamed again."

In answer, Avery spat in Prachett's face.

Prachett shoved himself upright, dashing the spittle away with a ragged and stained sleeve. "Lads, convince him."

"And this is the conservatory." Henrietta led Leah into a room full of potted plants. The evening light shone through the many windows, giving the greenery an almost-living glow. The scent of damp earth hung heavy in the air.

Leah looked around, nodding sagely. Sure, it was a nice room, but the charade was starting to grate on her nerves. Mrs. Harper would probably have a stroke if they were late to dinner, and Henrietta wasn't showing any signs of backing down yet. It was getting tough to maintain her patience with the girl. They'd already traipsed through half the huge house without any sign of the duke. And while the number of valuable and interesting antiques was impressive, Leah was starving and completely done with the hike.

"It's very nice. But shouldn't we be heading to supper now?"

The girl crossed her arms over her middle, her mobcap slipping to one side. "I told you, it's been delayed." She pointed toward the back of the room. "The orchids are quite lovely. They're by the windows, just there."

With a long-suffering sigh, Leah turned in the direction Henrietta had indicated. A delicate white flower sat in a small pot on a narrow table. She'd just bent to sniff it when the sound of a door slamming brought her head around.

She was alone. That little brat.

Leah crossed the conservatory toward the door, muttering under her breath the whole time. Grabbing the handle, she gave it a sharp twist.

It didn't move.

Shaking the heavy door, she tried again. It was locked. A curse escaped her and she slumped against the solid wood.

This had been a lot harder than she thought, and she hadn't actually had to do any work yet. Was her duke worth it? He had to be.

But what if he isn't, and I got a job as a housemaid for

nothing? What if Pawpaw is really sick, and I'm here chasing an adventure instead of being there for him? Uneasiness swirled in her middle, and she crossed her arms tight to stifle it.

But then the thought of Jamie and Micah's faces at their wedding popped into her brain. It had been so beautiful, as beautiful as *Pride & Prejudice* had ever been. Pawpaw's words echoed in her head. *You find him, and you marry him, so when I'm dead and gone I know you'll be taken care of…*She shoved herself upright, straightening her mobcap determinedly. Not only was this for her future and her happiness, this was for Pawpaw's peace of mind. Her man would be perfect for her, as perfect as Mr. Darcy for Elizabeth or Antony for Cleopatra, or even Romeo for Juliet—well, hopefully without the mutual suicide bit.

Wading through the plants, Leah headed for the nearest window. Here on the ground floor it should be as simple as yank up the glass and hop to the grass, just in time for dinner. Easy peasy.

Shoving a potted palm to the side, Leah stood on tiptoe to reach the latch. It was just out of her reach. Damn tall windows. Stretching farther, she was just able to flick the edge enough to loosen the catch. Her breath on the glass fogged her vision of the duke's grounds, so she almost missed him.

Almost.

Avery Russell was walking slowly toward the house, his face and arms covered with bruises and crimson splotches of blood. He looked like he'd been on the wrong side of a mugging.

"Avery," she breathed, fear streaming through her brain. "What the hell?"

Knocking the catch the rest of the way free, she shoved up the window with a bang and was tumbling free before her brain even had a chance to catch up. She had to go to him. Something horrible must have happened.

Her mobcap flapped wildly and strands of hair streamed free as she clapped a hand atop her head to secure her required headgear.

"Avery," she yelled as she ran. Damn, the yard wasn't that big. He had to hear her calling. "Avery, what happened? Wait a second, let me..."

Her skidding stop sprayed gravel beneath her boots. He'd entered the house without hesitating. He'd heard her, hadn't he? Why wouldn't he stop? Making up her mind quickly, she ran the last few steps that separated her from the door he'd entered and sprinted up the stairs.

She'd find out what was going on whether he wanted her to know or not. *But what about supper, and Mrs. Harper?* her logical side nagged. *You'll be in trouble if you're late. And you have to keep this job or you won't meet the duke, and Pawpaw...*

She shook her head as she rounded the landing and threw open the door of the duke's bedchamber. It would be okay. It had to be.

"Avery?" She kept her voice soft as she scanned the large bedroom. "Are you in here?" No sign of him. Ducking into the dressing room she'd sat next to him in, she scanned the smaller room for the valet. Nope. Not here either.

"Where did he go?" she said aloud, her hands on her hips. With a shake of her head, she turned to go. Her breath left her body when she clapped eyes on the bedroom's new inhabitant.

He was tall, with silvery gray hair and pale blue eyes that seemed dedicated to a slight smolder. He appeared to be in his early fifties or so. His features were angular, all hollows and shadows and sharp bones, with shallow wrinkles near his eyes and mouth. Slender, graceful, like a predatory cat, he moved into the room. Dressed in severe, unrelenting black, there was only one person he could be.

Suddenly remembering her role as maid, Leah sank into a deep curtsy. "Your Grace." She hadn't intended to sound so self-conscious, but she was face-to-face with a freaking *duke*. And not just any duke, but the duke that was destined to be hers forever. Wow. She hadn't imagined snagging such a sugar daddy, though. She'd have to think about how she felt about such a big age difference.

"Please tell Cook I shall dine at my club tonight." His voice was softer than she'd imagined. Still masculine, but refined, almost the polar opposite of Avery's deep and raspy male growl. He turned away from her with a polite nod. She stood rooted to the spot, confusion refusing to let her legs operate.

"At your club, Your Grace?" she repeated, just in the hopes he'd turn around. *Notice me*, she yelled in her head. *Come on, you've got to turn around and look at me!*

"Yes, thank you."

He dismissed her with a wave of his hand, not bothering to look up from the small wooden box he'd picked up on the bedside table. A gold ring glittered on his finger as he pinched, and a sniff sounded loudly in the room. Another pinch, another sniff. He tilted his head back and sighed, his longish gray hair swaying with the movement. Leah tried to swallow, but her throat had gone dry.

"Very well, Your Grace." Leah bobbed another unseen curtsy and let herself out of the room, closing the door with a soft click. Well, that wasn't exactly the meeting she'd pictured. It was tough to measure chemistry when the guy wouldn't even look at you. *And he looks old! Totally wasn't expecting that.* She dismissed the thought with a heavy breath. It would just take some time.

A clock somewhere bonged the hour loudly, and Leah winced as she turned and sprinted for the stairs. She'd have to find Avery later. She had about thirty seconds to get to the servants' hall and be seated for dinner.

But no matter how quickly she descended the stairs, she couldn't outrun the twinge in her chest. Her feet grew heavier with each step, slowing her progress. When she reached the bottom of the staircase, she plopped down on the lowest step and cradled her chin in her hands.

She'd met her man. He was handsome. His voice wasn't at all what she'd imagined. And—the thought of the snuffbox made her shudder—she hadn't wanted a guy with any kind of substance dependencies. But the duke wasn't what had slowed her, stopped her like a remote control car without any juice left.

She stood, turned, and ran back up the stairs as quickly as she'd descended them.

Pink-stained water dripped back into the basin as Avery wrung out the cloth. He dipped it again, letting the cool water soak the fibers. It was hardly the first time he'd tended to wounds here in his attic bedchamber, but he'd hoped that he'd finally left those days behind him. It seemed that he could not yet outdistance his past.

Wincing as he pressed the cloth to his swollen cheek, he blew out a breath. Prachett's men had thrashed him thoroughly, bruising and breaking his skin. They'd not spared him, only relenting when he'd agreed to fight in the Houndstooth. *Damn and blast.* He'd sworn he'd not set foot in the ring again. But what choice did they leave him? If Prachett and his men killed him, then his aunt could not last out the month. There was no one to purchase her medicine or to pay for her lodgings and care but Avery. He could not abandon her, no matter how it cost him.

"Bloody hell," he hissed as he draped the cool wet cloth across the welt on his upper arm. Drops of water ran in rivulets down his chest, dampening the fine spray of hairs on that side. He clamped the rag to his skin and set his teeth against the pain, squeezing his eyes shut. He blew heavy breaths from his nose, feeling the steady thump of his heartbeat in each welt, each bruise.

After another moment, the pain eased somewhat. He lifted the now-hot cloth and dipped it into the basin again.

Leah's anguished voice struck him like another blow from the crop. "Oh my God, Avery, what the hell happened to you?"

Six

VULNERABILITY. THAT WAS THE SENSATION THAT BUBBLED angrily through his veins, clenched his teeth, and closed his fists. The knowledge that he was exposed, bleeding and wounded, and she was seeing him in this state, turned him into more of an animal than a man. He didn't turn toward her, keeping his gaze locked on the small window in front of him. He could not show her his weakness, his shame.

"Get out." His voice was low and threatening.

The floorboards creaked with her steps. "Don't be stupid, Avery. You're bleeding. You look like you got hit by a pickup truck." Concern threaded her words, lending them an almost tender sound despite the insult.

He closed his eyes, trying to get his rage under control. Water trickled and dripped into the basin beside him.

"This is going to hurt. I'm sorry."

The cloth had barely grazed his shoulder when he gained his feet like a shot. Whirling, he glared at her. "I said for you to leave me be. I've asked for no favors from you. These chambers are mine, not yours. If you are discovered here, you'll be turned out into the street immediately. Besides, I've no need of your assistance."

He backed toward the corner and widened his stance unconsciously, staring at her beneath lowered brows.

She stood motionless for a while, the damp cloth still hanging from her fingertips like a dead creature. He mimicked her stillness, not letting his gaze leave her face.

Sighing, she let the cloth fall back into the basin with a fleshy plop.

"Okay, fine. So you don't need my help." She crossed her arms, and he struggled to focus on the throbbing pain in his ribs rather than the way her breasts rounded with the unintended frame. "I'll just stay over here, quiet and out of the way."

She flounced over to the only chair in the room and sat, keeping her blue eyes trained on his face.

They stood in silence, a pair of combatants unwilling to give the other quarter. Had she been a man, Avery would have been very tempted to give way to his baser instincts and thoroughly thrash the blighter. But this was Leah. Tall, beautiful, odd Leah, who insisted on helping tend the wounds of a nigh stranger. Despite his best efforts, he could not stay angry with her. Even though she'd invaded his private rooms, he could not ignore the selfless intention behind her reasoning.

"You can stand there and stare at me all you want. That's fine with me, but it's not going to stop that drip of blood that's about to hit your waistband."

He looked down. Blast it, she was right. He dashed the offending drip away, leaving a smear of blood to mat the curls of hair on his abdomen.

"Come on. Don't be such a hard ass. If you let me help you clean up, it'll go much faster, and we can both get down to dinner before Mrs. Harper throws a hissy fit."

"Surely it is not time for the evening meal?" At her nod, Avery cursed beneath his breath.

She shrugged, looking unconcerned. "They'll get over my being late. You were hurt."

"You must go."

She shook her head vehemently. "Nope, not while you're still bleeding."

He gritted his teeth in irritation. "You silly wench, go down to supper. If you're discovered in a man's chambers, you'll be ruined and cast out of the house. Smythe and Mrs. Harper would never allow you to stay."

Raising her brows, she crossed her arms. "Well, you'd better hurry up then, because I'm not leaving this room until your injuries are taken care of."

Despite the prickle of unease across his throat, he crossed the room to the basin again. Gripping the rag, he wrung it out and placed it on his broken skin with a hissing breath. Even though he desperately wanted to squeeze his eyes shut, he would not give her the advantage of losing his scrutiny.

"There. My wounds are being attended to. Now you may leave."

She laughed at him. "This is going to take forever. At this rate I won't get there in time for dessert, and then you'll be in trouble for helping me get this job."

Blast it—she left him no choice. His reluctant decision made, Avery laid the cloth back in the basin. "Be quick about it then. You must attend the evening meal."

He could not miss the self-satisfied gleam in her eyes as she stood. "Good. Sit down on the bed there."

He followed her instructions, his already sore muscles tight with apprehension. "This is very improper."

"Oh stop. I'm a servant, so nobody can give a crap about my reputation."

"In this household, even the servants are held to an impossible standard. And are you not a servant who has designs on a duke?" He tossed the bitter question over his shoulder and gave a hiss of pain when she probed at his rib cage.

"Yeah. But still. This will only take a minute." She stood upright, frowning at his rapidly darkening side. "I think you've got a broken rib. We'll need to wrap that up."

He did not disagree.

Her touch was tender on his wounds, soft and gentle as she cleansed the blood from his skin and bound his aching sides. He found himself relaxing under her ministrations, despite his better judgment. When he'd been bandaged and cleansed to her satisfaction, she cleared her throat.

"So you didn't say. How did this happen?"

Her question hung in the air, heavy and dark in its innocence. His teeth nearly drew blood from the inside of his cheek. She couldn't know about his past. She'd hate him like the rest of the servants, and God help him, he could not face that derision coming from her. She was nearly a complete stranger to him, but she'd been so kind. The dark world of the boxing mills and his past was no place for a beautiful creature like her.

"Avery?"

He sighed.

"It is not a tale for a lady's ears, and it does not signify in any case."

"But…"

He stopped her with a hand in the air. "It does not signify. But have a care, miss." He turned to her. "Men are not always what they seem."

❧

Leah swallowed hard, trying not to let her confusion show on her face. What could he mean by such a cryptic warning? *Men are not always what they seem?* Was Avery some kind of criminal or something? Had he been injured while doing something illegal?

"Well," she said, looking down at the basin of water to avoid the seriousness of his hazel gaze, "I'll remember that."

With confusion stirring in her brain, she turned to leave the room.

"Miss?"

Her heart fluttered with something odd when she turned to look at his shirtless form again. Even his bruises and bandages couldn't detract from the muscled beauty of his masculine form, but a half-naked Avery facing her was truly a sight to behold. His arms and chest were lined with muscle, nicely defined with a sprinkling of hair across his chest and thickening in a line down his belly, disappearing into his high-waisted breeches. But his eyes were as serious as the grave.

"Think on what I've said."

Leah nodded, trying to swallow, but her throat had gone dry. "I will," she rasped.

The door clicked shut behind her. His words dogged her steps as she made her way from the attic down to the servants' hall. What the hell did he mean? Was he trying to warn her away? But why? She didn't even know him that well, and she certainly wasn't here after him.

Leah laughed to herself as she skipped the last step to hop on the landing. It made sense. Of course he'd been concerned about propriety. Leah shook her head with a smile and hustled for the servants' hall. She didn't regret helping him at all, but she was grateful for the reminder. This place and time was different than what she was used to, and any tiny misstep on her part could have grave consequences. She'd be more careful.

"I trust," Mrs. Harper said when Leah entered the room, "that this tardiness of yours is not a habit, Miss Ramsey. No matter your relation to Cook, I shall expect the courtesy of your prompt attendance at mealtimes and whenever your services are required."

"Yes, ma'am," Leah said, hanging her head in what she hoped was an accurate portrayal of a chastened, meek parlor maid. "Henrietta was kind enough to show me the conservatory, and I lost track of time. It won't happen again, ma'am. Oh, and His Grace is dining at the club tonight, Cook."

After bobbing an apologetic curtsy, Leah slid into the chair beside Henrietta and smiled sweetly. The girl glared at her, obviously piqued that her scheme hadn't made Leah completely miss the meal.

Cook gave Leah a tight nod as she plopped a bowl of watery soup in front of her, along with a hunk of coarse brown bread. "There, lassie. You'll be needin' your strength now. You've much to learn and do tomorrow."

Leah murmured a polite agreement as she tore off a hunk of bread and chewed it slowly. Ugh. Dry and tough. Scanning the rest of the table's occupants, she took note of how they ate their soup. Mrs. Harper took tiny sips, perching on the very edge of her chair with her spine straighter than a yardstick. Cook hunched over her bowl, her lips pursed as she poured in the broth. Various footmen and a hawk-nosed man that Leah presumed was the butler ate with typical male gusto, refined as it was by the niceties of aping gentility. Henrietta and the rest of the maids chatted between sips and giggled like the young girls many of them were.

Satisfied that she wouldn't stick out too much, Leah soaked bites of bread in her soup and ate the bland broth without complaining. This was way too important to screw up.

Dinner was filling, if a little unsatisfying. Leah smiled at the maid who took her empty bowl. The thin girl didn't smile back. Sliding her damp palms down her skirt, Leah watched as the rest of the staff separated into groups. Where would she fit in here? Best to hang back and see.

The maids gathered in a corner around Henrietta, baskets of mending at their feet. They turned their backs to the room, eyeing Leah with mistrust from some and complete dislike from others. Leah sighed. It wasn't going to be easy to become one of the girls, apparently.

The off-duty footmen laughed as they shuffled a deck of cards. Leah stood, uncertainty holding her back. She knew better than to ask them to deal her in. She probably wouldn't know the game they were playing, and she didn't want the maids to think she was making a bid for the only male attention to be had. That would make things even worse, she was fairly sure.

So instead, she took a seat beside Cook and listened to the woman wax eloquent on the ways to prepare a leg of mutton. After an hour, she'd heard more than she ever wanted to know about sheep butchery. When the lady finally fell quiet, a smile pinned firmly to her lips at her own culinary genius, Leah saw her opening and jumped for it.

"Cook, why didn't Mr. Russell come to dinner this evening?" Whoa. Not what she'd intended to say at all, but her curiosity about the valet had momentarily preempted her mission to snare the duke.

Cook's smile slipped and she folded her hands primly in her lap. "I'm sure I don't know."

"Doesn't he normally eat with the rest of the staff?"

"Child, you'll do well to keep clear of Mr. Russell."

Confusion and offended loyalty for her new friend bubbled in Leah's chest. "But I thought you liked him. He seems really nice. What do you mean, I should avoid him?"

Cook stood and grabbed Leah by the hand, dragging her into the darkened kitchen. Her voice was a sibilant hiss in the dim room. "Mind your tone with me, miss. I've put me own position on the line by begging for yours, so you'll keep a rein on your tongue or you'll be out on the street. Mr. Russell prefers to be alone, and that's all there is to it. Do not speak with him; do not seek him out. I cannot be any plainer."

Leah's brow furrowed and she bit her lip at the woman's words, not liking a bit of it. There was a lot more going on in this house than it seemed. Avery was alone, but he seemed lonely too. Why wouldn't anyone associate with him? Weren't valets kind of high up in the ranks of domestic help?

When Leah didn't respond right away, Cook gave her arm a little shake. "Promise me, lass. I'll not leave go until you do."

"Fine, I promise." The words spilled out reluctantly and Leah pulled her arm free. The relief on the woman's red face was plain.

"Good. It is time to retire, so go up with the others. Not a word of this conversation to anyone."

Without waiting for a reply, Cook turned and left Leah in the empty kitchen. Leah crossed her arms and furrowed her brow. What conversation? As far as Leah could tell, Cook had talked and Leah had listened, even though she didn't understand a word of it.

Why would Cook be so adamant about Avery? It didn't make any sense.

"Ramsey, as penance for your tardiness this evening, you will finish the scrubbing up," Mrs. Harper said when Leah entered. In the few minutes she'd been with Cook in the kitchen, most everyone seemed to have cleared out. "You will find the scullery off the main kitchen there. Straight to your bed when you've done, and you are expected here for your tasks by five. I shall not be so lenient with your punishment if you are tardy again. Tomorrow you will learn your regular duties. Granville House is one of the most respected homes in London, and you must work to maintain that status with the rest of us."

"Yes, ma'am," Leah said dutifully to the woman's back as she exited the servants' hall, leaving her completely alone. Man, they didn't really go for friendly working relationships, did they? Or maybe it was just Leah. Maybe they could tell she was way more familiar with the intimate workings of *The Legend of Zelda* than with a broom. In any case, she thought as she wandered through the dim kitchen to the smallish room on the side, she would be pretty damn happy to see the end of her stint as maid, and she hadn't even done any real work yet.

Pushing open the door to the scullery, Leah ground to a horrified halt. "Oh, *hell* no."

It looked like an episode of *Hoarders: Regency Edition*. Sticky dishes were piled everywhere, layered with crusts and molding bits of food. Large pots were stacked to one side of a huge basin, which was filled with grayish water. Flies buzzed gleefully around the whole mucky scene.

Leah slammed her eyes shut. "This has got to be a joke." Even without the vision in front of her, the smell of old food was proof enough that reality had a really cruel sense of humor.

What do you want, Leah? You want true love? You want to find a man that Pawpaw can feel good about you marrying? Then here. Prove it. Do the best damn job you can. It's the only way you'll get the chance to win the game.

With a dejected sigh, Leah rolled up her sleeves and grabbed an apron. If she was lucky, she'd get this done in two hours, which would mean a good six hours of sleep. She could operate on that. She hoped.

Seven

SHE WASN'T LUCKY. NOT ONLY WAS SHE NOT LUCKY, SHE was almost completely sure that Mrs. Knightsbridge had put some kind of curse on her before shoving her through that mirror.

She didn't shove you. You practically dived face-first into that bureau's glass front. "Don't worry, Pawpaw. I'll go off and have an adventure and find a super-husband and everything will be perfect!" Typical Leah. Idiot.

The dishwater splashed into Leah's face as she slammed the plate down into it. A drop hit her tongue, and she nearly gagged. Wiping her face against her arm, she sighed and resumed scrubbing.

It was after midnight according to the bonging she heard from somewhere in the house, and she still had three pots to scour. Her hands were pale and wrinkled like raisins. Her nails were jagged, her mobcap was slipping, and to make things worse, a large brown spider was working in a dusty corner directly in front of Leah. She had to stand as far away from the basin as possible to avoid any chance of contact. Arachnophobia wasn't one of those things she could just suck it up and deal with.

"I've got my eye on you, you eight-legged bastard," Leah said aloud to the spider as she worked at a crusted-on bit of something. "If you move, you and I are going to have problems. I'm talking major issues. You should probably go ahead and pick out your casket, because—*EEeeeeeeek!*"

The spider moved. The pot clattered to the floor, splattering dishwater all over Leah, the clean dishes, and the spider, who skittered down the wall toward the floor as fast as his many legs could carry him. Letting out another bloodcurdling shriek, Leah ran for the kitchen and collided with a solid, muscled, male body in the scullery doorway.

"Help," she gasped into Avery's face, completely uncaring that her voice was thin and panicked. "There's a huge spider, and it was too close to me, and it ran and I don't know where it went."

He looked like she'd just grabbed an unexpected handful of Mr. Happy, but she couldn't do anything about that. The irrational fear completely blocked logic from her mind as she climbed Avery's body like a well-muscled ladder. Looking over her shoulder to make sure the spider hadn't followed, she twined her arms around his neck and her legs around his waist and held on for dear life.

❧

He'd known the lass for less than a day, and she'd just wound herself around him like the crust on a meat pie. She wasn't an overly fleshy girl, but she was surprisingly heavy when she clung to him like a petrified and hissing cat. Though his first instinct was to shove her away, breaking the unexpected and—if he was quite honest, painful—contact, he repressed it with difficulty. Spreading his feet apart to give him more balance, he carefully began to peel her from his body, making sure to move slowly and methodically, both to prevent distressing her further and causing his bruised body greater discomfort. Her panicked state would not facilitate his swift release.

"Stoppit, Avery, please. Holy shit, it's coming this way!"

She clung to him tighter, burying her face in his neck. The measured pace of his removal gave him ample opportunity to feel the soft vise of her thighs around his hips, the press of her breasts against his chest. The scent of sweet perfume invaded his senses, and tendrils of yellow hair tickled his cheek. The heavy ache in his bones accompanied a deep tingling of desire at the base of his spine.

"Miss Ramsey, release me." His voice was firm if muffled by the mobcap she'd pressed against his cheek. For every finger he removed from its grip at the back of his neck, another grabbed hold. "Now." He mustn't be seen with her this way; it would ruin her. His unease was growing into a creature that resembled her panic at the sight of the spider. He had to break their contact quickly. He could not harm her reputation, not when she'd been so kind to him.

"I can't. Kill it, please."

His voice was angrier than he'd intended, but he could not temper his response. "How am I to kill anything with you clinging to me like a vulture on a rotted corpse?"

"Ugh," she said, loosening her hold enough to look

him in the eyes. Her delicate nose wrinkled in disgust. "What a gross visual."

With barely disguised relief, he grabbed her around the waist and turned, pulling her free and setting her in a chair with a soft thump. His security was tempered with another, stranger sense of loss. How odd.

"Where is it? Did you kill it yet?" She peered around his hip as if looking for a brigand to come despoil her instead of a tiny spider.

"Wait there a moment."

He turned away from her and straightened his clothing. Scanning the stone floor beneath his feet, he stepped slowly.

"There it is! Oh my God, there it is by that bag."

Instead of examining the tiny spider that was making its way up the side of a sack of flour, Avery looked over his shoulder at Miss Ramsey. She'd clapped both hands over her eyes, drawing her feet up beneath her as if to keep them away from the slavering fangs of the bloodthirsty spider. It would have been humorous had her fear not been so real.

Taking pity on her, he knocked the spider from the bag onto a small piece of kindling, intending to usher the blighter outside.

"Don't take it on a transatlantic cruise, just squish it, for chrissakes!" Her choked voice chastised him.

Ignoring her, Avery walked slowly, turning the kindling to keep the spider from falling or jumping free. Shoving the kitchen door open with his knee, he bent down and deposited the spider in the bush beside the stoop.

"There, lad. Mind you stay clear of the kitchen and

Miss Ramsey. I'll not be allowed to spare your life a second time."

He smiled as the small creature disappeared into the darkened foliage. The door's hinges creaked as he pulled it shut.

She sat in the same position, feet tucked beneath her and hands plastered over her eyes.

"Is it safe?"

"It is. He will trouble you no longer, miss."

Avery watched as the tension slowly ebbed from her fingertips, her hands, then her arms and shoulders. Her feet slid to the floor, and her whole body melted like warmed candle wax. The corner of her mouth turned down, her cheeks were pale, and her demeanor was that of one utterly defeated.

"I'm sorry," she whispered, looking down at the floor. "Snakes I can handle. Mice are fine. I know it's stupid, I know, but those damn spiders scare the crap out of me." She looked up at him, her blue eyes shiny with unshed tears. "I'm so sorry."

His arms ached but not from the beating he'd taken. He didn't know why. Never before had he felt the urge to do something, to ease her discomfort, to shelter her by...holding her in his arms? No. The thought was insupportable. She had come here for the duke, and he could not stand in her way.

Abruptly turning away, Avery cleared his throat and clasped his hands behind his back. "It is of no consequence." Keeping his gaze trained on a stack of bowls, he fought to regain his composure. What had this woman done to him?

"I hate to even ask you this." Her voice was thin and

small. "Would you mind checking the scullery? To see if it had any, er, friends in there."

Without comment, Avery turned and walked into the scullery.

Pots and dishes were piled everywhere, mostly clean but for a pile of largish pots to one side of the washbasin. He stooped to pick up a half-scrubbed pot from the stones of the floor. This must have been the crash he'd heard when entering the kitchen. He set the pot upright by the basin and examined the corners of the room.

"There is no sign of any eight-legged compatriots, madam. I should think you are safe."

"Are you sure?" Her pale face peered around the corner of the doorjamb.

"Quite certain."

She entered the room slowly, eyes darting this way and that, as if she didn't quite trust his report. He said not a word as she moved with arms crossed tightly over her middle to stand in the center of the room.

"Thank you." She didn't look up at him as she spoke. "Again, I'm really sorry about that. I just can't handle spiders. I'm not normally such a wimp, so please don't think I can't do this, okay?"

"What do you mean?"

She gestured to the mound of dishes. "I know you and Cook are risking a lot by getting me this job. I can handle it, I promise. I don't want you to think because I wigged out over a huge, monstrously awful spider that I can't hack this job." She nodded and straightened her spine. "I'm kind of a bad ass, when I need to be."

He smothered the smile her odd words brought to his

face. "I have no doubt that you are." He turned to leave the room.

"Hey, where are you going?"

His feet stilled, and he looked back at her. She stood tall, but uncertainty still shadowed her eyes.

"I missed the evening meal. I had intended to find food."

"Oh," she said. "Okay." She turned back to her washbasin, and he moved to leave the room but stopped when she spoke again. Her voice was soft, uncertain.

"You could eat in here if you wanted. I've got to finish these pots before I go to bed, and it wouldn't be so lonely if you were in here. You don't have to talk to me or anything, if you don't want to. Just be here, if you wanted to, that is." She looked over her shoulder at him, and her wide, anxious eyes softened something in his chest.

"As you wish," he said, and turned to leave the room.

◈

Leah stared down into the dishwater, wishing it were physically possible to kick herself in the ass. What a completely stupid way to react to an itty-bitty spider! *Well, it had been pretty sizeable*, she argued with herself.

And for Avery to have seen her like that, completely overcome with panic over something so trivial? He must think she was a total wuss. But she wasn't. She muscled the largest pot over to the basin, just to remind herself she was tough. She grabbed the brush and started scrubbing, punctuating each mental point with another stroke of the coarse bristles. She was a *strong*, independent woman. She'd *built* sets for the community theatre, all by herself. She'd *made* her own iPhone app. She'd *beat*

Skyrim within a *month* of its release. But, she thought as she dropped the scrub brush down into the basin, at the sight of an eight-legged bug, she was a complete ninny. A brainless, spineless lump of humanity.

But she kept her head up and kept moving. She hadn't gotten this far in life by giving up. Well, not that she'd gotten too far, honestly. But she was a self-sufficient adult, and that counted for something, right?

"The scullery maid should be doing this washing." Avery's voice came from behind her. A scraping of wood against the stone floor accompanied his voice. "Why were you pressed into this duty?"

Redoubling her scrubbing efforts, Leah looked down into the pot instead of back at Avery. She couldn't tell him it was because she'd been late for supper. His *I-told-you-so* had to be more irritating than the usual. "Mrs. Harper said that the scullery maids were on vacation, or holiday, whatever."

"Are you still expected to do the duties of under-housemaid in the morning?"

She nodded and frowned down at a stubborn bit of burnt-on food. No matter how she scrubbed, it clung to the bottom of the pot like Scrooge with his last nickel. "Stubborn piece of shit," she muttered.

"I beg your pardon?" Avery's voice was just behind her head.

Startled, she dropped the brush into the washbasin. The resulting splash soaked the chest of her apron and dress. She staggered backward, straight into the surprised valet.

He sprang away as if burned, and she stumbled to catch herself before she fell on her ass. Crap, she spent a lot of time not being graceful in front of him.

Good thing he wasn't her destined true love. He'd have run away screaming by now if he was.

"Damn it," she cursed, wiping at her front. "I'm sorry. I'm not normally such a klutz." She looked up at him, confusion and helplessness leaking out of her ears. "It's just late, and it's been a really long day, and I…"

"Hush," he interrupted her. The corner of his mouth twitched, almost like he wanted to smile, but he didn't. Good thing, too. She'd have had to belt the shit out of him or burst into tears. "Sit just there, by the fire. It will dry your clothing. Finish that bread and cheese if you've a mind to."

He unbuttoned his cuffs and began methodically rolling the fabric up his muscled forearms. Leah swallowed hard at the purely innocent sight. Damn, the man had some nice arms, even though they bore some purpling bruises. Corded with muscle, they flexed with the simplest movements. Did valets do that much heavy lifting?

"You're not going to wash the dishes for me. It's not your job," she protested, but he shook his head.

"It is of no consequence. We'll have them done in a trice, and you can find your bed afterward."

"Oh gosh," Leah said, dropping her forehead to the table in front of her with a moan. "I forgot I've got to be up at the ass crack of dawn in the morning."

Avery barked a laugh, nearly scaring the shit out of her. "What did you say?"

"The ass crack of dawn," Leah said, laughing at Avery's shocked expression. "It's my somewhat colorful description for getting up too damn early."

He cleared his throat, smothered his smile with a more neutral expression, and continued scrubbing the next-to-last pot. "As amusing as your description is, I'd suggest you not use it around the other servants. They should probably not enjoy it as much as I."

"I'll take that under advisement," Leah said, smiling down at the cheese sandwich she was making. A sideways glimpse at the valet revealed that he was hard at work removing grime from what looked like a witch's cauldron. And it wasn't even his job; he just wanted to help her.

"Thank you for helping me." Her words came out without thought, but she was glad they had.

He didn't turn, but she thought his shoulders relaxed slightly. She popped a crust of bread into her mouth, chewing thoughtfully before speaking again. "So how did you end up here? Always wanted to be a valet?"

He paused in his scrubbing to laugh. "Not as such, no." The sound of bristles on metal resumed. "I had some little experience in grand houses before this one. My former employment rendered me unfit for service to most. But His Grace took a liking to me, so here I am."

Leah sat back against the wooden slats. "So what did you do before that made you 'unfit' to most?" She made air quotes, even though his back was turned.

"I worked with my hands."

The answer was cryptic, but his tone was even more so. Leah pursed her lips. "Like, making things?"

His laugh this time was bitter. "No, not at all." He didn't give her a chance to ask a follow-up. "It is of no consequence. What is your occupation in the land behind the wardrobe?"

Leah smiled. "That makes it sound like I lived in Narnia, which would have been awesome. But no. I'm an elementary school drama teacher." She pinched off another bite of bread. "I've got a great group of kids, and I couldn't imagine doing anything else. I mean, who else gets to play pretend for their nine-to-five?"

Water splashed as Avery emptied the pot. His muscles strained against the damp cotton of his sleeves as he lifted the large iron thing. "I am sure that the children enjoy their lessons with such a lovely teacher."

Leah's heart thudded at the compliment, but Avery didn't turn. He merely wiped the pot down with a rag and continued washing up. She took a bite of the food he'd given her, just because she didn't know what else to say. It would have been so much easier if Avery could be the duke. But even though he'd been sweet and had just called her lovely, he wasn't exactly coming on to her. She'd spent a lot of time in the friend zone, and this was shaping up to be that kind of friendship, sadly.

She swallowed methodically, flicking a little crumb from the corner of the table. As handsome as Avery was, she was here to romance the duke himself. That had to be it. She'd win his heart and waltz back through the mirror with her perfect man in tow. She hoped.

Eight

WHEN LEAH AND AVERY PARTED WAYS AT THE TOP OF the stairs, it was one o'clock. After that single compliment, he'd kept the conversation light, never venturing into the territory again. It had been a little disappointing, but even so, she'd really enjoyed talking with the strong, quiet man. She watched as he disappeared down the corridor, moving slowly. Must be his bruises hurting him. She shook her head. *Shouldn't have let him finish the pots.*

Leah's jaw cracked loudly as she yawned, and she covered her mouth with the hand that wasn't holding her candle. Four hours of sleep? It wasn't going to be fun, but she'd make it, she reasoned. It would be worth it in the end.

She found her door without much trouble and pushed it open with a creak. Soft snores echoed through the room from the occupants who were already in bed. Leah shook her head as she set the candle down on a small table. She really wasn't looking forward to sleeping with strangers, but what choice did she have? Hell, she thought as she peeled her damp dress off, she'd much rather go bunk with Avery than with the obnoxious little

Henrietta. Locking her in the conservatory? Come on. She'd have to do a lot better than that to get rid of Leah.

She spread her dress out on a ladder-backed chair near the fireplace, hoping it would dry by morning. Shucking her petticoat, she balanced on one foot as she removed her stocking. Another yawn knocked her off balance, and she grabbed the chair to right herself. The legs of the seat thumped against the rough wooden floor.

Leah froze as the snoring stopped. God, she didn't want to wake them up. It was going to be tough enough to sleep next to the prickly Henrietta without having to deal with her anger about being rudely awakened. She could just imagine the retaliation for that. And the other two, Sarah and…well, someone—she couldn't remember the other girl's name—had seemed nice enough, but she could just imagine the hell it would be living with three girls who couldn't stand her.

The even breathing resumed, and Leah sighed with relief. She made quick work of the rest of her undressing, and tiptoed to the bedside wearing only her shift and bloomers. Propping her hands on her hips, she stared down at the bed.

Grand. Just fucking grand.

Henrietta lay diagonally across the double bed, wrapped in the covers like a burrito. The only way Leah could fit in the bed at all would be to curl into the fetal position. Leah's eyes narrowed, and her hands fisted by her sides.

That was just about enough for today.

More gently than she wanted, Leah pushed Henrietta's legs over to the far side of the bed. The girl squeaked in alarm as Leah pulled the covers, lifting them up to straighten them with an irritated snap.

"What the bloody hell do you think you're doing, you stupid git?"

"Quiet," Leah whispered. She slipped beneath the covers beside Henrietta. "Don't wake the others. I had to make room. You were hogging the bed."

And for that, Leah got a sharp kick to the shin. Gritting her teeth, she rolled to her side and bunched the pillow beneath her head. As much as she wanted to return the favor, she wouldn't kick a kid. No matter how much this particular kid deserved it.

"Good night, Henrietta."

"Go boil your 'ead."

Leah closed her eyes.

To her surprise and delight, the face she saw in the darkness of her mind was aristocratic, thin, and handsome. Black hair shot through with distinguishing strands of silver framed it. A hand with long, slender fingers reached out to her, and she took it gratefully.

"Oh, my darling," the duke, looking at least twenty years younger, whispered as he swept her into a waltz. "I have searched the world over for you."

She reached up and touched his face. It was smoother than she'd expected, without the faint feel of beard stubble or any wrinkles at all. He was hard, not with muscle, but with skin stretched directly over bone. His hand was cool in hers, and the other bled a chill into the small of her back. She shivered.

"You are cold," he said in his too-soft voice. "Let me warm you."

She didn't resist as he drew her close in his arms. Her heart thumped faster in excited delight. Her destined true love was holding her in his arms. Could anything be more perfect? She rested her cheek against his chest with a contented sigh.

It was cold.

She was pressed full against his body, but instead of the comforting warmth she'd expected, he was icy from head to toe. Pulling away from him, she looked up into his face.

And screamed.

"You simpleton, wake up."

Leah sat bolt upright with a gasp, her eyes flying open. Sarah and the other girl were dressing across the room, the light from their candles dancing crazily as they chatted and giggled. Henrietta stood beside the bed, glaring down at Leah. In her hands was the blanket. No wonder Leah had dreamed about being cold.

"You will be late if you do not hurry. I shouldn't care if you were, but Mrs. Harper bade me wake you."

"Oh my gosh," Leah moaned, gripping her head. It ached with a thumping pain. What a freaking weird dream. But she didn't have time to analyze it. She swung her feet off the side of the bed and winced at the chilly touch of the wooden floor. Without a word to Leah, the other three girls left the room. If she hadn't been so absorbed in her own headache, it might have bothered her. As it was, she could barely stagger over to the drawer in the bureau that had been designated as hers.

The predawn sky was lightening slightly, but even with a candle it was tough to dig her way through the drawer. Finally her fingers closed around a small leather pouch she'd secreted in her skirt before making her journey through the mirror. She opened the zipper with relief and spread the contraband on the windowsill.

A toothbrush and tube of toothpaste. Tampons. A bottle of Advil and a box of throat lozenges for the cold that had been threatening her since last week. A bar of her favorite vanilla and coconut soap, and a stick of deodorant. A picture of Pawpaw, smiling as he worked on an ancient tractor. She popped open the bottle of Advil and swallowed two dry. Looking down at the picture, she said, "Morning, Pawpaw." She traced the photo with a fingernail. She'd ridden on that tractor many times as a child, her grandfather holding her securely in his lap. Things were so much simpler then.

Shaking off her reverie, she brushed her teeth with water from the pitcher and made quick work of washing off as best she could with a rag and her soap. She donned her uniform, wincing at the still-damp fabric. It couldn't be helped though. By the time her hair was all tucked beneath her cap, her stockings were on, and her boots were laced, the black of night had faded to the hazy gray of early dawn on the horizon.

She gathered up her treasure trove and replaced the pouch in the drawer beneath her dress. Her headache was starting to fade around the edges a little, and gratitude flooded her as she descended the stairs to the servants' hall. If nothing else, Jamie's journey had prepared her to rough it here in the past. It wasn't going to be easy, but she was sure she was up to the challenge.

Well, she thought she was, until she discovered just how much a pain in the ass being an underhousemaid could be.

"Good morning." Leah smiled at Mrs. Harper as she descended the stairs.

The white-haired housekeeper scowled at her. "You

are very nearly late again, Ramsey. Granville House servants are expected to be prompt at all times."

Fighting the urge to protest, Leah scrambled to her seat at the dining table. Nobody else seemed to be there for breakfast yet, but clearly Mrs. Harper had risen from the wrong side of the coffin. No use fighting that kind of bad attitude. Clearly this woman needed to roll a solid plus five to positivity.

"What are you doing?" Mrs. Harper's nostrils flared.

Leah put on her best contrite look. "Aren't we having breakfast?"

The housekeeper looked at her as if she'd shat in His Grace's boots. "You must work to earn your breakfast, girl. Now follow me."

Blowing out an exasperated breath, Leah rose and trudged after the housekeeper. Was she ever going to stop screwing up? It hadn't seemed like being a servant should be this hard. Hopefully she'd just polish a few pieces of silver and then have a good breakfast to make up for her lack of sleep. Longing for the coziness of her memory-foam mattress, she followed Mrs. Harper down the dim hallway.

"Attend me, Ramsey." Mrs. Harper's heels clicked on the polished wood floors, and Leah hustled to keep up with her. "These tasks are to be done every morning upon rising. The house must be cleaned and aired, all superfluous articles put into their proper places, the fireplaces and hearths brushed up. The hearths all washed with soap and water, then carefully wiped dry with linen cloth and new fires laid." Leah hurried into a sitting room behind Mrs. Harper, who didn't slow down at all. The woman opened the curtains and kept moving as she spoke. "Sweep all the carpets, then turn up the corners to sweep away the dust upon the floor. Dust the window sashes, and once or twice a week shake out the window curtains and hangings. Are you attending me?"

All Leah could do was nod her head numbly. Her brain throbbed, her headache having returned with a vengeance. The enormity of her new job pressing in on her, she followed Mrs. Harper through room after room as the housekeeper pointed out different tasks for her to complete. Why hadn't she smuggled a vacuum and some Magic Erasers through the mirror with her? This was going to take forever.

"Attend to His Grace's dressing room, and the dressing rooms of any guests we have in residence. Empty the slops, replenish the ewers with fresh water, clean the fireplaces, brush the carpets, sweep the room, and make ready for the valet to attend His Grace's dressing. Once these tasks have been completed, you may then, and *only* then, come down to your breakfast."

Leah stopped dead in the middle of the hallway, her jaw working soundlessly. Mrs. Harper had just listed about two weeks' worth of housework, and she was supposed to get all this done before breakfast?

"I'm sorry," Leah said, surging forward to intercept the housekeeper before she could launch into another list of duties. "I don't think I heard correctly. I thought you said all this had to be done before breakfast."

Mrs. Harper's mouth pursed. "That is what I said, yes. It is the duty of a maid in your position to assist in all these tasks. You are capable, I trust?"

"Of course," Leah said hopefully. *Assist* was a good word. There were other maids, so maybe that giant list the old bat had just rattled off was to be divided among them all. If not, Leah probably wouldn't be eating break-fast for a few days. Weeks, maybe.

"Now then," Mrs. Harper sniffed, "go along to your duties. Henrietta and Sara are attending to the breakfast room, so you may proceed to His Grace's dressing cham-bers. Once you have put them to rights, come down and attend to the library. I shall direct your movements thereafter."

After shoving a coal scuttle and cleaning rags into Leah's hands, Mrs. Harper shooed her toward the duke's dressing rooms.

Timing her footsteps with the throbbing in her head, Leah mounted the stairs, trying like hell to figure out where this adventure had gone so horribly wrong. She had a terrifying idea that *empty the slops* meant *take care of the chamber pot.*

She hadn't planned on cleaning the man's toilet before she'd even had the chance to say hello.

Avery rolled to his side on the thin mattress, his breath hitching as his injured ribs caught with the movement. Dropping his feet to the chilly floor, he rose, gritting his teeth against the heavy pain of his bruises. A deep breath blew the worst of the pain away, and he was able to bend and light the candle at his bedside.

Dashing chilly water against his face, he made quick work of his morning ablutions, careful of his healing skin. Much as he hated to admit it, his wounds were not as both-ersome as they could have been, thanks to Miss Ramsey's attentions. The rough cotton towel scraped against his throat.

Miss Ramsey. Leah. The memory of the strange and beautiful girl stirred feelings that it should not. But the concern on her face, the tender way she'd bandaged his ribs, the sweet scent of her…

He bit back a curse. He should not think of her, no matter how kindly she'd treated him. The girl wanted to repay his kindness in helping her gain a position in the house. Ascribing any more importance to the gesture would be folly. He did not have the luxury of courtship, and even were he so inclined, she was destined for a much more advantageous match than with a man such as he. Whether or not she would wed the duke, a woman that beautiful deserved a mate who was her match. And Avery was certainly the farthest man from that.

He dressed quickly, having wasted much more time considering Miss Ramsey than he could afford. Avery set his jaw and proceeded down the stairs to His Grace's dressing chambers. His duties would not wait for his dreams to end.

As he neared the dressing room, hissed curses met his ears. Quickening his stride, he arrived at the door just in time to discover the source of the commotion.

Leah stood with one slipper toeing His Grace's chamber pot across the polished floor, her skirts caught high against her thighs and her fingers pinching her nostrils shut. The lid slipped and clanged as she prodded the pot gingerly with her toes, her whispered oaths coming fast on the heels of each clatter.

"Miss Ramsey," Avery choked out, pointedly ignoring the delectable length of leg her indecent show displayed, "whatever are you doing?"

"I'm trying to get this out of here." She punctuated

her statement with a particularly hard shove of her slipper on the upper portion of the receptacle. Only Avery's quick thinking and faster movement prevented the chamber pot from tipping over and spilling its contents over the costly carpeting.

He set the pot upright, then lowered his brows into a glower. "You must be silent, or you'll wake His Grace. Take this down to empty into the slops jar outside the house. The night soil man collects it there."

She didn't release her nostrils, speaking in an odd, nasally tone. "I can't touch that."

"Whyever not?" Frustration ran rampant through his brain, and he fought to keep a civil tongue.

"It's someone else's shit. Literally. I can't possibly carry that without some kind of sanitary protection. Rubber gloves, a hazmat suit, a bomb shelter, something."

Avery tamped down the urge to throttle the beautiful chit. It was a very near thing. "You requested a position in this household. You informed me that you were capable of a housemaid's duties. Are you now saying that you misled me to acquire the post?"

An angry blush climbed her cheeks, only managing to make her look lovelier. "You know I didn't lie to you. I told you, I can do this job. But listen, I have zero desire to die of some horrible disease because of a cavalier attitude toward human excrement." She crossed her arms. Even in her plain, high-necked gown, her chest rounded with the pose.

His mouth went dry, and he nearly choked as he tried to swallow. Though he was irritated, his desire for her grew. How could it not? She was defiant, strong, and determined. The muscles in his legs tensed, readying him to cross the room to her. Instead, he bent down and lifted the chamber pot. Though he knew he should not, he could not resist a parting shot as he turned and crossed to the door.

"I shall remove the slops for you this time, Miss Ramsey. But perhaps you should rethink your decidedly unwomanly attitude before you meet His Grace."

Her shocked gasp followed him down the stairs, and he let a small smile of triumph stretch his lips. It had been the most egregious lie, but it had been worth it to anger her. She angered and frustrated him to no end. Let her taste her own medicine.

Passing Henrietta on his way down the back stairs, he nodded a polite greeting and tried to ignore the young maid's disdainful scowl. Even his fellow servant's dislike could not temper his satisfaction at having spoken so to Miss Ramsey. She was far too idealistic, and if he could disabuse her of her starry-eyed notions before she followed them into trouble, then so much the better.

His personal satisfaction was simply a bonus.

Nine

AVERY DISAPPEARED THROUGH THE DRESSING ROOM DOOR carrying that disgusting chamber pot and leaving a completely stunned Leah in his wake.

Unwomanly? Had he seriously just told her that? She looked down at the floor where the chamber pot had been only a moment before. The last thing in the world she'd wanted was to carry a toilet down the stairs to empty it in the backyard. But she hadn't asked Avery for help, and she certainly hadn't expected him to snark at her like that.

Biting her lip, she bent and rolled up the rug in front of the hearth. What could Avery have meant by that? Was it to be expected from a man who was unused to having a woman speak her mind? Or was it something more? She blew an exasperated breath as she straightened. She wasn't exactly the most graceful and soft-spoken of women, but did that make a difference in this time?

Mrs. Knightsbridge hadn't given her much to go on. As she dragged the rolled up rug toward the door, she recounted the lady's words.

"Your destined true love is in Granville House, the Duke

of Granville's Town home." She'd smiled, patting Leah on the cheek. *"Be careful, my dear, and do not settle for less than the man of your heart."*

Leaving the rug propped against the jamb like an overgrown and drunken Cuban cigar, Leah dusted off her hands with a decisive snap. It didn't matter what Avery thought. She liked herself just fine, and her destined true love would adore her just the way she was.

She grabbed the fireplace brush and began raking the ashes out of the fireplace. *What matters is that I meet the duke and let him decide. Mrs. Knightsbridge is right. I can't settle for less than the man of my heart. And it has to be the duke, right? That's how all the stories go.*

The pointed clearing of a throat brought Leah's head around. Holy crap, it was the duke himself. Almost like her thoughts had conjured him from thin air.

"Good morning. Where is Russell?" the duke said in a calm tone. "I have need of him."

Leah gripped the fireplace brush tightly, jamming it hard into the hearth to make up for the Jell-O in her knees. He was there, and he was in his nightclothes. His grayish hair was tousled, his wrinkled skin pale, his long fingers tapping against his leg lazily. This was a decisive man used to moving, to getting what he wanted. He was like a perfect statue, he really was. Like George Clooney or Sean Connery. She could work with that, right?

"He's just stepped out, Your Grace, to get something. He'll be back in a minute." She smiled, hoping her nervousness didn't show. She was talking to the duke, finally! "Can I get anything for you?"

"No, thank you. Inform me when he arrives," the duke said.

Her heart fell when he turned around and headed back toward the bedroom. Her hands shaking on the brush handle, she resumed sweeping out the ashes, trying like hell to keep her disappointment in check.

"Oh, there is one thing."

Her heart stuttered. "Yes, Your Grace?"

"What is your name?"

He smiled down at her, and his entire being changed then. The haughty pride that had surrounded him before melted into a pleasantly warm friendliness that Leah was dying to wrap herself in. His too-thin face widened, his brows lifted, and she could picture how he'd look if he was about twenty years younger and his eyes shined with love for her. She nearly sighed aloud in relief. *This* was the man she was here for.

"It's Ramsey, Your Grace. And my first name is—"

"Thank you, Ramsey." With a polite nod, the duke disappeared into his bedchamber, taking that beautiful smile with him.

The handle cut into her palms as she stared at the closed door.

Oxygen.

That was important somehow, wasn't it?

What was it for again?

She dropped the brush and flew toward the stairs. Avery. She had to find Avery. The duke wanted Avery, and he knew her name, at least half of it, and he wanted his valet, so where the hell was Avery?

And if she got to rub the duke's interest in the snarky valet's face, then that was just a bonus.

"Where are you off to, then?"

Henrietta's high-pitched voice thumped Leah in the

back of her neck like a slap from a long-dead tuna fish. Stopping on the landing, Leah turned and faced the younger maid.

"I'm doing my job. What are you doing?"

The younger girl shoved her mobcap back, narrowing her eyes as she stared. "You were to be attending to His Grace's dressing rooms, I was told."

"Exactly." Leah walked back upstairs, stopping by the doorway that Henrietta stood in. Her proximity forced the younger maid to look upward into Leah's face. Stiffening her spine and raising her brows, Leah said, "And you're supposed to be working in the breakfast room. So why are you up here?"

Henrietta's mouth opened, but only a half-formed squeak escaped it.

"So how about this? You do your job, and I'll do mine."

Turning on her heel, Leah hurried downstairs after Avery. If that little devil Henrietta wasn't careful, she'd get on Leah's bad side. And considering how many times Leah had gotten the best of Jamie at that age, it was a pretty safe bet that Henrietta would regret it.

"Avery!"

The valet in question entered the door from what Mrs. Harper had called the "area." He carried the thankfully empty chamber pot in front of him, the lid turned upside down. Leah jumped the last two stairs to get to him sooner.

"The duke is awake, and he asked for you. He smiled at me, and he said my name. I was right, this is going to work." The words poured from her like rain from a summer cloud. It wasn't so much to gloat, either. More to share her triumph with her friend. They were still friends, right?

Avery's nostrils flared, but he remained expressionless other than that. "I shall attend him directly. You can replace the chamber pot now, I trust?" He offered it to her, but she stumbled backward, warding the disgusting object away with waving hands.

"Can you take it up, since you've got to go anyway?" She might sound pathetic, but damn it, hot water was hard to come by around here. And she didn't even know if they've heard of bleach yet. "You're already contaminated."

He blew an angry breath. "I must attend to His Grace immediately. If you are capable of performing your duties, you must prove it now."

Leah shifted from foot to foot, searching her boggled brain for an answer to this problem. Gloves! Wait, they didn't have latex yet, did they. Maybe like, a towel or a rag she could wrap the pot in…

Avery didn't give her a chance to realize her half-formed flash of brilliance. He plopped the chamber pot in her hands and headed directly upstairs.

"Oh my God," Leah moaned, bolting upstairs after him as fast as she could. "I'm carrying a toilet." Bile filled her mouth and she swallowed hard, nearly stumbling as she hit the landing and skidded.

"Careful there." The thread of amusement in Avery's words nearly made her chuck the damn pot at his head.

"You're enjoying this, aren't you?" she hissed as they rounded the corner and entered the dressing chamber. "You think it's funny that I might die of some horrible disease because of the lack of sanitation here."

He rolled his eyes as he crossed to the bedroom door. "You shall not die. More's the pity, you shall live to empty many, many more chamber pots."

She didn't have time to snap back at him because he disappeared into the duke's bedchamber then.

Slamming down the chamber pot into the corner behind the screen, Leah stomped back to the fireplace and resumed brushing the ashes out with overly violent motions. God, that valet was such an asshole. Handsome as all get-out, but a real irritant. *Fortunately*, she thought as she tucked a loose curl back beneath her cap, *I'm on the right track. After seeing the duke smile, I know I was right about him. It's just a matter of getting to know each other now, and Mrs. Knightsbridge's prophecy will come true.*

She just had to stick it out that long, and things would fall into place. She hoped.

❧

"There you are, lad." His Grace's voice floated from the corner of the room by the window.

"My apologies, Your Grace. I am here to assist you." Avery stood with back straight against the wall, awaiting his orders. Though he'd been told time and again to relax in the duke's presence, he could not. In his experience, most so-called gentlemen were not to be trusted. Even though His Grace had given him no cause for alarm, his instincts would not give over.

The duke rose from his seat by the window, where he'd been looking out across the early-dawn-covered Town. Avery didn't take more than a single glance out of the pane. Something was not right. His spine prickled with warning.

"We shall ride out in two days' time. The Houndstooth tourney has been arranged." His Grace sank into the bedclothes, an eager smile on his face. "I'm told that you shall be the man to beat, Russell."

Avery's heart sank. He'd halfway hoped that the duke would refuse to allow him to fight. He should have known better. His Grace had discovered him in the mills, and though he'd been kind enough to give Avery a respectable position, he'd never made a secret of his continued support of the Fancy, those members of the ton who supported boxing. The other members would not take kindly to one of their favorites missing the famous Houndstooth, especially if Prachett was trumpeting about his supposed attendance.

"Very well, Your Grace." Avery bowed low and turned to leave.

"Russell."

Avery ground to an immediate halt. Turning, he watched as the duke's smile faded. "Yes, Your Grace?"

The nobleman closed his eyes, a picture of long-suffering. "The dowager duchess is hosting a rout tomorrow evening, and she has need of more staff. See to it that Mrs. Harper provides her with everything she requires."

"Yes, Your Grace."

Avery stood still as the duke yawned.

"You may take yourself off, Russell, and begin preparations for our journey. I'll ring if I have need of you."

The duke smiled at him, almost a gentle, fatherly expression, and waved in dismissal. Avery left the room with a mixture of relief and foreboding. The next tourney was set. He must fight once more.

The dressing room carpet was turned up at the corners, and Leah was nowhere to be seen. Filling his chest with air, he tipped his head back and stared at the beamed ceiling. He should not be disappointed at her absence. He should not think of her at all. But he was, and he did, and he could not resist searching the nearby corridor for her.

The doorknob squeaked softly as he twisted it.

"Miss Ramsey?" His whisper echoed down the long hall.

There was no answer.

You shame yourself, his mind seemed to chastise him. *Mind your duties. The chit is about her tasks, as well she should be.*

With his rationality restored, Avery turned and marched down the main stairs toward the butler's pantry. Mrs. Harper and Smythe must be informed of His Grace's journey and of the dowager's rout. The Duke of Granville's ancient mother did not entertain often, but when she chose to do so, it was a highlight of the ton. Most people lived in fear of the dowager, and rightly so. But they also desperately sought her good opinion. If she was entertaining, there would be such a crush that the servants of two households would be a necessity, not a luxury.

The timing, however, was less than ideal. If Miss Ramsey were to commit an error in service at the dowager's home, more than her own position would be at stake.

Avery's blood chilled as he rounded the corridor and knocked on the door to the butler's pantry. The dowager had been known to have unsatisfactory servants tossed into prison for the merest offense. There was not much time for Miss Ramsey to learn to serve properly.

"Enter," Smythe called.

Avery made a vow as he entered the small room. He must do his best to prepare her for the morrow. Whether he thought her mad or merely a dreamer, she could not last in Newgate.

She'd not go on his watch.

❧

The bucket of ashes was freaking heavy. Leah thunked it down on the top step, breathing heavily as she eyed the long back stairway to the servants' hall downstairs.

Take the bucket to the kitchens to dump it out. Grab a broom and go back upstairs. Sweep the dressing room, then dust it, then put the carpet back. Set the fire, however the hell you do that.

The list of chores swirled in her head, weighing her down, and she gripped the banister to stop herself from tipping forward.

The last thing she needed was a tumble downstairs. How did anyone remember this ridiculous list of stuff to do? No wonder all these servants were so pissy. Their brains were overworked as well as their bodies.

Leaning sideways to ease the crick in her back, Leah let her eyes flutter closed. If only she'd had a couple of hours more sleep, then maybe she'd be sharp enough to handle the enormity of this job.

A heavy metallic clang ripped her eyes open, and she watched dumbfounded as the formerly full bucket bounced down the stairs, scattering ash and dust in all directions.

Whirling, she caught a glimpse of a too-large mobcap and dark skirts disappearing into a nearby bedroom.

That little snot.

With Henrietta's name poised in an angry roar on her lips, Leah charged toward the door after her.

"Ramsey! Whatever have you done, you clumsy girl?" Mrs. Harper's voice stopped Leah short. Wincing, she turned and rubbed suddenly sweaty palms down her skirt. The housekeeper glared up at her from the bottom of the stairs.

"Mrs. Harper, I'm so sorry about that. I'd set it down for a second, and someone ran by and tipped it over," Leah explained lamely. "I didn't—"

"Blaming your faults on others will not be tolerated in this household. Sweep up these stairs at once." With a disdainful sniff, Mrs. Harper disappeared into the kitchens.

Longingly eyeing the door Henrietta had disappeared into, Leah trudged down the ashy stairs. Her morning had started out so promising, with that delicious ducal smile. How had it plummeted into drudgery so damn fast?

Watching her heroes in movies was proving to be much easier than trying to win one in real life.

Grabbing a broom from the kitchen cupboard, Leah returned and started sweeping up Henrietta's mess. The repetitive motions gave her more than enough time to think about home.

Pawpaw had been so insistent that she find her guy and get married. What was his game? Rounding up a largish pile of ash, she bit her lip and recounted all the doctor visits he'd had in the past year. There weren't many, certainly not enough to cause her to be concerned.

So why was he so adamant that she not be alone? What did he know that Leah didn't?

With the ashes returned to the bucket, and Leah sweaty, tired, and confused, she dumped them into the bin and headed back upstairs to finish the duke's dressing room. She'd have plenty of time to try to analyze Pawpaw when she got back. And if things kept going as well as they had been, she might just give up and dive through the mirror tomorrow. God, that made her sound like a damn weenie. She stiffened her spine. She'd never met a challenge she intended to back down from, and this wouldn't be the one to take her down.

"Ramsey?"

Damn it, she was really getting fucking tired of that Q-tip's haughty way of saying her name. Leah stopped on the third stair and turned. "Yes, Mrs. Harper?"

"The dowager duchess is hosting a rout tomorrow evening. You will help serve." The old bat didn't look happy about it, but she delivered the order with aplomb anyway.

Leah nodded politely. "Yes, ma'am."

A thread of interest wound through Leah as she continued mounting the stairs. Serve at a real duchess's party? See the glittering lords and ladies of the *ton*?

When the realization slammed through her, she missed a step. Clutching at the banister to prevent a fall, she gasped.

The dowager. The duke's mother. Holy crap, the woman must have danced with Methuselah. How was she still alive?

Leah righted herself and rounded the landing. Maybe she'd been wrong about the duke's age. If his mother was alive, then he had to be fairly young, right? Maybe he had one of those aging diseases that made you look a lot older than you were.

She entered the dressing room and started sweeping. She had to be careful, but this could be a very good opportunity to impress the duke and learn more about him. This could work.

Maybe her fairy tale would have a happy ending after all.

Ten

BREAKFAST WAS A LONG AND TIRING THREE HOURS LATER.

Cook set a bowl in front of Leah without a word. Apparently breakfast was lukewarm oatmeal-like gruel. Leah poked at the gelatinous mass with her spoon. It jiggled alarmingly, reminding Leah of that old B horror movie about the blob. *The Oatmeal that Ate London! Run for your lives!*

"Oh boy," she said beneath her breath. Clearly she hadn't gotten enough sleep.

"Ramsey, is the food not to your liking?" The housekeeper's brows had climbed to her hairline. The other maids had filled in the empty seats around Leah, and Henrietta especially looked pleased at Mrs. Harper's attitude. The little viper was really getting under Leah's skin. She'd have to think about how to get back at her for the ash bucket. That had been a prank worthy of Leah's best retaliation.

"No, no." Leah laughed uncomfortably. "It looks delicious." She took a big bite and nearly gagged at the too-thick texture. Blinking back tears, she swallowed the muddy-tasting gruel as quickly as she could.

"See that you finish it all." Mrs. Harper watched her like a skinny, cotton-headed hawk.

Leah nodded weakly. It was a good thing she could stand to lose a few pounds. On this diet, she'd be lucky to keep anything down.

The scraping of a chair near the end of the table brought her watery gaze upward. Avery nodded politely as he sat and began eating with refined gusto. Hmph. Must be an acquired taste.

A swig of lukewarm tea helped clear the gluey taste from her mouth, and the chatter at the table picked up shortly thereafter.

"Her Grace's routs are always such fun," Sarah was giggling to Teresa across the table. "All those posh lords and ladies."

"And their dresses, blimey," Teresa said, her pale face long with dreamy reverie. "I'd love to be puffed off like that."

"You?" Henrietta snorted. "A bony figure like yours would ruin those fancy clothes."

Teresa looked down into her lap dejectedly.

Leah resisted the urge to kick Henrietta's shin under the table. Instead, she opted for a more polite approach.

"I think you have a great complexion, Teresa. What do you use on your skin?" Leah swallowed another bite of gruel in the ensuing silence. Apparently they hadn't expected her to speak.

"Me mum would mix rosewater and cream, and apply it to her face. She let me do it too, when I was older and we could afford it." Teresa smiled down at her bowl. "It makes me skin softer. I do it whenever I can, even now."

"Vanity is a sin," Mrs. Harper admonished. "You'll cease this immediately."

Teresa's face went bone-white. "Oh no, Mrs. Harper, I didn't mean…"

"You'll do as you're told in this household." Mrs. Harper's chair scraped back. "The very thought of a maid taking such pains with her appearance is disgraceful. You are to be neat, pressed, and present yourself as a servant of His Grace, but to give yourself such a treatment is well above your station."

"Yes, Mrs. Harper," Teresa whispered.

"You'd all do well to remember that."

With a glare at Leah, the housekeeper left the table. The three footmen followed at her direction, leaving Leah with the maids and Avery. All the females at the table turned distrustful eyes on Leah, with the exception of Teresa, who had tears tracking down her pale cheeks.

"Teresa, I'm so sorry," Leah said. God, she felt like shit. "I just wanted to give you a compli—"

"You're poison, you are." Henrietta stood, her lips pursed in disapproval, much like Mrs. Harper's had been. "You intended to cause that trouble for poor Teresa, hoping that you can replace her as the upper housemaid. We'll none of us have aught to do with you." At her beckoning gesture, the other girls followed, including the still-sniffling Teresa.

Leah leaned forward with a groan, plastering her forehead against the rough top of the dining table. This was *so* not going well.

❧

Avery stared down into his bowl, unwilling—no, unable, if he were to be honest with himself—to look at Leah.

He should have spoken. He should have defended her against the false accusations that Henrietta had hurled on her. But how could he, when he knew that casting himself as her savior would harm her even further?

A movement drew his gaze as she sat up and glared at him. "Thanks for saving me there, cowboy."

Leah shoved her chair back to stand. He shoved another bite into his mouth to prevent having to reply.

She left the dining room without another word, and Avery stared at her departing back as if his regretful gaze alone could atone for his lack of action.

He was no gentleman. Never had been, by birth or by breeding. Did that excuse him? His mother's voice, echoing in his head from beyond her too-early grave, said not.

No matter what it cost *him*, he could have borne it to protect her. But how could he subject her to the jibes and taunts that would surely follow his public declaration of loyalty to the girl? She could have no way of knowing how much worse things could be if he were to cast his lot with her. His presence caused more problems than it corrected, and poor Miss Ramsey had more than enough trouble of her own.

Avery sighed regretfully as he left the now-empty table. He should know by now that nothing ever came of wishing things different. He had his lot, and now Miss Ramsey had hers. They would both manage as they could and leave the rest to the whims of Fate.

No matter how his heart ached with every pain she was forced to endure.

The rest of the day passed in a blur of normal duties and preparation for the dowager's rout at Tunstall Place across the square. With the large crowd that was expected, Avery would serve as footman with the others from His Grace's employ, and even Miss Ramsey was expected to assist. Cornering her to ensure her proper service was becoming more troublesome than he'd expected, but he persevered through the afternoon.

Until he was summoned by Cook.

"Mr. Russell," the old woman hissed as he made his way through the kitchens with a pile of freshly pressed cravats. "Meet me in the larder."

He nodded subtly and went on his way. He knew without her speaking what the summons meant. It was a play that they'd enacted many, many times before.

Once the cravats were put into their proper place, Avery descended the stairs again, winding around the corner of the kitchen to duck into the larder, unseen. Cook waited for him there, her sausage-curls wispy and haphazard from the heat of the kitchens, her cheeks flushed and eyes bright.

"The apothecary's boy came this morning." A small brown bottle was produced from Cook's apron pocket. "He said to thank you for your custom. I gave him your coin for it."

Avery took the bottle with a grateful nod. "I thank you, Mrs. Dearborn. My aunt sorely needs this. Her illness is getting worse."

Cook sniffed and dashed away a tear with the corner of her apron. "Millie was always a sweet girl. It's one of my greatest regrets that she took ill so sudden. She could have made a cook in some great house, for an earl or even a duke after my own time." She looked into Avery's face, sincerity thick in her words. "She was the best kitchen maid I ever had, and that's the honest truth. You tell her Mrs. Dearborn sends her love, and you take care of her, boy."

Avery gripped the bottle tightly, bowing deeply. "You may be assured of that. My mother would have wished for me to care for her youngest sister, and I've no intention of shirking that duty."

Cook straightened her apron and patted her curls. "Now, I've a goose to see to. I take it that you'll be off to St. Giles this afternoon?"

Hesitation sprang to his mind. He'd not yet spoken to Miss Ramsey, and it might be impossible to do so before the dowager's rout if he spent the evening away. But what choice did he have? His aunt could not do without this medicine. He nodded.

"I'll inform Smythe that you were called away." Cook shooed him. "Now, be off with you. I've a basket made up for Millie. It's by the door."

"You have my thanks, Mrs. Dearborn."

She left him in the larder with the bottle of medicine in his hand. Lifting the bottle to catch the beam of sunlight streaming through the crack in the larder door, he watched as the milky medicine bent the light, diffusing it through clouds of liquid. Strange that such a small amount of medicine could cost so much. And strange that such an odd woman as Miss Leah Ramsey had upset his normal balance.

Making up his mind, he shoved the bottle into his waistcoat pocket and headed up the back stairs to find

Miss Ramsey. He couldn't leave her to face the dowager without warning.

But he must be quiet about it. If anyone were to see him...

No. He'd not dwell on that.

Rounding the corner of the landing, he waited for Henrietta and Sarah to pass by.

"She won't last out the week," Henrietta's snide remark caught his ear. "Mrs. Harper should never have hired her on. I could have taken Fannie's position, and that's the truth. This girl cannot possibly do the job."

"What can Mrs. Harper be thinking, allowing her to serve at the dowager's rout?" Sarah followed Henrietta, the coal scuttle banging softly against the older maid's skirts. Avery stood aside and allowed them to pass. They did not acknowledge his presence at all. It was as if he was simply a stick of furniture. Don't trip on it, mind you, but certainly don't bother making conversation with it.

The cut had long ago ceased to bother him.

Continuing on his way, Avery mounted the stairs slowly so as to hear Henrietta's reply.

"I am glad that she shall serve. The stupid girl will anger the dowager, we'll make sure of that. This afternoon I am to instruct her how to go on. What a job I shall make of it!" Henrietta's giggles echoed in the stairwell.

Avery's stomach dropped. Damn and blast. Redoubling his speed, he mounted the stairs two at a time. He must keep Henrietta from ruining Miss Ramsey's chances of succeeding on the morrow. It really was too bad that he could think of but one way to keep her from her sabotaged lessons.

❦

"Are you sure it's okay for me to come with you?"

Miss Ramsey's voice floated over his shoulder as he led her through the streets. They'd left the fine parts of the West End many minutes ago and were now nearing St. Giles.

"There was no choice," he said patiently, holding an arm out to stop her from crossing in front of a hack. "The dowager's rout is tomorrow evening, and if you're to know how to go on, I must instruct you. Do not worry. Mrs. Harper has been told you've been sent on an errand for Cook."

They continued across the street, and Avery tried not to notice the growing concern on Miss Ramsey's face as she took in their surroundings. The fine homes had given way to crowded hovels, filth and garbage littering the streets. The warmth of Miss Ramsey's body soaked into him as she pressed close to his side. He repressed his desire due to her proximity, though it was a damned difficult thing to do.

"Mrs. Harper said she'd have somebody tell me what to do. God, what a stink. Where did you say we were going again?" Miss Ramsey's gloved hand pressed over her mouth and nose, and her forehead wrinkled in distaste. How strange that such a repugnant expression could look so lovely.

"We are going to my aunt. She is ill." He stopped to allow a tradesman's cart to pass before continuing. "But as for the rout, Mrs. Harper intended for Henrietta to show you how to go on. Henrietta wanted Fannie's position for herself. She made it quite well known that she'd be most happy if the dowager found you unsatisfactory." He bit back the part about prison. No reason to frighten the girl.

Their footsteps squished through the muddy streets

as they entered St. Giles. To distract her from the worsening conditions in the streets, he began reciting a litany of advice for the morrow.

"The dowager is His Grace's mother. You will need to be most careful while in her presence. Mind how you go there." He steered her away from a pile of filth in the street. "She does not tolerate mistakes from her servants. You've one chance to impress her, and once lost, you shall never have another."

"So, no pressure," Miss Ramsey said dryly, tucking an errant blond lock behind her ear. "Not only is my future mother-in-law a former duchess, she's also a terrifying dragon lady. Good thing I brushed up on my dragon-slaying etiquette."

She fell silent, and Avery let her take in the scene of the square.

It was familiar to him. After all, once his mother had passed on, he and his father had come to live here, in one of the shanties by the church. The foul odors, the calling curses loud in the air, the crowded conditions were all as native to him as breathing. He turned, and his throat closed at the shock on Miss Ramsey's face.

"Your sick aunt doesn't live *here*, does she?" Her words were thick with horror.

An odd mixture of shame and offended pride filled him. "It's not such a bad place. There's a roof over her head and enough food to fill her belly. If I had the means, she would make her home in a more comfortable situation."

She turned to him, biting her lip before speaking. "Avery, I'm sorry. I didn't mean…"

He dismissed her apology with a wave. "No matter."

"You used to live here, didn't you?"

Her insight nearly felled him. He drew himself up taller. "Yes, I did."

Her small hand curled around his arm. "No wonder you're so tough. You had to be, growing up here."

He cast a glance over to her. She was looking into his face, without pity, without any sign of condescension. She simply stated a fact, but there was a light behind her eyes, one that made him wonder if she esteemed him for overcoming his former hardships.

Though he longed to reach out, bathe himself in that light, he cleared his throat and continued. "Follow me, if you please."

Despite his longing at having her so near, he made sure to remain as close as her shadow as they wound their way through St. Giles toward his aunt's one-room hovel. Guiding her toward the next corner, he pulled down his hat and prayed as he passed the Wolf and Dove public house that no one would notice him. The first time he'd gone to a mill, which had been against his will, was at the insistence of the proprietor, Benedict Turpin. He'd won half a crown, as promised, but had made the acquaintance of Thomas Prachett in the bargain.

"Quickly now," he said in a low voice to Miss Ramsey, hustling her past the door.

"Russell, as I live and breathe," a cackle came from the door of the pub. The man leaning against the door spat into the street, then smiled with a mouthful of rotten teeth at Avery. It was Turpin, of course. One of Prachett's men. The one who'd introduced them.

Avery's stomach, having changed into a sack of lead, plummeted.

Then again, luck never had been much on his side.

Eleven

"Fancy meeting you here, you old devil." The man's accent was thick, making it hard to understand him.

Leah turned toward the voice, curiosity momentarily overtaking the nerves that had been ruling her brain. She'd been to some scary places in her day. Hell, once she'd had an overnight layover in Detroit. But even that hadn't prepared her for the harsh reality of the London slums.

Avery's shoulders, lined with tension before, tightened even further as he turned to face the one who'd addressed him.

"Turpin." He nodded coolly. "No time to waste, I'm afraid. I've an appointment."

The man stood half a foot taller than Avery, his brownish-white shirt splattered with stains across the front. His jacket was threadbare, the cheap fabric thinning in many places. "Come in for a pint, my lad, and tell us about the fine house you serve in. Fancy a bruiser like you polishing buttons and wiping a lordship's arse!" He tossed back his head and laughed, and Leah turned her head away quickly from the sight and smell of his open mouth. Ugh, she should have brought a sack of toothbrushes with her through that damn mirror.

"Another time." Avery turned on his heel and Leah stumbled in shock as he gripped her arm to steer her forward.

"At the Houndstooth tourney? You'll be there, won't you, lad?"

Avery didn't slow, apparently pretending not to hear the question.

Leah moved on her toes, driven by Avery's strong but gentle grip.

Shut up, she inwardly hissed to her fluttering heart. Anyone would think she'd been kissed passionately at the way her excited heart was thumping. She was apparently so desperate for human companionship that her upper arm had graduated to erogenous zone. At least, she tried to convince herself that it could have been anyone, not just the strong, quiet man beside her that was making her heart turn cartwheels.

Or maybe it was just the fear of the environment. She made use of their proximity to grip his coat in nerveless fingers. What had that Turpin guy meant by "a bruiser like Avery"? And what tourney?

She opened her mouth to ask him, but her train of thought was derailed when they crossed the road. The smell was awful, even worse than it had been before. Mud stood in the streets, fetid pools that made her wonder if they were just dirt and water or something else. The buildings, if she could be so generous, looked about ready to collapse at any moment. But the thing that made her want to close her eyes and not open them until she got back home was the faces.

There were thousands of them. Young, old, decorated

with visible dirt or wiped clean, it didn't matter, they all held the same expression—hopelessness. It saturated their gaunt cheeks, their pointed chins, but most of all, it haunted their empty eyes. It was like walking through a horror movie. She caught herself praying that Avery had never been among their number, although she knew better.

She curled her fingers tighter into his sleeve. "Avery, are you sure we should be here?"

"We've arrived." He pulled free of her grip and opened the door for her. Damn it, how did he sound so calm? And why'd he have to let go of her arm? She ducked through the low doorway into a narrow staircase. The smell wasn't as bad here, and she breathed a shaky sigh of relief. Even her normally strong stomach had been close to losing it at the conditions outside. How had he come through a life in this place?

The stairs creaked beneath their feet. At the top, Avery produced an ancient key and pushed it into the lock of the narrow door.

"Aunt?"

The only answer in the dim room was a hacking cough from the bed in the corner. The heavy, cloying scent of sickness and unwashed human filled the room. Avery moved inside, and Leah stuck close to his back. She didn't want to be here. She should have stayed back at the house. She could have figured out how to handle herself on her own, couldn't she?

No way to fix it now. She was in the middle of England with no way of getting back to Granville House except the man who was bending over a tiny bed by the room's single window.

"Aunt, I am here." His gruff voice was as tender as she'd ever heard it. A soft moan was the only answer from the rail-thin form beneath the covers.

Leah leaned to the side to get a better look at the woman.

A lank braid lay on the pillow. Her cheeks were sunken, her skin held the sickly pallor of the nearly dead. Her lashes, long and thick, rested on her sharp cheekbones. Apparently, the moan hadn't been in response to Avery's greeting at all.

Leah shifted her weight anxiously. This had once been a beautiful, strong woman. Now she lay here in this tiny room, dying all alone? Worrying the inside of her cheek with her teeth, Leah looked at the rough floorboards. It really put her own life into perspective, and Leah didn't care for the comparison. She'd been selfish and completely narrow-minded. But what could she have done differently?

The question seemed moot.

"How has she been faring, Mrs. Comstock?" Avery said as another woman entered the room behind them and dumped a bucket of water into the ewer.

"Millie is still breathing, Mr. Russell, but as to whether that's a blessing or a pity I cannot advise ye."

Leah watched as the thin, angry-looking woman wiped her hands with a rag. At least Avery's aunt Millie had someone nearby.

Avery straightened. "I have brought more medicine for her." He produced a small brown bottle from his jacket.

Mrs. Comstock took it from him and thumped the bottle. Leah bit her lip as the woman uncorked the top and poured a dose into a spoon.

"Mind yourselves," she admonished as she bent over

the sickbed. "You've no wish to be near when she swallows this draught, mark me."

Avery turned away as Mrs. Comstock brought the spoon to his aunt. Leah reached for his hand, wanting to comfort him, but he pulled away.

Mrs. Comstock pried open the sick woman's mouth and inserted the spoonful of medicine. Closing Millie's jaw with one hand and massaging her throat with the other, Mrs. Comstock forced her to swallow the dose. Millie fought weakly, hands batting at Mrs. Comstock's, but in her semiconscious state, there was no way for her to be a real deterrent.

The coughs began from deep within her chest, wet hacking sounds that made Leah wince. Once Mrs. Comstock was certain that she'd swallowed the medicine, she released the sick woman.

Then the real fight began.

Clawing at her throat, Millie heaved and hacked, almost seeming to want to vomit the dose back up. Leah took a step toward her, not knowing what to do but unwilling to stand by and watch the woman suffer, but Mrs. Comstock shook her head and held Leah back.

"She must bear it. It will be better soon."

Now Leah knew why Avery had turned away so determinedly. There was no way to watch and not feel horrible at Millie's condition. Taking her cue from him, Leah closed her eyes and wished with all her heart that the stranger's suffering would somehow get better. In reality, though, she knew it was probably a lost cause. There was no real medical care here. Millie might have had something as simple as a cold, but it had obviously turned into something that could very well rob her of her life. Leah squeezed her eyes shut harder. She hadn't wanted this. She'd wanted fun, an adventure, and if she found the love of her life, then great. She hadn't wanted to stand at a stranger's bedside as the stranger's life slowly slipped away. The image of her grandfather popped into her mind's eye, and she worked hard to keep from getting emotional. He was fine. There was nothing wrong with Pawpaw.

After long, tense moments, the coughing and gagging eased. Leah didn't open her eyes, her lids glued shut with unease.

"There now, that's better, isn't it?" The sound of Mrs. Comstock's movements drew Leah's lids open. The woman moved around the small room, fetching a cool cloth and laying it on Millie's brow.

"You can come closer now. The worst of it is over."

Avery turned, and Leah followed him to Millie's bedside. He knelt by the head of the bed, but Leah stood back, wanting to stick close to Avery for moral support but unwilling to interrupt what was obviously an emotional meeting for him.

"Aunt, I am sorry," he whispered. He started to reach for Millie, but drew back his hand just before he made contact.

Leah looked away, swallowing hard. Her throat had gone curiously dry.

She stood in silence as Avery bowed his head at his aunt's bedside. *He must be praying again.* He seemed to do that fairly frequently. She rubbed her damp palms across her skirt, blinking at the ceiling.

This was hard. This was damned hard—and unexpected. She wasn't a religious person, not really. She had beliefs, sure, but they seemed inconsequential when she was faced with a situation like this.

What was she doing here, really?

Millie's heavy breaths seemed to echo in the small room. Mrs. Comstock ducked from the room, saying something about broth for Millie.

Avery didn't respond, just kept his head bowed with his fingers only inches from his aunt's.

Leah took advantage of the silence to analyze him.

His shoulders were tensed as he hunched over the bed. His whole body seemed rigid, like he was fighting a large wave of emotion that threatened to suck him under. Following an instinct that she didn't really understand, she stepped closer to him and rubbed his back gently. As if in response to the strength she sent him, he took Millie's fingers in his own.

Maybe this was her destiny. Maybe, Leah mused as she blinked hard to shove back the tears, maybe she was being shown Avery's hell to make her grateful for what she had. For the love of Pawpaw and of Jamie, and of the rest of her family and friends. Or maybe she was being shown this so she could help people like this when she became a duchess.

Of course! When she became a duchess, she'd have money and power in this society. She could enact change. Help people. She could do something for Millie, and for the other poor, hopeless people that lived here. Sanitation would be the first thing to tackle. No wonder people got so sick here; there was no real way to dispose of sewage. Then, she'd—

Avery patted her hand. "Miss Ramsey."

Startled, she jumped and jerked her hand away. Mrs. Comstock passed them, bearing a tray with a bowl on it.

Leah fought the heat that climbed her cheeks. "I'm sorry, I was daydreaming. What is it?"

"If you're quite ready, we can return to Granville House." Avery rose to his feet, studiously avoiding her gaze. Had she embarrassed him? She sure as hell hoped not. She'd only wanted to help, but apparently she hadn't.

Leah nodded and turned to follow Avery to the door, but a sudden thought made her pause. Shoving her hand into her pocket, her fingers closed around a small box she'd placed in there before they'd left.

Maybe she didn't have to wait to become a duchess to help out a little.

"Mrs. Comstock?" She held the box out to her. "These aren't much, but they may help her feel better. They're lozenges. When she's awake, put one in her mouth and let her suck on it. The medicine inside will help her throat feel better."

Mrs. Comstock's face was wary, but she took the box anyway. "Thank ye, miss."

Avery looked at Leah briefly before turning back to Millie. "Good-bye, Aunt." His voice was low, rough.

There was no response. Millie lay still as death, the slight rise and fall of her chest the only indication that she was still among the living.

With a nod to Mrs. Comstock, and the delivery of a small bag, clinking with what Leah assumed was money, they descended the stairs into the dank and dangerous streets of St. Giles.

The afternoon light was long, and Avery led her briskly through the streets. Leah guessed he didn't want to be here after dark any more than she did.

She kept her questions to herself for several moments

as they crossed busy streets and avoided begging hands. But as the neighborhood got cleaner and less frightening, and the sun sank lower in the sky, she found guts enough to speak.

"So that's your Aunt Millie," she said. "Do you know what's wrong with her?"

Avery's eyes were dark, and his strides lengthened. Leah had to hustle to keep up with him. "It is a wasting disease. There is nothing that can be done to cure her. We must make her as comfortable as possible."

"How long has she been sick?" Leah stopped suddenly to avoid tripping over a young boy who was chasing a dog down the street. The mutt barked, and the boy yelled, and they both disappeared around the next corner.

"Three years." Avery pointed, and Leah walked in the direction he indicated. "There is a medicine that eases her coughing fits, but it is very dear."

"That's the medicine you brought her, right?"

He nodded.

Leah took in a grateful breath as they left the line of shanties behind. The smell wasn't good here, by any means, but it was certainly cleaner than in the depths of St. Giles. She looked over her shoulder and was unsurprised to see a wealth of emotion in Avery's tight-set jaw.

"You really love your aunt, don't you?"

He stopped, eyes flying open as if she'd punched him instead of asking him a simple question.

"We should be discussing the dowager's expectations for the morrow." He resumed walking as if she hadn't asked him anything. "Now, your duties will be to assist in serving. The dowager likes things to be prepared just so, so be sharp, pay attention, and mind how you go. The guests will arrive…"

He kept chattering, and even though Leah wanted to find out more about his past and his poor aunt Millie, she knew she'd have to do well at the rout tomorrow in order to keep things on track. She really did think things happened for a reason. And if her hunch was right, and she became a duchess, the first stop she'd make was the slums of St. Giles.

Avery had done the best he could, but if she could help Aunt Millie too, she'd do it in a heartbeat. Anything to keep him from bearing such a burden alone. *That's what friends do, right?*

The rest of the way to the house, he kept up his long string of to-do's for the party. She nodded, she asked questions, she kept from tripping on the long skirts of a tall-hatted woman, but Avery's insistence and seeming nervousness grew the closer they got to Granville House.

On the third time he'd reminded her not to speak unless spoken to, she kind of blew up.

"All right, fine, I get it." She threw her hands in the air as she stomped after him. "I'm not a complete idiot, you know. You can stop treating me like I'm stupid any damn time now."

He sighed. She nearly crowed in relief at the sight of Granville house in the distance. The lecture would have to stop soon.

"I know that you are not stupid, Miss Ramsey. But the dowager…" He trailed off, lifting his hat to shove stray strands of his honey-colored hair back from his face.

Leah tried really hard not to notice how golden it looked in the fiery light of the setting sun. They continued down the street, Avery's steps heavy and plodding, Leah's lighter and excited at the prospect of sitting down. And dinner. Her stomach was growling.

"The dowager will murder me if I screw this up." She finished the sentence for him.

He laughed uncomfortably. "That is closer to the truth than you think."

She bit her lip in consternation as he descended the stairs to the servants' entrance.

"Avery?"

He stopped before opening the door. "Yes, Miss Ramsey?"

"Thank you." Leah bowed her head. "For everything." The words weren't enough, but she didn't have anything else to offer him.

Avery didn't answer. He just gave a solemn nod and held the door open for her.

She passed him, wondering exactly what to make of the afternoon. There was a crap ton to sift through, that was for damn sure.

Avery disappeared up the stairs after making sure the coast was clear. Apparently, he didn't want anyone to know he'd spent the afternoon with Leah. She tried really hard to be irritated about that, but she couldn't. She unbuttoned the cloak she'd been given as part of her uniform and hung it by the door with a sigh. He'd been through a lot today, and despite that, he'd still made sure she knew what to do tomorrow. Her jaw cracked as she yawned. Besides, she was too freaking tired to be upset. Maybe later.

Mrs. Harper came around the corner in a white-haired cloud of irritation.

"Oh, Ramsey. There you are. Please take this tray up to His Grace's study."

Screw being tired. She'd just been given a ticket straight to ducal town.

"No problem." She bobbed her head to Mrs. Harper and took the tea tray.

"Mind your speech, my girl. His Grace and an associate are in the drawing room. Be quick now."

Leah walked carefully in the direction of the drawing room. Fortunately, she had a pretty good sense of direction. She'd had to develop one, because Jamie's was totally hopeless. After the third time getting lost in Jamie's neighborhood, she'd consciously developed the habit of paying attention to her surroundings.

Let's see, door, hallway table, portrait of the guy who looks like Jabba the Hutt, another door, another door, aaaaand drawing room.

She stared at the door. It was closed. She stared at her hands. They were full of tea tray, pot, cups, scones, cookies—well, biscuits—and all. She looked back at the knob and pursed her lips.

"Well, damn," she whispered.

Looking longingly at the floor—it'd be so easy to set the tray down just for a second to open the door—she instead turned and walked back the twelve feet to the hallway table. Setting the tray atop it, she trudged back to the doorway and opened the latch. Pushing it open only a couple of inches, so as not to disturb the duke, she crossed back to the tray.

The click of the latch hit her like the bite from a fire ant.

"You freaking son of a bitch," she fumed. *Damn drafty houses.*

Stomping back toward the door, she opened it further this time. She'd just returned with the tea tray, ready to push through the still-open portal, when the duke's guest came through it.

"No need to ring, Granville, I'll show myself out. Have a pleasant evening."

With a polite nod to his host, and not so much as a glance at Leah, the short, round gentleman headed toward the front door of the house.

"Your…Your Grace?" Leah poked her head into the drawing room. "I have your tea tray. Do you still want it?"

"Yes, thank you. Set it down, please."

The duke stood by the window, hands clasped behind his back as he looked out into the darkening night. His silvery hair seemed to glint like the moon he studied so thoroughly. Being careful not to let the expensive china clatter, Leah set the tray down on the table. With the duke's back turned, she allowed herself a long look at him.

His fingers were long, pale, perfectly manicured. Leah smiled to herself. Pawpaw had always said you could tell a lot about a man from his hands. Of course, he'd never met anyone like the duke.

"Ramsey, your timing is impeccable."

Leah jumped at the sudden statement.

"I'm sorry?"

"You have impeccable timing," the duke repeated, turning toward the room without really looking at her. "If you'd been a moment earlier, that idiot Waterson would have stayed another half hour."

"Glad I could help, Your Grace." Leah bit her lip and sank into a curtsy, wondering if her cheeks were as nuclear red as they felt.

"Be off with you."

She lifted her head in time to see that beautiful smile again. This time, it was accompanied by a mischievous wink. Holy shit, the man was stunning. Age difference? What age difference?

Quicker than her stunned brain could process, he'd taken his cup of tea and stood by the window again, an enigma of a nobleman looking out into the boundless night.

Leah left the room, trying like hell to keep her head and to memorize every word he'd said. This was going to turn into an excellent play one day, she just knew it. Or maybe an action-RPG adventure. Or a romantic comedy.

Shakespeare had nothing on the star-crossedness of Leah and her duke.

Twelve

AVERY DESCENDED THE STAIRS IN A FOG. PICKING UP THE sack of scraps Cook had left by the door, he slipped out into the now-chilly evening.

He didn't bother glancing upward toward the stars as he trudged toward the hounds' enclosure inside the stables. Even though he'd spent a long time praying for his freedom, he was convinced it would never come.

And, if he were honest with himself, what man who'd killed his mother deserved a better lot?

The heavy stable door swung closed behind him. A whinny of greeting sounded from the left side of the room, where the horses were kept, but he didn't pause there. He continued through the building until he reached a largish pen, filled with about a score of hounds. They jumped up on the fencing, tails wagging in greeting.

He reached over the gate to pet one of the hounds.

"Evening, Russell."

The sarcastic greeting, slurred from what was likely a bottle of cheap brandy, came from inside the tack room. Avery ignored it and doled out the scraps from the bag to the ravenous greyhounds. The excited yips and barks quieted as the dogs enjoyed their treats.

Tucking the empty sack into his pocket, Avery turned to leave. With any luck, he'd escape to his training room without further delay. The stable master was hardly one of his allies in the house, and he had no wish to be burdened by a discussion that could have no good effect.

"Off to the Houndstooth Tourney, I hear." Lachlan Mackenzie sauntered toward Avery, stumbling ever so slightly.

With a deep, steadying breath, Avery replied, "As His Grace wishes."

Mackenzie spat into the straw at Avery's feet. Lifting one grizzled eyebrow, the older man smiled mockingly and closed the gap between them. Avery stood his ground, knowing that to back away would be to invite conflict.

"Well, our lord varlet, how about a demonstration of your talents?"

The fist flew at Avery's face without warning. Relying on his years of fighting instincts, Avery ducked, spinning below the drunk man's blow and throwing his fist upward. His knuckles connected with Mackenzie's chin with a sharp crack, spittle flying at the force as the stable master stumbled backward and landed on his ass in the straw.

"You ruddy fool, you'll pay for that," Mackenzie slurred. Leaning on the hound pen's wall, he tried to gain his feet. His legs failed him, buckling beneath him and dumping him at Avery's feet.

Avery stared down at the drunken man, keeping his face pointedly blank. "Feel free to try again when you're not too foxed to walk." He shook out his hand and turned to walk away.

"Got your eye on that new maid, don't you, Russell?"

Avery whirled at the pointed slur. "Whatever gave you that impression?"

Mackenzie drew a hand across his mouth, leaving a bright red smear from his split lip. "Saw you walking with her. A pretty piece she is, all golden hair and smiles. She'll make a good toss. I've a mind to show her how ta' treat a man." His vulgar laugh echoed against the ceiling beams.

Avery wasn't sure how it had happened, but suddenly he had Mackenzie pinned up against the tack room door by the throat. The man's pale brown eyes bugged out and he gagged, looking for all the world like a desperate toad. Which, Avery reasoned, was not far from the truth.

"Mark my words, Lachlan Mackenzie: that maid is none of your concern, nor mine. You'll keep a civil tongue in your head about her, or I'll give you a sound thrashing that you won't forget for many a fortnight to come. Understand?"

Mackenzie nodded, feet drumming against the stable door uselessly.

"Good."

Avery let the stable master drop to the ground. Without another word, he left the horses, dogs, and drunkard behind for the relative privacy of his training room.

He tried like hell to empty his mind of all thoughts of Miss Ramsey as he removed his shirt for his exercise. With the soft light of the lantern, and the thin slivers of moonlight that shone through the high window, he could make out the pile of sand that his attackers had made of his last bag. Removing the mostly-empty sack, he replaced it with another and began the tedious job of scooping the sand into the fabric chute.

The repetitive motions did nothing to keep thoughts of Miss Ramsey at bay. He must think of something else, anything else.

His Aunt. Millie. She'd looked especially poor today.

Avery tightened his jaw as he watched the sand fall into the bag. Half full now.

The disease had been progressing faster these last few months. Surely the squalid conditions of her surroundings were of no assistance, but what could he do? With his wages from service and his winnings from the tourneys, it was all he could manage to keep her fed and in medicine.

The medicine.

He winced as he dropped the scoop back into its pail. The medicine that helped her also made her ill when she took it. But Leah had tried to help, and failing that, Leah had reached for his hand.

Damn and blast!

He swung at the bag and smiled inwardly at the stinging satisfaction of his knuckles. Miss Ramsey, not Leah. And she was none of his affair. None at all.

The bag creaked against the ropes as he pummeled it again.

His work this night would be most satisfying. He'd exorcise the demons in his head by punishing his body.

And wasn't that just what he'd been doing his whole life?

❦

The next day dawned bright and sunny, the perfect weather for a proper British party, Leah thought.

Well, maybe not the typical British weather, but beautiful anyway.

Leah tried to keep from yawning as she helped Cook load a basket full of her best scones. Apparently Mrs. Dearborn, the Granville House cook, was better at scone making than the Tunstall Place's own kitchen mistress. And the dowager demanded the best for her events, as Leah had been reminded, oh, about a billion times since she'd descended the stairs in the pre-dawn hour.

"Ramsey, tuck that cloth around the scones, and then the footmen can take this basket. Do be careful, girl."

Leah wasn't exactly sure how she could screw this up, but she tucked the cloth carefully anyway. The kitchen around her was a maddening mix of rushing maids and steaming pots, the noise and mayhem almost like opening night of a musical. It was like everyone expected the queen herself to show up at this rout.

Leah frowned as she shut the basket. She knew there was a prince regent about now, but was there a queen? She wasn't sure. Renaissance history she was much clearer on, but nineteenth century? Not so much. She couldn't remember one being mentioned in any of her favorite books placed during this time. She'd have to ask Avery later.

"Don't dawdle, Ramsey, you must hurry. The carriages are leaving in a moment. Take that hamper." Mrs. Harper's hands fluttered like deranged humming-birds as she shooed Leah toward the door.

Toting the basket, Leah hummed under her breath as she reached the fresh air and sunlight outside. The chaos she'd just left seemed far away, and she took a grateful, cleansing breath. Man, she'd needed that.

"Good morning, Ramsey."

A deep voice behind her made her jump. She turned to find out who'd spoken.

"Hello," she said, smiling politely to the stranger. "Do I know you?"

"No' yet," he said in the lightest trace of a brogue. "But I'd like to remedy that. I'm Lachlan Mackenzie, the stable master. May I take your hamper to the carriage?"

Leah smiled. What a gentleman. Her head tilted in the beginning of a grateful nod when the basket was lifted from her hands.

"I'll take it. Get into the carriage."

Leah wheeled on Avery, who now held the basket. Around the handle, his scarred knuckles were white with tension.

"Well, good morning to you too, sunshine. Is there a problem?" She glared at him, digging her toe into the gravel.

He leaned close to her as the Scotsman gave a mocking smile. Avery hissed the words into her ear. "Get into the carriage, and do not argue with me."

Mrs. Harper opened the door to the area, stifling Leah's retort. Ooooh, Avery was so going to freaking get it later. Glowering at him, Leah turned on her heel and half stomped to the plain black carriage that stood waiting outside the area.

What was Avery's deal, anyway? The stable master had been nice to her. He definitely hadn't been as macho-chest-beaty as Avery had. Avery was almost acting possessive of her.

That thought nearly made her trip on a cobblestone. Avery didn't feel that way about her, did he? In a fog, she climbed into the carriage and reluctantly took the empty seat beside Henrietta. A knot started in her stomach, tension and nausea combined. He hadn't said anything, hadn't given any indication he was interested in pursuing her. And on that somewhat awkward subject, what was she feeling for him?

She looked down at her gloved hands. She was here for the duke, wasn't she?

"Sara," Henrietta said loudly. Leah tossed a hard glance sideways at the little devil maid, her bullshit-alarm throwing off some huge signals.

"Yes, Henrietta?"

"Did you know that the dowager especially likes it when servants speak with her in a familiar manner?" Henrietta smoothed her skirt nonchalantly. "I am told that she and her scullery maid have a nice little tête-à-tête every evening."

Sara's jaw dropped in clearly overdramatic shock. Leah rolled her eyes.

"Oh yes," Sara nodded, her words wooden. She'd clearly practiced this hundreds of times. "The dowager does indeed like it when servants call her by her Christian name, Hyacinth."

"Yes. And she is also quite fond of…" Henrietta trailed off as Avery and another footman entered the carriage. Once they were seated and the door closed, the carriage creaked to a start and jounced along the road toward Tunstall Place.

Well, at least Henrietta and Sara stopped giving me advice that'll get me skewered by the dowager, Leah thought. Avery sat across from her, looking out the window. She took advantage of the silence to examine him and gauge her reactions. It was almost like a science experiment.

His hands folded in his lap, his jacket pressed and straight, his hair pulled neatly back into what he called a queue, his face solemn. His hazel eyes, clear and bright as they looked out on the slowly passing streets. His nose was crooked, and she caught herself wondering what had happened to disrupt the straightness. Her skin warmed as she took him in, and something in her chest loosened pleasantly.

They jounced over a rut, and she realized with a start that she'd been staring at him like he was a half-dressed Chippendale dancer. Heat climbed her cheeks and she looked out the window herself.

What the hell was wrong with her?

DUKE. She was here for the *DUKE*. Not for his manservant. Mrs. Knightsbridge had been clear. Well, sort of clear. And Avery had sworn that he was the last person on earth who could be meant for her. So she'd best get her brain in the game and start playing to win.

The carriage jounced along the busy and crowded streets, the air inside thick with tension.

Leah picked at the threads on her cloak. This was as awkward as a group blind date.

The footman beside Avery was checking out Sara, who was staring at the ceiling as if it was printed with the winning lotto numbers. Henrietta glared at Avery as if she could make him disappear for ruining her set-up of Leah's failure. And Avery stared out the window, a crease marring his forehead.

Dump them in a big house with some video cameras, and there was reality TV gold right there.

Fortunately, the carriage ride only lasted about fifteen minutes. They rolled to a stop beside a beautiful manor that looked a lot like Granville House, only not quite as fancy. Avery offered his hand to assist her from the carriage, but Leah ignored it and hopped down to the gravel alone. Sure, it was a childish move, but damn it, he'd acted like a caveman with Lachlan earlier.

Mrs. Harper, who'd ridden in the first carriage, clapped her hands.

"Henrietta, Sara, Ramsey, attend me."

Why do I get called by my last name? It was a stupid thing to let bother her, but it did. Just another way to keep her separated. She followed the other maids and stood behind them as Mrs. Harper doled out duties for the day.

The preparations took forever, but they passed by in such a whirl of activity that it was hard to really gauge the passing of time. There were tablecloths to be ironed, flowers to be arranged, china to clean, silver to polish, and enough other things to keep a platoon of Mr. Cleans busy for a good month. But with the army of maids and footmen from both Tunstall Place and Granville House, all of it got done in time for the party.

"Now," Mrs. Harper said in an excitedly hushed voice, "we must be ready when the guests arrive. Henrietta, Sara, you remain in the entry hall to assist with hats and coats and the like. Teresa, you can assist with the trays when they're rung for. Henry, George, do go and help Cook." She turned to address the butler.

"Um, Mrs. Harper?" Leah hated to speak, but she was tired of being ignored. She'd been standing there for twenty minutes waiting for her assignment. "Where do you want me?"

"Oh, anywhere, girl, do find something." Mrs. Harper dismissed her with a wave of her hand.

Stung, Leah turned toward the large drawing room that would see the most action. Maybe there was a tablecloth to straighten or a settee to dust or a chamber pot to empty.

She shuddered. Approaching footsteps made her turn.

"Miss Ramsey, I have but a moment, but do let me apologize for my behavior toward you this morning." Avery's voice was nearly a whisper.

"What is your problem?" Leah hissed back to him, picking up a vase of flowers and straightening the cloth beneath it. "You act like you don't give two shits about me and then you treat me like I'm some kind of helpless female who needs you. Which is it?"

His jaw worked silently for a moment.

"Russell, you're needed in the drive. His Grace has arrived," the Tunstall Place butler called.

Without another word, Avery gave her a quick look and strode away.

"Stupid man," Leah mumbled beneath her breath. She plucked a wilted leaf from a daisy. "What am I saying? They're all stupid."

The guests started to arrive. Backing into a half-hidden corner, she pretended to dust some figurines while she soaked in her first glimpse of true London gentility.

It was like being a guest at William and Kate's wedding, only without all the tabloid reporters.

There were beautiful women, wearing insanely decorated hats and beautiful, ornate gowns. The footmen took turns showing the ladies in, one by one. Their escorts, gentlemen dressed in tight breeches and colorful waistcoats, followed, straightening their jackets and laughing with one another.

Leah sighed with happiness as she pressed up against the half-wall that shielded her. God, this was beautiful. The gowns, the clothes, it was straight out of a dream she'd had in college—the one that almost made her go into theatrical costume design. It was only her inability to survive as the permanent houseguest on someone's futon that prevented her from chasing that dream all the way to Broadway.

But here, seeing such opulence firsthand? It brought back the feelings full force, and she happily swam in them.

Polite chitchat and laughter swirled around Leah as the guests made their way into the sitting room. The other maids and footmen scurried around in the background, but Leah didn't really pay them any attention. The real show was the lords and ladies, and she intended to enjoy it as much as possible.

She did until Henrietta, buried under several ladies' cloaks, shot Leah an evil glance as she passed. Startled, Leah dusted furiously. Whoops. She'd almost forgotten her charade. She'd have to be more careful when the dowager appeared. Speaking of which, where was the esteemed old dragon?

As if her thoughts had conjured the lady up from the underworld, the woman herself descended the staircase.

"Wymond, my dear sweet boy," she crooned in a deep voice that made Leah jump. Holy shit, it was an eighty-year-old Bea Arthur with a British accent. Leah smothered her surprised laugh with a half-choked cough. The dowager was tall, with a long face, pursed lips, and jowls, just like the Golden Girl—down to the mostly-salt-and-barely-pepper hair and everything. But who was Wymond?

"Mother," a soft male voice responded.

When Leah turned to see who had spoken, she dropped the Dresden shepherdess she'd been pretending to dust. The resulting clatter brought everyone's eyes to her, but she was still staring at the man who stood at the bottom of the staircase.

Holy shit, it was the duke. The duke's name was Wymond. How could such a beautiful man have such a dorky name? It was hard to tell which had shocked her more: the fact that his name was so unfortunate, or the fact that she'd called him a boy. He had to be pushing sixty.

She forgot about her supposed love's unfortunate name when the dowager rounded the bottom stair and glared at her.

"You stupid, thoughtless chit," the lady snarled, her formerly regal face now something that looked more like Emperor Palpatine about to shoot lightning bolts into Leah's body. "You shall regret that."

Oh, holy crap.

Thirteen

THE CLATTER OF PORCELAIN ON WOOD SLAMMED A HUSH
over the entry hall, servants and masters alike. Miss
Ramsey winced and righted the figurine she'd dropped,
but the damage was already done. Avery's anxious fingers
crushed the fabric of the greatcoat in his arms as if he
could crush the mounting tension in the room. If only
it were that easy.

How could she be so careless? He'd thought she
understood the importance of staying unnoticed in front
of the dowager.

Stealing a glimpse of Her Grace's face, Avery stopped
breathing. The dowager's papery cheeks were flushed,
her brows lowered, and her knuckles white on the
banister. This did not bode well.

She descended the last stairs and rounded the corner
toward Miss Ramsey with pure murder in her bearing.
Avery didn't know what she'd do, but he knew it would
not be pleasant. He had to act—and swiftly—if Miss
Ramsey were to outlast the encounter.

With only a small amount of regret, he extended his
leg toward a passing Tunstall footman. With his burden

of gentlemen's coats and hats, the poor soul never had a chance to avoid the obstacle. With a surprised squawk, he went flying and launched his burden directly at the duke and the dowager.

Chaos reigned.

A dark blue greatcoat settled over the dowager's head like a net, trapping her beneath it. Frantic cries came from beneath the billowing fabric as she fought to free herself.

A cane struck His Grace's nose before clattering to the floor. The nobleman clapped a hand to his face and screwed his eyes shut in discomfort. Maids and footmen, Avery included, rushed to assist the beleaguered pair. Miss Ramsey, Avery was relieved to note, disappeared into the sitting room during the confusion. At least the chit had the good sense to run.

"Who is responsible for this?" The dowager's voice echoed in the hallway once her maids had freed her from the predicament. "I demand that you speak up at once!"

"Your Grace, my apologies," the poor footman stuttered. He was pale as fine bone china. "'Twas an accident. I stumbled…"

The dowager's rage was thankfully curtailed by the duke's interruption.

"Mother, your guests are waiting." He sniffed, pinching the bridge of his injured nose. "Come, let us go in." He dropped his hand and offered his arm to her.

With a scornful look at the hapless assembly of servants, and an especially dark glare toward the unfortunate footman, the dowager allowed her son to escort her into the sitting room.

Avery sagged with undisguised relief. What a near

thing that had been. Despite his careful tutelage, Miss Ramsey seemed determined to worry him senseless.

A quick glimpse at the sitting room reminded him that the evening had only just begun, and that his self-appointed charge would have many more opportunities to offend tonnish society. With a long-suffering sigh, he ducked inside the sitting room door. If he were lucky, perhaps another rescue would be unnecessary.

He tried not to imagine the next scrape she'd find herself in.

Taking up a position opposite another footman, he stood like a soldier at his post, hands clasped behind his back, waiting to be called on. Scanning the room, he exhaled a calming breath when he caught sight of Miss Ramsey, who was, for once, exactly where she should be.

She, along with four other maids, was attending to the spread of scones, biscuits, jams, and assorted other refreshments on a long side table. Appearing to take her cue from the well-trained Tunstall maids, Miss Ramsey's movements were slow and methodical as she set a new pot of tea on the end of the table. She nodded to Harold, another footman, as he fetched a sherry for a guest.

Avery took heart at the sight, stiffening his spine against the sitting room wall. She'd avoided certain disaster already today. Surely she could manage to stay out of trouble now?

Gales of feminine laughter from her corner of the refreshment table drew his attention. He gripped his hands tighter behind his back. Damn and blast. Whatever was she doing, speaking so animatedly to Lady Chesterfield? He must prevent her from another catastrophe. Making a quick decision, he lifted a discarded teacup as a pretense and crossed the crowded room toward them. The Baroness of Chesterfield was known throughout the ton for her mischievous, capricious nature. Best for him to stand at the ready, in case of unforeseen circumstances.

If he survived this hellish afternoon without the chit causing herself irreparable damage, it would be a miracle sent straight from God himself. No one else could have a hope of accomplishing such an impossible task.

⤜∘⤛

Oh, she'd really fricking done it now. Leah clutched the teapot as if she could yank the steaming brown liquid back by sheer force of will. No such luck. It soaked into the shiny green satin of the woman's skirt, a large stain that would probably never come out. Ever.

She didn't know what had happened. She knew it wasn't really the maid's job to serve, only to see to the table, but when the woman had asked her for a cup, she'd agreed without thought. One minute she'd been pouring a cup of tea that the lady held out to her, and then suddenly the cup was three inches further to the left than it had been. The steady stream of tea had gone straight down, splattering against the woman's skirt like rain pouring from a rooftop.

"Oh my God," Leah moaned. "I am so, so sorry." Her hands shook as she put the pot back on the table and searched wildly for a towel, a cloth, something she could use to try to make this better.

The duke would kill her. His mother would kill her. And if there were anything left after those two were done, Avery would kill her twice. He'd tried so hard to keep her from fucking this up.

The woman laughed aloud, a sound that shocked Leah to the core. *What the heck?*

"Oh, look at what I've done! I've spilled tea all over my gown, what a clumsy fool I am. Dear, would you mind accompanying me so I can put myself to rights?"

She held her hand out toward Leah.

Stupidity gummed up the thought gears in Leah's head. *What?*

"Dear, can you assist me?" The woman smiled at Leah, the ostrich and peacock feathers atop her hat quivering sympathetically.

"Oh, oh! Yeah, I mean yes, of course."

The conversation around them resumed as Leah followed the lady through the room, past a shocked-looking Avery, and into an unoccupied parlor across the hallway. The woman shut the door behind them with a click, then turned a serious look on Leah.

Sweat broke out along Leah's forehead, and she stumbled backward a step. *Better get talking quick, girl, or you're screwed.*

"Ma'am, I am very sorry. I only looked away for a second, and the cup was—"

"Hush, dearie. We must speak before anyone follows us in here." The lady sat on the chair in the corner, completely ignoring her damp and stained skirt. "I am Amelia Florin, Baroness of Chesterfield. I noticed that you have an odd accent. Where were you born?"

"Um." Leah fought the urge to shove her hands into the pockets of her apron. *Show no fear, Ramsey. Play your role.* "I'm from the colonies."

"Stuff and nonsense. The truth, dear, we've no time for prevarication." A fan suddenly appeared in the woman's hand, and she opened it with a snap.

Leah gulped. "I'm from North Carolina."

"And when, precisely, are you from?" She started fanning herself, never letting her steely gaze wander from Leah's eyes. "I shall know if you lie to me, dear."

The sweat spread from Leah's forehead to her cheeks and chest. She wanted to pull the tight neck of her gown aside to get some air, but Lady Chesterfield's gaze kept her frozen like a tonnish Medusa.

"Twenty thirteen," Leah mumbled.

The woman rose, a self-satisfied smile on her face. "As I suspected." She made a circle around Leah, who stood ramrod straight, confusion locking her muscles in place.

"How…how do you…"

"My lady's maid is a most unusual girl. She used to serve in an earl's household as a parlor maid, if you can believe it. A certain Micah Axelby, Earl of Dunnington. When he supposedly ran off to the colonies, she came to be in my employ." Lady Chesterfield patted Leah's cheek. "Muriel has told me the most fantastic stories about a woman named Jamie Marten, and you know, I am inclined to believe her. A young woman who traveled through a bureau's mirror in order to find her true love. A bureau that has recently been purchased by the Duke of Granville. Now quickly, before they know we are missing. Are you also here to search for your true love, as Jamie was?"

Hope and relief slammed into Leah's forehead, and she swayed unsteadily. Her *yes* came out half gasp, half laugh.

Lady Chesterfield grabbed Leah's hands and held her steady. "And do you need assistance in that quest?"

"Holy crap, yes. It's tough to land a duke without any help. But why would you want to help me?"

Even though Leah desperately wanted to grab Lady Chesterfield's help with both hands and take off running, possibly do some parkour down St. James's Place, she couldn't help but be worried that this might be too damn good to believe.

But the woman's smile was as sincere and kind as any she'd seen. "Because I've had my own dear husband, and he was everything to me. Now that he's gone, I can amuse myself as I damn well please. And I like you, dear. You remind me of a very young Amelia Florin, and that's the truth." She pressed a delighted kiss to Leah's forehead. "Now, we must plan. Presenting you into society will not be easy, but we can do it if we are careful. Here's what you must do to avoid suspicion."

As Lady Chesterfield outlined her plan for the next twenty-four hours, Leah's excitement grew. Firstly, no more chamber pot emptying. Lady Chesterfield laughed when Leah offered to be a parlor maid in her house too. Leah didn't hide her relief at that. Everyone knew she wasn't cut out for the domestic servitude life.

After sponging off Lady Chesterfield's skirt with a damp cloth, they returned to the party. Leah was careful to keep her face calm and her hands steady as she tended to the refreshment table, but damn was she dancing inside. This was it! This was the way she'd imagined her trip into the past. She'd go to balls and routs and teas and soirees and masques and house parties and hunts and rides in the park…

"Ramsey."

She jumped. "Yes?"

"Fetch a fresh pot of tea," Mrs. Harper sniffed. "Silly girl, whatever you are dreaming of I can never know."

Damn skippy, Q-tippy, Leah thought with an internal snort. They didn't have drugs good enough to give Mrs. Harper a dream this awesome.

And in just a little while, Leah would be living it.

The rest of the evening proceeded uneventfully, fortunately. After two near disasters, Leah was petrified that the third time would be the charm. She managed to keep quiet and out of the way of the other servants and guests. But it was kind of tough to stay away from the duke. Now that she knew she'd get a chance to meet Wymond—holy shit, his name was *Wymond*?—on equal ground, she had to avoid him as much as possible. Their only time together so far had been so brief and unmemorable, at least for him, that Lady Chesterfield thought it would be best to keep their real introductions for society. After all, if anyone figured out that Leah was a servant, the duke wouldn't look at her twice—certainly not to figure out if she was good enough to marry.

So despite her desire to get to know him, Leah kept her distance while the party wound down, and he and the dowager said farewell to their guests. When there were only a few old women left, he kissed his mother on the cheek and took his leave.

Leah sighed in a mixture of relief and disappointment. Oh well. It'd all be worth it in the end.

She was hefting a tray toward the kitchens when she passed Avery in the hallway.

"Hey," she said, pausing for a second. "I didn't embarrass you too bad, did I?"

He gave a half smile. "Get about your duties, Miss Ramsey. No time to be dawdling now."

She smiled back, curious at the heavy twinge in her

chest as she turned and walked away from him. *Avery.*
She hadn't thought about leaving him at Granville
House. He'd been so kind to her, the only real friend
she'd had in this time before she met Lady Chesterfield.
And honestly, she wasn't sure how she'd get along
without him.

She set the tray in the bustling scullery and stepped
out into the area to catch a breath of air. The late
afternoon wind was chilly, and she shivered. Tilting her
chin skyward, she closed her eyes and filled her lungs.
Things were so odd here. Everything, not just the lack of
electricity and the ridiculous workload—the way she felt.

Back home, she knew what she wanted. She always
acted first and thought later. But here she found herself
second-guessing every move she made. What had caused
this crisis of confidence? Could she fix it? Should she?

A bitter laugh escaped her. Well, her second-guessing
wasn't getting her out of any trouble. As it was, she had
stepped in it way more often than not here. Avery would
probably be glad to see her go. She'd caused him enough
problems already.

She shook her head, straightened her apron, and
headed back into the fray. She had a rout to clean up
after, a bag to pack, and a resignation to give.

It was time for Leah to hurtle headlong into her
future. And that was just the way she liked it.

Fourteen

AVERY COULD NOT RELAX UNTIL THE CARRIAGES ROLLED to a stop beside Granville house. Even then, after the hampers were unloaded, and the servants had gone about their final duties of the night, tension lined his shoulders and clenched his teeth. Miss Ramsey may have avoided the dowager's wrath, but what could she have been doing so long with Lady Chesterfield? The woman was mischievous, clever, and as eccentric as any matron of the ton could ever hope to be. He did not know what she was about. How could he prevent Miss Ramsey from falling prey to a bored baroness's scheme? Simple. He could not.

The duke had gone straight from his mother's rout to his nightly amusements and would not be back until the wee hours of the morning. With his own duties completed and the preparations made for their departure on the morrow, Avery had nothing pressing to attend to, and his beleaguered brain made free reign of the lack. Pacing along the back edge of the dark garden, he set his mind to wander where it willed.

Miss Ramsey wanted the duke. She was beautiful enough

for any man, he was quite sure. And compassionate—he'd seen that in the way she'd looked at his ailing aunt. Why did he long to see her looking upon him with compassion and—dare he think it—regard in her eyes?

Spinning with a soundless roar, Avery plunged his fist into the oak's trunk. The tree shuddered, raining leaves down around him. His knuckles stung with the ache of fresh scrapes. The pain eased the anxiety that had built in his chest at the words he could not think.

He must not think them.

Shaking out his hands, relishing the numbing pain of them, he sank down onto a garden bench and looked up into the branches that had showered him with greenery. God could be so cruel. His father had taught him that.

In his mind's eye, he had always pictured God with the face of his father, sitting on a throne and pointing down at Avery with a scowl on his face. No matter what Avery had done, it had never seemed to please either of them.

He dug his fingers into the stone bench on either side of him. And when he'd decided it didn't matter and stood up for the one person in the world who'd loved him, she'd paid with her life.

He was not good enough to pursue Miss Ramsey. She had proved tonight that she was quick, clever, and strong enough to pursue the best in the land. And Avery was the farthest thing from what she deserved. He'd keep his distance, no matter the cost.

Shoving to his feet, he turned and walked toward the stables. Better to hit his training bag than an innocent tree anymore. If his dark thoughts were prone to destruction, then he should be in a safe place, away from living things that could come to harm because of him.

He'd just passed the entrance to the area when Miss Ramsey exited the kitchen door.

"Hey," she said, her beautiful smile stretching her lips. Her hair wisped out from beneath her mobcap, and her cheeks were stained pink with excitement. "I've been looking all over for you."

Even though he longed to smile back at her, he did not. He could not. Looking away, he spoke toward the stables.

"My apologies, but I must be on my way. I have duties…"

"Come on, Avery, even I know the duke is out on the town tonight." He flinched as she laid a careless hand on his forearm. "I need to tell you something."

Pulling free of her grasp as carefully as he could, he turned to face her. Her tone was much too serious to ignore, no matter how much he wished it were otherwise. He nodded toward the garden he'd just come from.

"If you must, then please speak in the garden. It is more private."

She walked in the direction he indicated. Tapping his thigh with anxious fingers, he tried to ignore the sway of her skirts. She drove him mad with the simplest of movements. Although he'd been with other women before, none of them made his blood fire in his veins like she did. With tremendous effort, he restrained the growing interest in his loins.

When they reached the bench by the oak, Miss Ramsey sat down and stretched her feet out in front of her with a grateful sigh.

"Gosh, that's better." She bent down and removed

her boots, wiggling her stockinged feet in the night air. "Holy crap, this feels good." Propping her ankle on her knee, she rubbed her abused toes.

He averted his gaze. What a pitiful man he was, tempted by a slender female foot. Clearing his throat, he clasped his hands behind his back.

"You wished to speak with me?"

She dropped her foot and looked up at him, the vibrant blue of her eyes shining with excitement and just a tinge of regret. She opened her mouth to speak, but just then a voice called from the kitchen doorway.

"Ramsey," Cook called. "Mrs. Harper is asking for ye. Look sharp, my girl."

Miss Ramsey groaned and shoved her feet into her boots. "That housekeeper makes the Stormtroopers look soft and cuddly. Can I catch you later?"

Avery nodded. "Of course."

She smiled at him. "Thanks, Avery. You're the best."

Worry grabbed hold of his spine as she walked away. Whatever she'd been about to tell him had been important. He did not know her very well, but he knew that she would not waste his time idly.

With a lingering glance at the setting sun, Avery set off toward the training room. Although he no longer felt the burning need to punish his body as he had before, the exercise would calm him.

And with the tempest roaring in his soul, that was a comfort he sorely needed.

୧୧

When Leah's head finally hit the pillow, she was beyond exhausted and was somewhere between La-La-Land and

Completely Punchy. She fought the urge to giggle as she rolled to her side with a smile.

No more scrubbing chamber pots and toting ash buckets. She was going to be like a Regency era Eliza Doolittle, only without the slipper fetching for Professor Higgins. She nearly cracked her jaw with a yawn as Henrietta flopped into bed behind her. Leah rolled her eyes as a bony heel connected with her calf. And to think she'd actually wondered if the little demon would miss her.

"Oh heavens! A spider!" Henrietta screamed.

The bed jostled violently. Henrietta's full-blooded shriek had Leah leaping out of bed and reaching for the nearest blunt object to defend herself with, in this case a heavy candlestick.

"Henrietta, where is it?" Leah brandished the metal object toward the room at large, searching wildly for the murdering eight-legged bastard as Sara and Teresa snorted with laughter. Wait, what?

"Oh," Henrietta gasped, doubled over with mirth. "Your face, you should have seen…" She collapsed on the pillows in a heap of full-throated laughter.

A chill settled over Leah's shoulders. The mocking laughter echoing in her ears, she set the candlestick down carefully and smoothed her shift over her hips. Slowly, methodically, she stepped toward the bed and the still-gasping-with-giggles Henrietta. Kneeling on the mattress with one knee, Leah leaned close to the young maid.

"You listen to me, and you listen good," Leah said in a low tone. The girl stopped laughing, eyes widening slightly at Leah's words. "I've let you off easy until now. But you've just messed with the biggest bitch you're ever going to meet in this lifetime, and she's had all she can take. Just remember that whatever's coming? You asked for it."

Henrietta wasn't breathing, just staring at Leah's face with the glassed-over look of someone who realized they'd stepped in a giant pile of trouble.

With a calm smile and a gentle "good night" to the room full of silent girls, Leah settled into her pillows once more with a happy sigh.

This was going to be so satisfying.

She had to get up early the next morning, but it was so worth it. Fortunately, her internal clock had been honed to a fine edge since college. Jamie had a nasty habit of forgetting to pay the electric bill.

All three of Leah's servant roommates slept like the dead. She kept all her delightedly evil snickering inside, though. No need to tempt fate.

When she'd laid out her plans to the best of her ability, she stuffed her pouch of contraband into the brown leather bag that Avery had given her. With her nearly nonexistent packing completed she descended the back staircase with a happy sigh. All she had to do now was tell Mrs. Harper she quit and hit the road for Lady Chesterfield's.

She'd be sorry to leave Avery and Cook, but the rest of them? Not so much. Lady Chesterfield seemed incredibly nice, and Jamie had told her all about the young maid, Muriel. She hadn't expected to actually get to meet her, so this was going to be awesome. Spending her days with people that didn't resent her? What a novel freaking idea.

She'd been sitting at the servants' table for about twenty minutes when the screams trickled down the stairs. Smiling, she picked at her fingernails. Any minute now…

"You stupid, evil, horrid woman!" Henrietta flew down the stairs, dressed only in her shift with her face completely blackened with coal dust. The very ends of her braids were coated with tar, and left sticky black spots on the white cotton. "What have you done to me?"

Leah pursed her lips and examined her cuticles. "I told you last night. You've brought every bit of this on yourself."

With a shriek of pure rage, the girl ran toward Leah with fingers curled into claws.

Leah didn't move. She wasn't concerned at all.

"Henrietta!" Sara descended the stairs, pale face wan. "Your clothes!"

"My clothes?" Henrietta whirled. "What is wrong?"

"They're…they're on the ceiling." Sara's voice trailed into a whisper.

"What? They cannot," she turned to Leah. "You did not…"

"I didn't what? I don't remember asking to be scared shitless last night." Shoving her chair back, Leah propped her hands on her hips and glowered down at the dumbstruck maid. "I didn't do what I did to get even with you. I did what I did to teach you a lesson. Actions have consequences, and I don't tolerate bullies. This is a little something called Karma. You get back what you put out. And so far, all you've put out is meanness. So here's what you're going to do."

Henrietta sank into the chair Leah pointed to. Underneath all her shenanigans and bullshit, she was still just a young girl. Teaching her this lesson would be the best thing Leah could do for her if she did it right.

"You're going to go wash your face. You're going to clip off the ends of your braids, because that tar isn't coming out. You're going to get your clothes down from the ceiling beams, get dressed, and apologize to Teresa and anyone else in the house you've tried to scare into giving you your way. And then you're going to not pull any of this shit again, or the next time something bad happens to you, it's liable to be a lot worse. Karma's a bigger bitch than you or I ever will be. Do you understand?"

Sullen tears tracked down Henrietta's cheeks, leaving pale white strips in the coal. "Yes," she whispered. She looked up at Leah with a pitiful frown. "I am sorry."

Leah nodded. "Thank you for the apology. Go ahead upstairs."

Sara followed a surprisingly meek Henrietta back upstairs, and Leah sank back onto the chair with a relieved breath. Hopefully the girl would think twice about her attitude from now on. Leah's retribution was pretty tame compared to what Henrietta deserved.

Biting her lip, Leah toed the leather bag with her boot.

Yeah, she'd taught Henrietta a lesson, but she didn't really feel good about it. The girl was young, and she'd had it hard, but that didn't excuse the way she'd been acting. Leah sighed and tucked a loose lock of hair behind her ear. She had done the right thing, she thought. Hopefully.

Footsteps on the stairwell drew her attention. She stood, grabbing her bag and holding it in front of her like a shield.

"Ramsey, whatever are you doing dressed in that manner?" Mrs. Harper looked down at Leah, wrinkling her nose as if she smelled something bad. Leah sniffed her armpit, she hoped subversively. Yeah, the basin baths hadn't been the most thorough, but she'd done the best she could.

"I've been asked to take a position in another household," Leah said, delivering the line Lady Chesterfield had given her with aplomb.

Mrs. Harper laughed aloud. "Whatever can you mean? Your service has been barely suitable in this home. Who could have…"

Leah smiled, biting back the snarky comments she wanted to fire back at Mrs. Harper. "Thank you for the kindness you've shown to me while I've been here. I won't ever forget you."

Turning on her heel, Leah marched toward the door. This wasn't exactly how and when she'd planned to do this, but damn it, she didn't want to spend another half hour here with Queen Q-tip. Ignoring the housekeeper's protestations, Leah closed the kitchen door firmly behind her.

And stopped dead.

Damn it, it was only five in the morning and still pitch-black out. What a way to botch her grand exit.

With a sigh, Leah leaned up against the wall. If that wasn't bad enough, she still hadn't managed to say goodbye to Avery. Well, this was great. Peachy. Glancing above her, she counted the windows. The one at the top was glowing softly with candlelight. With a grin, she bent down and scooped up a pebble. There was more than one way to get a valet's attention.

Fifteen

Tilting his chin skyward, Avery scraped the last of the shaving soap away. Wrapping his throat and cheeks in the soft, damp cloth, he sniffed as he wiped his skin clean. He tried not to think of the marks and bruises that this skin would very likely bear after the upcoming tourney. Tossing the cloth aside, he grabbed his breeches from the wooden chair by his bedside. He'd just buttoned them when a sharp pinging sound at the window drew his attention.

Glancing sideways with a bemused scowl, he picked up his shirt. Another ping rang through the room, followed by a third.

"Damn and blast," Avery muttered, tossing his shirt aside and going to the window. He must make haste for the last-minute preparations for His Grace's journey. This was a distraction he could ill afford.

Swinging the window open, he leaned forward to see where the projectiles were originating. A tiny pebble caught him on the bare shoulder, and he winced.

"Oh gosh, Avery, I'm sorry!" Miss Ramsey's voice floated up to him as he clapped a hand over the stinging spot. "I was just trying to get your attention. Can you come out here? I need to talk to you before I go."

"Go?" He suddenly forgot that he was only half-dressed in the unease her words draped over him. "Whatever do you mean?

She was barely visible in the predawn gloom, but when she glanced about, her blonde tresses whipped in the early morning breeze. He gripped the windowsill tightly, hoping that he'd misheard her.

"It's kind of a long story, and I don't want to yell it."

"I shall come down to you," he said, and shut the window. Jamming his arms through his sleeves, he made quick work of dressing, his thoughts all a-tangle as he did. How could she leave? Where would she go?

It did not signify. She did not know the dangers of this world. No matter her destination, he was determined to stop her. For how could he protect her if she left?

His footsteps echoed in the empty stairwell as he hurried toward the area. He did not have time for this. But how could he let her go?

Ducking past Cook, he slipped out the kitchen door.

There she stood on the steps that led up from the small area to the lane, one hand gripping the old leather case he'd given her, golden hair making a halo around her head. She gave him a small smile, and his heart thudded against his ribs. *Steady on, my lad*. He gripped his hands behind his back and stiffened his spine.

"I tried to tell you yesterday, but we kind of got inter-rupted." She took a deep breath, shrugging her shoulders in an exaggerated manner. "Lady Chesterfield asked me to come live with her, and I said yes."

"Lady Chesterfield?" he echoed incredulously. "Why has she asked this?" Avery's nails dug into his palms.

"Last night at the dowager's party, Lady Chesterfield told me that she knew about Jamie, my friend. She's going to help me with the duke and make me into a lady, à la Eliza Doolittle, I guess." Leah bobbed a grand curtsy with a grin. "Isn't that awesome?"

Avery's ire rose, bubbling in his gut like an overflowing river. "I do not know Miss Eliza Doolittle, but Lady Chesterfield is a bit of an eccentric. You should not accept her offer. You know nothing of her, nor she you." He couldn't control the hint of bitterness in his tone. She was leaving after all he'd done for her? "This is foolishness."

"Seriously?" Leah's blond brows crept high on her forehead. "Well, I'm sorry you feel that way. But I think I'm a pretty good judge of character, and this is a great opportunity. You've helped me a lot, and I appreciate that, but you've got to realize that I make my own decisions." The determined set to her chin fanned the flames of his temper, and he could remain still no longer.

"Do you?" Dropping his hands from behind his back, he took a step closer to her. "You make your own decisions? Is that why you decided you were destined for a man you'd never met? Are you the arbiter of destiny now as well?"

Her eyes widening, she stepped backward, bringing the bag in front of her as if to shield herself from him. "I…I don't…"

"Of course, my mistake, milady. Please. Do go and take up residence with these complete strangers. Of course, this is what you'd wanted all along, is it not? To be puffed up like some fine lady, to be able to court your duke on even ground? Ah yes. I can see by the expression in your limpid blue eyes that I am correct. I shall not importune you further, Miss Ramsey." He swept an exaggerated bow, nearly choking on his own bile-filled venom.

"Avery, please. Don't act like this." When he straightened, she stepped close to him. Reaching her hand upward, toward his cheek, she whispered, "Listen, I…"

He knocked her hand away, staggering backward as if burned. "Do not touch me." But that wasn't what he really wanted. He wanted to pull her into his arms and press his lips to hers, but he could not ruin her, no matter how much he wanted her.

Her fingers curled into a fist, which she dropped down by her side. "Fine. Have a nice life, Mr. Russell."

As she turned, the sweet, exotic scent of her tantalized him. She marched up the stairs toward the street.

"Miss Ramsey?"

She stopped but did not turn. "Yes?"

"I wish you well," he said in a low voice.

She nodded and then was gone, taking Avery's sense of peace with her.

A moment passed, then two, and with each heartbeat Avery's regret grew. When the torment grew too much to bear, he sprinted up the stairs to chase after Leah.

Her back was rigid as she strode quickly down the lane. She was nearly at the corner now. He watched her walk away for a long moment, warring with himself. What the devil was wrong with him? He should be glad to see the back of her. She'd caused him no end of trouble. So why did he long to chase after her and apologize?

He shoved a hand through his hair, suddenly realizing he'd not secured his queue. Damn. She'd done more than upset the household; she'd upset his internal balance. Best to get back to it. He had a journey to prepare for and a mill to attend. As distasteful as both propositions were, what choice did he have?

He turned and reluctantly made his way down toward the kitchen door, but voices ground him to a halt. A man and woman arguing? The woman's voice grew louder and more insistent.

"I told you, I'm not interested."

Miss Ramsey.

Without another thought, Avery leaped up the stairs and sprinted after her. Adrenaline pounded through him, forcing his footsteps faster. She needed him. He'd been right to worry. She was unprepared and vulnerable and in no position…

He stopped suddenly, gravel crunching beneath his boots. Miss Ramsey stood over Lachlan Mackenzie, who was moaning and grabbing his crotch as he lay in a heap on the gravel.

"Maybe next time a woman tells you she's not interested, you'll take her a little more seriously." She glared at the man and nudged him with the toe of her boot.

He would thrash Mackenzie. Later. For now, he directed his attention to Miss Ramsey. Her eyes were alight with anger, and her chest heaved with exertion and outrage. She was the picture of a warrior goddess, strong and decisive. The antithesis of a meek and demure female, but strangely he was drawn to her even more at the sight.

"Miss Ramsey, are you injured?" *You simpleton, she is obviously not.* But he could think of nothing else to say. If the stable master had laid a finger on her, Avery would not simply thrash him. He'd kill him.

She glanced over at him without losing her cross expression. "No, I'm fine. Just had to explain some basic communication skills to gropey-boy here." Hefting the bag in her right hand, she sniffed. "Well, I'm going to try this leaving thing again. See ya."

This time, when she turned, he reached out a hand and stopped her.

"Miss Ramsey." No, that was too formal. "Leah."

Her face softened slightly as she tilted her chin upward to look into his eyes. "Yes?"

I should not. I cannot. He must, and he did.

Stepping toward her, he closed the short distance between them. His hand trailed from her shoulder to the delicate curve of her neck, higher to tangle into the hair at her nape. Her lips, pink and pale in the breaking dawn, parted slightly on a breath.

"Avery?" The question was whispered, her eyes soft and confused as she looked up at him.

He let his actions answer. Bending low, he pressed his lips to hers.

Soft heat. That was the sensation of her mouth on his. His muscles trembled with the effort of holding himself still, of restraining the urge to draw her body tight against his and possess her completely. This was enough. It was more than he deserved and all he'd ever get. She was leaving here, leaving him, forever.

Her breasts just barely brushed his chest. He imagined he could hear her heartbeat, stuttering and thundering just like his own. She opened her mouth wider, and he let his tongue explore the wet recesses of her mouth.

God, she tasted so sweet. Like sugared mints, clean and delicious. He swallowed his groan and swept his tongue across her soft, full lips. No woman could be this perfect, this maddening, this…

A cough from the ground below them broke the spell, and Avery stepped back, reluctantly breaking the most incredible moment of his life.

He looked away from Leah, afraid of what he'd see in her face. He focused on the man lying in the dirt instead.

The stable master moaned and struggled to his feet. "You'll pay for that, Russell."

Avery moved between Leah and Mackenzie. The man was in no shape to threaten her further, but Avery would take no chances with her safety. Watching the stable master limp away, reality suddenly slammed into him.

Oh dear God, what had he done? If they'd been seen, she'd be ruined.

Shame filled him, replacing the fingers of pleasure that had warmed him at their kiss. "Miss Ramsey, I do apologize. I wish you much happiness."

Without stopping to see if his apology was accepted, he turned and strode toward the house. He must get away, must separate himself from her. She was too good for him.

He should never have allowed himself to soil her so.

Leah stared after Avery, wondering what the hell had just happened. She pressed a trembling finger to her lips.

He'd kissed her.

Well, that had been unexpectedly incredible.

He'd been sweet, tentative, but demanding at the same time. She blew out a shaky breath, willing her knees to stop threatening collapse. She needed to get herself together.

It was only a kiss. She'd been kissed before.

Not like that, her subconscious whispered.

She mechanically picked up the bag that she'd dropped when he leaned down to her, and walked toward the street. Her thoughts flopped around like rapidly breeding Tribbles.

He'd never given her any indication that he was attracted to her. As a matter of fact, every time she'd touched him he'd backed away like his ass was on fire. How was she supposed to read signs that didn't exist?

Had she completely screwed up this whole trip by chasing after the wrong man?

"Oy, watch ye'self!"

She staggered backward to avoid getting trampled by a horse and cart. The driver shot her a dirty look as he passed by. Walking around in such a daze was dangerous for more than herself. Shaking her head to clear it, she walked in the direction Lady Chesterfield had told her to go. *Walk now. Think later.*

She may not know exactly who she was here to fall in love with, but she did know she desperately needed a friend to talk to. Lady Chesterfield and Jamie's maid Muriel were the best shots she had at some objective advice. But she had to make it there in one piece.

The sun had risen by the time she made it to Hanover Square. Setting her jaw, she marched up the steps to number four and knocked. The large door squeaked open slowly, revealing an ancient-looking butler. His long, hooked nose sported a sizeable mole, and his eyebrows, well, *eyebrow*, was composed entirely of curly white hair.

"The servants' entrance is in the back of the house, miss."

She had to hand it to him. He used that beak to his advantage, looking down at her over it as if he was the king of England. Before he could firmly close the door in her face, as she assumed was his idea, a trilling, cheerful voice floated down the stairs.

"Graves, do let the poor gel in. She is our guest, not a common kitchen maid."

With a pained look, Graves stepped aside to let her in.

Lady Chesterfield, dressed in a flamboyant red robe, stood on the landing.

"Oh, my dear, how lovely to see you. Graves, take her things. Is that all you've brought? But of course it is, no matter. Come, come."

With an emotion that could safely be labeled ridiculously heavenly relief coursing through her, Leah trotted up the stairs after Lady Chesterfield.

"I'm sorry it's so early," she said as the older woman bustled into a bedchamber almost as large as His Grace's had been. "I hope I didn't wake you up."

Lady Chesterfield laughed as she pulled a velvet rope at the bedside. "No matter, dear, no matter. I shall rest when I've cocked up my toes. Now"—she clapped her hands together delightedly, eyes wrinkling at the corners as she smiled—"do sit down. Muriel shall bring us some chocolate, and then we shall make our plan of attack."

Leah sank into the chair that Lady Chesterfield had pointed to, relaxing gratefully into the softness. She hadn't realized how much tension she'd been carrying ever since she'd tumbled into Avery's arms from that mirror.

Avery.

Oh God, what had she done?

She was saved from her mental swan dive into melancholy by a timid knock on the door.

"My lady, I have your chocolate." A maid, probably about seventeen or eighteen, entered the room bearing a tray with a steaming cup atop it. Brownish hair curled around the bottom of her mobcap, framing her delicate, pale face.

"Muriel," Lady Chesterfield said, "this is our guest, Leah Ramsey. You are acquainted with her dear friend Miss Jamie Marten, or should I say Lady Dunnington?"

The maid nearly dropped the tray in her excitement. "Miss Jamie?" She set the tray hurriedly on the bedside table and rushed to Leah's side. "How is she? And my lord Dunnington? Mrs. Knightsbridge told me they were to wed. Was it lovely? I know it was the most beautiful ceremony, for they were so in love."

Leah had to laugh at the maid's excited outburst. "Muriel, you're exactly like Jamie described you. Yes, it was a beautiful wedding, and they're really happy."

It was nice to think about her best friend instead of the mess Leah had made of her own life recently.

The maid turned her shining eyes to Lady Chesterfield. "How may I assist your ladyship?"

The woman propped her hands on her ample hips and smiled broadly. "Our Miss Ramsey here is destined to wed the Duke of Granville. And we, my girl, shall help her."

"The Duke of Granville?" Muriel's tone was surprised, but not in a good way. "But he is so old!"

Leah shifted uneasily in the chair. Muriel had just blurted out her biggest misgiving about this whole shebang.

"Yes, dear, His Grace, the Duke of Granville." Lady

Chesterfield sniffed. "And mind your tongue, Muriel. As you know, a gentleman's age is of no real impediment to a match. I do not know His Grace personally. His mother is a harridan of the first water, I must own. Still, it is of no consequence. We shall see to it that our Miss Ramsey weds advantageously, you can be assured of that."

"Lady Chesterfield," Leah said, rising to her feet with only a slight wobble. "I might have been wrong about the duke. Mrs. Knightsbridge told me that my true love was in the Duke of Granville's household, but she never actually came out and said it was the duke." Unease swirled in her stomach as she looked at her hostess and the maid.

A quizzical smile appeared on the baroness's face. "But there are no other eligible gentlemen in the household."

Avery's face popped into Leah's mind's eye, and she laughed awkwardly. "Well, a gentle man, but not a gentleman, if you get me." Leah cleared her throat. "What I mean is, I kind of made friends with someone in the house. The duke's valet, actually. And I'm wondering if I may have made the wrong assumption about the identity of the man I'm supposed to fall in love with."

Pursing her lips, Lady Chesterfield paced in front of the wide hearth. Muriel looked on, fingers twisting her apron. The only sound for several long moments was the soft crackle and pop of the fire. Leah linked her fingers in front of her, willing her lungs to draw in oxygen deeply and evenly. Hopefully Lady Chesterfield could help her figure this out.

"May I be plain, Miss Ramsey?"

Leah nodded. "Please."

Lady Chesterfield continued, "In your position as a temporary servant in the household, it is only natural that you would develop a *tendre* for another servant, as a presumed equal. But"—she crossed over to Leah and laid a gentle hand on her shoulder—"I cannot think that your Mrs. Knightsbridge wished for you to marry a mere valet. With my patronage, you will be welcomed into society. You need not settle for a commoner."

Leah sank back into the chair as Lady Chesterfield continued.

"Is it not possible that your feelings were magnified by your difficult position? Should you not pursue what you had desired in order to discover its worth?" The woman grasped Leah's hands. "I only wish to assist you, dear. And I would be very remiss indeed if I allowed you to set your cap for a valet when you could have snared a duke."

Doubt began to creep into the edges of Leah's consciousness. She'd really enjoyed Avery's kiss, she knew that. But was it because she was so desperate for this to work? Was it because she was scared and lonely, and she'd mistaken his kindness to her for something else? Or was it because she was afraid to put herself out there and be rejected again?

Her grandfather would never let her relax if she settled for less than the absolute best. Only one way to know.

Her mind made up, Leah gave a tight nod.

"Let's do this."

Sixteen

THE CARRIAGE ROLLED INTO THE OUTSKIRTS OF HOLBORN, bearing Avery nearer to the mill. Avery rode up top with the driver, with His Grace comfortable on the inside of the conveyance. Breathing deeply, Avery looked down as the ground rolled along beneath the horses' feet. He must clear his mind, make himself ready to face his opponent. He must win this match. There was no choice for him.

A playful breeze tossed his hair, at odds with the churning in his guts. Prachett would be at the tourney today. He'd be expecting Avery to spin the match to his specifications. Though Prachett had never paid Avery for his participation in the underhanded dealings, he had forgiven a portion of Avery's debt.

But now that Avery owed Prachett nothing? He'd fight honestly. And, if all went well, he'd win.

The apothecary had sent a messenger around just before they'd left for Holborn. The medicine for his aunt's ailment would cost more the next time around, as the ingredients were becoming scarce. It was more critical than ever that he win today's purse.

They arrived by the ring much before Avery was ready. He disembarked from the carriage with thinly disguised trepidation. Prachett would be here soon. Avery's needs didn't matter to Prachett. He wasn't after the purse; he was after the hundreds, if not thousands, of pounds to be gained from betting on the right man.

"Hoy, Russell," Jenks, Avery's bottle man, called from the corner of the roped-off square that would serve as their stage.

"Jenks." Avery nodded a greeting as he stripped to the waist. The crowds were drawing closer to the ring, each man attempting to get the best vantage for the upcoming brawl. The shouts and raucous laughter did nothing to calm his nerves or fray them. He'd stopped thinking of them as humans. They were cattle, mindless animals that brayed and milled about while he did his duty.

He moved lightly back and forth on his feet, relishing the feel of blood pumping harder through his veins. As he moved, Jenks spoke.

"You're to face Martin Peters, a young scrapper just come up from Brighton. He lasted near two hours in his last fight, and would have won had Lockston not tripped him so underhanded-like. He'll be spoiling for a tough 'un, s'truth."

Avery nodded. "Then we shall give him what he asks for."

Jenks laughed, tossing a rag over his shoulder. "That's it, m'lad. His Grace will be glad of that, and the rest of the Fancy too, I'll wager. Becoming quite their darling, you are."

Jenks walked away from him then, leaving Avery to his exercises.

The earth was damp beneath his feet. Fortunately the rains had stopped early the day prior, or his bout would have been a much colder, more inhospitable affair. As it was, his breath fogged from his mouth and nose as he stretched his limbs.

Closing his eyes, he bent forward to stretch his spine. As it always did, the image of his mother leaped unbidden to his mind. He did not try to stop the horrendous memory from playing out, as he used to. Experience had taught him that was a useless endeavor.

They'd been delivering a meal to an elderly woman in the parish. On their return, his mother had looked at him and smiled.

"Do you know why I love you so, Avery?"

He'd grinned, looking up into his mother's face. "No, why?"

She'd laid a comforting hand on his back, rubbing softly. "Because you are kind and good. You help me to remember to smile."

She'd hugged him close to her side, and he breathed her in deeply. He'd been so young then.

The brigand had come upon them only moments later. The wild-eyed man had grabbed his mother's basket, spilling the food over the roadway. His mother screamed, grabbing for her young son. But Avery had ripped free of his mother's grasp to leap upon the man and defend her.

She'd fallen so quickly. The sharp crack of her skull on the rock haunted him even now.

And here he was again, ready to fight another man. It seemed that he killed her anew every time he stepped into the square to fight.

But this time, his violence ensured his aunt's survival. It was his atonement for his mother's death. He could never bring her back, but he could keep his aunt, her only sister, alive for her.

A prickle of warning spread across his shoulders, and he turned. Of course. Prachett approached, flanked by two of his men. The menacing smile on Prachett's face boded ill. Avery stood silent, filling his broad chest with air. Calm. He must remain calm.

"Russell." Prachett's voice slid over Avery like grease. "'Tis good to see you here."

Avery said nothing.

"It has been much too long since you've been among us. Peters is a newcomer and lost his first. You know where the bets will fall today, don't you, lad?"

Avery shook out his fists, wishing he could use them to pummel Prachett into the dirt instead of young Peters.

"The right people are betting against you. And you must make sure that they win."

Avery stilled, spearing Prachett with a look. "I cannot throw the match. The purse is too—"

Prachett's laugh cut him off. "Oy, Russell, you lost your purse when you refused to fight today. I had to pay my men to convince you. You'll fight, and you'll lose, and your life is the only prize you'll claim." Prachett stepped close, his men shadowing him. "If you wish to live, you'll make sure to allow Peters the victory. If you do not…" The glint of a knife flashed, and a sharp prick lanced his side. Avery froze, impotent anger crushing over him. "Peters will win. And make it look good, lad. I have use for you later, so I should hate to leave your body for the dogs tonight."

The knife disappeared, and Prachett and his lackeys walked away.

With a roar, Avery plunged his fist into the

earth. The crowd cheered at such an expression of violence and rage. He ignored it, focused only on his impossible predicament.

He must win, for his aunt to survive. He must lose to keep his own life. Avery slammed his eyes shut and shoved himself upright. What a damnable mess. There was no answer, no way out of this conundrum.

"Russell?" The duke's voice pierced his confusion. "Is all well?"

Avery dragged a heavy breath through his lungs. "Yes, Your Grace. My apologies."

The elderly duke nodded. "Many of the Fancy are counting on you today, my lad. Give us a good showing." He gave a smile, then strolled toward his private viewing box. The rest of the Fancy, tonnish ladies and gentlemen who supported and enjoyed the fights, were spread around him, all too eager to enjoy the bout with the Duke of Granville.

His employer wanted him to win. He needed to win. But Prachett would kill him for it. A dark grin spread across Avery's face. He knew what he had to do.

All too soon, it was time for his match. Jenks and Tarley, Avery's knee-man, huddled in the corner for a quick word.

"He's favoring 'is right side as he moves. Mayhap an old injury. Pound him there and you'll be home for an early supper."

Thanking Jenks for his advice, Avery turned to his adversary.

The boy was young, a half-score years his junior. Tall and muscled, he was fairer than a day in June. Must have been of Scandinavian descent.

His young opponent spat in the dirt before offering Avery a respectful nod.

Avery returned the gesture, and both raised their bare knuckles into the traditional fighter's stance.

The fight master called them to order, and then they were off.

Avery circled his opponent calmly, looking for an opening in the young man's defenses. It was easy to discern from Peters's movements that he'd been trained by Jackson, who was highly regarded as the master of fighting. A dark smile crossed Avery's lips.

This boy may have been trained by Jackson, but Avery had been nursing hellfire in his soul. Letting his baser nature take control, he grunted at the impact of the boy's fist. First blow was done.

Avery's own knuckles connected.

Peters staggered backward as the throng roared. Regaining his feet, Peters rushed toward Avery again. The valet was ready for him and used his opponent's forward momentum to deliver a blow to his midsection.

Peters coughed but returned a punch of his own to the side of Avery's head, leaving his ears ringing like cathedral bells.

Avery shook his head as Peters staggered off him, gathering his senses. This would not be a simple fight, so he must collect his thoughts and plan.

The fight wound on, the combatants trading blow for blow, the crowd jeering and celebrating by turns, and Avery growing more and more weary.

He dodged a blow that Peters aimed at his face and laid one across the chin. Peters grunted in pain, spitting blood. His right arm sagged as he coughed.

Sensing his opening, Avery pounced. Right, left, one after the other, blows rained down on Peters's right side. Across the ribs, the hip, the belly, the shoulder, Avery peppered his opponent with vicious jabs. Jenks had been right. Peters went down only seconds later.

Sides heaving with exertion, Avery stood over the man. The cheers surrounded him, yells and whistles of approval coming from all angles.

Except for one.

In one corner of the ring, Prachett stood silent, murder in his gaze.

Leah smiled so hard she thought her face would break. She had never felt so pretty in her whole damned life.

"Oh, miss," Muriel breathed, face glowing with approval, "you look lovely!"

The creamy-white gown flowed down Leah's hips, cascading in soft falls of muslin to the floor. Leah looked down, past the demure square neckline with just a hint of cleavage, past the empire waist to the lace-trimmed hem. Taking a deep breath, which was hard because of the whalebone and lace corset that Lady Chesterfield had insisted she wear instead of the modern Lycra and plastic one she'd brought with her, she smiled at the maid.

"Thank you so much, Muriel. Jamie told me so much about you, and it's so good to finally meet you." Leah hugged the girl, who stiffened in shock, but then relaxed into an awkward pat on Leah's back.

It was just so great to be out of the hell of servants' quarters that Leah kept hugging Muriel anyway.

"It's my duty, miss." Muriel pulled away with a

self-conscious smoothing of her apron. "Now, Lady
Chesterfield wishes for you to present yourself downstairs. Her sister, Miss Stapleton, will be joining you
for tea."

"Great," Leah said. It'd be nice to meet Lady
Chesterfield's family if they were as great as she was. From
the moment Leah had stepped into the house, she'd felt
like an honored guest. It was a wonderful change from
scrubbing fireplaces and emptying chamber pots.

Muriel led Leah down the hallway toward the stairs.
As she passed family portraits, smaller than those in the
duke's home but no less impressive, she wondered about
Avery. She'd overheard Mrs. Harper talking about the
duke's journey. Had Avery gone with him? It would be
so much easier if she could just send him a quick text to
check on him. Sighing to herself, she descended the stairs
and entered the drawing room. She'd spent the last few
days convincing herself Avery's kiss was a fluke. She had
a different destiny to chase…and Avery's broad shoulders
and warm hands weren't part of it.

"Ah, here she is." Lady Chesterfield rose in a flurry
of rose-colored lace and feathers. Leah was beginning to
wonder about all the poor little birds that were running
around in the buff because of her patroness.

"Dearest Leah, this is Miss Alexandra Stapleton, my
eldest sister." Lady Chesterfield gestured to a woman
dressed all in drab brown, who rose with a sour expression.

Leah bobbed a curtsy. "It's a pleasure to meet you,
ma'am."

Miss Stapleton shot Leah a dirty look. "Amelia,
whatever can you be thinking to bring such a creature
into your home? Graves has informed me of her previous

employment. You cannot present her into society. It would mean your ruination."

"Oh, rubbish." Lady Chesterfield plopped down on the cushions. Leah followed, grimacing inwardly while maintaining her polite smile.

"She is a quick study and infinitely clever. She shall take the ton by storm, you mark my words. And none shall doubt her origin once we've spread the tale of her relation to my dear Chesterfield." Lady Chesterfield fluffed her feathered collar.

Leah toed a discarded fluff beneath the tea table, wishing she were a thousand miles—or a hundred and fifty years—away. What if she failed? What if everyone found out that only last week she was nothing more than a dishwashing, dust-clad domestic? She stiffened her spine and laced her fingers together in her lap primly.

Miss Stapleton sniffed. "How can a mere servant, with no position or breeding, possibly masquerade as one of her betters?"

Whoa, nobody discredited Leah's acting skill. If they wanted to disparage the way she dressed? Fine. The extra weight she'd picked up after the shit with Kevin? Fair game. But her passion for acting was sacrosanct, and she'd be damned if she let a comment like that go without a fight.

"Alexandra, you must give Miss Ramsey a chance to prove herself. She is, well…" Lady Chesterfield took a sip of tea. "She is from a land much more advanced than ours. Also, she is an experienced actress."

"An actress!"

Lady Chesterfield could have said Leah had shoveled shit for a living and gotten a less horrified response than that.

Miss Stapleton splayed a hand across her nonexistent breasts. "Amelia, how could you sully your home with a woman of her stamp?"

Stamp? Leah scanned her memory, trying to make sense of the overblown reaction. Wait, did this woman think she was a hooker?

Leah shoved to her feet. "Pardon me, madam, but you are grossly mistaken. I was invited to live with the incredibly generous Lady Chesterfield, and she has no problem with my past. I would hope that such a beloved relative would trust the baroness's judgment." Leah let her nostrils flare slightly as she looked down at Miss Stapleton. With her raised chin and solemn glare, she was sure she resembled an avenging monarch.

"How dare you imply that I do not trust my sister?" Miss Stapleton hissed. "You are a charlatan. I knew it."

Lady Chesterfield sat forward and held up a calming hand. "Now, now, dearest sister, you misunderstand. Miss Ramsey is from a society much removed from ours. She bears no ill will toward me or you. I have seen to it."

Leah eased back down onto the sofa, not losing the firm set to her chin. She kept silent. As much as she disliked the deception, she knew it was necessary. She hadn't wanted to cause problems within Lady Chesterfield's family. Damn it, this was more complicated than she'd thought it would be.

Lady Chesterfield handed her a cup of tea, and Leah sipped it slowly. More drinking, less talking. That would be her motto for the rest of Miss Stapleton's visit.

Lady Chesterfield smiled winningly. "Now, I have asked you to come and to meet Miss Ramsey because we are preparing for her come-out."

"Come-out?" Miss Stapleton held her cup of tea out for Lady Chesterfield to refill. "She is of rather an advanced age for a debutante, is she not?"

Leah gritted her teeth together so hard she feared they'd crack.

"Sister, look at her complexion. She is as beautiful as any young miss in their first season. With her figure and my clever Muriel's coiffures, no one shall ever guess that she is past the first bloom of her youth."

So she was both a swindler and old now? This little trip wasn't doing a helluva lot for her ego.

"Well, if this is the course you are set upon, far be it from me to dissuade you. Do you have any gentlemen in mind for the chit? Mr. Rutledge, perhaps, or Sir Thomas Edwards?" Miss Stapleton brought her teacup to her lips.

Lady Chesterfield bounced in excitement, fluttering her feathers like a duck drying itself. "She is destined for a man much greater than that. None will do for our Miss Ramsey but the esteemed Duke of Granville himself."

Leah didn't know whether to laugh at Miss Stapleton's near-perfect spit-take or to be even more depressed.

"The Duke of Granville?" Miss Stapleton's hand shook as she set down her teacup and began daubing at the droplets on her gown with a plain handkerchief.

I don't know why she bothers. They're the same damn color. Leah hoped her eye roll went unnoticed.

"Of course." Lady Chesterfield laughed. "Miss Ramsey is more than capable of capturing his attention."

"It is not that," Miss Stapleton said, giving up on her gown. "It is only"—she darted her glance back and forth as if afraid someone would hear them—"he is of such an advanced age. He has his heir, and though he may wish to marry again, I had rather thought, well..." She trailed off.

"Thought what?" Damn it, Leah hadn't meant to say anything.

Miss Stapleton didn't bother to look Leah's way, keeping her gaze trained on her sister as she replied. "He might be searching for a different sort of woman. One with more experience in society, perhaps. The dowager duchess is rumored to be very demanding."

Leah opened her mouth to reply, but Lady Chesterfield waved her hand dismissively.

"Rubbish. Utter and complete rubbish. He is a gentleman, not a child, and as such will make a perfect mate for our Miss Ramsey. Now, dear sister, have you spoken with Lady Oberlin of late?"

The sisters began chatting about people Leah didn't know while the tea grew cold in her cup.

Their age difference was pretty damn obvious. But she'd thought that wouldn't matter as much in this day and age. Had she been wrong? Miss Stapleton had stared pretty hard at her sister when she'd said that. Did Miss Stapleton have designs on the duke? An elderly spinster probably didn't have many prospects in this time. Too bad eHarmony didn't have a Regency England branch.

Leah stared into the patterned carpet, the rich colors seeming to swirl under her gaze. If Lady Chesterfield helped Leah with the duke, then found out later that her own sister had wanted him, would she resent Leah for stealing Miss Stapleton's chance at happiness? Or did Miss Stapleton mean she thought Lady Chesterfield would be more suited to the duke? They had to be pretty close in age. But how could she abandon the possibility without even getting to know him? So he was older. That wasn't a deal breaker, right?

With a heavy sigh, Leah lifted the cup to her lips and took a swig of cool tea. She grimaced at the taste. What a complicated trip this was turning out to be. She really wished she had a friend to talk to—someone who understood her or at least knew her a little better than Lady Chesterfield or Muriel.

Someone like…

She bit her lip. Maybe she'd go calling once the less-than-pleasant Miss Stapleton had gone.

Seventeen

HE'D WON THE MATCH, BUT IF HE WEREN'T CAREFUL, HE'D lose his life. Prachett's threat was not an idle one. Avery had seen other fighters defy the man before, and the results were never pleasant. But what choice had he had?

None at all.

Beside the coachman atop the carriage, Avery huddled in his coat as they wound through damp and dank streets toward Grosvenor Square. The rain and cold might be miserable, but they were infinitely preferable to remaining at the Houndstooth and facing Prachett again.

Fortunately, the duke was not interested in the other matches and had opted to leave before the crowds. His Grace had been curiously silent, not congratulating his valet on the victory. Any other victory would have had the duke clapping him on the shoulder, cheering like a lad. But today? Not a word had left his lips. Yet another worry to be added to Avery's lot.

Avery shifted in the seat and winced as his muscles cried out in protest. It didn't matter that he was battered and bruised. He had won, and he must plan now for a way to avoid Prachett's anger. His aunt could not go without medicine. He'd bear what he must in order to protect his only family. He pulled his coat tighter against him as if it could keep out the coming trouble as well as the downpour.

The carriage pulled to a halt in front of Granville House. The coachman leaped down and opened the door for Granville while Avery clambered down slowly and painfully.

"Russell." The duke spoke without looking Avery's way. "You will attend me immediately."

"Yes, my lord."

Shivering with cold, wet to the bone, Avery hung his sodden coat by the front door. Smythe, who had taken the duke's hat and cloak, cast a glance over at him. Avery thought he may have detected the slightest hint of curiosity in the older man's gaze before the butler turned and walked away. As his footsteps echoed down the long hallway, Avery's thoughts turned to Miss Ramsey.

How was she faring with the curious Lady Chesterfield? Had she made her debut during the week he'd been gone? Was she being accepted, or was she shunned because of her lack of connections?

The longing in his chest intensified as he entered the duke's study. Wherever she was, whomever she loved, he wished her every happiness in the world. It was best that she'd gone. When Prachett caught up with Avery, he hoped that Leah would be miles, or years, away.

"Close the door behind you, Russell." Lord Granville settled into the chair behind his large desk, primly tenting his fingers.

Avery obeyed. The soft click of the latch felt like the gates of hell closing him in. Swallowing hard and setting his jaw, Avery turned and stood tall while facing his employer.

The duke didn't say anything for several long moments. His keen gaze raked Avery from the top of his head to the toes of his boots, missing nothing. The swelling and bruising on his body would go down in a few days, but for the moment, Avery knew he looked nothing like a duke's valet should. Would Lord Granville finally realize Avery's unworthiness for the position?

"I was approached at the tourney today by a Mr. Thomas Prachett." The words were spoken softly, but that didn't countermand their seriousness. "He said that you owed him a great deal of money, lad. What have you to say to that?"

Protests brimmed on Avery's tongue, but he bit them back. He couldn't tell the duke the depth of his involvement with Prachett. The fighting was one thing, but if Granville knew he'd been forced into throwing matches? He'd probably be out on his ear in a trice. He answered in as calm a tone as he could manage. "Prachett was my employer before you, Your Grace. My debt to him was repaid long ago. I owe him nothing."

"I gladly shouldered the risk of hiring you on." The duke rose slowly, the corners of his mouth drooping. "But I cannot risk scandal in this household. It bears on everyone under this roof, to everyone who bears the name of my family. You must understand the position I am in."

Damn you, Prachett. Rage bubbled in Avery's chest, the red poison thrumming through his veins. He let his lids slide closed. Breathing deeply, he controlled the anger and desperation. "Your Grace, it has never been my intention to cause you harm."

Lord Granville rounded the corner of his desk, straightening his waistcoat as he did. "The Swansdown Mill is occurring soon. While it might seem best to avoid the bout, I am sure that the bounder would use your absence to poison your—and by extension my—reputation. I believe it would be best if you put in a performance there. Your appearance there as my man should squash any rumor. I shall sponsor you, lad, and I trust that you are speaking the truth of your involvement with Prachett." The duke leaned heavily against the front of the ornate desk, looking older and more tired than usual. "I have made no secret of the fact that you are my valet and a fighter. But while society has looked the other way, I believe that Prachett may change that if we are not careful."

"Very well, Your Grace."

Lord Granville turned with a wave of dismissal. "Thank you, Russell."

Avery's shallow bow went unseen, and he left the room with his chin high, though his heart was heavy and his jaw was throbbing. Another bout? His bruises would be yellow and green, still tender. He had no doubt that Prachett would take his revenge for the loss today. Could he avoid the man?

He'd cost Prachett hundreds of pounds today. Prachett would kill for much, much less. He thanked whatever star watched over him that Leah had left the house before all this occurred. If she ran afoul of Avery's past, she'd likely never be seen again. He'd find some other way to get medicine for his aunt.

Avery mounted the stairs to the duke's dressing chambers, the burning pain in his muscles throbbing in time to his steps. He must see to the unpacking, and then he could retreat to his small room, shuck his sodden clothes, and lick his wounds in private.

When he opened the door to His Grace's rooms, a strange glint caught the corner of his eye. The bureau's mirror was shining oddly, almost shimmering like the surface of a pond in a rainstorm. Drawing closer, he reached out and pressed his palm flat against the mirror.

The glass was cold, and it sent a shiver through him.

Leah had fallen through the glass as if it were pure air. He'd caught her, pressed her intimately against him. However inadvertent the contact had been at the time, he remembered it with longing now.

She'd laughed with him, smiled at him. She'd never treated him the way so many others had before. She was a woman unlike any other, and he'd allowed her to leave him without telling her so.

Turning, he slumped against the bureau's slanted front, uncaring for the moment that his wet clothing pressed against the wood.

He'd wanted her. He realized that now. The way a man wants a woman, flesh to flesh and heart to heart. She wasn't the first he'd wanted physically, but she was the only one that the hole in his chest seemed to scream for.

"Leah," he whispered as he looked skyward. "Please be safe."

"Of course I'm safe. Why wouldn't I be safe?"

He whirled, eyes wide. She stood behind him, bold as brass. He almost didn't recognize her, coiffed and clothed like a debutante.

"How are you here?" Avery took a cautious step

forward, his heart thumping wildly against his ribs. "It is impossible."

She ran the few steps that separated them, throwing herself into his arms. Closing his eyes, he bent his head to kiss her.

Just before their lips touched, she said, "You're right. It's impossible."

He opened his eyes. He was still alone in the bedchamber.

Clutching his aching, pounding skull, he turned to his duties. It wasn't the first time an opponent had nearly cracked his skull, but the cruel daydream was particularly painful.

She'd never run to him.

Raindrops ran down the windowpane of Leah's borrowed room. She trailed her finger down the glass, chasing a droplet. Her reflection, wavy and dim, stared back at her.

Though she'd tried to leave after Miss Stapleton, Lady Chesterfield of course had other ideas. They'd gone shopping for, of all things, more feathers. The hole of Avery's absence wasn't healing as she'd hoped. It seemed to be growing wider and more jagged every day.

It wasn't as if Lady Chesterfield wasn't kind to her. She was. She'd gone to the trouble of procuring invitations to balls and teas and musicales, all with the express intent of wedding her charge to the Duke of Granville. She'd bought Leah dresses and hats, slippers and gloves. If Leah backed out now, she'd look like a scam artist hell-bent on fleecing a nice old lady. If nothing else, she wanted to prove that old bat Miss Stapleton wrong. She wasn't a bad person.

Leah's heavy breath fogged up the window. Pressing her forehead against the glass, she let her thoughts wander back home.

Was Pawpaw okay? He'd been so damn insistent that she find someone to marry. The old-fashioned notion wasn't that out of the way for him, but the sincerity and demanding nature of his request had been. She drew a little heart in the fog of her breath on the glass. Her grandfather meant everything to her. She couldn't imagine loving anyone more than the man who'd raised her, who'd shown her what family and loyalty and courage meant.

Courage. Leah's eyes closed and the memory of Avery's kiss came unbidden. It had been incredible, a kiss that she could replay a thousand times and never get tired of. The feeling that curled low in her belly and crept up to her chest was hard to define. There was lust there, a familiar and comforting friend. But there was something more. What the hell was going on with her?

Cupping her chin in her hands, she stared as hard as she could, trying to make out the street below her window. No use. The rain was coming down too hard. What a miserable day, and it fit her miserable mood to a T.

"Miss?" Muriel's head poked through the crack in the door. "I've come to dress you. Lady Chesterfield said that you're attending the Watersons' musicale tonight."

Leah yawned and stretched, shuddering as her joints popped like Rice Krispies. She'd been sitting here and wallowing too long, apparently. "Yeah, that's right. She said they can't sing worth a crap. This is going to be awful, isn't it?"

"Oh no, miss." Muriel pulled a gown, one of the many that Lady Chesterfield had commissioned for Leah, and yet another source of Leah's growing burden of guilt, from the tall oak wardrobe. Shaking out the pale cream and lace, Muriel spoke matter-of-factly. "Graves has told me that His Grace has returned. He's to attend tonight."

"His Grace? Like, the Duke of Granville, that His Grace?" Leah wrinkled her nose in uncertainty.

"Why yes, miss. Lady Chesterfield is quite pleased." The maid picked at a loose thread on the ivory gown. "Shall I help you to dress?"

Leah reached out and grabbed Muriel's hands, forcing the maid to turn and look at her.

"Muriel, listen. I need to ask you something, and I need you to promise me you'll tell me the truth."

Muriel nodded. "Of course, miss."

"Do you know anything about the duke? I mean, other than that he's kind of old and a duke. Is he kind? A good man? What is he like?"

"I do not know, miss." Muriel's face was serious if a little sad. "He was married before, but the duchess passed away in childbirth. His Grace's son is up at Eton. That is all I know, s'truth."

Leah dropped Muriel's hands. "He's got a son?"

Muriel shook out the gown again. "Yes, miss."

His heir. No wonder Miss Stapleton had said that. Leah wanted to smack herself on the forehead. Of course that was what she meant. Okay, a widower with a son. Wow.

Muriel sniffed, regaining her composure. "Now please, allow me to help you dress. Lawks, you shall be late if we do not hurry. Hannah is dressing her ladyship, so come."

Leah followed directions numbly, not sure what else to do. Things weren't going anything like she'd imagined. But what could she do at this point?

Muriel managed to get Leah dressed and ready by the time Lady Chesterfield descended from her room. Tonight, Leah's patroness was outfitted in a brassy gold satin, pheasant feathers towering from a simple-looking hairdo. Lady Chesterfield smiled in a long-suffering way as she rounded the bottom step.

"I trust you know, dear Miss Ramsey, what a sacrifice it has been for me to allow you the use of my personal lady's maid. My coiffure is much plainer than I would like, but that cannot be helped. But I must say"—she patted Leah's cheek with a proud smile—"you look ravishing, my dear."

"It's thanks to you and Muriel." Leah smiled back. "The clothes and hair are all you guys."

"No matter, my dear. The beauty is all yours. Tonight, you take the ton by storm!" With that proclamation, and a trilling, birdlike laugh, Lady Chesterfield sailed through the front door, held open by a dour-looking Graves.

Shouldering her evening wrap, Leah smiled at the butler.

"Good night, Graves. Thank you."

He acknowledged her words with the barest of nods. Oh well. He was a tough nut to crack. She followed Lady Chesterfield into the damp and drizzly night, wondering what the hell to do about the mess she'd made of this whole situation.

Eighteen

THE DUKE OF GRANVILLE'S CARRIAGE ROLLED TO A STOP in front of Waterson Manor. A tiger jumped to the ground and opened the door only a moment before the duke stepped out, dressed elegantly in white pantaloons, a black coat, and crimson waistcoat. Once Lord Granville was escorted into the house by the Watersons' butler, the boy resumed his position and the carriage rolled around to wait in the back of the manor.

"Pissin' down, it is," the tiger, Edmond, muttered as he jumped to the shiny wet cobbles. "Night not fit for man nor beast."

"Mind your tongue, lad. 'Tis fine enough for the likes of you," the coachman replied as he loosed the horses from their traces. "Oy, who's with ye back there?"

"Oh, 'im?" Edmond rubbed his hands together. "It's Russell."

Avery tossed his hood back and jumped to the ground. Riding on the back of the carriage, Avery was sure his employer hadn't noted his presence—exactly as he'd planned it. After all, how could he explain that he was there to assure himself of Miss Ramsey's well-being?

A note had been shoved beneath his door sometime during the night, and the contents had frozen the blood in his veins.

Russell,

I am most displeased. Your mission was clear, and you failed to carry it out. Do not be surprised if those you care for come to sudden harm.

Be ready for my instructions if you'd like to protect them. You know what I can do.

Prachett

Harm to himself, he could stand. Pain was a familiar friend after all these years. His aunt was safe enough with Mrs. Comstock watching out for her. But even thinking about Prachett harming Leah made rage thunder through him. He'd had to make sure she was safe.

Rounding the back of the manor house, Avery found his way into the back garden. He peered through the windows of the house.

People milled about, dressed in their lesser finery for a smaller gathering. But even the poorest-dressed among them still shone like a polished gem. They chatted and laughed easily, the cares of the world as foreign to them as the colonies.

Bitterness lodged in the back of his throat. He coughed quietly, then resumed searching for her.

His efforts were rewarded only a moment later. Leah followed Lady Chesterfield into the room, a delicate smile on her face. A footman took her wrap, revealing her creamy shoulders and smooth arms, framed as they were by the delicate ivory lace of her dress. She laughed at something Lady Chesterfield said, tilting her head back in abandon, revealing the slender column he'd love to kiss.

Lord, she was beautiful.

He curled his fingers into a fist as he fought the urge to go to her. He was nothing to her, nothing at all. She was here for the duke. And he was only here to see that she remained unharmed by Prachett or his men.

They couldn't know that this glittering debutante was the maid from Granville House, could they?

The rain had stopped, but the air was cold, thick, and damp. Music started in the house, the plaintive sound of a pianoforte seeming to echo the strain in his chest.

He slapped his hand against the brick.

Thinking of her was such foolishness. Why perpetuate a fantasy?

Avery turned and looked through the window once more. She stood at the back of the room, a polite smile on her face as she addressed the gentleman next to her. His stomach dropped. The gentleman next to her was none other than his employer. The man she seemed determined to catch.

Jealousy roared through Avery. He dug his fingers into the brick, gritting his teeth so hard they ached. He could not tear his gaze away from the couple.

Why should he care? Granville was a gentleman, despite his age, and would make an exemplary match for Miss Ramsey. He'd always been kind to Avery. So why did Avery want nothing more than to rip her away from the duke's side?

The song ended, and a polite smattering of applause sounded.

He spent nearly an hour by the bush in the back garden, growing more and more angry as Leah remained by the duke's side. Avery's employer took a glass of ratafia from a passing servant and offered it to her. A cold wind kissed Avery's burning skin, but it did nothing to cool his rage at the sight of the duke's hand brushing Leah's. She blushed, smiling down at the glass in her gloved hands.

Damn it.

It should be Avery she smiled at, Avery touching her.

He snarled as he ripped the bush beside him out of the ground, spraying damp earth in all directions.

When the haze lifted, he realized his hands were cut and bleeding. The holly's sharp edges had punished his impetuous actions with aplomb—and the Watersons' poor gardener would have an apoplexy.

He knelt in the damp earth, replacing the battered bush as best he could. Would his rages ever be controlled? Would he ever be the master of his own mind and body?

He flexed his sore palms, ignoring the trickles of blood that dripped to the ground below. His gaze locked on the group inside. The duke had moved to another part of the room. He stood by the front door, but where was Leah?

Avery's heart raced as he desperately scanned the room for her. Where had she gone? He must find her before someone else did.

The squeak of a nearby door's hinges chased him behind the mangled bush. He crouched low. Footsteps echoed on marble, disappearing only a moment later. Someone descending the stairs into the garden?

Maintaining his crouch and ignoring his protesting muscles, Avery ran alongside the manor toward the back garden. He had a feeling that the person wandering there alone just may be the woman he'd been searching for.

He bolted for a stone statue of a Greek warrior and knelt in the shadows cast by the lights of the manor's windows. His breath caught in his throat as the clouds moved past the moon, shining soft light down on her.

Her gown glowed, almost as if she were a celestial being. Her hair, a golden tumble of curls and braids, absorbed the moonlight, mesmerizing him. She shivered, rubbing her gloved hand on her bare upper arm. The longing seated deep in his chest intensified so much that he stood, intending to run to her. The aching pain in his body returned to remind him why that was impossible, but his heavy breath did not go unnoticed.

Leah turned abruptly, bright eyes wary. "Hello? Is somebody out here?"

Blast and damn. He stayed in the shadows, willing her to go back into the house, to remain in the safety of company. He could not go to her, not here.

"I know you're out here. I can hear you breathing." Her voice came louder as she drew closer. He flattened his back against the statue's legs. She must not find him here. She must not…

"Avery?"

His eyes flew open. There she was, the woman of his dreams, the one who haunted his waking hours. The one he could not touch, not under any circumstances. His one lapse would have to last him a lifetime.

"Miss Ramsey," he croaked. Clearing his throat,

he tried again. "Miss Ramsey. You must return to the house. You are not safe here."

"Avery, are you okay?" She reached out for him, but he dodged her hand, making sure to stay in darkness. "I can't really see you, but you don't sound all that good."

"I am well. Please return to the house." *Please, because I long to draw you into my arms, to make you my own. But you are so much more, need so much more than I can give. I've endangered you.*

She propped her hands on her hips, giving him a cross look. "Bullshit. Get over here where I can see you."

He shook his head. Maddening, infuriating, beautiful woman. "I cannot be seen. I do not have permission to be here. Return to the house. It is not safe for a female to wander outside alone."

"I'm not alone," she whispered, joining him in shadow. "You're here with me."

He turned away, though her words warmed him with violent hope. She must not see his face.

"You'll be missed."

She laughed softly. "I don't care."

He kept watch out of the corner of his eye. She stared at his face, squinting through the darkness. The moment her eyes adjusted to the dimness and she realized his injuries, horror painted her features and stabbed his heart.

"Oh my God," she whispered, stepping close to him. "You...you've been..."

"My dear Miss Ram," Lady Chesterfield called from the balcony. "Where have you got to, dear child?"

Leah tossed a look over her shoulder, and he took advantage of her distraction to look his fill. The delicate lace of her gown only hinted at her womanly charms, but the innocent décolletage flamed his interest as much as a daring gown would have. The ivory color only accented her porcelain skin, pinkened her lips and cheeks, and set off her golden hair to perfection. She was as close to an angel on earth as had ever lived, and she deserved the best man life could offer her.

"That's me," Leah griped as she turned back to him. "We had to pick a name so nobody could connect the dots to the maid at Granville House."

He stifled his sigh of relief.

"Miss Ram?" Footsteps echoed on the marble steps to the garden.

"Go," he said quietly, and though it cost him dearly, he gently pushed her toward the house. She stumbled from the darkness as he melted backward.

Lady Chesterfield's cry was nothing if not glad. "My dear, there you are. Lord Granville is searching high and low for you. Come, we mustn't keep him waiting."

Avery watched from the cover of the statue as Lady Chesterfield and Leah disappeared into the house. His chest burned with an intense ache he couldn't place, but he knew its cause.

He could not speak with her again. It was much too painful. He'd only brought trouble on her. He'd keep watch from afar and count himself blessed that he had met her at all.

&

"What a naughty girl to disappear in the middle of a performance," Lady Chesterfield clucked as she pulled Leah back toward the house. "I declare it is as if you've no interest in His Grace at all."

"That's not it, Lady Chesterfield," Leah protested lamely. "I just had a headache and needed a little air, that's all."

"Well, we must return before his interest wanes. Good heavens, did you injure yourself?"

Leah looked over her shoulder where Lady Chesterfield was mopping at a blood spot on the shoulder of her beautiful gown. The same shoulder where Avery had touched only a second ago. What had happened to him?

"It was just a bug bite that I scratched too hard," she said as Lady Chesterfield fussed. "It's not bad, I promise."

"You must be more careful, dear." Lady Chesterfield removed her own shawl and placed it over Leah's now-spotted dress. "Now, we must find His Grace."

Lady Chesterfield's winning smile and wink couldn't remove Leah's uncertainty. God, she wanted nothing more than to run out there and check on Avery. His face had seemed swollen, discolored even. It was so hard to see in the shadows, which he'd probably planned. She rubbed the shoulder he'd just touched. That was his blood. He'd been hurt and refused to show her.

"Miss Ram." His Grace's voice melted over her like warm butter. Distracted for a moment, she turned to him. She couldn't shake the feeling that he sounded a lot like her grandfather would if Pawpaw had a British accent. "I trust you are well."

Leah opened her mouth to answer, but Lady Chesterfield beat her to it. "Of course she is, Your Grace. I was just telling my dear niece about your new phaeton. It sounds lovely."

If Leah didn't know better, she could have sworn Lady Chesterfield had just fluttered her lashes at the duke. Leah stared harder. Nope, no question. Definite lash fluttering.

The duke laughed softly. "Yes, Miss Ram. I fear I have been frightfully rude in boring your aunt with such talk."

"Rubbish, dear Duke." Lady Chesterfield tapped his arm flirtily with her fan. "I have been most entertained."

An extended silence fell. Leah glanced first at Lady Chesterfield, whose cheeks held high spots of color, then over to the duke, who was looking directly at the baroness.

Well, damn.

Leah cleared her throat gently. "If you'll excuse me, I think I'd like some lemonade before the music starts up again."

"Oh, Miss Ram, I would love to take you and your charming guardian for a ride through the park tomorrow if you are both amenable."

Leah tossed a wan glance at Lady Chesterfield, whose eagerly nodding head reminded her of those creepy tree spirits from *Princess Mononoke*. She'd had nightmares for months after watching that movie.

"I'd be glad to," she said quietly.

"Of course you may go, dearest. But I am afraid I have a prior engagement, so I will be unable to join you."

The duke's face fell almost imperceptibly. "I see. Well, Miss Ram, we are to be a pair. I look forward to it then. I shall come 'round and fetch you on the morrow."

Taking Lady Chesterfield's hand, he bowed low over it, brushing her gloved knuckles with a light kiss. He repeated the gesture with Leah, who winced a little at the intimate contact. It was like hugging someone else's grandpa.

"I bid you good evening." He smiled at them again as he straightened.

"Good evening." Leah returned the expression despite the acid churning in her throat. Lord, what she wouldn't do for a Tums right now.

Lord Granville left then, even though the evening had only just begun. Leah was confused, but not sorry to see him go. It didn't look like the duke wanted Lady Chesterfield to shove Leah at him any more than Leah did herself. In fact, it seemed that the duke would much rather spend time with Leah's chaperone than with Leah herself.

The rest of the musicale was sort of anticlimactic after that. The music wasn't bad, and with everyone distracted, Leah was pretty much left to her own devices. She darted glance after glance out the window, hoping for a glimpse of Avery, an answer to why he'd acted so strangely and what had happened to him, but he was nowhere to be seen. She even sneaked onto the balcony once more, sprinting to the nearly naked Greek statue she'd seen him behind before, but he wasn't there.

Sighing, she slumped against the cold marble.

What was with him? And for that matter, what was with her?

She looked up at the stars, brighter here than she'd ever seen them at home. It was strange that despite the advanced technology of her time, she hadn't ever seen the heavens like they were here.

The twinkling lights above didn't offer her any answers. Bastards.

"What do I do?" Her lonely whisper faded into the

darkness. A raindrop kissed her cheek, then another her neck. She turned back to the house, her steps leaden.

How could she disappoint Lady Chesterfield? How could she let her chaperone push her toward the duke when she might have feelings for Avery?

The marble stairs were slick with raindrops, so she gripped the handrail tightly. At the top, she turned her palm over. Her glove was damp, dingy now with the dirt of the rail. His hand had been wet too, but with blood.

She let her lids slide closed and focused on dismantling the knot that had lodged in her throat. It wouldn't budge no matter what she tried.

Nineteen

THE NEXT DAY DAWNED SUNNY AND WARMER, WHICH should have made Leah happy. It didn't. She paced in the drawing room, wearing a carriage dress of powder blue that matched her eye color almost perfectly. Even the gorgeous costume couldn't pierce her melancholy armor. She glared at her reflection every time she passed the mirror behind the settee.

"You're a coward, Ramsey. An ungrateful and idiotic bitch."

Her "pep talk" didn't do much for her self-esteem or her confusion, so she gave it up and flopped down sideways on a wingback chair in the corner, legs draped over the arm. Worrying the inside of her cheek, she stared at the ceiling and concentrated on breathing deeply. Maybe extra oxygen would clear the fuzz from her brain.

A noise at the door grabbed her attention. A dark-haired maid toting a bucket and a broom had entered the room and ground to a halt at the sight of Leah.

"Oh, I apologize." The maid blushed as she stammered, hands fumbling on the broom handle. "I did not know you were here."

Leah smiled encouragingly at the girl. Man, did she ever understand how the maid felt. "Don't worry about me. Do what you need to do."

"I couldn't, miss. 'Tis no trouble." She started backing out the door.

Leah's feet hit the floor. "It's cool, come on. I could use someone to talk to."

Though her face was wary, the maid set her bucket by the hearth and began sweeping the ashes. Déjà vu slammed into Leah. Such a short time ago, she'd been in this girl's position. How amazingly things had changed.

"I'm sorry, I don't remember your name."

"Eliza, miss," the maid said as she dumped a load of ash into the bucket.

"Can I ask you a question, Eliza?" Leah rubbed the brocade fabric of the chair arm as she spoke. The nubby texture was soothing somehow, and boy did she need something soothing. As soon as she got back home, she was going to book a two-hour massage.

"Of course, miss." Eliza turned from the hearth, her face a giant question mark. It was probably weird for her to be approached like this.

Oh well, let's get it done.

"If you were supposed to be with someone, but you weren't sure about them, what would you do?"

Eliza shook her head, mobcap flopping. "I do not understand, miss."

Leah stood and ticked off points with her fingers. "Okay. Say you're part of an arranged marriage. Your parents, your guardian, everyone you know expects you to love this guy. But you know he's not the right one for you. In fact, he's perfect for someone else, but they don't see it at all, and they want you to marry him too. What do you do?"

Eliza resumed her sweeping as she replied, "I shouldn't want to disappoint everyone. I should wed him."

Leah's brows lifted. "Even if you thought you might have feelings for someone else?"

Eliza lifted the bucket full of spent ash and faced Leah with a matter-of-fact expression. "If I were so lucky as to be promised to a man of standing, then I should wed him. There are not many so lucky in the world, miss."

Leah's damp palms slid down her skirt. "I see. Thanks for your answer."

"My pleasure, miss." Eliza nodded. "May I fetch something for you before I go?"

"No, I'm fine."

Eliza bobbed a quick curtsy and took her bucket from the room.

Leah's heart thudded against her rib cage and she resumed her pacing. Okay. She could do this. Open mind, keen observation, and level head. For the moment, she had to play the part and get to know the duke. Lady Chesterfield would expect it. But while she did it, she'd be thinking, planning. She'd find some way to fix this.

She ground to a halt and glared at the ceiling. Damn it, why did Avery's stupid face keep popping into her head at the most inconvenient times? Stupid, handsome, silent face.

"Oh, Miss Ramse…er, Miss Ram, there you are." Lady Chesterfield fluttered into the room, trailing her obnoxiously purple shawl behind her. "Lord Granville has arrived for your turn about the park. Make haste, my dear."

"I thought you had other plans today," Leah said wryly as Lady Chesterfield dragged her toward the foyer.

"Oh do be quiet, girl."

Feeling suspiciously like she was about to take a nosedive into the fang-covered pit of the sarlacc, Leah followed Lady Chesterfield into the foyer, where His Grace was waiting. He greeted her with a polite smile.

"Miss Ram, you are looking quite fine."

"Thank you, Your Grace," Leah said as she accepted her wrap from Graves. "You look very nice today too."

He offered her his arm, and she took it. With a last glance at Lady Chesterfield, Leah walked with the duke toward the high two-wheeled carriage with its pair of black horses.

She didn't say anything as he helped her into the carriage. She didn't know what to say, or what to do even. It had been easier last night, while surrounded with other people and with music, albeit bad music, to distract her. And with Lady Chesterfield, who seemed to thrive on conversation with the duke. But here? They were alone, other than the maid who rode silently on the back of the phaeton to assure Leah's respectability. Kind of a nerve-wracking turn of events. Leah swallowed hard and screwed a smile to her face. Hopefully it looked normal.

The duke smiled at her once he'd settled into the seat beside her. "Shall we be off?"

She nodded and pulled her wrap closer around her. "Yes."

His head tilted and he furrowed his brow. "Pardon me, but have we met before? I know we were introduced last evening, but your face is somehow familiar."

Leah laughed nervously. "Oh no, Your Grace. I only

got here last week, and before that I lived far away. There's no way we could have met." She patted her hair self-consciously. *Pull it together, Ramsey. Don't blow it, or Lady Chesterfield might get in trouble because of you.*

"I see." He seemed to take her explanation. The reins flicked over the horses' backs, and they were off toward the park.

He was quiet for a moment, and Leah used the time to compose herself. She had to keep it together and figure out a way out of this mess.

"Miss Ram," the duke said as they turned into the park, "may I be frank with you?"

"Please," she said, sitting up straighter. It'd be great to have someone tell her what the heck to do.

"I am not in the habit of squiring young ladies about." His voice was soft, higher pitched than she'd have liked, but it wasn't a girly voice. He was easy to listen to, actually.

"Then why are you taking me? Not that I'm not enjoying it, because I am," she hastily corrected herself.

He glanced over at her. He was attractive, she had to admit. Maybe she was just intimidated by his age, position, and obvious wealth. Not out of the realm of possibility. Kevin had been rich, and she hadn't exactly fit in with his family.

"That is the question, is it not?" He rounded a corner on the park's path, and the scattered other carriages along the way had disappeared. She swallowed the sudden knot in her throat. They were alone.

"Yes. I guess it is." She stared straight ahead.

He cleared his throat. "Perhaps it is best to admit the truth. I am entertaining the notion of marriage."

Well, shit. She dropped any pretense of looking forward. "What?"

"I am not proposing marriage to you, Miss Ram." He laughed, flicking the reins as another carriage rounded the bend. "I have my heir and am simply considering the matter."

She smiled politely as he looked over at her. "Ah. Okay."

He grew somber. "My first wife passed away many years ago. I had not realized how lonely I'd become."

"I'm sorry," Leah whispered. Reaching over, she laid a hand on his. Even through their gloves, she could tell how cold his hands were, and it sent a shiver through her. Poor man. Poor, lonely old man.

"It is of no consequence." He patted her hand, and she withdrew. "Shall we continue?"

She nodded, and the carriage rolled on.

Avery pulled the brim of his hat lower over his eyes. He was dressed in a coat much too heavy for the finer weather of the day, but he'd had no choice. He could not be discovered.

He'd followed the duke's phaeton to Lady Chesterfield's manse. His hands had curled into fists when he saw his employer's hands on Leah's waist, handing her up to the high seat atop the conveyance. Jealousy seethed beneath Avery's skin, but he tamped it down with effort. He could not afford the distraction. He must keep her safety in the forefront of his mind. Another note had come in the night.

Russell,

The Swansdown approaches. You will face Brookers,

and you will lose. If you do not, she will pay. I have gotten some quite interesting information as of late about a lady you seem to care for.

Make no mistake, we know who, and where, she is.

Prachett

He followed them at quite a distance, making sure to keep the phaeton in his sights. Fortunately, the horse he'd secretly borrowed from his grace's stables was quite well-mannered and even quick when needed. The nag was not of good stock, but he had spirit. And his nondescript color and markings were perfect to blend into the crowded lanes of the park.

He wished he could hear what they were saying. What caused Leah's brows to lower as she responded to the duke or what caused her to smile, throw back her golden head and laugh.

Was she falling in love with him? That was what she'd wanted all along, from the moment she'd landed in Avery's arms. But he could not resign himself to the idea.

Blessed hell. His hands tightened on the reins. What if she were to marry Granville? She'd be a duchess. And Avery would have to see her every day. He could look but never touch. When he pictured her lying in the duke's bed, hair strewn about her with a lovelorn smile on her face, Avery inadvertently jerked the reins.

"Steady boy, ssssh," he said in a low voice to the horse beneath him. He patted the gelding's neck. "I'm sorry there, chap."

He had to keep his wits about him. Prachett had many spies, many men who were more than willing to exchange information for the promise of coin. With difficulty, Avery pried his gaze from the pair in the phaeton and scanned the area. He did not have the luxury of remaining at her side to protect her at all hours, so he must be vigilant when he had the opportunity.

The phaeton turned about and headed toward him. Avery didn't hide his open sigh of exasperation. The duke had to be returning her to Lady Chesterfield, and that meant Avery himself would be expected at Granville House very soon.

He steered the horse onto a half-hidden side path and waited. He'd let the pair pass by and then continue on his way.

The sound of wheels on the gravel pathway warned him of their coming.

"So that's what you meant." Leah was laughing as she spoke. Avery fought for control. He must not run after her and pull her atop his horse, riding hell-bent for Gretna. She was not his and never would be.

"'Tis true, I admit." The duke's voice was amused as well. The bloody bastard.

As the carriage rolled past the pathway, Leah adjusted her hat and turned toward the duke. Avery's heart stuttered when he caught her gaze. Her blue eyes went wide, and her mouth formed an *O*, but he shook his head quickly and turned away.

"Is something the matter?"

"No, nothing at all, Your Grace. Sorry." She smiled at the duke and Avery's rage climbed even higher. He was nearly shaking with it now, an anger so fierce that it threatened to burn him from the inside out.

He must breathe. He must retain control.

Though he wanted nothing more than to follow them and take Leah away from his employer, he stayed there, atop his horse on the forgotten path. His eyelids slammed shut and he fought to ease his tension.

She is not yours, lad. She is not yours.

He had to have her.

For he was quite certain that Leah Ramsey was his one shot at salvation. Without her, he'd drown in his anger, guilt, and loneliness for the rest of his days.

Twenty

He hadn't meant to come here, but when he realized the route he'd taken, it was too late to change. Lady Chesterfield's home loomed just ahead, and the temptation of seeing Miss Ramsey was much too difficult to ignore.

Berating himself with every step, he continued toward the home. He'd simply glance through the windows and ascertain if she'd returned in good health. Then he'd be about his business, with her none the wiser.

He dismounted and tied his horse to a nearby lamppost. It snorted and tossed its head as if to tell Avery how foolish he appeared.

"I know, lad," Avery said in a low voice as he patted the horse's neck. "I'll return in but a moment."

The afternoon shadows were growing longer, and Avery moved carefully to avoid being seen. This time of day was not the most active for the servants of the household, but there was sure to be someone about.

Each window he peered into revealed nothing more than empty furniture and the odd maid or footman. He grew more concerned when he looked through the window on the west side of the house. It was apparently the drawing room, and Lady Chesterfield sat alone, having tea as she wrote at a small table beside the settee.

Why was Miss Ramsey not there? His tension grew. Surely she'd returned from her ride with the duke by now. Had one of Prachett's men accosted her?

He crept around the back of the house, careful to give the servants' entrance a wide berth. A small garden lay before him, its plantings beginning to burgeon with life. He'd just risen to look through another window when a sound caught his ear.

"Pawpaw, what am I supposed to do?"

He whirled without a sound, kneeling behind a holly bush. He was careful of the leaves this time. Leaning to the side, he found the source of the voice.

Leah was there, her back to him as she sat on an old stump. Her attention was focused on something in her lap.

Relief flooded him. She was here, and she was alone. He'd remain a moment longer until he could verify her well-being, then he'd take his leave without her knowledge. He hoped.

"Maybe Mrs. Knightsbridge was wrong about all this." She sighed, tilting her head skyward. A yellow curl kissed her cheek as it swayed with her movement. His breath caught as she was silhouetted in the sun's dying glow. Had there ever been a woman so lovely, so perfect?

Without conscious thought, he was suddenly moving toward her, abandoning his hiding place. The inner voice that had kept him from seeking out her touch was silenced as if it had never existed. He only knew that he had to kiss her, and kiss her now, before she was lost to him forever.

The sound of his footsteps on the path grabbed her attention, and she looked up, surprise on her face. Her beautiful blue eyes were confused—and then excited.

"Avery," she said, rising and turning to him. A small portrait was gripped in her hand, and he caught a glimpse of an old man with Leah's eyes standing by a strange carriage. She must have been speaking to the portrait.

"Leah," he breathed, and without another thought he pulled her into his arms. Stiffening with surprise, she froze at first, but then melted into him, her softness against his hardness fitting perfectly. Her soft lips parted on a breath, and he drew her in, deep into his lungs. His tongue traced the soft edge of her lower lip, and he groaned deep in his chest at the sweet taste of her.

His body stirred, his hands roaming the planes of her back, then lower to cup her buttocks. Blood surged to his groin as she returned his kisses, sucking on his tongue and tangling her fingers in his hair. He pressed his hips into hers.

She writhed, as if she couldn't get close enough. His hand caressed up the curve of her waist to settle just beneath one of her breasts, its hardened nipple practically begging to be touched.

Leah erased any moment of doubt, pressing his hand against her breast. He released her mouth, but only to let his kisses trail down the column of her throat. She tilted her head back in abandon.

"Avery," she whispered, hitching a leg over his hip. God, her core pressed against his erection now, so hot it almost burned. "I want you."

The words were exactly what he wanted—no, needed—to hear.

He nipped at the tender flesh of her neck, wanting to mark her, claim her like an animal would. Her mewl of passion only spurred him on. Dipping his head, he trailed kisses down the delicate curve of her shoulder, to the neckline of her lovely blue gown.

The creamy swells of her breasts begged for attention, and he was loath to deny them.

Cupping one breast, he worshipped the other with his tongue and teeth, licking and nipping kisses on the tender skin. She pulled at his hair, ran her hands down to his hips, brushed the stiffness in his breeches.

God, it was not enough. He needed to see her, all of her. He needed to sink himself deep into her, feel her as she welcomed him into her bed and her body.

Into her life.

Forever.

Oh God, what am I thinking?

His eyes flew open. He staggered backward, dropping all contact with Leah. She swayed, nearly falling as he fought to regain his senses. He'd been dreaming. He'd been mad to do that to her. He could not be what she needed.

"Leah, Miss Ramsey, I..." He had no words. His manhood throbbed with frustrated lust, but he ignored it. "My apologies, Miss Ramsey."

"Don't stop. Please..." Her hand trembled as she pressed it to her swollen lips. Her eyes were wide, dazed, and wanting.

"I should never have forced myself upon you so." Avery bowed deeply, cursing himself. "You have my sincerest apologies. It shall not happen again."

"Wait just a goddamn minute." She glared at him.

"You didn't force anything on me. Couldn't you tell how much I wanted that?"

He glowered at her. "There is no need to prevaricate, Miss Ramsey. The fault is mine."

She stomped toward him, mayhem plain in her gaze. "You're going to answer some questions for me in a minute, but first you need to get something through your thick caveman skull. I wanted that. I want you. You didn't trick me into kissing you, so get over yourself."

His frustration and confusion battled for the upper hand. "Over…myself?"

She sighed. "Forget it. Did you get into a fight? Because no offense, but you look like hell." Her brow furrowed as her gaze raked over his still-swollen cheek.

He set his jaw. "It is no concern of yours."

She barked a bitter laugh. "The hell it isn't!" She lost some of her vitriol as she pressed a warm palm to his cheek. "Listen, Avery. I'm not sure what's between us right now, but I do know that I care about you. I can't help if you keep shutting me out."

He wanted so badly to turn his face into her palm and press a kiss there. To lay his head in her lap and tell her he'd put her in danger. To apologize for jeopardizing her chance at happiness with the duke.

"Miss?" A young female voice floated into the garden. "Are you here, miss?"

"Shit, that's Muriel." Leah tossed an irritated glance over her shoulder. "Can you wait here while I get rid of her?"

"I must go," he said, disguising his relief at the interruption. He had to get away from Leah before he lost his head again. She wreaked havoc on his already tenuous control.

She looked at him, hurt in her gaze. His heart ached, but he stayed motionless.

"Okay. See you later, I guess."

She walked away, leaving him alone by the stump of the old oak.

He'd bungled that properly.

❧

Leah tried like hell to keep from crying as she walked away from Avery. The tears weren't so much from sadness as they were from being frustrated, pissed, and straight up horny. The man had just left her with the feminine equivalent of blue balls. *Blue ovaries?* She sniffed and swallowed her emotions, pinning a pleasant expression on her face for Muriel.

"Sorry, I needed some fresh air," Leah said to the maid. "What's up?"

"Your new gowns have arrived from the modiste. Lady Chesterfield bade me fetch you."

"More new gowns?" Leah pressed a hand to her forehead. A monster headache was starting to zoom around her skull like a *Mario Kart* party was going on in there. "But she already bought me a closetful."

Muriel laughed as she led Leah into the house. "Miss, Lady Chesterfield would not dare to arrive at a ball in a previously worn gown, and she would not see her protégé do so either."

Leah trailed after Muriel, trying to find some happy. Damn it, it wasn't there. She was too riddled with anxiety to do anything but keep moving forward like a shuffling zombie. She'd have to do something drastic to clear these cobwebs, and soon. There were two men in her life, two very different men, and even though she was pretty confident she knew what, and who, she wanted, she had to do something to make sure.

An entirely wicked idea popped into her head, and she grinned. This was going to be delicious.

"Are you well, miss?" Muriel said, tilting her head.

"I'm fucking spectacular," Leah said, then clapped her hand over her mouth with a laugh. "Sorry, Muriel! I'm good. I promise."

The maid gave her an odd look but continued on her way. Leah had to fight to keep from skipping up the stairs. Tonight would answer her questions and ease her pent-up tensions. Oh, this was going to be incredible.

The night was so cold her breath fogged out in front of her. She wrapped her cloak around her tighter and kept on trucking. *At least this is the ritzy part of town*, she thought. *If I had to walk through St. Giles in the dark alone, I wouldn't make it fifteen feet.*

Not that she actually owned anything worth stealing.

The streets were completely empty of people. A shiver skittered down her spine, and she walked faster. Maybe she should have begged Muriel to come with her. As soon as the thought popped into her head, she shoved it off with a laugh. Yeah, she should totally have asked the innocent teenaged maid to hold her hand as she hauled ass to seduce her man.

The thought warmed her as she spied Granville House ahead. Seducing her man. Avery. He'd bolted; he'd nearly driven her crazy by revving her up and leaving her wanting. But they'd finish what they'd started tonight. She refused to take no for an answer.

The servants' entrance was locked tight. Damn it. She resisted the urge to thump her fist against the heavy door in frustration. It wouldn't do any good.

She shoved herself upright and nodded. Time for Plan B.

The conservatory on the ground floor was her target. She hoped the room that Henrietta had locked her in—gosh, weeks ago now—would still have its window unlatched.

She found it without trouble, careful to avoid the stables on her way. She didn't want to run into that asshole of a stable master.

She breathed a relieved sigh when she reached the window. Finally. Bracing the heels of her hand on the window, she shoved upward with a grunt.

The window didn't budge.

She bumped it, trying to encourage the seal to break. The window didn't so much as squeak.

"Damnit," she hissed. "What the hell do I have to do to get in this place?"

The front door was out. Smythe probably slept on the damn welcome mat. She could probably go around the bottom floor and try all the windows, but what if someone saw her? They'd throw her into prison before she could explain.

She looked up at the stars. Maybe one of them would have mercy and grant her a wish.

The moon's soft glow reflected off a shiny leaf of ivy.

Ivy.

The trellis!

She rubbed her palms together briskly. It couldn't be much more difficult than climbing a tree, right? She'd been awesome at that when she was about ten.

Of course, that had been a long time ago.

She shook her head as she tucked the ends of her skirt up. No way. She could do this. She could do anything she put her mind to.

What about that time you got kicked out of Zumba?

"Shut up," she muttered to herself as she gripped the trellis. "That instructor was a sadistic bastard."

The wooden trellis creaked and groaned under her weight. The ivy was thick, and it was tough to figure out where her slippers would fit. But she kept her gaze locked on the windows of the top floor. She could get to him—she could. She had to.

She reached sideways, aiming for a thin spot in the foliage. Her fingers slipped, and she tilted dangerously. Pulling at the tendrils of vine, she pulled herself back toward the house. Her heart thumped and her breath came in little gasps.

"Damn, that was close."

She looked toward the ground and gulped. She'd never been afraid of heights, and she wasn't really afraid now. It was more the falling she had issue with.

No. She wasn't going to fall. She was going to haul her ass up this trellis, make love to Avery, and if she ever got home, she'd invest in a rock climbing class.

Hey, you never know when shit's going to come in handy.

Drawing even with the top of the trellis, she breathed a relieved sigh. Okay. Here she was. Now, which window was Avery's? The trellis stretched wide, covering the bottoms of three top-floor windows. She could look down, see where the area was…A quick glimpse downward was enough to make her nausea rise. Nope, not looking down there anymore. Too damn scary.

She'd have to do it the hard way.

Moving to the closest window, she peeped above the bottom edge.

Several moments passed before her eyes grew accustomed to the dimness inside. She blinked several times before the vision cleared. Henry, one of the footmen, lay sprawled atop the covers, completely nude. Ugh. She hadn't needed to see that. Fortunately, his roommate Oliver was fully clothed in the small bed across the room. Typical. The men got beds to themselves.

Hand over hand, foot over foot, she Spider-Manned it to the next window. When she didn't think about the terrifying ground below, this was actually kind of fun.

With a whispered plea for luck, she lifted her head over the bottom edge of the window.

It didn't take as long for her eyes to adjust this time. When she saw him, her breath caught.

Avery lay on his back, arm cast over his eyes to block out the beam of moonlight that highlighted his chest and face. He was gorgeous, dressed in nothing but his breeches. She couldn't help but wish he'd been the one who slept in the buff. She might have been satisfied just hanging out here like George of the Jungle on a vine with a view like that.

Who was she kidding? She wanted to watch out for his tree.

A quick glance across his room confirmed her suspicions. Nobody else was in the room. She didn't know why the other servants ostracized him, but it happened to be pretty convenient at the moment. Gripping the windowsill, she moved higher, stretching for the window latch. Thank God, it opened with the barest push. Third-floor windows were so much nicer than first floor!

She hoisted herself up onto the windowsill, tumbling into his room with a thump. Wincing, she glanced at him. Whew. He'd just turned over with the noise. Good to be a sound sleeper.

Her palms stung with the effort she'd used to grip the trellis, but she rubbed them against her skirt and ignored the tingling. What was a little discomfort? He'd obviously been through much worse in the past week or so.

Shedding her cloak, she moved toward him and knelt at his bedside. Her fingers trailed just above his chest, tracing the edges of greenish-yellow bruises. He'd been beaten severely, or had gotten in a bad fight.

Her throat closed, and her eyes stung at the thought of Avery in pain. God, what a hardheaded bastard. He got in trouble way more than he should. The memory of the time she'd bandaged him slammed into her. One man shouldn't have to bear this much crap. But he did, and he'd never complained, not once.

It wasn't pity or even compassion that moved her to lean over him and take his lips in a fervent kiss.

It was something much, much deeper.

Twenty-One

His lips were so warm. She lost herself in them, delighting in the stubbly texture of his five o'clock shadow against her chin. He shifted beneath her, and she curled her fingers into the muscles on his broad chest. The man was solid as a brick wall, and the feel of those firm muscles under her made her want to purr.

His mouth opened, and she capitalized on the opportunity. Her tongue slipped between his lips, tasting his warm mouth. She knelt on the narrow bed's edge, wanting to lie atop him, stretch out, and feel every part of him touching her.

Way too soon, he pushed her away.

"Leah," he rasped, eyes wide and confused with sleep. "What are you doing here?" He sat up. She made use of the extra space on the narrow bed, plopping down beside him.

"I came to finish what you started," she said, hoping she sounded a lot more confident than she felt. She didn't have much experience convincing men to sleep with her. Her list of conquests wasn't nonexistent, but it was kind of on the short side. She leaned forward, hoping he'd take the hint.

"What do you mean?"

Well, shit. She bit her lip. Better to show than tell, right?

Crawling toward him, she braced her palms on either side of his lean, muscled abdomen. "This," she whispered before kissing him again.

As kisses go, it wasn't the best she'd ever had. Avery pulled away after their lips had touched for only a brief second.

"What's wrong?" she said, raking her hair from her face in frustration.

"You must not...I should not..."

"Avery, please. I want you. Don't say no."

His face was tortured, beautiful even though the expression was heartbreaking and his injuries were plain. She had every intention of getting him to spill his guts about why he looked like the poster child for a new Rocky movie. But right now, there was something they both needed much more than conversation.

"Please."

His brain lost every trace of sleep. He blinked, trying to clear the vision of Leah lying over him, hair falling like a curtain around them both. She could not be here. In his bed. Asking to lie with him.

But she was.

As gently as he could, he pushed her away.

"You do not know what you are asking," he said, standing and lighting the candle at his bedside. She only looked lovelier in the dim light. "How can I ruin you?"

His muscles tensed, and he fought to keep their trembling secret. Excitement and willingness thrummed in his body, but he must deny it. He cared for her too much.

"It's not ruining, Avery." She unfolded herself and came to him. "I'm not a virgin, and I want you as much as you want me. And there are things that we need to settle between us, feelings that I need to explore." She laid her head on his chest, and he did not resist the urge to fold his arms around her.

He rubbed her back and closed his eyes. All the reasons he should abstain pelted him. She was not of his time. She was not his wife. Prachett would use her against him, harm her.

But when he looked down into her open, honest, and beautiful face, he could not deny either of them.

"Leah," he whispered, pressing his forehead against hers. Their kiss was filled with her enthusiasm and his barely contained joy. She'd accepted him. She could not know what that meant to him.

Bending low, he scooped her against his chest, bearing her back to the bed. Her hands curled around his neck and she nuzzled his chest.

"You have the best body," she said as he lay her gently on his mattress. Her eyes glowed with desire as she traced his chest with a finger.

He smiled. "I would like to return the compliment, but I cannot see as much of you at the moment."

Her laugh warmed his heart as well as other parts of his body. She sat up with a wink. "Let's fix that then, shall we?"

His mouth went dry as she turned and presented her back to him. "Can you help me out of this?"

He was no fool. He knew what he wanted from her and what she'd expect from him. But faced with the reality of a warm, laughing Leah in his bed, he found himself frozen with an emotion he could not name. Not fear, or anxiety either. More the sense that the world around him was changing at a lightning pace, and there was not a thing he could do to stop it.

If he wanted to stop it.

"Are you okay?" She looked over her shoulder at him. "Avery?"

He shook off the thoughts and moved close to her. "All is well." His fingers moved sure and strong, deftly loosing the buttons that flowed down the back of her dress. He concentrated on the task, doing his damnedest to ignore the throbbing ache in his groin that needed to be sated.

He pushed the gown from her shoulders, and it pooled around her torso. His moan of frustration at the numerous layers of underthings that lay beneath the gown wrenched a giggle from her.

"I know. It's a crazy amount of underwear. We'll get through it together, though, right?"

He pressed a kiss on her shoulder. "I cannot wait."

He pulled her to her feet, and together they removed layer after layer of frilly, womanly undergarments. He'd not thought he could grow so hard at such a simple act as undressing her, but she was irresistible. She teased and kissed by turns, stoking his fires by touching him whenever and however she could. By the time she stood barefoot, wearing only her shift, he was ready to toss her onto her back and plunge into her. Control. He must retain control.

"Well," she said, running her fingers beneath the waist of his breeches. "I think we're even here. What do you say we get rid of the last of these clothes on the count of three?"

"I don't think I can wait that long," he said, gripping her shift and lifting it over her head. His breath caught deep in his throat.

"Good Lord."

She stood naked in front of him, her arms at her sides, not bothering to hide her exquisite nudity. He did not know whether to stumble backward to look his fill or to press her full against him.

She was so lovely. Her full, high breasts pouted and teased him with their erect nipples. Her waist sloped delicately, flaring out to beautifully shaped hips. He could happily stare at her all evening, but she clearly had other notions.

"It's your turn," she said, stepping close and unbuttoning his breeches. "I want to see you too."

He didn't move as she bent to lower his breeches. He couldn't. He was transfixed by the sight of her delectable bottom as she bent over in front of him. It was too much pleasure for a man, it truly was.

"Oh, Avery," she whispered, kneeling in front of him. "You're beautiful."

Before he could ask to what she was referring, her soft hands had wrapped around his manhood. She pressed a kiss to the weeping tip, and he fisted his hands at his sides. Control.

"Can I suck you?"

The image of her sweet mouth wrapped around his rod nearly drove him beyond the brink. He shook his head, his hair tickling his shoulders.

"I would not last if you did."

"Later, then," she whispered, and pressed another kiss to the swollen head. He titled his head back, throat working.

Her hands ran up his body, from his groin to his abdomen to his chest, winding at last around his back. Her nipples dragged across his chest, her belly pressed against his erection.

"Touch me," she groaned against his throat. He was more than happy to comply.

Starting at her hips, he indulged his fingers in the direction they wanted to travel, upward toward her breasts. His hands closed over the sweet, soft mounds, lightly flicking over their erect tips. She pressed against him, smiling as he touched her.

"Like that," she whispered, rubbing her hips against his.

Something in his lust-filled brain snapped, and he stopped thinking. He acted.

"Put your arms around my neck," he directed. Once she obeyed, he cupped her buttocks and lifted. Obligingly, she wrapped her thighs around his waist. He nearly wept when her slick mound made contact with his erection.

He moved backward and sat on the bed, leaving her straddling his lap. In this position, it was easy to lean forward and capture one of her beautiful nipples in his mouth.

She tangled her fingers in his hair as he sucked, his tongue flicking against the bud, his teeth grazing it. Her hips writhed against him, bathing his hardness in her sweet slickness. It would be so easy to slip inside her this way, to claim her as his. But he wanted to make this last.

He moved to her other breast as her hands roamed

his body. He forgot all his bruises, forgot all the reasons why they should not be doing this. None of that mattered when her hands wrapped around him again, moving up and down in a rhythmic motion that drove him mad.

"Leah," he whispered after releasing her nipple from his mouth with a soft pop, "I cannot last much longer if you persist in that."

"I can't last much longer either." She seemed winded, her eyes dark and lips swollen. "Feel me, Avery. See what you do to me."

She slipped from his lap and stretched full-length on the bed.

Could there be anything so beautiful on earth?

"Please touch me, Avery." She'd fisted her hands into his sheets, and her breath was coming much quicker. "The way you're looking at me is driving me crazy."

"How am I looking at you?" He could not resist asking the question, though he could empathize with her desperation.

"Like you want to devour me." Her breath came in gasps as her eyes darkened.

He did. He wanted to taste her. Kneeling between her legs, he parted her folds and lowered his head to her. The scent was intoxicating, sweet and musky and womanly. He could breathe her in forever, but if he did that, he'd never know her taste. And that was a pleasure he'd not forgo.

He licked the lower part of her folds and moved his way up as her hips writhed against him. When his lips closed around that swollen nub at the apex of her mound, she gave a mewling cry.

"There! Oh my God, right there, Avery." The sheets twisted in her grip.

"As you wish," he breathed against her hot, wet flesh, and then complied.

Twenty-Two

AVERY SEEMED DETERMINED TO COAX HER TO HEAVEN with his mouth alone. But she wanted much more than his mouth.

She got a portion of her wish when his finger slid inside her. Her muscles spasmed around it involuntarily, and she let out a long, low moan.

"Are you trying to drive me crazy?" she panted.

He gave her a wicked smile as he inserted another finger. "Perhaps."

"Please, Avery," she whispered as she pinched her own nipples, wishing he was close enough to kiss. "Don't make me wait."

She lifted her arms to him and he stretched full-length atop her. Their mouths and hands were suddenly everywhere. They rolled and tangled, tasting, touching, licking, and sucking. Leah wrapped her legs around his hips and bit his shoulder.

"Now," she said, tangling her hands in his long hair. "I need you inside me."

He lifted himself above her, a fine sheen of sweat coating them both in the candlelight. "Are you sure?"

She gripped him and guided him to her entrance. "Yes, Avery."

They moaned together as he slid slowly, inexorably home. Leah's eyes flew open as he began a rhythm that tapped the deepest places within her.

She dug her nails into his hips as he drove into her. His deep breaths, mingled with almost animalistic growls, filled her with a deep sense of pride, want, and something else she couldn't name.

He looked down at her for a moment, then their mouths connected. Leah took his tongue into her mouth, sucking it in time with his thrusts. His hands cupped her ass, bringing her higher and tighter, forcing his thrusts deeper into her.

"Avery," she gasped against his mouth.

He buried his head beside hers and continued the rhythm that would either make her come or kill her with desire, and at this point, Leah didn't really care which. He'd made her feel like a goddess, and now his thick heat lay hard in her channel, so deep she thought he touched her womb.

He reached between them and pressed against her clit.

She bit back her scream as her world exploded. Her inner walls gripped him as she kissed him, hard, trying like hell to make the moment last forever.

This was her man.

This was the one she'd been sent to find.

❧

His body felt light, almost as if he could float away with no cares at all.

He was still sheathed within her heat. She held him

so tightly, arms and legs wrapped around him as if she'd never let him go.

He held her tightly, bracing himself on his forearms so as not to crush her. He never wanted to let her go either.

"As much as I hate to make you move, I think maybe you'd better." Her voice was thick, slurred against his chest. She pressed a kiss there before he lifted free.

"My apologies," he said, running a hand down her leg. She was softer than linen, warmer than summertime. And she'd shared herself with him.

Before he could voice any of this, she reached out and traced a particularly deep bruise on his ribs.

"I don't want to kill the mood, but I need to know." She looked into his eyes, concern threading her words. "How did you get all these bruises?"

He looked down at his hands, knuckles scarred and callused. She'd shared her all with him. Could he deny her similar intimate knowledge of his own life? He slammed his eyes shut. Even now, after what they'd shared, he could spare her the pain of association with him. If she loved the duke, she'd be safe.

"Before I tell you, I must know." He gripped her hands fervently. "What are your feelings for the duke?"

Her jaw went slack, her eyes wide.

"I cannot believe those words just came out of your mouth!"

She swung her legs over the side of the bed and stood, a flag of golden hair trailing behind her as she went.

"Well, I have a right to know," he said, rising from the bed as he tried to tamp his anger. "Do you still intend to let him court you?"

She stilled, holding her petticoat in front of her like a

shield. "You don't really know me at all, Avery Russell." She resumed her dressing, furious.

He had to stop her. He had to tell her. But would she spurn him?

In the end, it would not matter. He could no more have her than he could have the throne of England.

His words hurtled free like a bird escaping a cage. "I fight."

Her movement ceased again. "What?"

"Pugilistic tournaments. Boxing, if you'd rather." His palms were suddenly drenched with sweat. It was only when he tried to dry them on his breeches that he realized he was wearing none.

"But why?" She crossed to him, pressing her palm against his chest. "Don't valets make enough money? Is it for kicks, like a hobby?"

He looked down into her wide blue eyes. Despite her bravado and knowledge of a world so foreign to him, she was really quite innocent of the harsh realities of his life.

"The medicine for my aunt," he began, but a sharp rap on the door interrupted him.

Leah's face lit with alarm.

"Behind the bureau," he mouthed at her, motioning as he grabbed his breeches. "Quickly."

She flew on silent feet, disappearing as a voice called out with another knock. "Russell?"

He lowered his brows as he opened the door. "Henrietta? Whatever are you doing here?"

She looked past him into the room, greedy eyes searching for something. "I was going to the kitchens for a light. Our fire had gone out." She turned to him, a knowing smile on her face. "But I heard voices coming from somewheres over here. You wouldn't know about that, would you, Russell?"

"You must be mistaken," he said. "You know female maids are not allowed in this part of the house. Now please remove yourself from my chambers."

Henrietta tried to push past him and enter his room, but he blocked her way with his body.

She delivered the killing blow with innocent aplomb. "I merely wished to greet my dear old friend Ramsey."

His stomach sank, but he fought to keep his face neutral. "You are incorrect. Do not spread your lies further."

She opened her mouth to argue, but he shut the door in her face.

He fought the urge to slump against it. He must get Miss Ramsey away before Henrietta's suspicions became convictions. Thomas Prachett was sure to have a spy hidden amongst the Granville House servants. With his ear pressed against the door, he sighed in relief as Henrietta's footsteps disappeared down the hallway.

He rounded the corner of the bureau. "Leah?"

She had curled up in a tiny ball on the floor. Her hands covered her eyes, and she shook like she'd been beaten.

Heart lit with alarm, he bent low and scooped her into his arms. "What is the matter?"

She pointed with a trembling finger. "Spider."

Guilt pummeled him straight in the chest. He bore her away as quickly as he could, depositing her on the bed.

"I am so sorry," he whispered against her hair.

"Can you get rid of the spider first?" Her voice was thin.

Reluctantly, he rose from the bed and returned to the corner she'd been forced to hide in, swallowing her terror as he lied to Henrietta. Not only had he besmirched her name and reputation, he'd forced her to cower like a criminal as her fears overtook her. He was a bastard.

The spider was nowhere to be seen. After a thorough examination, and only a bit more regret at the deception he'd enact on her, he stomped softly on the floorboards.

"Did you get it?"

He nodded as he returned to the bedside. Though he desperately wanted to hold her again, soothe her fears and ease her worries, he knew he could not. He stood over her, looking down as her shivers eased.

This was no life for her. He was a servant, with no home or funds to support her. Every groat he wrenched from his hardscrabble life went directly to his aunt's upkeep. How could he doom her to a life of wanting? Of domestic servitude, when clearly she was used to a life much more like that she'd enjoyed at Lady Chesterfield's? And Prachett could not be held at bay forever. Though she hadn't seemed disgusted at his former occupation, she would be at the dishonesty inherent in his dealings with Prachett. And once she learned that, she would then revile him as everyone else did.

He could not have her. Though the words lanced his heart with their brutality, he knew there was no alternative.

"You must leave. If you are discovered here…"

She sat upright with a cross expression. "Avery, we have to talk about that. Listen, I…"

He pressed a finger to his lips. Footsteps grew louder as they approached.

"Henrietta is returning," he mouthed. "Be silent."

The hurt in her eyes almost did him in, but he hardened his heart and turned away. After three heavy breaths, he turned back.

She was gone, his window open.

He bolted for the casement and leaned out. She was halfway down the trellis already.

"Leah." His whisper was rife with the anger he wished he could roar at the thoughtless chit. "What are you doing?"

"I'm leaving. Isn't it obvious?" She let out a small cry as her foot missed its hold, and he fought the urge to leap out after her. The trellis could not hold their combined weight, he was certain.

"Do not be so rash," he said, gripping the hair atop his head in frustrated fear. "I never meant for you to—"

"I know that, you doofus." She jumped the last few feet to the earth, stumbling as she righted herself. The roar in his ears quieted somewhat as she glared up at him.

"I don't want to cause you any problems, but we have to talk. Soon."

She turned and walked toward the street, her dark cloak quickly hiding her from his worried, watchful gaze.

"The little idiot," he snarled as he threw his shirt and boots on, throwing open his door and bolting down the stairs after her. "To think she walked alone in the streets and climbed the damned trellis three stories up. I've a mind to throttle her."

But as he threw open the kitchen door and sprinted after her, he knew that while there were many, many things he'd like to do to her, throttling her was not one of them.

Thoughtless, beautiful fool.

Twenty-Three

LEAH KEPT LOOKING OVER HER SHOULDER ALL THE WAY back to Lady Chesterfield's house. She had the odd feeling that someone was following her. But even though she kept watch, she could never see anyone.

It was probably Avery, wishing he could kick her ass for sneaking into his bedroom and nearly getting him caught with his pants down.

It was pure pleasure to kick off her boots and flop into bed with a sigh. She stared at the ceiling, wondering what tonight had meant for Avery. Had it clarified the feelings in his heart the way it had for hers?

She rolled over onto her belly, bunching the pillow beneath her chin. When she was younger, she'd liked nothing better than getting lost in a book, a movie, a video game. When her life was more interesting, like when things with Kevin were heating up, she left her escapist life behind and enjoyed living in reality. But when things had fallen apart, she'd run to those comfortable old friends immediately, drowning herself in the distraction.

Avery was confusing but exciting. Would he get tired of her too? Would he want to come back to the twenty-first century with her? If not, she'd be back to burying herself in her apartment with nothing but Mario and Mr. Darcy for company.

Her dreams swirled with the worries she couldn't leave behind even in unconsciousness.

❧

Avery awoke with a sense of foreboding.

With a steadying breath, he rose to his feet and crossed the room. A small square of paper lay innocently by the crack at the bottom of the door. The plain, rough paper crinkled under his hands as he unfolded it. In the moon's predawn glow, he read it.

Russell,

Your lady friend, or should I say Miss Ram, visited you quite late last night. Terrible things can happen to a young lady on the streets of London after dark.
The Swansdown is set. You know what to do.

Prachett

Avery gripped the note so tightly that the paper ripped.

There was no question of obeying Prachett now. No matter what it cost him. He'd do anything to keep Leah safe.

Even lose his own soul.

❧

The carriage bounced along, making Lady Chesterfield's ostrich feathers wave excitedly. Leah sat across from her, glumness hanging over her like Eeyore's little black raincloud.

It had been almost two weeks since she'd seen Avery. Two freaking weeks. During that time, the duke had been their almost constant companion, showing up at every function she and Lady Chesterfield attended. He'd sat between her and Lady Chesterfield at the theatre, the two of them making *The Taming of the Shrew* much more about the societal tête–à–tête than it was about the performance. Leah despised people that talked during movies. Plays? Oh, her blood had bubbled like acid that night.

Too bad they hadn't gotten her subtle hints. She couldn't have been outright rude, or Lady Chesterfield would have either passed out or killed her, neither of which appealed to Leah.

Garden parties, balls, soirees—he was there for them all. It was probably a good thing, but Leah had a hard time viewing it that way. To hear Lady Chesterfield talk, the rest of the ton had had a much harder time swallowing the Leah-is-the-cousin-of-the-late-baronet story than His Grace had. The Duke of Granville's attention had gone a long way in convincing the rest of society to accept Leah the way they had. Lady Chesterfield couldn't be happier. She smiled, she laughed, she flirted with the duke. Leah was beginning to wonder why her patroness wouldn't admit she was halfway in love with the duke herself. It was obvious to everyone except Lady Chesterfield.

The carriage rolled to a stop in front of another large home. Leah bunched her soft-blue ball gown up in her hands to descend from the carriage. She didn't remember who was throwing this shindig, or even what the hell day it was. It was just another night that she'd be expected to dance with His Grace, converse with His Grace, simper at His Grace. She considered shoving a finger down her throat so she could puke in the bushes and go home. Play cards with Muriel or scrub a chamber pot or two. It'd be less of a pain in the ass than being here, she was pretty sure.

"My dear Leah, come now." Lady Chesterfield gestured with the fan.

Leah trudged toward the door, her heavy stomps sounding more like she was wearing combat boots than fine kid slippers.

"Stand straight, my dear. Good heavens, are your stays not laced snugly?"

Reluctantly Leah stiffened her spine. "No, it's fine. I promise. Sorry." If they tightened this corset any more, she'd need to be re-inflated when she took it off. She sighed as deeply as she was able to when she handed her wrap to a waiting footman. There were many long hours between now and that blessed corset removal.

"Amelia, darling," an approaching woman cooed to Lady Chesterfield. "I have not yet had the pleasure of meeting your charming protégé."

Introductions, dancing, more introductions, more dancing, chatting, warm and disgusting lemonade, it was a carbon copy of almost every night she'd had since moving into Lady Chesterfield's home. It was hard not to think of all the books she'd read, all the movies she'd seen. This wasn't elegant; this wasn't magical. It was a damned bore. Where was the romance of the whole thing? It seemed to have gotten trampled beneath expensive kid slippers and the feet of aristocrats.

Leah's smile started slipping as she stood in a group of young people who were cheerfully gossiping about some countess she didn't know. A longing glance at the clock revealed that it was approaching midnight. People were being nice enough to her, but she didn't want to be there.

She wanted to be in an attic room, snuggled on a thin mattress with Avery's strong arms around her.

"Miss Ram," the high male voice intruded on her fantasy, and she jumped.

"I'm sorry," she said, turning to Granville. "I was daydreaming."

"Dare I hope that I took part in your dream?" His teasing smile wasn't as hopeful as his words.

"Oh, you," she said, smiling tightly and thwapping him on the arm with her fan. She should have smacked him harder. "I'm pretty sure we both know better than that."

"Would you take a turn with me about the room?" He held out his elbow to her. She gave a desperate glance to her conversation-mates, but there was clearly no help there. The two young gentlemen appeared completely in awe of the duke, and the ladies were all shooting daggers at Leah.

Just her luck.

"Yes," she said, trying to make it enthusiastic. She slipped her hand in the crook of his elbow and the two of them moved toward the edge of the crowded ballroom.

"Quite a crush, is it not?"

"It is," she agreed, opening her fan. The slight stirring of air across her throat helped, but it wasn't enough. "It's a very nice ball."

"I had hoped to dance with you earlier, but I was detained."

"Oh?" She scanned the crowd for Lady Chesterfield. A chaperone to run interference would make the conversation much easier.

"Yes," he said, patting her fingers gently. "As a member of the Fancy, I attend many of the tournaments. There have been some exciting events of late, and our next bout promises to surpass them. Lord Charleston requested my assistance with a matter related to it, or I should have been here in time to claim my waltz." He nodded to an acquaintance as they passed.

"Fancy?" she repeated, tilting her head toward him. The name was completely unfamiliar, and she had to admit talking about anything other than waltzing was a great idea right then.

"The Fancy. Ah, I forget that you have lived abroad for so long." He smiled down at her like she was an ignorant child, which she guessed she was, to him. "Boxing tournaments, Miss Ram. But they are not a tale for such a proper young lady as yourself."

"Oh, Miss Ram." A young man with a rose-colored waistcoat came up to her with a smile. "I do beg your pardon, but I believe it is time for our dance."

"Of course, Mr. Lowell." She turned to the duke. "Will you excuse me, Lord Granville?"

"Quite reluctantly," he said, bowing over her hand. "Perhaps afterward, I may again claim your attention? There is a matter that I wish to discuss with you."

Crap, crap, and triple crap. She took a deep breath and put on her most polite act. "Yes, to be sure."

As Mr. Lowell led her onto the dance floor, she

worried the inside of her cheek. Her brain whirred like a wind-up robot toy. The duke and boxing matches. Avery's bruises and muscles that were much too nice for a valet to have...Could Granville have been forcing him to fight? That didn't seem likely. Granville was too nice.

She curtsied to Mr. Lowell as he bowed, and they began the quadrille. Fortunately, she'd been practicing Regency dances since she'd first planned to marry Mr. Darcy, so she only had to pay a minimum of attention to the steps.

Avery fought, and the duke was a member of the Fancy. What was she missing? Weren't fights like that illegal? But there was something else, and she wished she knew what it was.

"You look quite fine tonight, Miss Ram." Mr. Lowell nodded as he gripped her hand. They stepped together in a line with another couple, moving to the music.

"Thank you," she said. Turning, they moved through the formation and took their place at the end of the line.

"If I may, Miss Ram." He paused as another couple passed them. "I should like to drive out with you in the park if you are amenable."

The thoughts of Avery and the duke and back alley boxing matches slammed to a halt. *Oh, crap.*

"I'm sorry, Mr. Lowell, but I don't think that's a good idea."

"Oh." His face fell as they came together again for the last pass of the dance. "My apologies for being so forward."

"Oh, no." She stumbled a little through the step. He steadied her. "It's nothing like that, it's just..." She trailed off as the music ended. "I wish I knew what to say."

He shook his head ruefully. "I understand, Miss Ram. I do wish you every happiness."

He left her on the edge of the dance floor. She stared after him with complete befuddlement.

When she was single, men never looked at her twice. Why was it that once she'd found the man she wanted, they seemed to be lining up in droves?

Sometimes the Fates had a really twisted sense of humor.

"Chased the young pup off, I see." The duke laughed as he approached her. His silvery waistcoat matched his hair tonight.

"It wasn't like that. He had, erm, another person to dance with."

The duke nodded knowingly. "It is quite close in this room. Would you care to walk onto the balcony with me? There is something I would ask."

"If you'd like, Your Grace," Leah said, though her eyes searched for any distraction she could plausibly use.

They passed through the crowd, which parted to let them through like Moses and the freaking Red Sea. Leah shook her head inwardly at the deference everyone showed to Granville. She'd been no better than these people only a few weeks ago. She'd only seen the title and hadn't looked past it to see the man himself.

Not that Granville was bad. Quite the opposite. He was a sweet old man. But he was perfect for Lady Chesterfield, not her. Her heart was too full of someone else.

The night air was fresh with a hint of chill. Leah drew in a deep breath gratefully. It had really been stuffy in there, too many people and too many layers of undergarments. She'd never take her regular old cotton bra and panties for granted again.

"Miss Ram," the duke said, placing a hand on her arm and turning her to face him, "I had hoped to speak with you about a matter of some delicacy."

A little knot caught in Leah's throat. "Of course," she said. Uh-oh. Had she been reading his signals wrong? She hadn't thought he was really into her, but he seemed to be nervous. If he proposed to her right now, she'd fall over in shock.

The duke took a deep breath. "Your aunt, Lady Chesterfield." He stopped, looking out over the darkened lawn. Leah followed his gaze. He wasn't really looking at anything.

"My aunt?" she prodded.

"Yes. Of course. Your aunt." He looked down at her, smiling in a nervous but fatherly way. "Has she made mention of me?"

So that's the way he's rolling. Relief nearly made Leah sag. "She talks about you all the time."

His eyes lit up. "She does?"

Leah nodded. "I think she really likes you."

"I see."

They fell silent. Leah worried the inside of her cheek, wondering what she should do to help this along.

"You know, Your Grace," she said, looking down at the toes of her slippers, "I think she's really interested in you. Why don't you ask her to the park? Or the theatre?"

He clasped his hands together behind his back. "The dowager duchess is not in favor of my marrying again."

"Oh. Oh. I see." The memory of his mother made Leah shudder. The poor man. "But you don't need her permission, right?"

"No, of course not." He pursed his lips. "But my

mother can make things, well, difficult, to say the least. Since her dowry repaired the family fortunes, I find myself somewhat dependent upon her good nature."

Leah nodded knowingly. "Well, you could always—"

A shot rang out. The lamppost beside them shattered, raining glass onto the ground beside them.

Twenty-Four

AVERY RAN AFTER THE CHESTERFIELD CARRIAGE. Thankfully, with the glut of conveyances leaving at the same time, Leah and her chaperone were forced to move slowly along the lane toward the home in Hanover Square.

He kept his breath even as he followed at a distance.

Staying out of sight had not been easy for the past weeks, but he'd had no choice. After the Swansdown came the Berford. Prachett had demanded Avery lose at both tourneys, promising to harm Leah if he did not comply. Though the lies gnawed at him daily, he did as he was bidden, losing to boxers who he could have readily beaten. The duke had never mentioned anything, but Avery knew that his actions must look suspicious.

Besides, staying near to Leah would only have strengthened the connection that should never have formed at all—that had put her very life in danger tonight and all the nights she'd been in his life.

Then why do you follow her still? his subconscious mocked him. He had no choice. The gunshot tonight had been a warning from Prachett's men; he knew that.

To ensure Avery's continued assistance, they would do much worse to Leah.

Ignoring the thought, he ducked behind the manor house just beyond Lady Chesterfield's. He watched from the cover of shrubbery as Lady Chesterfield and Leah descended the carriage and headed into the house.

He sighed with relief, as he did every night when she'd returned home safely. The carriage rumbled to a start, heading for its home in the stables.

Guilt chased him, ever his constant companion. He should not follow her. He should not steal after her in the night like a thief. But it was his fault her life was in danger. He must protect her if he could.

"Sorry, Lady Chesterfield. I forgot my fan in the carriage."

Leah's voice floated to him, the sweet sound drawing memories that he longed to relive. He ducked lower as she descended the front steps and followed the path the carriage had taken toward the stables.

Indecision gnawed at his gut. He should leave. He should not speak to her, should not make his presence known. She'd be angry with him. She may even hate him for neglecting her, no matter his good intentions.

He stole after her anyway. Her presence was a lure he could not deny. Pressing his back against the chilly stone wall of the stable, he waited.

Her voice was indistinct as she spoke with the stable lad. A light laugh whipped Avery across his chest. She sounded so happy, so free. He looked downward, to where his hands were fisted in front of him. He should stay away. Her life was better without him.

"Avery?"

Reflexively he brought his fists upward into a fighting stance, dropping them a split second later when he realized that Leah was looking straight at him, a delicate white lace fan in her hands.

He stood straight and cleared his throat.

"Yes," he said, frantically searching his brain for an appropriate reason for his presence. "Miss Ramsey. Good evening."

Her fan thwacked across his arm. "What the *hell* is your problem?"

"I beg your pardon?"

She gripped him by the hand and dragged him farther into the shadows. He tried to ignore her closeness, but the scent and heat of her body wrapped around him. When she turned to him, fire in her eyes, it was all he could do not to kiss her.

"I have been waiting to hear from you for *two freaking weeks*." She punctuated her statement with a finger to his chest. "I thought you'd died or something. Where the crap have you been?"

He caught her hand against his chest, pressing it to his thumping heart. "I have been closer than you know."

She delivered a soft kick to his shin. He grunted as she connected with a still-healing bruise. "What, are you stalking me now? Because that's not sexy at all, even if you were a sparkly vampire."

He shook his head in confusion.

She rolled her eyes. "Never mind. But seriously, I've missed you."

"I have missed you as well," he whispered, and bent his head to hers. She jerked sideways, avoiding his kiss, and disappointment flooded him.

"No way," she said. "No kissing until we've talked some things through."

A noise from behind him grabbed his attention, and he pressed a finger to Leah's lips. Together they watched as the stable hands left for their quarters, apparently having finished their duties for the evening.

"Come here," Leah whispered, and led him into the warmth of the stables.

The heavy scents of horseflesh, leather, and straw perfumed the air. Avery lit the lamp by the doorway, and together he and Leah made their way to an empty stall near the back of the stables.

The lamp's metal hook rasped as he hung it above the stall door. Words ran rampant through his brain as he rehearsed them silently. He must remember all the reasons that he and Miss Ramsey could not be together. Never mind Prachett. He'd been careless before. He could have left her with child, after all. There was nothing he could give her, no provisions he could make to ensure her happiness and well-being. Their encounter had been a mistake. They had no future together, and he must convince her of that.

But when he turned and saw her there, pale-blue gown seeming to make her skin glow in the lamplight, all his carefully chosen words dissipated.

"Tell me the truth, Avery. Have you been following me?"

She'd set her fan on the narrow window ledge and had her hands on the curve of her hips. His pulse quickened as her décolletage heaved with emotion.

"I have."

She lost some of her irritation at his honest confession. "Why?"

He took a step closer to her, drawn despite himself. "Because there are evil men about, and you are an innocent."

She barked a laugh, tilting her head back in mirth. With that graceful column so exposed, he was sorely tempted to taste her lovely skin. He did not.

"I'm about as far from innocent as you can get, dude. I can take care of myself."

He shook his head. "You mistake my meaning. There are threats that you are unaware of." Unable to resist her anymore, he wrapped his arms around her waist and pulled her to him. "I would see that you come to no harm."

Her arms wound around his neck. "Why do you care so much?"

His kiss was the only answer he could give.

All his reasoning why they should not lie together burned up in the heat of that kiss. She pressed herself eagerly to him, opening her mouth to receive him. He groaned as he tasted the wet recesses of her, reveling in the feeling of her hands wandering the planes of his shoulders and back.

His erection pressed full against her belly, hardening him further. The décolletage of her gown seemed to call to him, begging for his attention. Who was he to ignore such a summons? He pressed fiery kisses along her throat, in the sweet space between shoulder and collarbone, finally to rest his lips atop the swell of her left breast.

"Avery," she whispered in a throaty voice. "I want you too, but you have to promise we'll talk afterward."

"Of course." He'd have promised her the moon in that moment. Though he was not proud of his too-hasty answer, it seemed to please her.

Leah divested him of his trousers, eyes alighting when she spied his erection. Her attention only served to harden him further.

"You've missed me too, haven't you?"

She didn't give him a chance to respond before she took him into her mouth. Her hot, wet mouth closed around his length and his knees buckled. Gripping the wall to steady himself, he threaded his free hand into her hair.

She took him deeply, throat working around the sensitive tip of him. He never looked away. He couldn't. The sight of her beatific face as she moved her hand and lips in concert was the most sensual thing he'd ever seen.

"Leah," he whispered, "you must stop."

At his words, she ran her tongue up the underside of his shaft. A drop of crystalline fluid appeared at the tip. Avery gritted his teeth to stop the flood of pleasure that threatened to sweep him away.

He must regain control of this. Of her.

Gripping both her hands in one of his, he laid her back into the sweet-smelling straw. She pulled against his grip, but he tightened his hold. The way she smiled, writhing and twisting against him, was proof of her approval.

He kissed her deeply, mastering her mouth with sweeps of his tongue. With his free hand, he lifted the fine satin of her skirt. Silk stockings covered her legs, but he knew the fine fabric could not match the beautiful flesh between her legs for softness.

She moaned her passion into his mouth when his hand parted her wet folds. Her thighs fell open, and he settled between them eagerly.

"Avery." She'd torn her mouth from his, gripping the length of his hair in both hands. "Please, please take me."

He couldn't. Not yet.

Releasing her hands, he rose on his knees and lifted her hips to his face.

"Oh God!"

Her cry was muffled by the yards of satin and lace that covered his head. Her taste was as incredible as it had been those weeks ago. He spread her petals wide, licking and sucking every part of her most precious flesh.

Her movements quickened, becoming frantic.

"Avery, please!" Her high, thin plea broke through to him, and he relented.

Entering the well of her body with two fingers, his lips closed on her fluttering, swollen bud.

She screamed.

He held on as the spasms wracked her, coming slower and slower until she stilled. He unearthed himself from her skirts and smiled down at his beautiful, dazed-eyed angel.

"More," she whispered, holding her arms up to him.

He needed no second invitation.

Falling atop her, he kissed her mouth with all the fervor he'd shown to her tender flesh only moments before. She quickly matched his intensity, gripping his shoulders and moaning as he probed at her entrance.

"Are you ready?"

"God, yes," she cried.

He plunged into her, high and hard. They cried out together as her warm sheath welcomed him home. Avery trembled as he held his upper body aloft, hips moving instinctively.

"You are so beautiful," he whispered as he thrust. "Leah, oh, Leah."

Her name was a litany, a prayer that was necessary to his continued life. Her throaty cries quickened his movements as he strained for that peak, for the both of them.

He grew harder within her as her channel grew wetter, more swollen around his length.

She buried her face in his shoulder as her pelvis moved to meet his.

It felt so wondrous, so completely incredible, he wanted it to go on forever.

But then he reached between them to fondle her swollen button. Her explosion took him along with her.

They came together, her body wringing every last drop from his. He shook with the effort of holding himself upright. He must not crush her, but he wanted to remain there, sheathed in her warmth forever.

His world, in that moment, was perfect.

A nearby whinny caused them both to laugh, but it broke the spell of the moment. Reluctantly, Avery rolled to the side and gathered a panting Leah against his chest.

She pressed sweet kisses against his chest. "You're pretty damn good at this."

He laughed. "You are exceptionally skilled as well," he said, toying with a blond curl. "An admirable trait for the woman I love."

The admission surprised him, but once the words were uttered, he was glad of their release. He did love Leah Ramsey. She was altogether too headstrong and impetuous for her own good, but she was also selfless, caring, and compassionate.

His love could not change their circumstances, but that did not negate its value.

"Oh, Avery," she whispered, and brought his mouth down to hers.

Their lips had met for the briefest of seconds when the creak of a door sounded.

"Miss Ramsey?" a young maid's voice called. "Are you here?"

"Hi, Muriel," Leah called in a shockingly calm voice as she smoothed down her skirts. Avery picked straw from her hair as she continued, "Sorry, I was just playing with some kittens I found in here. Go ahead, I'll be right up."

"Are you sure, miss?"

Avery swept Leah into his arms for one last kiss. With a regretful sigh, she pulled free of his arms.

"Here I am." She left the stable with Muriel, not looking back in his direction.

Once he'd dressed, he picked up her discarded lace fan and tucked it into his coat pocket.

He'd tumbled her in a stable. What a common, lowly beggar he was. But try as he might, he could not regret what had passed between them. He could only resolve to abstain from future lapses.

But that conviction, as he left the empty stable behind, was shaky at best.

Twenty-Five

LEAH PEERED OUT HER BEDROOM WINDOW AS unobtrusively as she could. Even though her bedroom overlooked the stables, she never saw Avery leave. He'd probably followed her out, the high-handed, ridiculous, sexy bastard.

Muriel picked pieces of straw out of Leah's skirts, her scolding comments about young ladies who play with kittens in ball gowns going right over Leah's head. She was too sodden with afterglow to give a crap about ruining an expensive dress.

Avery loved her. The confession had come in a roundabout way, sure, but he'd said it all the same. In a fog, Leah lifted her arms over her head at Muriel's command. While enveloped in the column of her beautiful dress, a sudden thought struck her.

She hadn't told him that she loved him too.

Well, shit.

He had to know that, right? She hadn't had a chance to say the words, but he had to have gotten the gist of her feelings by the way she jumped him like a bullfrog in heat. *Wait. Do bullfrogs go into heat?*

Muriel's yawn startled Leah as her nightgown settled around her.

"I'm sorry, Muriel. I didn't mean to keep you up so late. Go ahead to bed, okay?" Her swift hug must have startled the maid, because she jumped.

"If you have all you require, then I shall see you in the morning." Muriel pulled away with a tired smile and headed for the bedroom door.

Leah sank onto the edge of her fluffy, comfortable bed.

Muriel probably had to get up at o'dark-thirty, just like Leah had during her brief stint as a maid. It had to be after two in the morning. While Leah had been wound up in Avery, the poor girl had been stuck waiting for her, probably wishing she could just go to bed.

When had she become such a self-absorbed bitch? After Kevin, she'd thought she learned what it felt like to be used. She'd never thought she might be thoughtlessly using people herself.

Lady Chesterfield and Muriel would both be getting a sincere apology tomorrow, she promised inwardly as she sank into the covers.

And Avery would get his return declaration of love as soon as she saw him again.

She smiled as she drifted off to sleep.

❧

Her eyes opened only a brief second later. Sunlight streamed through the window, making her soft peach bedroom glow. She stretched luxuriously, relishing the tenderness of her thighs.

"Avery." She couldn't help but say his name aloud. The sound made her feel warm, safe, and loved. What a man she'd found, and she hadn't had to slay any dragons to do it.

A soft knock on the door drew her into a sitting position. "Come in."

Muriel appeared with a tray.

"Good morning, miss. I've your chocolate here."

Leah grinned. "Great. Bring it over."

Muriel cocked her head curiously as Leah held her hands out for the tray. "You want the tray in bed with you, miss?"

"Hand it here." Leah set the tray on the foot of the bed and scooted over. "Now here. Sit with me."

"Oh, miss, I couldn't." Muriel shook her head, but an embarrassed smile was beginning to spread across her face. Leah patted the spot next to her.

"Come on, I don't bite unless you ask."

Muriel giggled and settled on the edge of the bed next to Leah.

Picking up the cup of chocolate, Leah smiled at the maid. "See? I'm not so scary." She took a deep whiff of the chocolate in the cup. It smelled like heaven, but she passed it over to the maid anyway.

"Here."

Alarm crossed Muriel's face as she took the cup. "But it's yours, miss. Is it not to your liking? Shall I have the cook make a fresh cup for you?"

Leah grabbed Muriel's arm to prevent the maid from running to the kitchens and overhauling them to produce the most perfect cup of hot chocolate the world had ever seen. "It's fine, you goof. But I want you to have it."

Muriel settled back down as Leah smiled wryly and continued, "I haven't exactly been the most courteous houseguest. I kept you up way too late last night. You've been so wonderful to me the whole time I've been here, and I've taken you for granted. And believe me, anyone who can empty chamber pots for a living really deserves much more of my gratitude. So thank you."

Muriel's head bob nearly spilled the chocolate gripped in her eager hand. "It was my pleasure, miss."

"Drink up." Leah's flop into the pillows wrenched a giggle from the maid. "We can chat and relax for a few minutes before you go attack whatever dust bunnies and dirt devils are on your list for the day. I can even help if you want."

"It wouldn't be proper, miss." Muriel's eyes closed in bliss as she took a sip of the hot chocolate.

"You haven't known me too long, but I promise that I can be improper with the best of them." Leah winked.

They fell quiet for a moment as Muriel sipped the chocolate. A memory sparked in Leah, about a story Jamie had told her.

"Muriel, wasn't there someone you were interested in? A footman or something?"

The maid's cheeks went red. Leah hastened to fill the gap.

"Sorry if the question is rude. I just wondered if the two of you were still together."

Muriel stared down into the cup. "He became a sailor, miss. He's in the Royal Navy. I've not heard from George for nigh on a year now."

Leah didn't know what to say, so she rubbed Muriel's back. "I'm sorry."

Muriel drained the rest of the chocolate. "Never mind that, miss. When he returns, we'll wed. I'm sure of it."

Leah nodded and smiled. "That's the spirit."

❧

Leah didn't get the chance to make good on her offer of housecleaning assistance, because Lady Chesterfield called for her only half an hour later. Muriel helped her dress, and Leah descended the stairs feeling a little more at peace with the world.

Only one more apology to go through, then she'd start focusing on the future. Rounding the bottom of the staircase, she laughed to herself. How would Avery take to life in the twenty-first century? The thought of him on a motorcycle was definitely appealing. As was the thought of him in full armor as he jousted at the Renaissance Faire. For that matter, she couldn't think of a situation that he wouldn't be sexier than Magic Mike to her.

"Good morning," she greeted Lady Chesterfield with a smile. The lady was seated at the head of the dining room table, a plate of breakfast in front of her. She nodded to Leah, her smile unusually subdued. For that matter, she was only wearing a few feathers in her hair today. A frown wrinkled Leah's brow as she helped herself to the breakfast spread on the sideboard and took her seat at Lady Chesterfield's side. Something was clearly bothering her patroness, and Leah had more than a sneaking suspicion that it was probably her own fault.

"Are you feeling okay, Lady Chesterfield?"

The older woman cleared her throat. "I am well enough, my dear. But when I woke this morning, Graves informed me that a missive came for you." She picked up a folded paper that Leah hadn't noticed before. "It is from the dowager Duchess of Granville. Naturally, as your guardian and chaperone, I read it."

"Naturally," Leah agreed drily. Privacy was a luxury she hadn't realized she'd miss so much.

"Her Grace has decided that you are entirely unsuitable for marriage to her son." A little tear formed in the corner of Lady Chesterfield's eye. "Oh dear Leah, whatever can you have said to give rise to this opinion? I only hope you have not lost your chances with him."

Leah's fork clattered to the table. "I'm so sorry, Lady Chesterfield. But listen. The duke isn't really interested in me at all, he wants—"

"Never mind that, my dear. We may yet have a chance to set things right. I shall ask dearest Granville to accompany us to Ranelagh Garden in two days." Lady Chesterfield's eyes glowed. "You shall apologize for whatever it is you have done to anger the dowager. I am certain that in such a romantic setting, dear Granville must come up to scratch, no matter what the dowager feels." With that, Lady Chesterfield patted her feathers. A self-satisfied smile spread across her face.

"No, I don't think you understand. I don't love the duke."

Lady Chesterfield stared at her, brows climbing in question. "But of course you do not, my dear. Love is what occurs between a husband and wife after many years of marriage. You will come to love him."

Her chair scraped back and she stood to go. She gave a little pat to Leah's cheek. "Your world of the future must be quite different from this. But you must trust me, dear. I know how you are to go about things in this society. I'll not lead you astray." She turned to leave, but before she reached the door, she looked over her shoulder at Leah.

"My dear, I shall never forgive myself if you do not

marry advantageously. You are too precious to squander yourself on anything less than a peer of the realm." She disappeared through the door, leaving Leah's jaw hanging open. No matter how hard she tried, she couldn't quite convince it to shut.

So much for her apology. So much for laying things out on the line, thanking Lady Chesterfield for her kindness but firmly stating her feelings for Avery. So much for planning her exit ASAP.

She munched on a piece of bacon dejectedly. It appeared that she had another couple of days to figure out exactly how to get Lady Chesterfield to realize that *she* was perfect for Granville, not Leah.

Why hadn't she stayed home and started collecting cats or something?

Twenty-Six

HE'D NEVER BEEN A DREAMER. THOUGH HIS REALITIES were not always pleasant, they were better than being caught unawares. His beliefs had not changed, but his dreams were much stronger than they'd ever been in the two days since he'd seen her last.

Several times, he'd shaken himself to regain control of his mind from the memories that replayed through it over and over. Leah smiling up at him, straw in her hair and laughter in her eyes. Leah's kisses, passionate and fervent. Leah sinking to her knees...

He dropped the brush he'd been using on His Grace's coat. The clatter of the heavy object on the polished floors brought some clarity to his foggy mind. Scowling, he picked up the brush and resumed his brushing on the sleeve of the duke's fine, blue coat. He must hurry and finish his duties so that he could watch out for her.

That night in the stable had not changed his station, nor had it magically gifted him with the means to support a wife. He'd revealed his feelings to her, but he should not have. She had come to land a husband, not ensnare herself with a boxing valet, his bedridden aunt, and a puppet master named Prachett.

Avery's strings would be jerked again on the morrow. He was to face Emersen in the Jackford. Their match was sure to be the biggest draw in years. The underdog, Russell the bruiser, against the as-yet-undefeated Emersen? With Prachett's careful planning, the odds were stacked against Avery. If he were to win, Prachett and his cronies stood to make thousands of pounds.

"Bloody fool," he hissed under his breath. He was an idiot for forgetting reality for that night in the stables—and for nearly every minute since then.

The door opened behind him.

"Your Grace." He turned and bowed without looking up. "You have returned early. Is everything well?"

Instead of his employer's gray-haired form, Prachett stood in front of him. A self-satisfied smile crossed his face, an expression so unpleasant that it tensed Avery's spine.

"What are you doing here?" Avery nearly spat the words, clenching his fists at his sides. "How did you get in?"

❧

Ranelagh Garden wasn't at all what Leah had expected. She and Lady Chesterfield arrived and were shown to His Grace's private table in the Rotunda. An orchestra played somewhere nearby, their soft refrains a sharp counterpoint to the boisterous crowd around them. Lords and ladies of the ton filled the Rotunda, but more normal people were scattered along the various paths through the garden.

"Are we early?" Leah wasn't sure why she was

bothering to talk to Lady Chesterfield. The woman hadn't bothered to listen to a word Leah said for the last two days. She'd tried to reason with her. She'd yelled; she'd even mustered up a tear or two. But nothing she said could convince her patroness that she wasn't, and never would be, in love with the Duke of Granville.

"Oh pish-posh," Lady Chesterfield said. "You look ravishing."

Yup. She didn't hear a word.

Leah lowered into her chair carefully. She didn't want to crush the silver gown that Muriel had taken such care stuffing her into like a Thanksgiving turkey. Lady Chesterfield started babbling about the fireworks that would happen later, but Leah didn't really pay attention. She kept scanning the crowd for a familiar handsome face, one that didn't belong to a duke.

Of course, why should she expect Avery to show up tonight? This place was huge. It wasn't like he could hang out by a window and keep an eye on her. She tried to get mad about the high-handed way he'd been watching her, but she couldn't. He made her feel safe and loved.

And honestly, what more could she want out of life?

"Miss Ram, here he is. Good evening, dear Granville." Lady Chesterfield's excited curtsy nearly pitched her forward into the duke's thighs. Fortunately, she righted herself without toppling, the green feathers of her bodice trembling as she fluttered her fan coyly.

"Thank you for coming. Our Miss Ram has been beside herself with joy since you agreed to meet us here."

Though Leah's *Bullshit!* went unsaid, she hoped it was clear in the intense height of her eyebrows. If anybody was thrilled, it was clearly Lady Chesterfield.

"It was my pleasure, indeed." The duke smiled and offered his arm to Lady Chesterfield. "Should you care to take a turn about the gardens?"

"Oh, I cannot," Lady Chesterfield said with all the sincerity of a zombie pledging to give up eating brains. "But do take dear Miss Ram for a turn."

❧

Prachett ignored the question, pulling off his gloves one finger at a time. "Do you know why I picked you, Russell? Out of all the boxers, do you know why I selected you as the man to beat Emersen?"

Avery stood rigid, mind ticking quickly. There was no such thing as a simple query from a man like Prachett. Every word he spoke was calculated, designed to give him the upper hand. But why would he risk so much as to enter a duke's household? His Grace would not return until late this evening. Avery had been about to leave himself, in order to watch out for Leah.

"I do not." Avery ground out the words. "But I have done as you've asked. The last two fights were lost on your demand, so you can have no quarrel with me."

"I chose you, dear Russell, because you've forgotten." Prachett ran a finger along the duke's bedside table, lifting a heavy brass candlestick lovingly before replacing it. "To think that you, a vicar's brat, fight barefisted in the mills like the very hounds of hell are nipping at your heels. Though you left us, you still belong to us. And to see you like this?" Prachett gestured at Avery's solemn clothing, perfectly respectable for a servant of his rank. "You forget who you are."

"I know who I am. But you are trespassing, and you

must go. Now, Prachett." Avery set his jaw firmly as he gathered the discarded cane and coat. The conversation was turning into a dangerous one, and he must keep his wits about him. "His Grace will return at any moment."

⁓

Leah reluctantly stood and took the duke's arm.

"We'll be right back," she promised Lady Chesterfield.

"Do take your time, and enjoy the air." The older woman simpered as she looked up at the duke. "His Grace will ensure your well-being." She fluttered her lashes like a preteen at a boy band poster.

Leah's teeth hurt, she clamped them together so hard.

She didn't waste any time. Once they'd exited the Rotunda and found their way onto a dimly lit path, she spoke.

"I'm really sorry about this. I've tried to tell her that you're not really interested in me, but she's not having any of it." Leah kicked a leaf off the gravel pathway. "She's like a damn dog with a bone."

"Amelia is quite determined." Granville patted Leah's hand on his arm. "She does want the best for you."

"I know." Leah sighed. "But her idea of the best and mine aren't really even on the same planet."

Granville smiled as the orchestra grew fainter behind them. "Her tenacity is one of her most admirable traits."

Leah couldn't stand the lovelorn look on the duke's face. "Listen. Why don't you go back there? Have some time alone with her, and tell her how you feel."

"I should not leave you alone." Granville looked back longingly.

"I'll be fine." Leah laughed. "Go. Seriously. I'll stay on the path right by the box."

"I should not. It is not safe for a young girl."

"I'm older than I look," Leah grated. "For crap's sake, go talk to the woman."

She nearly had to shove him into the box, but the delighted sound of Lady Chesterfield's voice assured her that she'd done the right thing.

Dragging in a deep breath, Leah smiled at her surroundings. Here she stood, in nineteenth-century England, in one of the famous pleasure gardens. She was dressed like a princess. All she had to do now was find her valet.

Picking a path at random, she whistled as she walked. It was a beautiful night, and her man was here somewhere. She knew it.

❧

"Tell me," Prachett said, ignoring Avery, "what do the other servants think of Russell the bruiser?"

"That is not any of your concern."

"Ah." Prachett stood tall as he towered over Avery, his thin chest heaving and his eyes glowing with a strange light. "I see. And your Miss Ramsey. What is her opinion?"

The words were soft, but the threat therein was unmistakable—as was the knife that was suddenly pressed against his ribs.

"Stay away from her." Avery growled the words as he planned his move. He could disarm Prachett if he stepped into him, threw his elbow, and...

Three of Prachett's men entered through the duke's dressing chamber.

Prachett stretched out a finger and drew it across the valet's throat, pausing for a moment over the pulsing vein there. Avery fought the urge to swallow and kept his gaze locked firmly ahead. Blast and damn.

"You'll face Emersen tomorrow, lad." Prachett leaned close, whispering the words in his ear. "And do you know to what lengths I shall go to ensure your victory?"

Avery kept the image of her locked in the forefront of his mind, abandoning all attempts at pretending she did not matter to him. Leah. His angel. The only bit of heaven he'd see in this life or the next, he was certain.

"Your lady is in my keeping. If you lose tomorrow, she will die." Prachett's words may as well have been a bullet, for they shot Avery straight in the heart.

The gravel crunched beneath her slippers. She shivered, rubbing her arms briskly. The night had turned chilly.

"Avery?" she called him in a quiet voice. "Are you there?"

She'd probably gone too far. The strains of the orchestra and laughter of the partygoers was hard to hear now. She'd passed the last lamppost a few minutes ago. Reluctantly, she turned to go back.

A twig snapped close by.

"Avery?"

Something went over her head, and she dropped into fight mode without hesitation. Her elbow connected with soft flesh, probably someone's belly. She kicked viciously, but her toes bent backward as she hit some-one's shin. Pain arced through her foot. Stupid flimsy slippers. That kick had hurt her more than her attacker. Her struggles were ineffective as the sack tightened around her. Before she knew what was going on, she'd been tied up and was being toted like a Christmas tree atop a Bronco.

Her screams for help were just warming up when a blow landed on her skull and everything went dark.

❧

Avery's knuckles had gone numb nearly an hour before. That didn't stop him. Keenly aware of Prachett's presence on the other side of the cottage door, he kept up his movements. Every blow, in his mind's eye, landed straight in the man's face.

How dare the bastard go after Leah? How dare he use her for his own gain? Avery grunted as he gave the sand bag a body blow.

And is that any different from what you've done to her?

"I love her." His words were lost in the sound of the ropes overhead creaking wildly as the bag swung.

He loved her, but he could not protect her. Gripping the bag, he rested his head against it, his breaths coming quick and heavy.

Prachett had her. If Avery lost to Emersen in the morning, he'd kill her. Steel lined Avery's backbone as he stood. He could not let that happen.

Damning the consequences, he pulled his shirt over his sweat-dampened skin. Prachett and his men had brought him here to fight, and so he would. He would fight, and he would win, no matter the cost. His body would suffer, but that did not matter.

Leah mattered.

He lay on the narrow straw mattress and stared at the ceiling. Though he wanted nothing more than to break through the door and go to find her, he knew that would only cause her more harm.

He'd play this game to win, and once he had her safe, he would break the men who'd dared lay a hand on her, bone by bloody bone. And Prachett? Prachett he would kill.

Sounds swirled around Leah, penetrating the painful haze that surrounded her brain. She groaned and tried her best to put her hand against her aching head. It felt like she'd drunk about three cases of beer and then had a *Dance Dance Revolution* competition. She hurt everywhere, and dammit, why couldn't she move her hands?

Oh. She was still trussed in some kind of burlap sack. Lovely.

"Help!" Her scream was only half the volume she'd intended, because the sound of her own voice echoed through her skull with a ricocheting pain.

"The liddle bird's awake." A rough male voice with a coarse accent came from somewhere above her. She scowled in the darkness of her cloth prison. Of course the shitheads were still there. She'd be smart about this and be quiet and obedient until they untied her. Then she'd go all *Kill Bill* on their asses.

Leah bit her lip and moaned as another pain speared her head. What had they hit her with, a freaking bat?

"Oy, darlin', you can't be comfortable like that. Let me 'elp."

Her gorge rose as a broad, sweaty hand rubbed up her calf to rest behind her knee. This wasn't happening. There was no way she was tied up and helpless. Nothing bad would happen to her.

Even though she tried her damnedest to block out the reality, the touch on her leg became more and more insistent. She pulled away, but her bonds made moving more than an inch or two nearly impossible.

Another voice joined the first, and then Leah knew real fear.

"Untie 'er, then we can 'ave us a lark." The sour smell of cheap alcohol drifted through the weave of the bag, and Leah coughed. Drips of the stuff trickled down her nose and chin.

"You bloomin' idiot, don't lose all me brandy!"

"The chit was thirsty," the second man laughed. "Untie 'er legs, at least. I've a mind to get between 'em."

Leah gagged.

The hand drifted down to her ankles, and the first rope loosened. She fought the urge to stretch, to help restore the circulation in her feet. She had to keep still until they untied her more. Her chances wouldn't be good then, but they'd be a helluva lot better than they were at the moment.

The knot on the next rope must have been tangled, because it took them several moments to loosen it. Leah used the time to think.

What had happened to Lady Chesterfield and the duke? She should be really pissed at herself for wandering down that dark path in the garden, but right then, all she could think about was getting out of there and seeing Avery again. Tears leaked from the corners of her eyes as pain needled the bottoms of her feet. The circulation's painful restoration opened the floodgates, and her silent tears quickly changed to sobs.

She'd fucked this up. All of it. From the minute she'd

fallen through that mirror, she'd been determined to go about things her way. And she'd been wrong every fucking time. When was she going to learn to think before she tossed herself face-first into everything? Life wasn't a storybook adventure, and bad shit happened. Pretending otherwise hadn't done her any favors.

The rope knotted at her knees finally loosened. Panic welled in Leah's throat, and even though her feet and legs still prickled with the pain of the fresh blood flow, she kicked out as hard as she could. She could cry later. She had to live now.

Her heels connected with someone's face. The sharp crack of the blow made her smile.

"You goddamn bitch." Something hit the floor. She hoped it was a mouthful of his teeth. Bastard.

A blow glanced off her shoulder, and she jerked in pain. She didn't regret her rebellion, though. She'd do it again. She wouldn't stop as long as there was breath in her body.

Four hands rubbed along her legs as she kicked out. They gripped around her ankles, stilling her motions. Panic sped her heart and she thrashed as hard as she could. But there were two of them, and only one of her. It didn't look good.

"What are ye doin'?" An angry voice with a Scottish sounding accent rang through the room. It was kind of familiar, but where had she heard it before? The grip on her legs disappeared, and she clamped her thighs together as tightly as she could.

"Havin' a bit of fun, s'all," the first man mumbled. The second man's reply was garbled, sort of far away. Leah strained to understand it, but the bag muffled her perception.

The conversation continued on the other side of the room, and Leah huffed her frustration to cover her fear. She'd rather be pissed than scared. After her one lapse into desperate sobs, she wasn't interested in trying that again.

A few minutes later, a door slammed shut and silence reigned. Relief soaked through her. Inwardly thanking the weirdly familiar Scotsman, she pulled at her bonds. They held fast.

Time dragged along like a two-legged dog. The tingling in her feet and legs abated finally. The alcohol dried on her face. The sharp ache in her head reduced itself to a dull throb centered just above her left ear. She was hungry. She had to pee. The hope that someone had followed them to wherever the hell they were dissipated as the minutes—hours? days?—passed.

She had a lot of time to think, and she used it. She thought of Muriel and Lady Chesterfield and their many kindnesses to her. She thought of Jamie and Ella back home, and wished she could give them big hugs and giggle at Monty Python movies again. She thought of Pawpaw, and the tears flowed fast and freely. Would she ever see him again? Would she ever be able to tell him about Avery?

And the valet who'd chased her down and stolen her heart? She thought of him most of all.

If she survived this, the first thing she'd do was tell him she loved him. It couldn't wait another second. He had to know that he meant everything to her.

Twenty-Seven

THE NEXT DAY DAWNED GRIM AND GRAY, LIKE AVERY'S mood. He rose early, energy humming through his muscles. The sooner he beat Emersen, the sooner he could rescue Leah.

Leah.

She was in danger because of him.

His anger simmered just below the surface, fueling the fire in his muscles as he stretched in the ring. Prachett's men, including one Lachlan Mackenzie, stable master to the Duke of Granville, milled nearby. Avery gave Mackenzie a dark smile. He knew where the betrayal had come from now and would recompense him accordingly once Leah was safe again.

The crowds came. Fine lords and ladies, common laborers, the young, the old—they filled in the gaps at the sides of the square, elbowing and crowding to get closer to see the bouts. The first match lasted nearly two hours. Cribb and Gulley pounded one another until the blood flowed like wine. Cribb was the victor, when Gulley lay in the dust and did not rise.

All during the long match, Avery kept a watchful eye

on his jailers, waiting for an opening. One never came. He'd have to fight his way out through his opponent.

"Emersen's a tough 'un," Jenks said as Gulley's men cleared the unconscious man from the ring. "His guard is high, and he's lightnin' quick. Best to hit him low and often if you're to have a chance, lad."

"Aye, and mind your feet. Be light and fast, he's no' used to that," Tarley chimed in. "Won't be easy, but you can win if you pull your head from your arse."

Avery took the jibe without comment. Jenks and Tarley didn't know about Prachett's manipulation of both Avery and the matches. They only knew that Avery had lost two matches he could have easily won.

"I will do my best. You have my word."

Avery stepped into the ring to the hisses and jeers of the crowd. Emersen was the clear favorite. That was what Prachett counted on.

Avery stood at the line and nodded to his opponent. Emersen, a ruddy beast of a man, stood over six feet tall. He towered over Avery, thicker, stronger, in every way his superior.

Avery widened his stance and raised his fists. There was no force on earth that could stand between him and Leah. Not even this beast of a man.

They came together like two leviathans, with a crash. The noise was deafening as the crowd cheered at every landed blow.

Bruises and blood, fists and grunts flew as they pummeled each other. Round for round, blow for blow, they were as perfectly matched as any pair of combatants could be. As the hours dragged on, and the warriors slowed, only one thought kept Avery moving.

Leah was in danger, and it was his fault.

This man kept him from rescuing her.

In the twenty-third round, with Avery's vision clouded by blood, his fists swollen, cut, and aching, bones broken and head spinning, he saw his opening. A quick stumble, a simple misstep, and Avery laid into Emersen without mercy. Right and left, over and over, he let his rage pour through his fists.

The crowd went silent as Avery stood. Emersen moaned but did not rise.

The victor did not waste a moment on the loser. He only had eyes for one man, the man standing in the corner of the ring, gloating at his victory.

Prachett.

The distance between them melted away as if it were nothing. Avery grasped Prachett's coat, shaking the man as if he were a dog with a bone.

"Where is she?"

Prachett coughed, clawing at Avery's hands. "Let me go."

Avery lowered Prachett to the ground, but he did not release him. "Damn you, you perfidious cheat, where is she? I lost the matches as you told me, and won this one, now I'll have her back."

Murmurs ran through the crowd.

"Cheat?"

"Wot did he say?"

"He lost purposefully?"

A shrill voice penetrated the fog of anger surrounding Avery. "Thomas Prachett has been manipulating the fights for his own gain!"

The crowd surged around them, carrying Prachett away from Avery in a tide of outrage.

"Where is she, Prachett? Damn you, answer me!"

There were too many people between them. He cast about for another answer.

Prachett's men had scattered, unwilling to be caught with their master now that the scheme had failed. But one was not as fast as the others.

"Mackenzie." Avery caught the stable master by the neck. "You will tell me what I need to know, and you will tell me now."

✑

Shouts woke her, though she hadn't realized she'd fallen asleep. Angry male voices—it was hard to tell how many—arguing and cursing one another. The sharp crack of gunfire made her jump, and she struggled to sit up. Her body groaned and protested, but she managed to prop herself against a wall. She pushed against the wall with her bound hands behind her and struggled to her feet.

Damn it, if only she could freaking see! She could run while they were distracted if she just had a peephole. But while the weave of the bag was loose enough to allow oxygen to flow to her, it wasn't large enough in the dim room to give her a clear line of vision.

She had to do something. She was tired of lying here and waiting for someone to either kill her or rape her.

Her scream was so loud it nearly pierced her own eardrums. She stumbled but pressed back against the wall to steady herself. Let them ignore that if they could.

✑

Avery was nearly out of his head with worry by the time he located the secluded hovel in the woods that

Mackenzie had confessed was Leah's prison. His horse had pulled up lame, and he'd had the devil of a time finding another. She'd been in their custody for nearly a full day. Anything could have happened to her. How could he know the brigands Prachett had hired would leave her unharmed?

Blackhearted devils. If they'd hurt her, he'd kill them all with his bare hands. Gladly.

He circled the area, making the best of the fading daylight. There were no lookouts posted. Of course, Prachett knew that Miss Ramsey was not really of the ton and therefore had no powerful allies to come to her aid.

Cold rage had replaced the angry passion of the morning, and Avery was glad of it. He could examine the situation much more clearly and rescue her that much sooner.

The mare picked her way over a thin stream, and Avery dismounted once they'd reached the other side. He tightened the makeshift bandage on his forearm, wincing as pain blossomed. There was very likely a broken bone, but he had no time to tend to it. There would be time enough once Leah was safe.

The reins rasped softly against the branch of a young willow as he tied them. With a whisper of gratitude to the black mare, he crept through the twilight woods toward the cabin. He moved swiftly and silently, taking care to step on damp earth. Bodies milled by the door of the cabin, and he crouched to better count his opponents.

He'd only counted four of them when angry shouts echoed through the woods and a shot rang out. Leah's bloodcurdling scream pierced his heart.

His feet pounded against the earth as he bolted for the cabin. Had she been shot? Oh God, had he come so close only to lose her like this?

The duke's voice ground him to a halt at the last ring of trees before the building. "Oh my darling, are you harmed?"

"No, no, I'm fine." Her voice rang clear, though her tone was thin.

Leah. Avery sank to his knees in relief at the sound of her voice. She was whole. A strange sensation pricked at his eyes, but he rubbed it away. He staggered to his feet, ignoring the nerveless feeling in his legs. He must go to her. He must assure himself that she was unharmed.

He rushed past the duke's carriage but pulled up short at the sight inside.

His Grace's arms were around Leah, locked in a passionate embrace. Her beautiful lashes dusted her cheeks as her arms were wrapped around his neck in the picture of perfect pleasure.

Avery's heart crumbled to dust in that moment.

He waited for a breath or two, hoping, praying that the vision was false. When the duke murmured to her softly, Avery slammed his eyes shut and staggered backward.

She hadn't stopped him.

He turned and strode for the horse, ignoring the looks of the men who milled around the front of the cabin.

He'd been too late. Much, much too late.

The sight of their embrace seared itself into his brain, a throbbing reminder of what he'd lost. A dark laugh escaped him as he freed the black mare from the willow. Had he expected Leah to throw over a duke for the love of a valet? A poor man with no home, no coin, and a past that put her in mortal danger?

He'd been so stupid. So very stupid.

⁓

The journey back to London was a long and lonely one. Along the way, he recounted each and every one of his sins in the past few months. The list lasted him until he reached the outskirts of Town, and even then he was certain he'd forgotten a few.

He must return to Granville House and claim his meager possessions. Then find employment somewhere. He was certain he'd get no reference from His Grace after the way he'd declared his participation in Prachett's scandal. The lack would make things more difficult, to be sure, but he'd as soon never speak to His Grace again after the embrace he'd witnessed. The man had rescued Leah when he had not, and that made him a better mate. She deserved nothing less than a duke.

Avery slammed his eyes shut as the pain locked its grip about his heart again.

"Leah, why?"

The whispered question was unanswered, as he'd expected. A man such as he did not deserve answers.

He'd failed her. He'd allowed her to come to harm. How could he blame her for choosing the duke?

He dismounted at Granville House's stables, rubbing down his horse and returning the tack to its proper place. The young stable lad eyed him curiously but kept his distance.

His steps were leaden as he moved toward the house. He could not remain at Granville House with Leah as its mistress. Though his sins were many, and his punishment justly deserved, that was a pain he could not endure.

The chatter in the servants' hall died as he entered the room. Scents of boiled mutton and cabbage greeted his nostrils, but he paid no heed to the growling in his belly. He could not stomach any more derision from his fellow servants, even to satisfy his hunger. With a polite nod to the gaping maids and dumbfounded footmen, he walked toward the stairs.

"Russell."

Smythe's voice stopped him. Avery shut his eyes but did not turn.

"Yes?"

A chair scraped back and a gentle, fatherly hand lay on Avery's shoulder. "Sit. Eat. You must be weary."

Avery waited a heartbeat for a blow to fall. It didn't. "May I ask why?"

The hand disappeared, but Smythe did not. The man's voice was gentle as he spoke. "Mackenzie left not long ago, raving about Prachett, the mills, and your involvement. We had assumed the worst about you, and Mackenzie fostered that bad opinion. We've wronged you, my lad, and we would make it right."

The kindness nearly felled him. He took a deep breath and faced Smythe.

"I thank you, sir."

Smythe held his chair out for him. Mrs. Harper brought a wet cloth for him to wipe his hands and face, and Cook served him a double portion of mutton. Teresa promised to tend to his wounds once he'd finished his meal, and Henrietta looked at him as if he were an avenging warrior returning home.

The delicious food was tinged with both acceptance and bitterness.

He'd found his place only to have to leave it behind.

Twenty-Eight

LEAH WAS LIMP. THERE WAS NO STRENGTH LEFT IN HER body. It had all been wrenched away by a euphoric glee that stemmed from not being tied up and smothered by a burlap bag anymore. When the duke had removed that barrier between her and the world, she'd been so overcome that she'd hugged him.

He'd patted her back, comforting her. He really was a good man.

"Thank you so much for saving me," she said. "I don't know why they took me, but I'm so grateful you came."

"It is my fault, dearest Miss Ram." He patted her hand. "I should never have allowed you to wander the paths alone. It was foolishness."

"Yeah, it was pretty stupid of me." She rubbed at her wrists, taking in her surroundings. "Granville, what men do you have with you?"

His brows arched curiously, but he answered, "My driver, the tiger, and two footmen."

She couldn't help but be disappointed. Where the hell was Avery? "I'm sorry, I'm feeling a little faint. Can you take me back to Lady Chesterfield's?"

"Of course," Granville said tenderly, and snapped his fingers. A man leaped forward and fetched the carriage, which had been parked just out of sight.

Granville handed her into the carriage, and she settled herself on the plush seat. As soon as the conveyance rumbled to a start, she lay her head back against the cushions.

This wasn't right. None of this was right. Why had those guys taken her? She didn't have anything they could want.

Avery's absence wasn't the only thing that smelled funny. That Scottish accent had been really familiar. She frowned. Wasn't the stable master Scottish? The one that had tried to get fresh with her that time?

Mackenzie—that was his name. Could his have been the voice that had stopped the jerks from violating her? On the one hand, she was really grateful he'd stopped them. But on the other, what was he doing there at all?

The carriage's sudden stop scared the crap out of her. She jumped, clutching at her thundering heart to keep it from leaping out of her chest. Sunlight streamed through the carriage windows.

Oh. She'd been asleep.

"Why have we arrived at Granville Place?" The duke's expression was cross as he called up to the driver.

"My apologies, Your Grace. I had thought…"

"We must return Miss Ram to Lady Chesterfield's." Granville turned back to Leah. "I do apologize, my dear. However, since we've arrived at my home, is there anything that you require?"

Leah shook her head quickly. "No, thank you,

Granville. I need to get back to Lady Chesterfield. I'm sure she's really worried."

Granville nodded. "Of course. But allow me to fetch a horse for the return journey. I must go and speak with the magistrate as soon as possible regarding this matter. Those responsible will be punished."

"O…kay." He had descended the carriage before she could get the whole word out.

She watched as he entered the house. A glimpse down the street caught an unexpected sight.

Avery, wearing a coat and hat and bearing a leather bag similar to the one he'd given her, was walking away from Granville House.

She'd hit the pavement before her brain caught up. Hauling her wrinkled and dirty skirts up, she took off running toward him.

"Avery," she called, heart pounding with more than exertion. She hadn't realized how desperate she was to see him. He was her sanity in this freaking crazy world. "Avery, wait!"

He didn't turn, only walked more quickly away from her.

"Oh, the hell you are," she snarled and put on a burst of speed. She caught him as he rounded the corner, grabbing his arm and pulling until he stopped.

"What is wrong with you? Didn't you hear me?"

He didn't look her in the eyes, just kept staring straight ahead.

"My apologies, Miss Ramsey."

"Wait, where are you going?" Her heart thumped even louder now. Something was wrong—horribly, horribly wrong.

"That is none of your concern." His soft reply pierced her through.

She stared up into his face, trying to understand what was going on. But no matter how she framed it, it didn't make any sense.

"You owe me an explanation."

He laughed bitterly. "I have done enough to you. You have made your decision, and I was a fool to ever think otherwise. I wish you a wonderful marriage."

He bowed curtly and walked away before she had a chance to form a reply.

"Avery," she whispered. No, no, *no*! What was she doing? How could she let him walk away?

She picked up her skirts to run after him again. "Avery!"

Her shout was drowned out by the hoof beats of an approaching horse. She glanced over her shoulder, and the sight brought her to a halt.

The carriage and the duke were there behind her. "Come, my dear. Amelia is beside herself with worry."

With a reluctant glance toward Avery, Leah allowed the duke to help her into the carriage.

Lady Chesterfield clucked like the chicken she'd probably murdered to have such a fluffy feathered gown. The duke left after entrusting Leah to her doting chaperone's care, promising to call on them tomorrow.

"I have never been so worried in all my days, dear Leah. Are you harmed in any way?" Genuine concern threaded the woman's words.

"I'm fine." Leah sniffed. "I'm just tired. Do you mind if I have a bath and go to bed?"

Lady Chesterfield's pudgy hand patted Leah's cheek. "Of course, my dear. But I must say how dashing the duke appeared carrying you into the house!"

"Yup. Totes dashing." Leah's dry tone sailed right over Lady Chesterfield's head.

Leah trudged up the stairs, looking forward to no less than thirty-six hours of total oblivion. And then she'd figure out how the crap to get back into Granville House and activate the mirror to get her home.

Man, she was going to need weeks of therapy to get over this so-called adventure.

Hushed voices from inside Leah's bedroom piqued her interest. She slowed, reaching for the door handle but hesitating as she tried to place the voices inside.

Muriel was there, but that other voice...so familiar...

"Ella!" Leah threw open the door and hugged her friend tightly. "Oh my God, I am so incredibly happy to see you."

Ella pulled away long before Leah was ready to let her go. But then Leah saw her face. Her cheeks were tear-stained, her eyes red. Ella wasn't a crier. Something was up.

Leah's chest tightened to a near-unbearable level. "What's wrong?"

She knew it before the words left Ella's mouth.

"It's your grandfather. He's bad, Leah. It was a heart attack, and they don't think he's going to last much longer."

And with that, Leah crumbled inside. The last reserves of strength that had held her upright, had dared her to believe that she and Avery would reconcile, that she could take him home and they'd be happy and Pawpaw would feel better and not have to worry about her, melted away. The world shimmered, and she stumbled.

Ella grabbed her shoulders and looked into Leah's face. "Come on, don't do this. He needs you to be strong."

"How?" Leah whispered, tears already burning her cheeks. "How can I be without them both?"

Ella shook her head, confused. "I'm sorry, sweetie. We have to get back to the mirror as soon as we can. Mrs. Knightsbridge is having trouble keying into the right times now, and if we don't hurry, we might end up in ancient Egypt or something." Ella pressed her forehead to Leah's. "Come on. Keep it together for me, okay?"

Leah nodded numbly. Ella and Muriel flew around the room, making preparations for their hasty departure.

How had things gotten so bad?

Avery's heart, which had hardened over his last night in Granville House, had grown cracks since he'd seen her again. Even on the duke's arm, she'd still been the most beautiful thing he'd ever seen. She made him want to believe he was wrong about what he'd seen.

His stride shortened, and he stopped. Tilting his chin skyward, he searched the beautiful blue sky for answers.

There were none.

A nearby park beckoned, offering sanctuary from the crowded street. Avery sank onto a bench not far from the entrance.

He had bungled things. All of them. He'd not been there for her when she'd needed him. He'd not protected her from that blackguard Prachett. And now he was running away like a beaten dog with its tail between its legs.

Anger stirred in his belly.

How could he be such a coward? How could he abandon her with no word of apology? He loved her, damn it! He loved her and he'd fought for her. He loved her and he'd take revenge on the man who'd dared lay a hand on her.

He shoved himself to his feet and took off for Granville House at a dead run. The duke would help him. He must help him. If he felt even half of what Avery did for Leah, then he'd tear hell apart with his bare hands to get revenge on Prachett.

The meek valet had disappeared, but Prachett had finally woken the sleeping monster that had lain dormant within Avery for so long.

Twenty-Nine

Smythe answered Avery's knock on the area door.

"Russell." A smile stretched the butler's lips. "You've returned?"

"Only for a moment, Smythe." Avery set his bag down by the door and removed his coat. "I must speak with His Grace. Is he at home?"

Smythe shook his head. "No, he has not yet returned from Lady Chesterfield's home. I have not yet informed him of your decision to leave us."

"Thank you, Smythe. I will speak with him myself." Avery mounted the stairs.

The door to His Grace's bedchamber squeaked softly as it opened. Avery stepped inside, his spine straight and his heartbeat steady. He wasn't surprised to see Prachett rise from a seat by the fireside.

"You have ruined everything," Prachett said in a surprisingly calm voice.

Avery prowled closer to him, his knuckles tingling with the need to plow themselves into the man's jaw. "You deserve to be ruined. How dare you lay a finger on her?"

The rage rushed over Avery, and this time he relished the power it brought. He leaped onto Prachett's back, bringing the thin man to the ground with little effort. His fist connected with the man's head. He pulled free as Prachett rolled to his back, snarling.

Avery ducked as Prachett threw a punch of his own. From his lower position, Avery shot forward, his shoulder landing in the man's midsection. The two tumbled to the Aubusson carpet, trading blows. Avery's were practiced and punishing, Prachett's were well placed and cruel. Rolling to the side to avoid a vicious right, Avery grunted as his lower back connected sharply with the foot of the bureau. Pain rippled through him, but he ignored it, pushing to his feet.

"I'll have you killed," Prachett snarled. His face was a mask of crimson, a cut on his forehead seeping blood. "You dare to touch me? I'll see you gutted for this."

"If I die for such a righteous cause, I have not lived my life in vain." His calm answer covered his approach. Pulling back his arm, he smiled. "This is for Leah." Avery's left fist met Prachett's jaw with a sickening crack. The man stumbled backward, both hands clapped to his now-broken chin. "And this is for me." Avery's right fist shot outward, finding its mark in Prachett's soft belly.

The man doubled over with a cry and then collapsed against the cupboard at the bedside.

Shaking out his stinging knuckles, Avery turned to walk away. He was finished.

The mindless shriek of rage behind him was the only warning Avery had. Ducking instinctively, he managed to avoid the bullet as the shot rang out. Glass rained over him, glittering shards falling like spring rain onto the blood-spotted carpet.

The sting of gunpowder burned his nostrils as he raised disbelieving eyes toward Prachett. The dueling pistol still hung from the man's fingers, smoke curling lazily from the barrel.

"I said you'd die," Prachett whispered, smiling with his ruined mouth. He dropped the empty pistol and reached upward into the halfway open drawer. The glint of metal caught Avery's eye as the man drew a matching gun from the cabinet. "Now do it, worthless brat."

Avery should have been filled with regret, with sorrow for his actions that had brought him to this untimely end. But as Prachett leveled the pistol at him, all the valet could think of was her.

Leah. His angel.

She'd freed him of his torment after all.

Even as he turned to run, he knew it was futile. At this range, the man would not miss twice. When the shot rang out, Avery let himself fall forward.

"I love you," he whispered into the floor. "Leah, I love you."

Leah stopped suddenly, causing Ella to plow into her. She clutched at her chest, trying to steady the ragged thumping of her heart. Something was wrong. Something horrible had happened.

"Pawpaw," she whispered, tears tracking down her cheeks. "No."

"Leah," Ella said. "My phone is gone. It was here a second ago."

"Did you drop it?" Leah tried very hard to concentrate, but her head was in a fog of distress. God, if it wasn't Pawpaw, what had happened? It was almost like someone was breakdancing on her grave.

"No, I didn't. My thumb drive's gone too." Ella swayed, clutching her temples. "I'm sorry, but I feel so freaking weird right now. I'm dizzy, kind of sick."

"I am too." Leah's stomach dropped. A sudden thought speared her, and she dug in her bag for the leather pouch she'd brought with her. It was gone. But she'd placed it in the bag only moments before they'd run from Lady Chesterfield's house, so where could it be?

Her fingers grazed over a glossy paper in the bottom of the bag. She snagged it and brought Pawpaw's picture into the sunlight. It faded into nothingness in her hand, as if it had never been there at all.

"Shit. Ella, what the hell is happening?" Leah tried to keep hysterics out of her voice, but she wasn't that successful. Panic ruled her brain. "Everything we brought with us from home is gone. What does it mean?"

"The mirror," Ella whispered as she absently rubbed at her pocket. "Something must have happened to it."

They looked at each other for a split second, then took off at a dead run for Granville House. Leah tried not to think of what it all meant. She tried not to imagine the worst. She tried to keep a level head as she and her friend wound their way through streets crowded with horses, carriages, and pedestrians.

She failed miserably.

People stared at them as they ran. Some shouted, others cursed, but none stopped them, a fact for which Leah was incredibly grateful. After all, two unescorted women running headlong in the nicest areas of London was a sight that nobody was used to. Damn it, if only Avery were with her! She could take all this shit if she knew that he'd be there for her.

But he wasn't. And he wouldn't ever be again because he thought she'd chosen the duke over him.

"Slow down," Ella gasped behind her. "I can't breathe."

The ache in Leah's side intensified, and she slackened her pace to match her friend's. The air burned in her lungs as her slippers pounded against the cobbles. Ella's too-large slippers, borrowed from Leah's closet, as was the gown she wore, caused her to stumble. Leah grabbed her friend's arm and the two rounded the corner to Grosvenor Square.

"There," Leah panted, pointing. "That's Granville House. Third one on the right."

The last few feet seemed interminable, but they finally descended the steps to the servants' area. Leah pounded on the door as Ella bent over, trying to catch her breath.

"Cook! Mrs. Harper!" Leah's hand stung with the blows she landed on the door. "Please, somebody open up!"

Nobody came. Leah kept pounding, but eventually Ella grabbed her arm. "Nobody's answering."

Leah shoved the door open and led Ella through the empty kitchen. There were pots on the stove, bubbling away. The whole place looked like it had been deserted suddenly. What the hell was going on?

Leah shook her head and kept moving. They had to get upstairs to the duke's bedchamber and get to the mirror. Either they had to get through it and back home so she could say her good-byes to Pawpaw, or the thing was broken and they were totally fucked.

The house was unusually quiet for midday, and the

silence worried Leah. There should have been servants everywhere, going about their normal daily duties. But they'd wound their way through the back stairs, the length of the hallway, and made it to the duke's chambers before they saw anyone.

"Leah, look." Ella pointed.

Leah squinted down the main stairs. Smythe's back was to her, and he and two of the footmen were carrying something large down the stairs. A rolled-up rug? She shrugged.

"Quiet," she told Ella. "Follow me."

Leah pushed open the duke's bedchamber door. She clapped a hand over her mouth to cover her desperate cry.

The mirror had been shattered, and most of the pieces were missing.

She and Ella were stuck in 1817.

Thirty

THE MIRROR'S BROKEN PIECES CLINKED SOFTLY IN THE
sack across Avery's back. Wincing, he pulled the stallion
up, forcing the beast to slow from a headlong gallop to
a walk. Even though he must hurry or risk capture, he
could not afford to damage the mirror further.

He'd never expected for the last hour to proceed as
it had.

When he'd landed on the Aubusson carpet of His
Grace's bedchamber floor, he'd believed himself to be
dead. It had taken several heartbeats for him to realize
that he'd not been struck by the bullet.

"Russell." The duke's voice, tremulous but triumphant, wrenched Avery upright. His Grace stood by the
doorway, a smoking derringer in his hand. Prachett had
slumped to the floor, blood pooling out from the wound
in his skull.

Avery's legs trembled as he pulled himself upright.
"Your Grace. Why?"

The duke dropped the gun and wiped his hands on
his waistcoat as if to remove the invisible blood from
their surface. His eyes, though aged, were clear and

untroubled. "Did you think that I'd allow him to harm you any further? Lad, you have borne too much for too long."

Avery took a deep, shaky breath and nodded. "My apologies, Your Grace."

"None are necessary. I only wish that I could have stopped his evil before it progressed as far as it did."

Gesturing to the corpse on the floor, Avery said, "What are we to do now?"

"You must go." His Grace pulled the bell rope. "After the altercation at Jackford, they will suspect you first, being a fighter yourself. I shall rid us of the body and inform the other servants of the need for silence."

Moved beyond words, Avery bowed. "Thank you, Your Grace." He tilted his head toward the shards of glass behind him. "May I have the broken mirror? It is very important."

The duke laughed. "Have whatever you like, lad, but be quick about it."

Avery had gathered as many pieces of the mirror as he could before stealing away on one of the duke's horses.

He entered the outskirts of St. Giles with both relief and trepidation. Such a fine horse would surely draw attention in this part of the world, but he had no other choice. If he were to have any chance of restoring Leah to her true home, he must see Mrs. Comstock as soon as possible.

The horse snorted as Avery pulled back on the reins. He tossed them and a coin to a nearby lad with the promise of more if the beast was still there upon his return. Carrying the sack as gently as he would a newborn babe, he ascended the stairs to his aunt's chambers.

"Mrs. Comstock?" His soft-voiced question floated through the close room. "Are you about?"

The woman rose from his aunt's bedside, a basin in her hands and a cross expression on her face.

"What'll you be wantin'? She's no better, if that's the word you're after."

"Mrs. Comstock, may I be plain?"

She nodded, setting the basin aside and drying her hands on her apron. "I prefer it."

Avery set the sack gently on the rough wooden table. "I have need of your talents, Mrs. Comstock. Your magical talents."

The woman's scowl deepened. "I've no more dealings in the Old Ways."

"It is of vital importance." He'd beg if necessary. Leah must be allowed to return home if it was her desire.

Mrs. Comstock sighed and gestured to the bag. "Show me."

When the pieces of the broken mirror were revealed, her countenance darkened. "This is strong magic, this is. Not only time magic, but love-findin' magic as well. A true sorceress did this."

"But can it be repaired?" The question was more of a prayer.

She pursed her lips and shoved her straggly hair from her forehead. "I will do me best."

A wave of relief crested over him. "Thank you, dear lady."

"Do not thank me yet. I've no guarantee it can be repaired, but I'll do me best."

⚜

Leah and Ella took their time on the way back to Lady Chesterfield's. After all, they had no reason to rush anymore.

They'd be living the rest of their lives in this century.

Leah kept her mind blank. She could not afford to think of Pawpaw or Avery or of the way she'd cost her friend her future. *One slipper in front of the other. Don't look right or left. Don't think of the fact that Avery is probably in Scotland by now, and Pawpaw is probably...*

She tripped and sprawled in a sobbing heap on the walk in front of Lady Chesterfield's house. Ella knelt beside her, pulling her up into a sitting position. It was several minutes before Leah could breathe enough to speak.

"Come on. Let's get inside."

Ella nodded numbly, and together they made their way into the house.

"Leah dear!" Lady Chesterfield's voice floated down the stairs. "Whatever has gone on? Muriel has been frantic since you departed so hastily." She drew up short when she saw Ella.

"Lady Chesterfield." Leah fought to keep her voice steady despite the tears that wouldn't quit. "This is Ella Fowler. She came to take me home because my grandfather is very sick. But...the mirror..." Leah stared at the polished floor beneath her feet, struggling to regain control of herself.

"Oh. Oh, my dears." Lady Chesterfield gathered them both to her feathered bosom. Leah clung to her gratefully, despite the gray feathers that tickled her nose.

The baroness took them into the sitting room and ordered a big pot of tea. Muriel brought it in and she and Ella stepped into the hallway to talk in hushed voices.

Leah stared down into the cup of tea she clasped in both hands, wondering how to make sense of this.

"I must apologize to you, dearest." The settee sank as Lady Chesterfield settled herself beside Leah.

"For what?" She didn't look up from her teacup. Little rings of tea spread out from the tear that fell into her cup.

Lady Chesterfield laid a warm hand on Leah's back. "I did not consider many things in the way I assisted you. I assumed that you were as other young ladies of my acquaintance are—in search of a husband of rank and means. But I was quite wrong."

Leah's glance wandered upward. "No, you were doing what you thought was right. And I didn't want to hurt your feelings, so I just went along with it. I should have told you that I had feelings for Avery before I even got here." Her voice fell to a whisper. "I'm sorry."

Plucking the teacup from Leah's hands, Lady Chesterfield gathered her into her arms again. "There is no need for it. In the end, my dear, all I have ever wanted was to be a part of your success. The tale of your friend Miss Marten sparked my imagination as nothing has since I dreamed of fairy tales in my youth."

"You've been amazing, Lady Chesterfield."

As Leah hugged her patroness, she closed her eyes. Nothing had gone the way she'd thought it would, but she had been really lucky to find such a generous and kind friend. She just hadn't wanted to move in with her. She'd sort of thought she would bring her true love home with her.

The fresh memory of Avery's rejection wrenched a sob from her.

"My lady?" Muriel appeared in the doorway. "You and Miss Ram have visitors."

"We are not receiving," Lady Chesterfield said calmly as she patted Leah's back.

"But it's His Grace, the Duke of Granville, and a servant. A male servant, miss. And he said something about the mirror."

Leah's heart leaped. "Does he have light brown hair tied in a ponytail? And hazel eyes and scars on his knuckles?"

Muriel's head had only dipped in half a nod before Leah was running into the entryway. Completely ignoring the duke, she ground to a halt the moment she saw Avery holding a large object wrapped in brown cloth.

"Avery," she whispered, the words seeming to emanate from her bruised heart. "You came."

He set the object on the entryway table, slowly and carefully. The duke and Lady Chesterfield withdrew to the sitting room.

Leah fisted her hands at her sides to keep herself steady. She wanted nothing more than to throw herself at him and bury her face in his broad chest, but considering the way they'd parted last, she wasn't sure she'd be welcomed. And another rejection from him might just break her beyond repair.

But then he turned, though his face was bruised and battered, and opened his arms to her.

With a glad cry, she ran to him. She clung to him as though they were adrift at sea and he was the only thing that kept her from sinking. It wasn't really that far from the truth.

"Leah, my angel, Leah," he said in a rough voice

between kisses that he dropped on her hair. "I am here, I am sorry, I love you."

"I love you too, Avery." She turned her face up to him and accepted his kiss eagerly. For a moment, her hellish reality slipped away in the wonderful feeling of his body pressed firmly against hers, his lips and mouth possessing her, his arms holding her tightly. She tangled her fingers in his hair and kissed him with all the desperate passion she felt.

All too soon, he raised his head.

"I must speak with you," he said seriously, though he never stopped touching her. "It is important."

"If you're here to tell me about the mirror, I know. It's broken. Ella came to tell me that Pawpaw is really sick, and when we tried to get back, it was gone." Darkness returned to blanket her, though it wasn't nearly as dark as it had been before with Avery beside her. But even the presence of her true love didn't change the fact that her grandfather lay on his deathbed and she couldn't go to him. She pressed her cheek against Avery's chest, taking comfort in the firm beat of his heart.

"Yes, it was broken when Prachett…" He trailed off. Leah looked at him darkly but let it pass. "But Mrs. Comstock and I have done our best, and we've managed to piece some of it back together."

The words rumbled through her, and she raised incredulous eyes to his face. "What?"

He pointed to the flat object on the table. "I gathered up as much as I could and took it to her. It is not a large portion, but it should be sufficient for you to pass through."

"Ella too?" Leah pulled back enough to gesture toward her friend, who stood beside a silent, staring Muriel.

Avery nodded in greeting. "That should be manageable."

Relief sapped her, and she nearly fell backward, grabbing Avery's muscled arm in just enough time to prevent it. "Oh, thank goodness. You're coming too, right?"

Hope and bitter disappointment crossed his expression right after one another. He looked downward, avoiding her gaze. "I cannot."

Her fingers curled into his shirt. She wanted to yell, to throw a fucking fit. It was either that or cry, and she was so tired of being soggy. "Why not?"

"Muriel, come in here with me, okay?" Ella's voice barely registered in Leah's mind, as did the soft click of a closing door behind them.

Avery tossed a glance toward a pointedly staring Graves. "Is there not somewhere we can be more private?"

Leah took his hand and led him up the stairs, ignoring the huff of disapproval from Graves. Damn it, if this was the last time she saw her Avery, she was going to make the most of it.

She led him into her bedroom and closed the door. In the soft, comfortable room, he appeared even rougher, wilder, more masculine. His clothes were rumpled, his cheeks had stubble, and his eyes were dark and wild. He was the most beautiful thing she'd ever seen.

Sitting on the edge of the bed, she patted the space next to her. "Sit with me. Tell me the whole story—what happened when you left me, how the mirror broke, and why you can't go with me."

His smile was dark, but he sat beside her. He took her hand and spoke softly.

"I owe you an apology, Leah. I saw the duke embrace

you, and I let myself believe that you would choose his rank and wealth over anything you felt for me."

"It's okay," she said, laying her head against his bicep. "I've done stupid shit too, and I can't blame you for getting the wrong idea. What made you change your mind?"

His fingers burned a trail along her throat. "I could not allow anyone to harm you without retribution." Avery sighed and lifted her chin. "I must tell you that I am responsible for your abduction."

She gasped. "What?"

"A man named Thomas Prachett. Many years ago, I accepted a loan from him. I needed the money to secure a place to live for Aunt Millie. In return, he demanded that I cheat in the mills." Avery looked away, as if the words were distasteful to him. "When he decided he had need of me again, he used you to ensure my cooperation."

Everything clicked into place in Leah's head. "I thought I heard Mackenzie, the stable master, while I was being held in the cabin. Was he one of Prachett's goons?"

Avery nodded.

She paused, enjoying the small circles Avery drew along her collarbone. "If I ever meet Mr. Prachett, I'm going to kick his nuts into his throat."

Avery's fingers paused. "You will not meet him. He is dead."

Leah drew back in horror. "You didn't kill him? Oh God, tell me you didn't. He might have been a bastard, but I don't want his blood on your hands."

Avery's quick head shake reassured her. "No, I did not. I did thrash the blighter, but he drew a dueling pistol. I ducked and the shot hit the bureau's mirror. His Grace came to my aid, and his shot killed the man."

Somewhat relieved, Leah settled her head against him again. "Good. It was self-defense then, not murder." She laid a hand across his broad, muscled thigh. "But if you and Mrs. Comstock fixed part of the mirror, why can't you come with me? I'm sure they'll be looking for someone to blame for Prachett's death, so it'd be best if you got out of here, right?"

He gathered her close to his chest, whispering into her hair. "It is not my choice to remain here, love. But the mirror is not large enough for me to pass through."

Leah's heart dropped through the floor. "You're kidding."

He held her tighter as she fought the tears. "I am sorry, Leah, more sorry than you know. But it is for the best. My aunt is worsening, and I cannot allow her to languish without care. You belong there, and I..." His voice dropped out. He cleared his throat as her tears soaked the cotton of his shirt. "I must remain here."

She wanted to scream, to curse the Fates for being so damned cruel. She'd been through so much to find him, and now he was being ripped from her forever?

"I'll stay with you." She rose on her knees, cupping his face with both hands. "I'll stay here with you and we'll be together."

"I may well be hanged for murder. I have no money, no home, nothing to care for you—"

"I don't care!" She pounded his chest with her fists. "I don't have anything if I don't have you! Don't you fucking get it? I love you!"

He took her lips in a desperate kiss, and she clung to

him tightly, their mutual sorrow burning into passion. This would be the last time they'd be together, and she clung to each second as if she could burn it into her memory.

After all, those memories would have to last her a lifetime.

Thirty-One

AVERY SENSED HIS OWN DESPERATE NEED TO POSSESS HER in her passionate caresses. He knew what she was feeling because it was the same searing pain that beat in his chest.

His anger at their impossible position would do no good. His need to rail at God would gain him nothing. But he could give her his love, himself, to carry with her on her journey.

And he would.

He covered her body with his own, their mouths meeting and parting, delving deep and nipping lightly. Her hands roamed his body, playing along his broad shoulders, down the arms that held him suspended above her. Pulling his shirt upward, she arched her back.

"Please, Avery." She pressed a kiss to his throat. "We don't have much time."

Her words were no less true than they were painful. Rising on his knees, he pulled his shirt over his head. Her fingers fumbled on his breeches.

"Let me, my love."

She nodded, eyes darkening as he removed the last

barrier and released his erection. He knelt beside her, hand delving beneath her skirts as her own soft fingers wrapped around his length.

"You're the most beautiful man I've ever seen," she said as he lifted her skirt to reveal her soft, white thighs. "I love to touch you."

His hand trailed across the dark blond hair that crested her most secret flesh. "There cannot be a woman as lovely as you are to me." He looked into her eyes, and his next words came without his forethought. "I would love nothing more than to have you as my wife."

Tears sprang into the corners of her eyes, and she shook her head vehemently. "Stop talking. Come here and love me."

She held her arms out to him, and he covered her body with his own. His tongue explored her mouth as his hands explored her body, loosening the buttons of her gown to release her breasts from their confinement. She gasped as his hand covered her pebbled nipple through the thin barrier of her shift.

"Avery, please," she begged as she wrapped her thighs around his hips. "I don't want to wait. I want you inside me."

Though his body roared to claim her, he resisted the urge. He must make this last; he must carve this moment into his very being. Ripping her shift away, he bared her breasts to his hungry gaze. Her stays forced the beautiful orbs higher, and he took advantage of their perfect frame.

He bent his head and captured the tip of her puckered nipple between his lips.

Her fingers tangled in his hair and her hips thrashed as he flicked the tight bud with his tongue. He clasped

her soft, round buttocks with both hands as he loved
her breasts. Her body was made for him, though she'd
had lovers before him, and would in all likelihood
marry someday...

Growling, he refused to think of the future. This was
their moment, and it was their forever.

He covered her breasts with his kisses, and he ravaged
her body with his touch. His fingers delved between her
folds as he kissed the pale column of her throat, lightly
sucking the pulse that fluttered there.

She was so wet, her silky skin parted easily to allow
his fingers entry. One, then two, slid within her heat,
and she gasped.

"Avery," she moaned, raising her hips to force him
deeper. "Don't make me wait, please."

Though he wished he could draw their encounter out
for hours, days, their lifetime, he knew that he could not.
Kneeling between her parted thighs, he lifted her hips to
receive him.

Poised at her entrance, her wet heat beckoning him,
he hesitated. Looking down into her wide eyes, as blue
as a summer's day, he smiled.

"You are mine, Leah. My own angel."

And he slid home.

There was nothing like that moment. Even in the
times they had come together before, he had never
known such pleasure as sinking himself into her heat.
Holding her close to his chest, he stilled himself for a
moment, letting himself sink deep into the cradle of
her body.

"Oh please," she panted. "Please."

He moved against her in a rhythm that felt as natural as

breathing. Breathing her in, he smiled. Her scent would forever be burned in his mind, that sweet exotic perfume that he had never smelled before and never would again.

Their bodies strained together, soft cries and intimate touches building in intensity until Avery thought he'd die from the pleasure. Her heat thrummed through him, almost as if they were connected in more than body. She buried her face against his chest, pressing kisses wherever she could reach.

When her cries grew more desperate, and her movements more frantic, he reached between them and found the hidden place, the one that seemed to call out for his touch more than any other part of her exquisite body.

She exploded and, a second later, so did he. He muffled his hoarse shout as he poured himself into her, shuddering as her body wrung every last drop of his response from him.

He stayed there for several ragged heartbeats, waiting for the world to stop swimming about him. When it did, he rolled to the side, gathering his bedraggled, half-dressed, and well-loved angel to his chest.

"I love you, Leah," he whispered. "I shall never love another as I love you."

"Oh, Avery." She closed her eyes. "I love you more than anything, and I always will."

They dressed quickly but with more kisses and touches than were wise. Though he'd just had her, he wanted her again. He wanted to chain her to his bed and never let her go. But she needed more than he could provide, and though the thought broke his heart, he'd let her go.

They descended the stairs, hand-in-hand, only a few moments later.

The duke and Lady Chesterfield sprang apart when Leah opened the sitting room door. Avery wanted to laugh at the obvious blushes on their faces, but such an expression was beyond him then.

Ella and Muriel entered the room behind them. When Avery would have released Leah's hand, she gripped him tighter. He could not help but be relieved. Her touch was a commodity that would be ripped from him all too soon.

"Everyone," Leah said. "This is Avery. I love him."

Ella nodded pleasantly. "It's great to meet you, Avery."

"He and Mrs. Comstock repaired as much of the mirror as they could, but it's only big enough for you and me to pass through."

He could not help but be proud of the way her voice remained steady though her hands were shaking like leaves in autumn.

As Ella and the young maid carefully lifted the mirror and brought it into the sitting room, Leah stepped into his arms.

"Are you sure you can't come?"

He tangled his hands in her yellow curls, holding her tight. "Even if the mirror were large enough, I cannot abandon my aunt."

"I know."

Their last moments together passed too quickly. Ella touched Leah on the shoulder, a compassionate look on her face.

"Leah, are you ready?"

His angel pulled free of his embrace, wiping the tears from her eyes. "Yeah."

"Wait," he said, and she turned. He swept her into his

arms, kissing her with all the love and longing that lay in his broken, bleeding soul. She returned it with equal fervor, clinging to him desperately.

Too soon, he lifted his head.

"You must go." His voice was broken—but so was his heart.

Ella stepped through the mirror first, squeezing through the small opening with a fair amount of struggle. Leah went after her, dipping her slipper through the cracked glass. It disappeared as though she were stepping into a pond instead of solid glass.

"Love me forever?" Her tears glittered like jewels on her reddened cheeks.

"As you wish," he whispered as she disappeared.

⁓

Leah thumped to the floor of Jamie's house, narrowly missing landing on Ella's head. She rolled to the side to avoid crushing her friend.

"Are you okay?" Ella asked, coming to her feet.

"No, but it doesn't matter." She clamped the lid on all thoughts of Avery. Pawpaw was her focus right now. Once she'd seen him and demanded that he feel better, she could fall apart the way she was longing to.

"Come on, let's get to the hospital."

Fortunately, Leah's suitcase was still there from her aborted housesitting trip. She threw on some jeans and a T-shirt, yanking her hair into a ponytail and scrubbing ineffectually at the tearstains on her cheeks. Within ten minutes, the pair was on their way to Concord Memorial Hospital.

Ella tried to draw her out in conversation a couple

of times on the short drive, but Leah couldn't really respond. Casual conversation was completely beyond her right then. She was starting to realize how Jamie had felt when she'd had to leave Mike behind. This was a pain that she wouldn't wish on her worst enemy.

When they finally arrived and checked in at the visitor's desk, they sprinted up the stairs to the second floor. When they got to the closed door of room 217, Leah ground to a sudden halt.

"Are you okay?" Ella asked, concern in her voice.

"Do you mind going in first?" Leah wrapped her arms around her middle as if she could stop the anxiety from knotting itself around her guts. "To see if he's okay?"

"Sure." Ella nodded and pushed the wide door open.

Leah slammed her eyes shut, unable to face the hospital room. What if they hadn't made it? What if she'd left Avery behind and lost Pawpaw too?

"Leah, come in," Jamie called softly.

With a deep breath that didn't do jack to steady her nerves, Leah entered the room.

Pawpaw, that strong and capable man who was always moving, always laughing, always looking out for her, was lying pale and still as death on the hospital bed. Leah covered her mouth in distress. There were so many monitors, IV bags, cords, and tubes. She could only see half of his face because of the oxygen mask.

She rushed to his side, taking his hand as gently as she could. Mike and Jamie moved from their seats at the bedside to make room for her, and Ella stood in the corner while Leah looked down at the man who'd raised her.

"Pawpaw, can you hear me?" She rubbed at his

callused fingers. "It's me, Leelee. I'm here now. I'm sorry I was gone when you got sick." She looked down, trying to get a handle on her emotions. "But I'm here now. And I found that man, you know. You would love him, Pawpaw. He's amazing and strong and kind, and he loves me."

The only response Pawpaw gave her was a slight wrinkling of his brow. She squeezed his hand tighter.

"I promise you'll love him. But you have to get better so you can meet him, okay?"

Mike and Ella left the room, and Jamie laid a warm hand on Leah's shoulder.

"The doctor came by. The tests aren't looking as good as they'd like. But don't give up hope, okay?"

Jamie hugged Leah from behind, wrapping her arms around Leah's shoulders. Leah's eyes fluttered closed as she took solace in Jamie, grabbing her friend's forearm with her free hand. The world had crashed down around her, and though things couldn't get much worse, her best friend was there for her.

"Love you, James," Leah sniffed.

"Love you, Leah," Jamie replied, tears in her voice.

They stayed that way, Jamie holding Leah, and Leah holding Pawpaw's hand, for long moments, until a soft knock on the door drew Leah's attention.

"Come in," she called as Jamie straightened.

Ella came in first, a curious smile on her face. "Leah, Mrs. Knightsbridge is here to see you. She has something for you."

Leah stood reluctantly. She didn't want to let go of Pawpaw, but Jamie patted her hand.

"I'll stay with him. Go ahead."

Jamming her hands in her pockets, Leah moved past Mike into the hallway. Mrs. Knightsbridge, dressed in plain cotton dress with white sneakers, was standing by the door and smiling widely. To her left stood a broad man, not too tall, with long, light-brown hair, the color of dark honey. Hazel eyes, a crooked nose, and muscles that were clearly defined in the tight black T-shirt he wore.

Leah's heart stopped.

"Avery!" Her cry was much too loud for a hospital, but she didn't care. She launched herself at him and wrapped her arms around him. "How are you here?"

Mrs. Knightsbridge laughed as Leah kissed him, not giving him a chance to answer the question. "I believe I can answer that. He and the duke replaced the mirror, so why did you not think I could bring him to you afterward? The time stream is becoming more stable again, so I was able to time his arrival much more advantageously. It is some of my best work." She preened as Leah turned, keeping a death-grip on Avery's hand.

"Mrs. Knightsbridge, you are amazing." Leah hugged the woman, who laughed again.

"It is no trouble, no trouble at all."

Sobering, Leah turned to Avery. "I'm beyond thrilled that you're here, but what about your aunt?"

His expression darkened and Leah's heart fell.

"She lasted but a day after you'd gone. Her illness had progressed so much that she could not eat."

Leah pressed a kiss to his lips. "I'm so sorry."

He cleared his throat. "She is free of pain now. How is your grandfather?"

"Pawpaw's not so good. Can you come with me?"

He nodded. "I will do whatever you wish of me."

Leah threaded her fingers through his and led him into the darkened hospital room. Mrs. Knightsbridge followed.

"Avery, this is my Pawpaw, Milton Ramsey."

Leah held tight to Avery's arm and closed her eyes. Things should be so perfect now. This was what she'd wanted, right? To feel whole, to be loved, to have Pawpaw satisfied that she'd have someone to lean on. Why did the last piece of the puzzle have to be such a tough one? Why couldn't she flip a switch and make her grandfather whole again?

A terrifying series of beeps screamed through the room, ripping Leah's eyes open. "Pawpaw!"

Pawpaw was sitting up, pulling at his monitors and tubes. "Get these blasted wires off me. Man can't breathe wrapped up in all this mess." He stopped, blue gaze trained on Avery. "Who in the sam hell has his paws all over my Leelee?"

Adrenaline flooded Leah and she grabbed her grandfather's hand. "Pawpaw! Are you okay?"

He coughed and pulled the oxygen mask away from his bearded chin. "Can't stand this plastic over m'face. Leelee, get this thing off me."

"Jamie, go get the nurse, please." Leah turned back to her grandfather, grateful tears tracking down her stinging cheeks. "Pawpaw, you have to leave that on. You need the oxygen."

Pawpaw reluctantly stopped pulling at the mask and instead settled his steely gaze on Avery. "Who are you, son?"

"My name is Avery Russell, sir." Avery bowed deeply, the courtly maneuver making Leah's heart swell with pride. "I love your granddaughter, sir, and I ask for your blessing on our marriage."

Pawpaw didn't say anything for a long moment. His gaze raked Avery up and down. Though he was flat on his back in a hospital bed, he was clearly the one in control. Though Leah longed to slip a reassuring hand in Avery's, she stayed still. This was between her two favorite men on earth, and if they didn't like each other, life was going to be pretty freaking difficult.

Several seconds later, her grandfather nodded. "I'm not against the idea, but I need to get to know you first."

"Pawpaw, you know I don't need your permission to get married, right?" Leah's dry tone covered her complete excitement that he hadn't dismissed Avery's request outright.

Avery spoke up before Pawpaw could respond. "It is only right that we apply for his blessing. It is clear that you are precious to him."

Pawpaw laughed, the sound slightly muffled by his oxygen mask. "I like this fella, I do."

Jamie pushed through the door, a nurse right on her heels. At the nurse's insistence, they cleared the room and let her check Pawpaw's vitals. In the hush of the hallway, Leah turned to Avery, winding her arms around his neck.

"What do you think of Pawpaw?"

Avery smiled, rubbing her lower back gently. "It is easy to see where your adventurous spirit originated. I like him very much."

"I just hope he's okay." Leah pressed her head against Avery's chest, breathing him in.

Only half a heartbeat later, the nurse pushed open the door. She smiled at the tense group around her.

"He seems to have turned the corner," she said. "It's

kind of miraculous, actually. I'm going to call his cardiologist and get him down here soon. In the meantime, try to keep him quiet."

Leah hugged Avery in relief as the nurse walked away. Ella, Jamie, Micah, and Mrs. Knightsbridge went back into the hospital room, leaving the two as alone as a pair can be in a hospital hallway.

"I didn't know I could be this happy," Leah whispered. "What did I do to deserve so many good things?"

Avery smiled and bent his head to kiss her. Just before their lips met, he said, "My love, you have brought light into my darkened life. I cannot hope to make you as happy as you have made me."

Leah's heart soared as her valet kissed her. He wasn't Mr. Darcy, he wasn't a duke, he wasn't a fairy-tale hero.

He was so much better than that.

Here's a sneak peek at

the geek girl and the reluctant rake

by Gina Lamm

ELLA CHEWED HER BOTTOM LIP AS SHE HELD HER PENCIL tighter. The cape just wasn't right. Something about the way the fabric curled and flared against the hero's muscular bum didn't make her happy.

Carefully adding more shading didn't help. Using the corner of her gum eraser to fade it a bit didn't either. The clock ticked loudly, and she glared up at it.

"For chrissakes, I know it's late. Nagging me isn't going to help."

Her pencil descended to the board again.

"I wasn't nagging you. I just wanted to see if you needed anything."

Ella screeched as her pencil went skittering over the drawing, leaving a jagged line in its wake. The studio's owner, Anthony, stood in the doorway of her office, grinning at her. His dark hair fell over one eye, clearly gelled to stay there.

"Holy crap, Anthony, you scared me."

Anthony proceeded into the room, flopping onto the ratty couch that occupied the opposite wall. "Sorry. I just wanted to see if you needed anything. It's not like you to hang out here this long."

"I'm okay, really. Finishing up now."

Steadfastly ignoring Anthony's presence, Ella stared down at the line drawing. There. It wasn't perfect, but it would be good enough, she hoped. Whisperwind Comics' offer was an incredible break for her, and if she could land the lead artist spot on Admiral Action she'd have a steady paycheck for at least twelve months. A nice setup in this business. Being a comic artist, her lifelong dream, wasn't exactly the most stable of careers. But she'd loved Admiral Action since she was old enough to tie her dad's blue bathrobe to her back and zoom around the living room. She couldn't screw this up. It was too important.

Mentally crossing her fingers, she wrapped the board and carefully slid it into her portfolio with the others. She'd have to hand-deliver these to the inker.

"Hey, Ella?"

She looked up from packing her messenger bag. "Yeah?"

Anthony sat up on the couch, eyes narrowed in thought. His leg trembled a little bit, and Ella stared. "Are you okay?

"Yeah," he laughed, an unfamiliar, nervous tremble in his voice. "Yeah." He cleared his throat.

Bemused, Ella shouldered her bag, grabbed her portfolio, and went over to Anthony, who was still struggling to speak. She sank down on the couch next to him, careful to perch on the edge.

"What is it?"

He didn't look over at her. "I just wondered, um, I mean…"

Ella shoved her black braid over her shoulder. "Anthony, can you spit it out? I need to get to Max's before he cuts out for the night."

Anthony slammed his eyes shut and the words shot

out of him like fizz from a shaken-up Dr. Pepper. "Would you go out with me?"

Ella froze. She hadn't heard that right. One of her eyebrows had climbed all the way to her hairline, and it simply refused to let go. Her other eyebrow seemed to be twitching a bit. She searched for the right words, the ones that would indicate that she had zero interest in the poor guy without crushing him. She didn't need a romantic entanglement right now. Her career was finally taking off, and the last thing she wanted was to screw that up with a boyfriend. Anthony was nice, but he wasn't her type. At all. He tried too damn hard, with his skinny jeans and ironic lens-free glasses. When she jumped back into the dating pool, she wanted it to be with somebody who wasn't ashamed to be who he really was.

"I mean," Anthony's laugh climbed even higher. "If you're not interested, that's cool. I know it's weird, since I own the studio and you sort of work for me. We're friends. I mean, we should just be friends. Probably."

"No, I mean, yes we're friends. And you're right, it's kind of odd. Listen, I should probably get this to Max. I'll see you later." She grabbed her bag and her portfolio and bolted out the door before she could pry her eyebrow back to an acceptable level.

Slumping against the side of her rusty yellow Jeep, Ella blew out a heavy breath. That had been a way-too-narrow escape. Anthony had been after her to go out with him for a while, but he hadn't actually come out and stated it so clearly until now.

Ella glanced up at the rapidly darkening sky. The cloud cover was too thick to see any stars, but she wished anyway.

"I just want to be happy," she whispered to the sky. "I think this job will do it, but if not? I'm sort of clueless. So if anybody's up there, I could use a little luck."

Maybe someone upstairs had heard her plea. Maybe not. Either way, she was determined that her life was about to start.

❧

April 2nd, 1820

Patrick Meadowfair, third Viscount Meadowfair, smiled tightly as he bowed his farewell to the young debutante. Turning on his heel, he wound his way through giggling debutantes and avaricious mamas. His toes ached inside his boots. Damn chit was possessed of two left feet, and that quadrille had seemed interminable.

Almack's was becoming more and more like a slaughter, and gentlemen of his age and circumstance were the preferred victims. If not for Amelia, he'd never show up there again.

The young lady in question waved him down before he could claim his greatcoat and make his escape into the bitter night. It was unseasonably cold for April, and the chill ran down to his bones. He had the sneaking suspicion that the shiver had less to do with the weather than it had with the company. Chaperones lined the walls like hungry vultures.

"Meadowfair," Amelia called him over with another desperate wave of her gloved hand. "You must come and meet Mr. Cuthbert. He's ever so amusing."

Patrick smothered his irritation and made his way to her side. He'd known Amelia Brownstone since he was a young man of eleven, and he'd been thrown from his pony on her family's property. The tiny girl had announced that he was her prisoner, and marched him nearly half a mile to Brownstone manor. Thinking she was amusing, he'd played along at the time. Things hadn't changed much since then.

"Mr. Cuthbert," Patrick said smoothly after Amelia made the introduction.

"Your lordship," Cuthbert said with a bow and a bob of his shiny bald head. He grinned broadly at Amelia, who winced. "'Tis a pleasure to make your acquaintance. Such a fine lord as you, yes. I was just telling Miss Brownstone here about my new cattle. A beautiful matched pair of bays, you see, with…"

Just then, the orchestra began again, and Amelia grabbed Patrick's arm. "Oh, do excuse us, Mr. Cuthbert. The viscount had reserved this dance ages ago, and I mustn't disappoint him."

Before the surprised Mr. Cuthbert could respond, Amelia and Patrick had maneuvered their way into the crowd of waltzing couples.

"You know I cannot rescue you again tonight, Amelia. This is our second waltz. The dragons would have us wed."

Amelia thumped his shoulder surreptitiously. "Do be quiet, Patrick. I cannot think with your preaching."

Patrick's eyebrows winged high. "Preaching? Dear girl, you were the one who summoned me like a fishwife hawking her wares. I believe that I'm entitled to a bit of friendly advice."

"I suppose," she blew out the words like they tasted foul. "Thank you for rescuing me from that wretched bore. Mother insisted that I meet him."

"Is your father still determined to see you wed this Season?"

Amelia nodded, biting her lip in consternation. "He still refuses to believe that I love George as I do. He'll never let me marry a poor clergyman, Patrick. Since Father has no heir, he's determined to see me well settled."

She turned her face up to him, and his heart softened at the pain in her light blue eyes. "What am I to do? He's threatening to force me to wed the next man to ask for my hand. I couldn't bear being separated from George forever."

He considered as their feet moved through the swirling patterns of the waltz. It was a knotty problem.

As much as Patrick cared for Amelia, he knew better than to offer for her himself. She'd drive him mad with her machinations and schemes. And besides, he was only nine-and-twenty himself. Much too young to be leg shackled.

"Don't worry. I'm sure you'll think of something. You always do, more's the pity." He mumbled the last bit.

She laughed, and the sound made Patrick smile.

"I suppose you're right. If only you were more of a rakehell, Patrick. Then we could plan a scene that painted George as my rescuer." She sighed dreamily, but Patrick's innards twisted. This did not bode well. He knew her lovesick little brain was churning, and he was quite certain that whatever plan she'd make would be singularly dangerous to his…

"I've got it! Patrick, I know what we must do." She gave a gleeful hop just as the violinist's string popped and the song ended.

"I have a definite feeling that I'm not going to like this plan," Patrick said as he escorted her from the floor.

"You'll adore it! All the ladies will flock to you

afterward, you'll see. Women do so love a rake. Meet me in the park tomorrow at dawn, and I shall lay down what we must do."

Patrick made his bows, and escaped into the chilly night.

Coming Spring 2014

Acknowledgments

This book tried to kill me. It tried its best, but in the end, me and my army of love won over!

To Commander in Chief (and husband) Scotty. Your unshakable faith in me is quite undeserved, but it keeps me moving! I love you more than marshmallows.

To Co-Generals Mom and Dad. Your constant questions about the state of the book kept me working when I wasn't motivated. Thank you!

To Sergeant Frog, I mean, Sister. Heather, you're a great source of comfort and kick-assery. I can't do this without you!

To Private McBoing-Boing. Jason, I'm so proud of you. Keep working on being the best guy you can be!

To Princess Dawn. The first, the incomparable, the best beta reader. Thanks for nagging me to give you something to read!

To Empress Denise. Your friendship is invaluable to me. If not for you, this book might not have gotten started. If not for you dragging me to the beach, there's no way I would have finished on time. I owe a TON of this one to you. Thanks for always being there. I love you bunches. To the careers!

To the Medical Corps, led by Stephanie. You'll never know how much you, Dave, Jodi, Gabe, Keith, and even crazy Lee have meant to me. Just hanging out with you guys gives me strength! Mario Party next week?

To my dancing ladies who've never forgotten me. This is to Shell, Jenn, and Krysti! May we all wiggle in the same space soon.

And to my special ops team. Without these ladies? There is no book. Frances Black and Jennifer Mishler, my kick-ass agents, and Leah Hultenschmidt, the bestest editor ever. You guys make me want to be a better writer. I can't tell you how much I value your opinions. I live in fear of disappointing any of you, and I hope that you'll allow me to continue bringing smiles, entertainment, and spicy scenes into your lives! Thanks for all your wonderfulness!

About the Author

Gina Lamm loves geekery, but don't let that fool you. She's also an overly dramatic theatre rat with a penchant for reading scary books too late at night. She belly dances too much, tweets too often, and lives her life with a passion that could be considered foolish. She's addicted to stories and loves nothing more than penning funny, emotional tales of love, lust, and entertaining mishaps. Married to a real-life superhero, she lives with her beloved family in rural North Carolina, surrounded by tobacco farms, possums, and the occasional hurricane. When not writing, you can usually find her fishing or playing *World of Warcraft*. Badly. Visit her online at www.ginalamm.net anytime.

WHITE-KNUCKLE SUSPENSE IN A TALE
OF HORROR SO REAL IT COULD
HAPPEN TO YOU TODAY...
AND BE IN BLACK HEADLINES
AROUND THE WORLD TOMORROW...

**Look Up and You Will See
Death on a Black Lava Slope
One Hundredth of a Second Away . . .**

This is the gripping, alarming, fascinating thriller of 190 people aboard an airliner headed for disaster. Some will live, some will die . . . some will survive to find out why it happened . . .

MIKE DUCKHAM, the pilot, the onetime hard drinking, womanizing, much decorated ex-RAF fighter-pilot. He would know the reason why . . .

GEORGE RAVEN, the flight engineer, who liked to laugh at everything; who warned of a nasty storm over that "bloody volcano" . . .

MAC PHERSON, the medical half of the British investigating team, who realized the public would never know how many deaths could have been avoided . . .

STELLA, the stewardess. Her beauty could turn heads; had she turned Mike's . . . and filled him full of guilt?

PETER NYREN, the first officer. He had quarreled with Mike and bedded down with Stella . . . now he had to call the heading . . . right on the nose.

JOHN HOWLETT

Tango November

For all those who helped

Tango November
A Bantam Book / .published by arrangement with
Atheneum Publishers, 122 E. 42nd St.
N.Y.C. 10017

PRINTING HISTORY
Atheneum Edition / June 1977
Bantam edition / April 1979

Bantam Books are published by Bantam Books, Inc. Its trade-
mark, consisting of the words "Bantam Books" and the por-
trayal of a bantam, is Registered in U.S. Patent and Trademark
Office and in other countries. Marca Registrada. Bantam
Books, Inc., 666 Fifth Avenue, New York, New York 10019.

International Aviation Phonetic Alphabet

A—ALPHA	N—NOVEMBER
B—BRAVO	O—OSCAR
C—CHARLIE	P—PAPA
D—DELTA	Q—QUEBEC
E—ECHO	R—ROMEO
F—FOXTROT	S—SIERRA
G—GOLF	T—TANGO
H—HOTEL	U—UNIFORM
I—INDIA	V—VICTOR
J—JULIETTE	W—WHISKEY
K—KILO	X—X-RAY
L—LIMA	Y—YANKEE
M—MIKE	Z—ZULU

Prologue

Mike Duckham left home as light faded on a warm September evening. He slipped away as he liked to do quietly and with a minimum of fuss, though little Clara had come running from the nursery following him downstairs, repeating good-byes in her singsong voice. She would not be hushed, stretching to open the front-door latch and standing on the gravel to call farewells at five-second intervals as the car backed out of the garage.

Mike had been laughing from the driver's seat but when Julia ran from the house to gather up Clara those endless good-byes were singsonging in her head and she touched wood on the door lintel as she carried the child back inside. She would remember forever the heavy sweet apple smell of that evening; the white car with its whiter exhaust smoke moving away down the drive; Mike's hand waving out of the window.

It was trouble from the moment he signed in; three night flight legs after a four-day rest; a delayed plane;

the voluble wearisome George Raven for flight engineer; and a sour-looking Peter Nyren standing in for a first officer who was off sick. "Sorry," said the scheduler. "There's no one else available."

They sat around with the girls in the crew room listening to a series of bad knee-slapping George Raven jokes. When flight dispatch confirmed the delay Mike Duckham left the others and retired to his office to clear up some of his paperwork. He should have been sociable, especially with Peter. It was an obvious occasion to patch up their quarrel, but Mike was tired and flat. He'd lain in bed all afternoon without even approaching sleep, and now his eyes were drooping and his neck beginning to ache. Off-duty he'd have felt like a stiff drink.

G-FETN, "Tango November," had been held up in Germany. A false fire warning during a military charter flight into Stuttgart had meant checks on the number two engine, and by the time the plane returned to base at Gatwick its schedules were running over two hours late. Distant girls in the terminal building coped with frayed tempers and the particular anger of one youthfully dressed not-so-young man on his honeymoon. Departure was further delayed when Duckham requested another report on the number two engine. The log entry at Gatwick repeated the German engineer's: "Checked for hot gas leaks. Fire wire checked. Ground run and found serviceable."

Tango November was an American-built 119, a T-tail design with the three engines grouped at the rear, similar in size and configuration to a Boeing 727, in silhouette to a Tupolev 154—a good-looking monster, shining under the airport lights as Duckham walked out to climb on board. He smelt the weather. It was a humid still night and no doubt they'd be back in time for some early morning fog. The old Death's Head fighter pilot grinned somewhere in Duckham's skull. *If we get back.*

Flight GC 523 taxied out for takeoff at 01.25: a crew of nine and 181 passengers—two holiday charters totaling 87 bound for Sicily; 40 members of an Italian society from New York already in the twelfth hour of their journey; and a private social club booking of 54 for Malta.

Soon after takeoff the company radio came up with information on one of the holiday passengers, Mr. Julius Janius, the honeymoon man. They had found out who he was and requested Duckham to give him a bit of the treatment. Mr. Janius had been a well-known young tycoon in the far-off Swinging Sixties. Once they had reached cruising level Duckham moved back into the passenger cabin. The senior hostess indicated the honeymoon couple with a discreet nod of the head, and Duckham stopped to address the man by name.

"I'm sorry about the delay, Mr. Janius" . . . and the bullshit worked its usual magic—the name, the fact of being singled out from the crowd. Mr. Honeymoon was very mollified; his new young wife very impressed.

Tango November had flown a Seaford One Standard Instrument Departure, climbing to 29,000 feet over the French coast. A wrong 'un. Twenty minutes beyond Rambouillet the flight engineer noticed the oil temperature rising on the constant-speed drive to the number one generator.

"Switching essential power to number two generator."

"Trouble?"

"Oil temperature on number one generator. I've taken her off the line and I'm running it isolated."

A minute later the engineer spoke again. "Temperature's still up, skipper. Tripping the CSD." Number one generator was disengaged irrevocably now—useless until it was serviced and reset on the ground.

"White rabbits," said the flight engineer. "Looks like we got a bad battery as well. It's charging too high."

A wrong'un. As they passed the coastline over Genoa they were given the weather report from Sicily: Taormina-Peloritana was socked in; runway visual range down to 1,800 feet; cloud base at two hundred feet—the bare minimum required.

"Hercules Tango November, you are clear to the beacon Kilo Lima at flight level one one five." Air traffic controller at Taormina–Peloritana. His English was heavily accented but his voice was clear.

"Roger, Taormina. Descending to one one five."

The T-tail 119 was moving four miles above the Mediterranean at 450 knots southeast into the mocking clarity of a clear dawn sky, ninety tons of silver bird sinking slowly toward an isolated bank of cloud on the horizon.

The Italian voice in the headset dropped its formality: *"Good to hear you, Hercules."*

The flight engineer slapped his knee and laughed. "Blimey! He really can talk English."

"Sorry we're late, Taormina. Can we have the weather again."

"Stand by, Hercules."

The engineer laughed again. "He's licking his finger and sticking his hand out of the window." Flight engineer George Raven, thirty-nine years old, ex-RAF, voluble to a fault.

"Taormina weather at o three hundred hours. Light rain. Wind one four zero at five knots, cloud base at six hundred feet. Runway visibility at 1,950 feet. QNH one zero zero six."

"Thank you, Taormina." Thank you for nothing, Duckham thought.

"He's creeping the RVR up. He'll push it to two thousand if he wants us there."

George Raven, sideways behind the pilots, hadn't stopped chattering all night, but for once Duckham shared his sentiments. He still wasn't sure where he would put down. Twelve months ago he'd have given up this borderline visibility and settled for Malta. Visibility in Sicily was bound to clear after sunrise.

But twelve months ago he hadn't been a fleet captain, and the finer points of airline economics had never influenced his decisions. They were nearly three hours late tonight, and there was a large party waiting in Malta for the return flight to Gatwick. If he went straight to Malta now there would be no room to take the new party on board, and that would mean a couple of extra legs flying between the islands. Another two hours' delay compounded for Saturday's schedules.

"There's a nasty storm echo waiting for us." The flight engineer was chirping again, one eye on the weather radar. "It's that bloody volcano, that's what it is. The biggest tit south of Mont Blanc and north of Kilimanjaro. It picks up all the dirty weather that's lying around."

Duckham looked at the scattering of pale green storm dots on the radar. He knew the island from hairier times and remembered suddenly and briefly one moment of terrified panic in a Mosquito thirty or so years ago. It had nearly killed him once, that mountain.

"It's a lousy runway if it's wet." The flight engineer, feeding some more bad news to Duckham's insides.

"Approach and descent checks," said Duckham to shut him up, and the three men took up their check lists.

"Seat-belt signs."

"On."

"Radio altimeters."

"On. Decision height set."

"Flight instruments and transfer switches."

"Checked and set."

"Air condition and pressurization."

"Set."

"Fuel."

"Set for landing."

The checks went on, voices, eyes, and hands reacting mechanically. Duckham took up the instrument-approach chart for Taormina–Peloritana. 1943, he was thinking. His first year of operational flying. Out over the Med. He and his wingman had been shooting up trains on the Italian mainland and a 109 had chased them home—home being one of the recently captured Sicilian fields. Sigonella, was it? They had flown into a bank of cloud to lose the Messerschmitt, then found it so rough inside they'd forgotten all about the mountain.

Peter Nyren called out an altitude check from the seat beside Duckham: "Five hundred to ninety to one one five." Duckham nodded but one half of his mind was still wandering.

Ten feet above the trees they'd been when they came out of the cloud, both of them sick with the turbulence, and flying straight for that mountain. This would be the first time in thirty-two years that he'd been back on the island.

"One one five."

Duckham reacted automatically, easing back the wheel: "Check. Leveling at one one five."

The tower spoke again. *"Hercules Tango November. Runway visibility clearing to 2,100 feet."*

George Raven slapped his knee again. "What did I tell you! They want their landing fees tonight."

"Roger, Taormina. We'll give it a try." Duckham pushed reminiscence away and buzzed the galley. Stella Pritchard came quickly through the door to clear empty plates and coffee cups. A swift breeze of scent and she was gone.

Idiot, thought the young first officer. I haven't even said hello yet.

First officer Peter Nyren, twenty-nine years old, a graduate of Hamble Flying School, 1,547 hours' flying time, and unlike George Raven silent but for procedure since they had left Gatwick two hours ago. It was the first time he had flown with Duckham since one happy and hilarious trip to Malaga ten weeks ago. But their relationship had changed radically and for the worse since June.

"There's the mountain," the flight engineer sang out behind him, and Peter looked up briefly from his instruments and through the side window. They were over the northern isthmus of the island now, 1,000 feet above the level of the volcano and fifteen miles or so to the north of it. Peter had seen it once before, two weeks ago, smoking lazily into the sunshine. It looked harder now, a white-dusted cratered lump silhouetted against the dawn sky, protruding a few hundred feet clear of the dark storm clouds gathered to its north and west.

A blue light on the instrument panel flashed with a repeating bleeper. Nyren jumped at the noise and had to refer to his chart before confirming position.

"Outer marker. Kilo Lima." He wasn't concentrating and he knew the captain would have noticed his delay. Duckham didn't miss much.

"Hercules Tango November to Taormina. Checked over Kilo Lima and taking up the hold."

"Roger, Hercules. You are cleared down to seven thousand feet on altimeter setting one zero zero five."

"Roger. Cleared to seven thousand feet. Confirm altimeter setting."

"Altimeter setting one zero zero five."

Pressure dropping, thought Duckham. That storm center moving nearer?

The plane was banking into a long right turn, its rate of descent now perceptible to the 181 passengers in the two sections of cabin. Their imminent arrival at Taormina had been announced and three of the uniformed girls were moving up and down checking seat belts. Two hostesses were securing the carts and containers in the forward galley. The senior hostess was packing away the duty-free boxes in the tail galley. She was given an OK through the door from her number two and she called the cockpit.

"Seat belts checked. Both galleys secure for landing."

Duckham acknowledged. He looked up for a moment through the window at the primrose-dawn horizon. By way of a farewell, for five seconds later the cloud enveloped them and they were blind, back into the darkness, on their way down toward unseen mountains. Thirty-six years of flying experience did little to diminish the apprehension that began to tighten Duckham's stomach and accelerate his pulse. "It's none or a crowd," his old RAF instructor used to tell them. It was beginning to look like a good crowd on this flight: one bad generator; a doubtful battery; Peter Nyren sitting there like a broody hen not quite on the egg; a wise-cracking smartass of a flight engineer who wouldn't stop talking; a plane load of delayed and disgruntled tourists. And now, a storm, marginal visibility, a bloody mountain, and a half-assed airfield, which only the first officer had ever flown into before. Serve the moody bugger right if I made Peter fly it in, Duckham thought. It was Peter who now warned him of their approach to clearance.

"Five hundred to go to seven thousand."

"Hercules Tango November approaching seven thousand."

The airport voice was casual and confident: *"Roger, Hercules. Reclear down to four thousand for ILS on Runway two nine."*

"Roger. Cleared for ILS on Runway two nine."

"Call me when procedure turn complete."

"Roger." Duckham looked over at Peter Nyren.

"Time me fifty seconds. Gear down and landing checks."

"Spoiler switches."

"Armed."

"No smoking signs."

"On."

"Antiskid."

"On and check."

"Five hundred feet to four thousand feet. Ten seconds to fifty seconds."

The approach turn had taken them out over the sea. It was time now to head themselves back at the island and the airfield, hopefully to find the Instrument Landing System.

"Gear down and three greens."

"Four thousand feet."

"Leveling out at four thousand."

"Localizer alive."

A voice laughed in Duckham's ear. "Miracle number one." George Raven was swiveled round to monitor the letdown.

"Established on the ILS. Four thousand feet."

"Roger, Tango November. Call me on outer marker."

Nyren called out as they picked up the landing system on their instruments. "Glide slope alive."

The Raven laughed again in Duckham's ear. "Miracle number two!"

"Shut up, George!"

They were on the glide path beamed up at them from the airfield, the magic thread that would, all being well, guide them down to the threshold and the moment when they made visual contact with the runway. The blue light and bleeper activated again.

"Outer marker." Peter Nyren paused to check on the letdown chart. "We're two hundred feet too high."

"Hell! It checks out on my side. I'd say it looks good. Confirm glide slope your side."

Peter confirmed: "Check on the glide slope."

The flight engineer muttered again behind Duckham: "Bloody marvelous. I bet they changed the slope and forgot to tell anyone."

"OK. Let's have a bit of quiet. *Tango November over outer marker.*"

"*Roger. Tango November, you are clear to land.*"

Tired ground staff on the apron at Taormina–Peloritana began to hear the approaching whine. They had been waiting five hours for this one delayed flight—two fuel attendants, a tractor-tug driver, six baggage handlers, four immigration officials, a couple of policemen, and the travel couriers with their bus drivers.

It was around half past five (GMT plus two) on a cool, wet morning, the 119 settling steep, sitting elegantly back on its tail. So far it had made a perfectly normal approach: the synchronized green-red-green of the warning lights visible to the ground in patches where the cloud thinned; their blip fading from a distant radar screen as the plane descended below the profile of the hills; the 15,000-pound thrust turbofans a slow whistling roar over a sleeping stone village. But the last nine minutes of many lives were already counting down. The 119 was Tango November, the black headline all round the world in tomorrow's newspapers.

Part One

1

    "Taormina calling Hercules Tango November—" The call was repeated twice through shattered headsets before the radio faded on the flight deck.

Two minutes after impact survivors started to move and cry out in the wreckage. Of the 190 passengers and crew less than half were yet medically dead. The senior hostess in her folding seat at the back of the plane found herself able to move. The left-side engine under the tail had torn into the fuselage on impact, smashing the galley bulkhead against which she had been sitting, cutting a space open for her to fall into, still strapped to the broken wall. No one around her seemed conscious. The shouting was farther forward. It was three and a half minutes after impact when she had freed herself from the straps and the wreckage. She tried to activate the left-side rear emergency exit, but the tilt of the fuselage had jammed the exit against the ground outside. The ventral staircase that let down under the tail was smashed and locked solid. The right-side emergency exit was tilted too high for her to exert the

necessary pressure to open it. She started to crawl
forward on her hands and knees around bodies and a
jumble of loose and broken seats. "Is there anyone
there?" She repeated the question over and over, crying
to herself for all those motionless and distorted people.
She remembered their faces row by row, some of them
angry, some of them forgiving, a couple of them drunk,
most of them eventually asleep. Fire, she was thinking
to herself. She could smell kerosene.

Kerosene from ruptured fuel lines was draining
slowly into the accumulation of wreckage at the tail.
Five minutes after impact the fuel level rose high
enough to make contact with the still hot left-side
engine. The fuel ignited and progressively through the
next ten minutes passengers between rows 31 and 22,
immobilized by injuries, began to choke or burn to
death. The senior hostess, still crawling forward
through the debris in the cabin, had reached row 23
before she finally succumbed to the fumes. She died,
unconscious, a minute and a half later.

In the midsection of fuselage the tilt of the plane had
thrown cabin wreckage against both left-wing exits, and
none of the passengers between rows 13 and 19 were in
a fit condition to clear these exits. Their only chance of
evacuation was through a gap where the fuselage had
split just forward of the main bulkhead in the midplane
toilet. No one saw the gap and the only people to
escape from this wing section of the 119 were the air
hostess Stella Pritchard and a five-year-old girl called
Trixie. They had both been thrown through that gap as
the crash occurred.

In the darkness and the confusion there were only
isolated cries of distress or pain. Two passengers from
one of the few rear-facing rows of seats in the forward
section had escaped without major limb fractures and
the noise they were making in the attempt to free
themselves convinced everyone else that a rescue party

was already at work. But fourteen minutes after impact the heat of the fire below the tail created enough draught to counteract the lateral ventilation of the northwesterly breeze. The poisoning effect of carbon monoxide with cyanide from burning plastics began to spread from row 21 forward to the fuselage break, and the presence of cyanide in the atmosphere made it impossible for anyone to hold their breath or control their respiration.

The realization of fire in the narrow fuselage created panic among the conscious survivors, a deformed, contorted hysteria of people trapped, gassed, and unable to move. It was in that ugliness and with that fear that most of them died.

Air traffic control in Catania had been alerted by telephone from Taormina and they raised the alarm for a missing plane some nine minutes after impact. A coast guard helicopter and an Italian air force Sea King on exercise were both diverted to search.

The smoke of the fire was finally spotted by the coast guard helicopter thirty-four minutes after the crash. Fifteen more minutes passed while the helicopter moved inland and up the long slope of the mountain. It was flying dangerously near to its own altitude limits and proceeding with appropriate caution. Forty-nine minutes after impact the wreckage was positively identified, and the helicopter landed as best it could on the rough lava. An air hostess and a little girl were found clear of the wreckage and apparently still alive. They were covered with blankets to await stretchers. The air force Sea King arrived a few minutes later. Marker flares were lit and the pilots joined the coast guard in their attempts to clamber into the wreckage.

Twenty miles away in Catania police woke the procuratore generale and informed him that a major disaster with fatalities had occurred. The procuratore detailed an elderly and senior magistrato to take charge of rescue and investigation. The magistrato issued an immediate request through the prefettura for assistance from NATO air force bases.

Sixty-one minutes after impact the first heavy rescue and fire-fighting helicopters arrived overhead, an Italian air force Boeing-Vertol 114 and a USAF Sikorsky S-64 Skycrane.

Tino G. on his first visit back to his parents' homeland was bent double and buried under seats and other bodies, his own body broken and in pain. He could feel the warm wetness of blood down his legs and could sense unknown hideousness where his bent-up stomach was holding wounds together. He hoped no one would ever realize how long it had taken him to die and he wondered if anyone would find the fragments of the autographed guitar he had been holding between his knees.

The words of a song were running through his head without their tune, which he could not remember.

Sweet dreams and flying machines
in pieces on the ground.

2

The night duty officer in the Department of Trade and Industry glasshouse on Victoria Street read off the telex at ten minutes past six on that Saturday morning. The message followed the outlines of International Civil Aviation Organization protocol, but the facts were sparse, and the duty officer checked for further information with Reuters and Associated Press before calling the duty senior inspector at his south London home. It was 06.17 (GMT plus one hour) when Ralph Burden picked up his bedside phone.

"There's an accident AFTN, sir." The duty officer read out the details on the telex: a 119 belonging to Hercules and registered in Britain had crashed on the slopes of a mountain in Sicily. "I checked with the news agencies. There's no indication of damage or casualties."

Burden's duty list was lying under the telephone, and he made his own calls without stirring from bed, alerting two members of the standby team for departure and dictating messages for the RAF pathologist and dentist at Halton. As an afterthought he left word with the night staff at the undertakers in Edgware Road. Four calls in seven minutes, clipped, unapologetic, naked for the lack of facts.

The PBX operator at Halton was having more difficulty with his messages. The dentist had gone away for the weekend, and the pathologist wasn't answering. The operator listened to the ringing tone for two minutes, then used another line to check the number through the exchange. Mac Pherson, the operator was thinking with a grin, hung over with drink or sex.

European headquarters for Hercules flights, were temporarily accommodated in crowded offices at Gatwick, where the busy end-of-season Saturday had been in disarray all night. Tango November had left for Sicily and Malta nearly three hours late, and there were four holiday charters throughout Saturday that were bound to inherit the delay. The flight coordinator had been searching for possible ways to juggle their seven 119s variously engaged in Europe and the Near East. Between them, flight coordinator and computer were just about cracking the equation when the crewing officer took an outside call in the next office and banged with pale-faced urgency on the glass partition. Associated Press was asking for the crew and charter details of a crashed plane in Sicily. It was Hercules flight's first notification of disaster, and within a minute its entire switchboard was lit up with incoming calls from the other press agencies and newspapers.

A disaster-procedure team was hastily improvised and an office and telephone lines borrowed from a neighboring airline. But it took twenty minutes to obtain confirmation of the accident from Italy, and no one seemed able to give them an assessment of casualties and damage.

The disaster team began to contact the travel companies who had contracted the charters, and the families of the nine crew members involved.

Julia Duckham was in the kitchen when the telephone rang. She'd been up early expecting her husband back any time for a meal. His bed was already made up in the black-painted dressing room he used for daytime sleeping. He had called last night from the airport to tell her about their delayed departure and to warn her he would be back later than expected.

"You'll never guess who I'm flying with."

"Not Peter?"

"The P_2 went sick and Peter's on standby. If he wants to make friends I might bring him back for breakfast."

Why bother with him, Julia had thought, but she'd prepared enough food just in case. One of Michael's early morning specials, neither breakfast nor supper: a cress soup, kidneys, bacon, eggs, sausages, tomatoes, a bowl of autumn raspberries from the garden, and a glass of wine to help him sleep.

Even at seven in the morning the sound of the telephone caused her no anxiety. The superstition of the evening before had long since passed away, and she assumed the call was Mike to say he was on his way from Gatwick.

But she didn't know the voice on the line at the other

end, a soft southern-states American drawl trying to establish the need for calm optimism. "Mrs. Duckham, I am afraid there has been some kind of an accident. . . ."

She was in no way prepared for it, not on this particular morning with the sun slanting across the garden, Mike's meal spread in readiness around the kitchen, and the children pattering and laughing upstairs. She shouted out loud in alarm and disbelief.

Peter Nyren's next of kin was his widowed father, the elderly vicar of a thin village congregation in East Sussex. The vicar's reaction to the bad news was almost professional.

"I'm sorry," he said. "Oh, dear, I'm so sorry," as though the soft-voiced American needed his comfort. He replaced the receiver without saying another word.

It was seven in the morning and the enormous Georgian vicarage felt cold and empty. Canon Ash Nyren walked to the end of the garden, through the broken lych gate and the overgrown graveyard to an even colder church.

The village women heard him on their way to applepicking half an hour later, the church organ grumbling away full of discord from arthritic fingers and uncertain legs.

Later in the morning the old man remembered to pray.

3

In Washington it was twenty past one in the morning, and Larry Raille's bedroom telephone woke all four members of the family. "British registered Hercules 119 in Italy," the National Transport Safety

Board night operator told him, and Raille, with a glance at his frowning wakened wife, moved the phone into the kitchen to make his calls. "Don't forget we're having a party Monday," her scowl had told him. "Eight people, all from NASA."

Another twenty-two and a half hours, thought Raille, and someone else's name would have been penciled in on the roster. He had arranged to keep Sunday and Monday free. Raille placed telephone calls to Rome and London and asked the NTSB operator not to put through any other calls. It was the third 119 "incident" in two months and he had no intention of playing "Washington ear" for any political lobby. In California it was not yet bedtime and in California there were many thousands of jobs dependent on the long-term future of the 119. The 3-W plane they had called it at first, for its greatest sales potential was thought to be with the Third World. "Easiest plane in the world to fly," a company test pilot had told Raille at someone's party. And a mildly drunken company salesman had entered on cue—"Even a monkey could fly it"—before lurching across the room to buttonhole an African air attaché.

Larry Raille frowned at the memory. Washington was a difficult place to maintain constant professional objectivity. But cadre pride kept the more susceptible regulars of the National Transport Safety open-minded about such things. Only the politically appointed board members were sometimes suspect, and Larry wanted engineers, not politicians on this trip. The investigation would already be complicated enough: an Italian crash; an American plane; British registration—three nations with a legal claim to participation.

"Is it a bad crash?" The eldest Raille boy was standing in his pajamas by the kitchen door.

"No one seems to know."

"You're going to miss the party."

"It looks like it."

"You could ask someone to go in your place."

"That's not the way we work, not unless we're sick."

"You could be sick."

"I'm not a sick kind of person."

"Gee! Mom is really going to be mad—" and the boy's eyes were gloomy with apprehension as the open line came to life again: a disorganized Italian air force clerk from Rome, fluent in English, but otherwise ill-equipped to answer Larry Raille's queries.

There was nothing specific about damage, casualties, or apparent scenario of the disaster, except that the site was accessible only to helicopters. "There are reports of survivors inside the plane," the clerk told him. "But the plane is also on fire."

Not very cheerful, thought Raille. The poor old 119 could have done without another gruesome crash. "Albatross," the world press were beginning to call it. Ninety people had been killed only three months ago shortly after takeoff from Nairobi.

Half past one. It was the wrong half of the clock for transatlantic flights. Larry looked at his time charts. Italy was on Eastern European time. Even if he found seats on a nonscheduled charter they'd hardly make Sicily before the next nightfall. There seemed no point in waking anyone up yet.

But another voice appeared on the open line.

"Colonel Parker for you, sir. USAF Travis."

That lobby's been working fast, Larry thought. They don't like this one.

"Got seats for you on an exercise flight," Colonel Parker told him. "Three seats. We'll have your team over in Sicily in five hours."

"That would be a great help, sir."

Three seats and five hours to Sicily? Probably the new swing-wing bomber, the "B1," or whatever they were calling it.

"Can you get 'em all over here inside a half hour?"

Half an hour? He hadn't even alerted them yet. He looked down the address list on the duty roster. He'd have to pick the men who lived within shouting distance of the Travis air base: one man for his Italian and the second for his knowledge of the 119. Both of them promised to be at Travis within thirty minutes.

Raille dragged his bags from the wardrobe: three ready-packed bags, a hot weather bag, a cold weather bag, and an equipment case. The plane had crashed on a mountain. He threw some heavy clothes into the hot weather bag and checked the climbing gear. His wife didn't even turn to watch. A year ago she'd have been up out of bed and packing for him.

He called good-bye to her when he was ready.

"I'm not putting it off," she said. It was the party she was talking about. "I'm not going to make a fool of myself. Not after six months cultivating them all. I'll do the talking whether you're here or not."

Larry Raille had no doubts on that score. She'd missed out on the moon. But by all that was New England holy she'd have her man on Mars or thereabouts, carved into the history books.

4

Tango November had set a multitude of telephones ringing in Rome that morning as officialdoms tried to rouse themselves from summer slumbers or disguise the extent of unauthorized weekend absenteeism. There were also warnings for people whose interests might be served or threatened by the fact of the disaster: those who suspected that they could be making money; and others who wondered if they shouldn't be preparing lines of retreat.

In the midst of high-level fluster and bluster one very unimportant call was made to a cheap two-room apartment out in the concrete jungle along the Tuscolana, half a mile or so short of Cinecittà. "Sharlie" Barzizza was wakened by the ringing, and when no one else stirred he got up himself to answer it. There were six of them on mattresses around the room, eight if you counted two girls who had stayed the night. The mattresses radiated haphazardly from the center of the room, each one surrounded by the owner's pile of clothes, records, books, and suitcase, and in Sharlie's case his cameras.

The phone was in the kitchen, the single luxury the tiny apartment had permitted itself. More of a necessity than a luxury, for on five of the six mattresses were hopeful and unemployed young actors, and Sharlie a hopeful but impoverished photojournalist—one of a new generation of Roman *paparazzi* struggling to make a living now that cosmopolitan dolce vita had moved elsewhere.

The call was for him. "An airplane has crashed on Etna," the voice said stuttering on its ls and ns. "A 119 full of tourists." It was Citto from back home.

"So what am I supposed to do? Jump in my helicopter?"

"It's your mountain, man. And the only big story we'll get a chance at this side of Christmas." Citto Risarda from the Catania newspaper that had published Sharlie's first pictures.

"I'm busy here," Sharlie lied.

Citto ignored him. "I'll call Air Sicily at Ciampino."

"I don't want to come home."

"They'll take you down on a cargo flight."

Sharlie put the phone down and stared out through the windows at a tired end-of-summer morning already hazy with dust and filtered sunshine. Soft, lazy September was somewhere else beyond the dirty city or these

weed-grown concrete suburbs. Saturday. Today and
tomorrow were reserved for hustling pictures of soldiers
and their girl friends up around the station and the
barracks and the nearby streets and piazzas where the
buses from the provinces set down their passengers.
"Develop and print while you wait" was the gimmick,
and Sharlie used a tiny darkroom behind a chemist's
shop rented by the half hour. But it was a hard way to
make the week's bread.

An air crash on Etna. Mongibello. "Your mountain," Citto had said, for Sharlie had spent his childhood in the shadow of its gently smoking cone. He
remembered the violence of the eruption as he had
photographed it one winter night nearly a year ago: the
explosions of flame and stone from the crater; and, a
long way below, that slow oozing of molten lava from a
wound on the mountainside. Citto had taken him up
there within hours of its starting and they'd seen the
rocks still buckling apart as the lava exit elongated
itself.

The shapes on the bedroom mattresses were still fast
asleep, only one of the visiting girls awake, winking at
Sharlie as he stepped over her to return to his corner.
He wondered whether she'd come and lie with him if he
beckoned. They were all actresses or models, the girls
who came here, most of them happy enough to hook a
tame photographer to do their portfolios for them. He
sat on the mattress and looked over at her, but she'd
turned over and gone back to sleep.

Sharlie pulled out his camera bag. He didn't really
want to go back to bed, not in this miasma of sweat and
sex. Anyhow it'd take him an hour and a half to walk
into town unless he had money for the tram. By Saturday morning it was usually a question of choosing
between a tram and coffee.

Nine o'clock Air Sicily flew from Ciampino, he

thought, and Ciampino airport was only twenty minutes' walk down the road.

News had traveled in inverse ratio to distance. Twenty-five miles from the mountain reporters in Catania had read of the crash on the tape machines from Rome. When they called the hospitals for news of casualties the hospital staff knew nothing of casualties or crash. "In fact," said a receptionist, "don't send anyone here. Everyone's gone away for the weekend."

The news editor of the local daily had assigned four reporters to cover various aspects of the crash. The investigative role was given to Citto Risarda, tubby, polite, apparently innocuous as he peered at everyone through thick lenses. But since the Alitalia crash at Punta Raisi he had become a minor expert on the shortcomings of Italian airports—shortcomings usually well-concealed. At Punta Raisi they were trying to blame the dead pilot.

A couple of hours after the crash Citto's battered old Giulia was squealing up the hairpins off the *Statale* 185 and through the sci-fi perimeter fence of Taormina–Peloritana. The airport was quiet, uninhabited it seemed, gleaming in the early morning sun. The rain had shined the tarred joints in the tarmac, had cleared the air and given body even to the dust-colored earth in the shrubbery around the parking lot—waist-high sprigs of oleander. The shrubs were the only clue to the airport's newness, for everything else, concrete, tarmac, metal shutters, and dirty glass had been baked into premature age by the sun and the wind on this high plateau. Citto left his car at the main passenger entrance and walked round the outside of the terminal building. Every door was locked and only the distant throbbing of an engine suggested the presence of man or men's creatures.

Citto was not surprised. The crash had occurred in the province of Catania and rescue was being organized from Fontanarossa and Sigonella. This new airstrip was over the border in Messina province and there was little they could offer in the way of assistance or equipment. The night shift would have gone home when Tango November was posted missing, and the day shift on a Saturday didn't start here until half past eight.

He peered through barred glass at the departure concourse: two flag-carrying airline desks repeated forever in two large wall mirrors; a marble floor; half a colored glass mosaic; empty patches of brick that should have been decorated with pictures or friezes. The young architect who had won the local *concorso* would hardly recognize his masterpiece. The contractors here lacked finishing power. Even the clocks had stopped, reading twenty to six in identical lines endless through the looking glass. Rome money had paid for these buildings. The runway and aprons, financed from Brussels, had been more carefully completed.

Citto listened to that distant diesel engine splutter and fade. A few moments later a truck pulled away from behind the maintenance buildings and onto the road beyond the parking lot—a dirty black oil tanker just near enough for Citto to read the top line of its Catania license plate. He turned back to his car, resigned to a thirty-minute wait before anyone would arrive to answer his questions.

The tanker crept down the hairpins and joined the main road in a crashing of gears. A young red-haired man with a flushed and fleshy face and an oil-stained suede jacket nursed the heavy monster down into the valley and back toward the small town at the foot of the hills. He parked the tanker on a wide dirty pavement and walked along the main street under the balconies back to where he'd left his green and luminous orange Ferrari Dino in the Agip Garage on the east side of town. Flavio Consoli.

5

Halfway up the mountain the plane lay broken-backed on a ridge of black lava at the end of a splintered swathe through thin chestnut and scrubby pine. Smoke from the burning tail section spread out suddenly for the space of half a mile through the rocks and trees as the Skycrane maneuvered to aim a final load of foam. Death and damage done, the fire surrendered, and the giant helicopter sideslipped away looking for a landing patch. On the ground rescue teams moved back toward the wreckage in clumsy scrambling movements over the corrugated black pumice.

Tino G. heard them returning. He waited for the sound of their feet on the ladders, then resumed his low and painful cry.

Bowed old Turi heard him. He'd been listening to that intermittent cry since he had first arrived, and the cry hurt him because he could do so little to help.

Turi Pennisi had been picked up from the road nearest to the accident site by one of the early police helicopters. He was medico condotto, the local state doctor, with a multitude of responsibilities covering life, death, disease, and sanitation in a half-dozen villages and hamlets scattered under the volcano. For two hours he had worked in the shattered fuselage, directing rescue with the air force medics, until he was sure there was no one left alive except that voice trapped in the mess at the front of the plane. Thirty-four survivors had been evacuated, many of them close to death, and Turi did not give them much hope for survival in the butcher-shop hospitals along the coast. Not on a warm Septem-

ber weekend. One of the ferrying pilots had told him
that they had already run out of both blood and
plasma, and that an SOS had gone out to the ships in
Catania harbor for sailors to volunteer transfusions.

Turi's coat pulled and flapped in a gale of rotor
blades. Grappling hooks had been lowered from the
huge helicopter overhead. They were going to try to pry
open a hole near the smashed cockpit in an attempt to
speed the rescue of that trapped voice. One of the
blackened sweating policemen gave Turi a swig at a
water bottle. Considering the inaccessibility of the
wreck, carabinieri and air force had seemed quite well
organized in operating their standby procedures for
earthquakes or eruptions. Both teams had been deployed by the elderly magistrato who had legal charge
of salvage and rescue.

The grappling lines tightened and the wreckage began to part in an unearthly shrieking of metal. The
magistrato helped Turi squeeze himself into the widening gap. "Check the bodies of the crew if you can find
them—three of them."

"If they were up front they'll be dead."

"I have to have official confirmation." He wasn't too
sure of himself, this elderly magistrato. He was following textbook procedures.

The engineers from the helicopter had calculated
well. They had told Turi that the front exit and the
corridor between galley and toilet would be impacted
upward, but still relatively clear, and sure enough on
one side Turi could sense a possible way into the
wrecked cockpit. On the other side he felt the wall of
accumulated debris where seats and bodies had built up
against the front partitions of the cabin. Four seats, one
on top of the other, had jammed across the aisle behind
the galley, and the trapped voice was pinned somewhere inside that giant sandwich. It was six hours since
the crash, and bodies were cooling. Turi moved his

hands from flesh to flesh. He found a braceleted wrist that moved suddenly, rings on stiff fingers—a severed arm that fell across him as he let it go in sudden horror. Then under it he found a leg, still warm, and as he touched it the voice cried again for help somewhere just below him.

Turi called out: "You hear me?"

Tino G. heard the voice, muffled but very near, an Italian voice talking in careful English. "I am a doctor," the voice said. "You must tell exactly what you hear to me. You hear me touch your leg?"

Hear? *Sentire*. He means "feel," thought Tino G. "I think so." His words were breathless.

"You have much pain?"

"My chest."

The boy was bent double, his feet and head on Turi's side in the wall of wreckage.

"I can't breathe right."

"Your mouth and your throat it is clear?"

"My chest."

"You not talk. I give you morphine for the pain."

Turi had found one of the boy's arms and followed it back to the shoulders. "We have to free you out of here very careful. It take a long time. You understand that?"

"Yes."

"I am going away to tell the engineers how to free you. You understand?"

"Yes."

Turi listened to the boy's breathing. It was short but it was strong. "You must not be afraid. I come back. I not leave you. What is your name?"

"Tino G."

"G?"

"It's a nickname."

"I come back soon, Tino G. OK?"

"OK."

Turi pushed himself back to the hole and called to

the engineers telling them how the boy was lying. They
would have to use jacks and hacksaws to shift the
wreckage inch by inch, and Turi told them he would stay
inside with the boy. The magistrato asked him again
about the cockpit crew. "I must have confirmation."
Turi squeezed feet first into the concertinaed chaos of
the cockpit. He could see nothing in the darkness but
he felt three bodies, cold, and very broken. Then moving sideways to turn himself Turi found a fourth body
with them, dead like the others, and even more broken.
A woman.

The drama of the fourth body brought the salvage
operation to a halt. The magistrato forbade any more
movement or evacuation of bodies from the wreck,
except the work directly concerned with freeing the
trapped boy. All other evidence was to be preserved
intact for technical and forensic examination.

Only two men were allowed to continue: officials
detailed by the magistrato to search for the so-called
"black box" flight recorder. The two men left the scene
later in their own small helicopter, their canvas carry-
alls heavy with salvage or equipment. But no one actually saw whether or not they had yet found the "black
box."

An hour or so after Turi's unexpected discovery the
press-agency teleprinters began to carry the dramatic
news of a flight-deck intruder and the possibility of an
attempted hijack. An addendum to the drama was the
confirmation that all members of the Tango November
flight crew were dead.

There'd been little for Julia to do except wait. She
had sent the children next door with a request to keep
them away from the radio or TV. She had rung up
Mike's first wife in Richmond, her stepdaughter's

school in Kent, her own sister in Guildford. She could tell them all so very little. "No one knows what has happened."

She had seen Mike alive, seen him injured, dead, shattered beyond recognition. She'd seen him laughing as he had laughed waving from the car last night; brooding and worried as he had sometimes been during the nine months past. She saw him crying as once he had cried when their love and her physical contentment had finally coincided.

She told herself Mike would have called or telegraphed if he'd been alive. She heard little Clara's singsong good-byes of the previous evening. And each time the telephone rang she thought she knew. But every time she was mistaken. Once it was her sister, Pam, driving up from Guildford; then her stepdaughter's school to say she would be sent home in the afternoon; finally a cheerful ironmonger in Woking to say that a spare chain for the lawnmower had arrived. Julia saw Mike again, driving the lawnmower like a racing car in and out the borders, and up and down the orchard.

She thought of 190 other families also waiting in this agony.

Then, just as she heard Pam's car turning in the drive, that soft southern States drawl phoned her from the Hercules office at Gatwick, definitively, conclusively. When Pam came upstairs the two sisters cried for the memories of two separate loves.

6

Taormina–Peloritana came slowly back to life, personnel, buses, and cars gathering for the Saturday-morning traffic: four holiday charters from Germany and Scandinavia; and Air Sicily cargo services from Rome and Bari. They would be the last flights into the airport for some time. The ministry in Rome had already announced the closing of Taormina–Peloritana to all commercial traffic—"until the cause or causes of the crash have been reasonably established." The atmosphere at the airport was accordingly muted and no one particularly anxious to discuss the crash.

Citto Risarda watched the activity from a stone bench in the flight-arrivals building, moving every now and then for a hesitant stuttering word with one or other of the airport officials. He was told that there were no records available of radio conversation with the doomed plane, and emphatically no record of malfunction in the landing aids at the airport. The clocks, Citto noticed, were in operation again and back on time.

When the first charter flight arrived, a DC-9 from Bremen, he followed the two pilots to their coffee break at the bar and talked with them in stumbling English. No, they told him, there had been nothing wrong with the landing approach that morning. The ILS system was operating normally. "But then," the German captain said, "you would not expect anything wrong on a warm sunny day."

"So you say this is a safe airport?" Citto asked.

The German laughed and held up a hand. "You want I count the safe airports south of the Alps and Pyrenees? We make not even one hand of fingers."

"So you say it is not safe?"

"I say already—on a warm sunny day is like parking my car. Now you tell me what was the weather last night."

Citto shrugged. "I don't know. It was OK in Catania. Around the mountain the weather changes every five miles."

The pilots finished their coffee and turned away.

Citto persisted. "What happens in bad weather?"

"Once I land here in a storm. Next time I go some place else. Your mountain he is like a bad animal in a storm."

The two pilots returned to their DC-9 for the journey home, and Citto wandered outside onto the veranda enclosure. An Air Sicily Viscount was settling in to land, and Citto watched it through binoculars. The whole operation looked so simple, the plane and its shadow meeting with light puffs of smoke and scarcely a ripple on the wide white runway. That lump of volcano was far away, not more than a hill with a pretty plume of smoke, and a scattering of innocuous-looking clouds.

The Viscount was the morning flight from Ciampino, and Citto moved back into the building in the hope of seeing Sharlie. There were half a dozen reporters who had hitched an unauthorized ride down from Rome, all of them making a beeline for the telephones, anxious no doubt to arrange passage to the scene of the disaster. Sharlie was behind them, unshaven, definitely leaner and hungrier, but still carrying the same battered plastic bag of cameras and lenses. Sharlie Barzizza. Barzizza had been just a kid when they'd first known each other, Citto a young cub reporter and the boy another potential delinquent from the Catania waterfront, until he had discovered his natural talent photographing a street fight with a stolen camera. Citto had placed the pictures with his newspaper and thereafter shared stories with him, using him for the paper whenever the staff photographers were unavailable. Nine months ago they had climbed the mountain together and Sharlie had made big money with his pictures of the exploding crater and the lava flow. After that he had bought new cameras and gone north to make his fortune in Rome.

The boy wasn't waiting at the baggage counter. The camera case and one duffle bag were always, as Citto remembered, his only companions. Citto caught up with him outside: "Sharlie!"

The boy turned, the look in his eyes defensive until he saw who it was.

"Were you in the middle of another job?" Citto asked.

There was the slightest hesitation before the boy replied. He had, thought Citto, contemplated telling an untruth. But he grinned instead and said no. Citto guessed that things in Rome hadn't been going too well. The Levis were threadbare, his shoes splitting.

Sharlie laughed again. "I just jumped on the plane and came as I am." He had seen Citto's once-over up-and-down assessment of his appearance. He indicated his clothes. "I didn't have time to change."

The other newspapermen were moving from the telephones and toward them at the door. Citto drew Sharlie aside. "I've got a ride up onto the mountain."

Sharlie was still defensive. "What's your deal?"

He wouldn't have asked that question nine months ago. He wasn't believing his good luck. That was another sign of hard times.

"Just a friendly thought," Citto replied. "You give us first refusal on the pictures—and me 10 percent if you make your million out of them."

"A million?" Sharlie laughed. "I could do with a couple of thousand right now."

"You've still got a chance. No one's been in there yet, not as far as I know, and the first good pictures out are going to sell all over the world."

"What's the ride?"

"Army helicopter. A friend of a friend. A favor returned for past favors received."

"Whereabouts on the mountain?"

"Somewhere between the Citelli and the Val del Bove."

"Rough country."

"That's why no one can get in or out, except by air."

Christ, thought Sharlie. I hope I don't run out of film.

7

The interior of the plane was dark and cramped and hot and stinking, and Tino G.'s midriff was still trapped tight in an interlocking maze of seat frames. It felt to the boy as though his body were being held together by that wreckage and he was convinced that when they finally freed him his various components would fall apart like a broken machine. But at least his two extremities had been freed and his breathing was easier. The Italian doctor was still with him, encouraging him now to talk and keep himself conscious. Tino G. had been telling him about the journey, remembering everything in the clearest detail, surprising himself with his own clarity of mind. He had thought that after accidents people were supposed to forget things.

They had left from JFK airport in New York in a big DC-10, plush and ugly, like the inside of a large and badly designed movie house. They were pushed out somewhere in England in the middle of the night. They'd been treated like refugees while they waited for a delayed connection, abandoned in a large airport terminal with nowhere to sit, and children crying and mothers going bananas and the bar shut up for the night until they raised hell about it. Then in the second plane a pretty hostess fixed him a drink and asked him to sing because she saw the guitar. So he'd sung a couple of his own songs and earned himself another drink from the Brooklyn family in the seats behind him.

That was the family with the little girl who'd been playing hide-and-seek while they came down to land. The pretty hostess had to go looking for her because they were all supposed to be strapped in. Then something happened and they were climbing again, flying with violent rocking movements. People were getting scared. There was a storm, they said. Then they came out of the cloud and it was clear and there was a big red sun rising out of the sea. All the people in the plane started clapping. "The sun was so big and round and perfect," said Tino. "And what a color. Like a hole in the world." Then down they fell again and there was the pretty girl sliding around and other people screaming. And then the bangs. He had been sitting facing backward with the guitar between his knees and the force of the crash had broken the seat and the belt so he tipped back head over heels. After that he couldn't move any more.

Tino G. was freed at midday. He cried out once with pain when they finally moved him, and old Turi swore at the men to be careful. The boy had been bent double but his back was not broken and they unfolded him slowly onto a stretcher. His midriff was a mass of wood splinters and blood. Turi couldn't make out what had caused the damage until one of the other men produced one half of a smashed guitar from the sandwich of wreckage.

Turi had been with the boy for three hours and he stayed with the stretcher now as they scrambled it up the lava slope to the waiting helicopter. At first the boy had looked about him at the world outside that dark nightmare of wreckage and bodies: at the sky; at trees; at the shape of a mountainside; at the sweating, tired faces watching him. But before the helicopter took off Turi could see the boy's consciousness fading, the color of his skin changing, and a sudden mist of sweat glazing his face. Turi held the helicopter two minutes while they put the boy on a saline drip, and then told the pilot to make for the nearest town at the foot of the mountain. It was a small hospital, inadequately staffed and equipped, but they would lose another twenty minutes flying him into the city. Something had gone badly wrong. After six hours of great resilience the boy had suddenly lapsed into deep shock. Probably one of those splinters, Turi thought, shifted by the inevitably crude movements of rescue and causing some bad hemorrhage inside him. It was almost impossible now to find the boy's pulse. The heart was racing and the blood pressure very low. One of the medics was holding the boy's legs high and Turi was using the oxygen mask on him. The copilot radioed details of the boy's condition and police stopped traffic in the streets outside the hospital to make a landing area for the helicopter.

Turi knew the waiting surgeon—a competent man by local standards, but elderly, and already exhausted with emergency operations on earlier survivors from the crash. At least they'd organized a roomful of potential blood donors to cover all but the more obscure blood groups, and the elderly surgeon had opened the boy up within five minutes of arrival to find the suspected hemorrhage. A lacerated liver, they told Turi as he left the hospital. Turi wondered if it wouldn't have been wiser to take the risk of the longer journey and go for the larger hospitals in the city.

He walked out into the hot sunlight and returned in a taxi to his village and his own patients neglected since early that morning.

Turi need have had no qualms about his decision. There were twenty-nine casualties from Tango November in the larger city hospitals but only three qualified doctors to cope with them. An offer of medical assistance from a NATO base had been rejected earlier in the day by hospital administrators unwilling to admit inadequacies in their weekend staffing arrangements. Of the twenty-nine victims four had already died and another twenty-three were "critical" or "dying." The two exceptions were the air hostess, Stella Pritchard, and the little girl found with her, but neither of them was yet conscious of their good fortune.

8

Thirty miles away up the coast five men were gathering for lunch on a restaurant terrace overlooking one of the small bays to the north of Taormina.

The youngest of them, a fleshy moist-faced man was the last to arrive, announcing himself with a roar of green and orange sports car and a swirl of gravel. Flavio Consoli had changed his oil-stained suede jacket for a white suit, the combination of white suit, black eyebrows, and dark red hair silencing a table of young American women as he passed by. He turned to look at each of the women in turn before joining the other four men on the edge of the terrace. His father, the Avvocato Consoli, was the only one to nod a welcome. Two of the others were politicians who had been driving since early morning to make the meeting. They were not tolerant of unpunctuality in the young. The fifth man was obviously a subordinate. He sat apart from the others keeping his silence until he was asked to talk. When he did speak it was in a low but very clear voice, a voice used to making itself immediately understood. Captain Duckham would have recognized the voice of the air traffic controller from the tower at Taormina–Peloritana.

He answered questions about events that morning, describing in detail the conversations he had had with the crew up until the moment he had given clearance for landing.

"And the airport instruments were all functioning?"

The controller shrugged. "There was a bad storm. Aural Direction Finder beacons without a Visual Omni Range—that's all there is. The plane could have been anywhere in the general area."

"That's just a theory."

"Yes, sir."

One of the politicians joined in. "You are sure about the ground conditions?"

"Visibility was marginal. It was up to the pilot to decide."

Avvocato Consoli had a suggestion. "It is a possibility that this plane was in fact nowhere near the airport. If its own instruments were at fault, for example."

The ATC shook his head. "The plane passed right overhead. I don't know what happened. I think he headed for the factories."

The avvocato stood up from the table. "Another of your theories. I'd be grateful if you kept them to yourself."

Just how "grateful" was explained to the air traffic controller as Avvocato Consoli walked him back to the waiting airport car.

When the avvocato returned to the lunch table he did his best to reassure two nervous politicians. "The young man will not misbehave."

One of the politicians smiled. "That's obvious. It's Rome I'm more worried about."

"I've spoken with Rome this morning." Consoli poured wine for them all. "Rome will be all right. The ministry's shorthanded. Their senior investigators are all out on a couple of military crashes up north. They can only send technicians."

"Where does that leave the investigation?"

"In our court. The technicians will come. But our local procuratore is holding the reins, with one of his older magistrates."

"The Americans and English will be sending investigators."

"They won't be down till tomorrow. And they can only work on what evidence is available. If I make myself clear."

"What about flight recorders?"

"We can be confident that flight recorders will not be found on this occasion."

Waiters served lunch, but only young Flavio seemed interested, attacking his shellfish risotto with delighted appetite. Silence was broken once during the meal as a train passed on the single-line track below the restaurant terrace. Under the noise it made, only the two politicians could hear what the avvocato had to say.

"We're lucky the plane crashed where it did. The procuratore in Catania is a personal friend."

The politicians nodded. The implications of such a friendship did not need elaboration.

They passed from pasta and rice to fish; from fish to fruit; from fruit to coffee, Flavio slowing with his digestion, his eyes dulled like those of a satiated python. Then as his father paid the waiter, Flavio asked a question across the table.

"I don't understand how you can be so certain about the flight recorders. Surely they would show if the plane headed for the factories?"

No one bothered to answer him.

The avvocato and one of the politicians departed in a chauffeur-driven car on a mission of persuasion to Messina, the second politician went in the opposite direction, home to Palermo. Consoli's fleshy young son watched them drive away, then tipped the parking attendant to look after his sports car until the evening. Flavio had seen the four young American women grouped around a sun umbrella on the beach below the railway.

9

For all his preparations and intuition Avvocato Consoli had been mistaken in two of his assumptions. Both American and British investigation teams were already on their way—the Americans courtesy of a hastily improvised USAF proving flight; the British courtesy of Hercules Flight (Europe).

In the absence of a standby aircraft of their own the Hercules flight manager had chartered a Trident for the ninety stranded passengers still waiting to return from Malta in Tango November. This relief plane had been routed via Sicily to convey company representatives to the crash, and travel facilities on the plane had also been offered to the Accident Investigation Branch of the Department of Trade and Industry: Ralph Burden with two AIB Engineers; and, if they arrived in time, an RAF pathologist from Halton, his assistant, and two operatives from a London firm of undertakers specializing in the identification of aircrash victims.

Takeoff had been delayed to wait for the medical team and in the interval a box of files had been delivered to the plane by the Hercules safety officer—personnel details on the Tango November crew. Access to such files was now the legal right of the official investigation, and Burden, as accredited British representative signed a receipt.

Pink and blue files: hostesses and flight crew. Burden opened each file quickly and briefly: First Officer Peter Nyren; Flight Engineer George Raven. Burden knew neither name. He looked at the photographs in the cabin crew files. Pretty girls all of them, in neat tight jackets and buttoned skirts. The captain's file was underneath.

Michael Edward Duckham. The shock of recognition froze Burden for a moment. He looked again for the details. They were unmistakable. Duckham, M. E., born 1922. "Dixie" Duckham, no more, no less. D.S.O., D.F.C. with two bars. 23 Squadron: one-time hard-drinking, womanizing crown prince of north Norfolk. The absolute fighter-pilot prototype, prematurely lined young face, sunken eyes, and a head that never stopped moving side to side over each shoulder like a nervous bird. Definitely an image for the adulation of younger members of the squadron. Burden did not need the file photograph to picture him. "Dixie" Duckham. You silly old sod, he thought, breaking all rules of objectivity. You come all that way and through all that war and down all these years, just to fly into a ruddy mountain half a step short of retirement. I should walk off this job, Burden thought. Telephone the chief. Tell him I know this Duckham. Or knew him. The chief wouldn't worry about that, though. It was thirty years ago. You don't know people any more after thirty years.

"Your colleague has arrived, sir." The steward was leaning over him. Burden looked at his watch and out of the window at his elbow. They were two minutes off the promised departure time and Mac Pherson had appeared trotting briskly across the apron, an Indian assistant trailing behind him with a heavy instrument case. Even the reporters hushed as Pherson banged loudly up the steps and into the cabin. He entered, bearded and huge, and announced himself, as was his habit, in thunderous tones: "Dr. Pherson." He grinned as he saw Burden. "Bloody man put the chopper down in some field wrong side of the motorway."

Burden stood up, bent under the luggage rack, to shake hands. "Good of you to break a weekend, Mac."

Pherson subsided into the aisle seat and kicked himself backward with his feet testing the seat mountings. "Hope this rotten little soapbox doesn't fall." He turned to Burden. "Couldn't find a dentist. He'll fly out tomorrow. What's the story?"

Burden passed him the sheet of notes attached to his formal authorization. They summarized the circumstances of the accident: hour, date, place, company, plane—

"Another 119? Time they grounded the bloody things."

His silent Indian assistant installed himself in the seat across the aisle.

"That's Sanju. He's training with us," Mac explained, not very *sotto voce*. "Jolly bright little chap. Do him good to see a bit of blood."

The plane moved and Ralph Burden stared out at the tarmac as the Trident taxied to takeoff. He remembered suddenly the tail-jarring grass track takeoff of the Little Snoring Mosquitoes. It was Dixie Duckham who had led Burden into the night sky on Burden's first active mission, talking him into position as Ralph strained to keep the silhouette of the other plane in sight. "Take it easy, sonny" . . . the two years' difference in age had been a lifetime in those days. "Drop her back. I know you love me, but you're more than halfway up my backside."

Mac was busy telling Burden some story. Women or booze. Ralph heard not a word. While Sussex dropped away below them Ralph felt instead the dancing tracer of a Junkers smacking through the fuselage below him, and heard Duckham's voice shouting in his headset: "Left foot down! Throw it around!" Burden had been paralyzed with fear, frozen in the sky. The voice afterward had been sweet and acid: "You got three lives up here, sonny, and you just lost two of them."

Michael Edward Duckham, fleet captain for Her-

cules Flight Europe. Age fifty-three, 18,711 hours flying time. Seven hundred and seventy-nine days of his
life in the air, one twenty-seventh part of his living to
date.

Ralph Burden's mathematical brain could cope with
statistics in a file, but was not sure it yet wanted to
reconstruct memories of this one-time fellow combatant. A pilot always has a reasonable chance in a
forced landing with a better seat and a better harness
than the poor old passengers. Come this evening,
Burden was thinking, and I might be talking to Duckham in a hospital bed.

But the Trident captain came on to the public address two hours into the flight and put an end to wishful
thinking. "There has been a message on our company
radio regarding the list of casualties. The dead are now
estimated at around one hundred and sixty. That includes all members of the flight crew."

A few minutes later the Trident captain appeared in
the cabin and introduced himself to Burden and Pherson, leaning over the empty row of seats in front of
them: "Dixie Duckham, wasn't it?"

Burden nodded. "You know him?"

"Met him once or twice. Nice man."

"No more indications of what happened?"

The captain shook his head. "Nothing that we've
heard."

"Do you know the airport?" Burden asked him.

"I've been in and out most of the summer. You'd
better come and sit in with us. Get the general layout.
Though it seems they're trying to divert us."

"Any reason?"

"I expect they'll close the field for a few days. They
get a bit hysterical after an accident, you know, shutting everybody up in prison and impounding everything.
That's what it's like in Spain anyhow. I cracked up a

car there once. You'd never believe the hoo-ha. He stood up to go. "You coming up front?"

Pherson shifted his bulk and his tray of breakfast sandwiches to let Burden squeeze past. "Don't let this clown anywhere near the steering wheel," laughed Mac. "The last time he did it he dropped nine tons of dried milk into the sea."

Burden followed the captain forward, past the subdued Hercules party, and through the end door into the cockpit. He shook hands with the first officer and settled into the jump seat.

The captain grinned over his shoulder at him. "What did he mean, 'dried milk'?"

"Dried milk and bananas. Vital military supplies. I put an old RAF Hastings down in the sea. One of the landing-strip islands in the middle of the Indian Ocean."

The Trident pilots wagged their heads sympathetically and asked no more questions. Burden's embarrassment was too obvious.

1953, Burden was thinking. A Hastings C.1 on a night flight from Singapore through the tail of a tropical storm and trying to land in the dark. Overtired and blinded by the storm, the inquiry had suggested afterward. Extenuating circumstances they'd been trying to give him and he had accepted it on day one of the inquiry. Day two, and after a night lying awake with his conscience, he had gone back and told them, thank you very much but such excuses were not really valid. It was error of judgment. Eventually he had worked it out for himself. The landing strip ran straight off the beach without approach lights and the runway lighting crossbars were accordingly shorter and fewer than normal. It had been a late-night landing with no hut or hangar lights to give an alternative visual reference. Someone who didn't know the strip could assume they were higher than they really were on approach. On that particular occasion Burden's copilot had been sick from the storm and Burden had excused him from the routine readoff of altitudes that would have told them something was wrong. They had "landed" a hundred yards short of the beach, soft as a feather, with an hour to unload some of the bananas before the Hastings finally decided to sink. Not surprising that the crash and its diagnosis had obsessed Burden. It effectively ended his flying career. A couple of years later he had entered the AIB as a crash investigator.

"If you can't beat 'em—" The Trident captain was grinning over his shoulder at him. Mindreading. But the headphones called and Burden was spared further conversation.

Hercules Special, Sierra Sierra. Turn right to one four zero to take up approach for Catania Fontanarossa. Taormina–Peloritana closing to commercial traffic from 14.00 hours."

"*Roger, control. Our estimated time of touchdown at Taormina 13.50. Request permission to continue with approach. We are noncommercial with government personnel on board."*

The captain winked at his first officer. "The weather's all right. They can't shut the door on us, not unless they park trucks across the runway."

The headphones replied after a long delay. EEC or NATO goodwill had triumphed. "*Hercules Special. Continue approach on one five zero for Taormina."*

They were over the tiny volcanic islands around Stromboli, each island with its capping of cloud. Inland on Sicily they could see cumulus gathering against the north and west flanks of Etna. Burden scribbled on his note pad: Kilo Lima at one one five. The checking-in point for the hold was at 11,500 feet over the outer marker beacon, giving a reasonable 700 feet and 15 miles clearance from the mountain. The descent pattern

circled the outer marker and the approach turn swept
eastward out to sea and back over the coastline on
heading 289°. The outer marker beacon was crossed
for the final time 11 miles short of runway threshold at
5,000 feet. The final approach followed a long valley,
wild and rough with ridges and ravines, but the airport
was over 2,000 feet on a plateau at the end of the
valley and the glide path 3,000 feet clear of any danger.
Distance from Etna was maintained throughout the
approach at around 15 miles and high ground around
the airport was no more of a problem than skyscrapers
in a city approach. Considering the terrain it was a
safer approach than many of the Alpine airports, or the
seaside wind traps at Naples and Palermo.

The runway was plainly visible from six miles out,
wide and long, carved out of the plateau. It seemed that
whole ridges had been flattened, slopes ironed out,
ravines filled in, and the equivalent width of two or
three highways laid out over a length of two miles.
Smaller taxiways led from either end of the runway to
the airport buildings half a mile to one side. It had been
an enormous feat of engineering at goodness knows
what kind of astronomical cost.

The Trident came in, dwarfed by the size of the
landing area, the touchdown scarcely detectable on the
smooth runway. A nice piece of Italian road building,
thought Burden.

"Feels lovely."

"Perfect until it rains." The captain laughed. "They
forgot to put in any drainage. First time I landed here
in the wet the water knocked two flaps off."

They taxied round toward the buildings and Burden
turned to the side window to keep the distant volcano
in his view. It looked almost innocuous, the profile
broken on one side by cloud and on the other side by
smoke from the crater. It was only the near horizontal
angle of the smoke that gave a clue as to the mountain's

11,000-foot altitude and the extremes of wind and weather around its central craters. Burden wondered where on the slopes the crashed plane was lying.

The Trident drew up by International Arrivals as casually as a car drawing up outside a house. The front exit was open almost before they had stopped, and as Burden said good-bye to the pilots the two of them were already into their pretakeoff checks preparing for a swift refueling and departure.

The captain gestured apologetically at Burden. "If they're shutting up shop at 14.00 we've got six minutes."

Burden closed the door on their activity. Cowboys, the computer half of his mind might have said of another crew, but he liked the way these two had flown, methodical, unfussed and good humoredly arrogant. Definitely ex-RAF.

A wall of heat hit Burden on the stairs at the front of the plane. Ninety-three degrees in the shade, after fifty-six at Gatwick. A bronzed and shirt-sleeved Italian air force captain was waiting for them on the apron with a helicopter.

They squatted on metal benches and took off one minute after the Trident, Burden watching their 130-knot shadow as it moved like a tiny cloud over a hilltop village, a green valley of orange or lemon trees, eroded ridges, and the dried-up bed of a winter torrent. He'd never been in Sicily before. It had the scrubby white-rock biblical look of Crete or Cyprus. That is, until they came out onto the seaward slope of the volcano where, in contrast, the mountain contours were rich and green, endless cultivated terraces falling some fifteen miles down from the tree line to the shore, chestnut woods on the higher slopes, citrus, vineyards, and a multitude of villages lower down. To the north of the mountain and perched above the sea Burden identified the hilltop resort of Taormina from his map. To the south, where the land flattened, the coast was dominated by the city sprawl of Catania. The Italian captain touched his arm and pointed.

"Taormina—" The rest of the words were lost to Burden, but the captain was gesturing bed and sleep with his face against the palm of one hand. Taormina was presumably to be their accommodation base. It looked an unhealthy long way from the scene of operations.

They were under the volcano now, rising evenly with the slope like a gigantic cable car.

"Lava!" A sudden bellow from farther back in the hold where Mac was gesturing like an excited schoolboy stabbing a finger at a window. They were passing over a black corrugated ridge of solidified lava that had flowed in some recent eruption from high on the mountain, bisecting and burying everything in its pyramid-shaped path. The pilot swung away momentarily to show them where the lava had changed course, surrounding but not quite entering the highest of the mountain villages.

"*La Madonna!*" The pilot shouted back at them with a smile. Whether the tone was deprecating or adoring Burden could not tell. The captain explained that the village priest had marched out to meet the advancing lava with the Madonna and the statue of the patron saint from the church. The lava had obediently altered course and only one house had been destroyed.

Burden called across to the captain. "How high is the crash?"

The captain showed him the spot marked on the map. "A thousand six hundred metres." Over 5,000 feet.

"Like so—" The captain described the attitude of the wreckage pointing southward, tangential to the

mountain, and about eighteen to twenty miles distant
from the airport. A long way off course on any possible
approach or overshoot.

A road moved into sight below them, zigzagging
through the chestnut woods, glittering and moving like
a river. A road jammed solid with vehicles reflecting in
the sunlight. It was a sudden shock to see so many
shining cars in such a lonely place, and Burden remembered the time it had taken the AIB inspectors to work
through the lines of sightseers on the evening of the
Trident disaster at Staines. Sure enough the jam below
them was interspersed with the occasional flashing blue
light of an immobilized police or Red Cross car. Columns of multicolored human ants wound and undulated
through the lava ridges and the trees—the sightseers
from the cars. But the crashed plane was too far for
them to reach on foot and by the time the helicopter
banked to land the countryside was once more bare and
uninhabited.

Burden caught a glimpse of the wreckage before they
descended: a trail of damaged woodland and the plane
fairly compact, still more or less contained within its
natural length and width. A low-speed crash. On the
lava slope above it white sheets had been laid to mark
the only vaguely horizontal patch of ground clear of the
trees. The Vertol put down slowly to join the other two
helicopters already on the site.

The elderly magistrato, hot, tired, and ill at ease, met
them with his attendant carabinieri. He was unsure how
to treat these new arrivals and while he could realize
the importance of their technical inquiry, he still felt he
had to safeguard the priority of his own legal investigation. He warned them through an interpreter that no
technical evidence was to be removed from the site, and
told Mac that all pathology and identification would
have to be done under police supervision. But at least
Mac's status was not queried. The Italians had not yet

found a local pathologist prepared to take charge of the 170 bodies.

The magistrato detailed carabinieri to keep an eye on the Englishmen, then clambered thankfully into a helicopter and left the site to return to his office in the city.

Burden and his party paused on the ridge above the crashed plane to film the general picture before moving in closer. The plane had hit a low ridge of lava that protruded from the general woodland and scrub. The fuselage had split on the major bulkhead just forward of the wing, the front half shunting up at an angle along the gradient of the ridge, the rear half grounded and badly fragmented on the lava. The left side wing had disintegrated in the trees just prior to the main wreckage, and the right side wing was broken into four sections scattered over the lava ridge. The attitude of flight seemed to have been left wing low, and the grounded fuselage was tilted at that same angle. A hundred-yard trail of wreckage and luggage stretched out behind the tail where the lava protrusions had ripped the cargo holds under the cabin floor as the plane slid to its final position. The fire had started at the rear of the cabin where roof and walls had been destroyed but had worked forward with steadily decreasing effect until by the wing section there was little evidence of burning. The T N of Tango November were the only two surviving if blistered registration letters at the root of the tail. Golf Foxtrot and Echo had disappeared with the central engine through the fuselage and into the blackened ruins. Only the two-toned magenta-and-black Hercules strip remained unmarked, rising with that high white soaring tail toward the unshattered unburnt rudder and stabilizers thirty feet above. Forward of the fire and the break the cabin was relatively intact except for the odd buckling and peeling of fuselage skins. But the front portion was hopelessly smashed, a telescoped broken nose of cockpit piled at all angles into the lava. Some-where in there, thought Burden, is whatever is left of Dixie Duckham.

Citto and Sharlie watched the new arrivals from the juniper scrub twenty yards or so above the wrecked plane. Sharlie was changing a film in his camera, and Citto was scribbling notes for a paragraph of prose that he hoped would accompany some of his friend's pictures.

"So different from a car crash," he had written. "The car is intimate, the smashed car an obscene reminder of how near we all are to sudden death or disfigurement. The broken airplane instead is the shattering of a myth; the frailty of apparently infallible technical sophistica-tion, a reminder, for those who need reminding, that only birds can really fly."

The two of them had been there now for nearly three hours, virtual stowaways on a military helicopter, and tolerated only so long as they kept their distance from the wreck. Official access to journalists had not yet been granted, and with the arrival of the investigators, journalists were not likely to be admitted until tomor-row. Which gave Sharlie an eighteen-hour advantage with his pictures. He had taken over ninety exposures of the plane from all possible angles, and their tame air force pilot had told them he'd be leaving in ten minutes' time.

Citto was watching the investigators. They had un-loaded themselves and their baggage from the helicop-ter and were pulling boots and coveralls over their clothes before they moved down the slope toward the wreckage. They were all a bit wild, as befitted mad Englishmen. There was a tall bearded giant of a man striding out with great ferocity, a turbaned Indian shadowing him like a slave; but the boss here was undoubtedly the old worn face with the thin mouth and

the sharp eyes, peering about him with great suspicion
as though he expected to find the wreckage already
desecrated.

Police, soldiers, air force personnel, and the two
truant journalists all watched as the Englishmen, clown-
like in boots and coveralls, split up around the broken-
backed fuselage. They seemed like a parody of anxious
tourists with their bags of camera equipment and their
haste for pictures. One of them perched suddenly with
pad and pencil like a sketch artist in a ruined temple.

Above them the cloud crept lower and the sun disappeared.

10

Lunchtime and afternoon news on Italian radio
and television emphasized the presence of that fourth
body on the flight deck of the doomed plane. It was
generally assumed, with the usual reservations, that the
crash had somehow resulted from an attempted hijacking. Terrorist specialists were already on their way
south from London and Munich, dispatched by Scotland Yard and Interpol. Though there had been no
exchange of views and no collusion it was nonetheless
clear to various authorities in Rome, and subsequently
in Catania, that a "hijacking" solution would satisfy
many influential parties. After all, a plane, an airport
and a major charter flight company were all at stake.

"Naturally it's pilot error," said one off-the-record
voice in a telephone conversation from an unnamed
embassy. "But I'm sure you'll find the poor guy had
someone's gun stuck in his back."

Early indications suggested there would be no
straightforward solution to this particular "incident."
Left alone it would end up as one of those half-

explained crashes. A little innocent arm-twisting here and there was instinctive and inevitable.

A helicopter pilot later that afternoon received a call from the avvocato Consoli.

"Have," the avvocato wondered, "any oranges been found?"

"Both of them found and both disposed of," he was assured. "Dropped from a great height into impenetrable undergrowth."

Consoli thanked the pilot, assured him that his work would not be forgotten, and privately hoped that the man had chosen undergrowth well away from any road or mountain path.

One trail of evidence had already been laid, albeit unwittingly, by a dirty black oil tanker parked on the outskirts of a small town in the valley below the airport.

Citto was hurrying with Sharlie and his rolls of film to a darkroom in Catania, but when he saw the truck he stopped for a closer look. It was pulled up on a wide dirt sidewalk. Citto walked round it, sniffing at the offloading pipes coiled untidily along the chassis. It smelled like gasoline. Certainly not the kerosene that fueled jet engines.

Sharlie joined him on the pavement. "You want a picture of that thing?"

"With the license plates."

"Is it breaking some law?"

"It was up at the airport this morning."

"So?"

Citto grinned and shrugged. "I'm just a compulsive collector of useless information." He picked up a scrap of paper lying in the gutter and rubbed oil and dust from the offside door to reveal the owner's name:

ETNOLIO, Fuel Distributor, with an address in one of the larger villages on the slopes of the volcano.

It would have been an exaggeration at this stage for Citto to have claimed a theory. But there were two small details beginning to nag him: this truck on its refueling mission that early morning, and those dead clocks set on 05.40 in the airport buildings. Tango November had crashed, they had been told, "some time between 05.35 and 05.50."

11

Passengers though they were, the "go team" from Washington crossed the Atlantic the hard way with oxygen masks and on hard sit-up USAF observers' seats. And for all their trusty official positions they were politely kept out of the cockpit throughout the five hours from Washington to Taormina. The bomber and its equipment were far too hush-hush. The only concession to their job was on landing approach at Taormina when they were given visibility through a side window and the descent-and-approach dialogue was relayed on their intercom.

Not that the colonel had been anything but courteous. He seemed to Larry Raille a very senior man to be flying an ordinary transport mission, and it was plain he had higher priorities than flying on this particular trip. In fact he spent a long time with Raille back in the radar hutch making a rather bad hash of a psyching job, talking at great length of the many virtues of the 119—"the most important subjumbo medium-range transport in the history of aviation; the standard multi-purpose plane for the 1980s."

"Don't worry about the Italian officials," said the

colonel with a nod and a wink at Raille's impassive face. "They want to extend their manufacturing license on military helicopters. They're not going to play Jack and the Beanstalk with us."

The colonel could have saved his breath. Raille, a very nonpolitical animal, was concerned only that the lecture had effectively ruined any chance he might have had of sleeping.

His two go-team colleagues had slept heads down on the chart table. They were all of them bleary and tired when they stumbled down the ladder onto the blazing afternoon tarmac at Taormina–Peloritana.

Cloud was still creeping down the mountain, and all but one of the helicopters had been withdrawn. Apart from the carabinieri and an air force salvage team Burden's men were alone, scattered over Tango November, still photographing, annotating or sketching on their pads. Burden was in the burnt-out tail section of the cabin, his face covered with a mask against the smell, showing two groups of carabinieri how to label the carbonized bodies, how to plot their positions on a plan, how to roll up the remains intact into plastic sheets.

Pherson, helped by the silent and ever-attentive Sanju, was doing a similar job with the unburnt bodies in the forward cabin. They were working as fast as they could in the cramped conditions, unraveling the jumble of human and structural debris, plotting each tiny piece of aircraft, body, or clothing onto a plan, trying to penetrate into the cockpit area for the evacuation of the bodies inside. They had been told that the local doctor who had supervised the morning's rescue operation had arranged temporary facilities for autopsy and cold storage in a nearby village, and Mac wanted to begin pathology on the flight crew that same night before deterioration had progressed too far.

It was after two hours of work that he finally called out to Burden: "I think we've found your buddy, old man." He led Ralph on hands and knees into the dark cavern of wreckage that had once been the cockpit. The windows were lost in folds of the crumpled fuselage, and Mac was using lamps to illuminate the salvage. Burden saw both pilots from behind, still strapped in, crammed down into their seats with their heads at odd angles so that they seemed like stunted dwarfs. The cockpit had shrunk, stove in on three sides, and the two men were embraced grotesquely by the instrument panels and controls.

"No point in looking at him," Mac told Burden. "There's nothing much left of his face." Mac gave him instead Duckham's passport, and Burden nodded recognition of the photograph. He stared at the back of that head and neck: the hair was thick but graying, curled round below the ears, the remains of a headset hanging loose. Burden retreated from Duckham's death.

"Looks to me as though he knew he was coming down," said Mac. "His hands and feet are right for landing. And he went for his fire levers."

Burden nodded again. He was seeing a young fighter pilot barely twenty years old at the end of an evening's briefing, left hand held high with his navigator's right as the crews walked out and separated to their planes. He was hearing Dixie Duckham's voice calling to them all in the darkness: "We all have to die and we only die once. Enjoy it, my friends."

Somewhere above them a helicopter was maneuvering slowly out of the cloud, the Vertol carrying the American investigators. Burden climbed down from the wreckage and turned up the slope to meet them, his mind still trying to relate the image of the twenty-year-old fighter pilot to the gray-haired body in Tango November. He heard his name called and came out of his

dream. He saw Larry Raille on the lava above him and
he waved a greeting.

He'd never worked with Raille but he'd met him at a
couple of ICAO conferences in Montreal—a "jigsaw"
and "crossword" man who loved the fitting together of
evidence and the satisfaction of reconstruction.

"Any miracles?" Raille asked.

"It's going to be a bastard," said Burden. "Not even
a recorder."

"Broken?"

"If they're still under the tail they're probably
smashed. And if they're not in the tail they've been
pinched by the local sheriff."

"Any Italians from their air ministry?"

"They haven't got a team together yet. They've only
sent a few technicians. I'm afraid that means the local
judiciary has rather taken over."

They picked their slow way down the slope toward
the wreckage. Raille gestured with one hand, miming
the landing approach of a plane. "Low speed, and all
set for landing. Was it still dark?"

Burden laughed without humor. "You won't believe
it, but no one really knows what the visibility was like.
It wasn't dark, but there could have been cloud cover."

The investigators gathered by the remains of the
flight deck, Mac towering over all of them as he
climbed down from the wreckage. Burden and Raille
agreed on the composition of groups and read out their
deployment of manpower. The Italians themselves
would organize and man the groups investigating
weather, air traffic services, and the postmortem on
evacuation and rescue. Witness statements would be
collated by a combined team. Raille would be in charge
of site investigation and specifically attached to systems
group. The examination of airframe, power plant, and
maintenance records would be largely handled by a

group of specialist engineers from the manufacturers concerned, due to arrive next day, and they would come under Raille's general supervision. Mac was in charge of human factors group, the aeromedical and crash injury aspects of the investigation. Burden was to head operations group, investigating the history of the doomed flight and flight crew. Again Ralph Burden wondered if he shouldn't opt out of that particular job. Memories of Dixie Duckham had seemed to hang over him all day like ghosts of ill omen.

Raille was asking Mac about the bodies of the cockpit crew and the supposed hijacker.

"Give us another hour and we'll have them out tonight."

"Maybe you need some more men?"

Mac shook his head. "There's only room in there for two of us." He turned back up his ladder to rejoin Sanju in the tangled remains of the cockpit.

The other men were breaking up in twos and threes around the plane, forming the groups within which they'd be working for the next few days. The two chief investigators walked together back along the slide of wreckage and down into the avenue of splintered trees, Raille busy with his camera clicking off a methodical round-the-clock picture of the whole disaster area.

The avenue of damaged scrub and woodland tapered away to their right as they faced it from the tail of the plane.

Burden described an angle with one forearm: "Left wing down. The line of damage on the outside of the arc is very regular—until the wing breaks. It must have been in one heck of a turn."

"Away from the mountain."

"We're at five thousand feet here. That's the check-in altitude on the outer marker. He could have been at normal approach height on a correct heading and the

only thing wrong being he was fifteen miles too far to
the south. He comes out of the cloud, sees where he is,
tries to bank, and he can't make it."

"Anything's possible at the moment."

"It'll be damn near anyone's guess if we don't find a
flight recorder."

"You really think the magistrate took it?"

"We didn't get here till after two o'clock. They had
time enough to find it."

"Why would they do that?"

"To let everyone know how important they are."

They reached the end of splintered death row and
turned to view the distant plane.

"Poor son of a bitch," said Raille. "He must have
seen what was happening to be turning like that."

Dixie Duckham, thought Burden. Trying to fight his
way out of the mountain.

12

The elderly magistrato, sticky and dirty from
the scene of disaster, was back in his office reading
through textbooks and old reports. But there were few
precedents for him to draw on and no colleagues along
empty Saturday afternoon corridors to share the
burden.

The magistrato in the next room would have been
the ideal choice today—a young man from the north
who had done his national service in the air force. He
came from Turin, and he was appropriately self-confident and energetic. So after two hours at a deskful of
books and papers the elderly magistrato telephoned him
at home, with apologies, suggesting his participation:
"Your technical experience could be useful."

The younger man agreed. He was not one for false modesty.

Disgruntled representatives of the world press were gathered in the bar at Catania Fontanarossa airport, their numbers growing with the arrival of each flight. Notwithstanding the chaos of extra traffic diverted by the closing of Taormina–Peloritana the authorities had set up their press office at the airport and what little information existed was being released there. Access to the crash site was promised the next morning and there seemed nothing more to do except wait. The few intrepids who had set out cross-country by car and on foot returned defeated; the flying of private planes and helicopters had been banned in the area until further notice; short of parachuting off the top of the mountain there was no way of reaching Tango November.

They had been allowed to question the men in charge of the rescue operation and at the end of the afternoon the air traffic officer who had been on duty in the control tower was also produced to read a statement.

It had been, he assured them, an entirely normal and satisfactory landing approach until the final moments before touchdown, when the plane had seemed to veer away. After that he had had no further communication with the pilot. There had been no Mayday call and the coded "hijack" signal had not been used. Visibility at the time had been poor but quite safe—cloud cover at 1,000 feet, and runway visibility at 900 yards.

The statement did not quite coincide with what the officer had told Consoli and the politicians at lunchtime. Nor was it a completely full account of what had happened that early morning. But the reporters were not given a chance of elaborating on the statement. It was regretted, explained an air force officer, that since the traffic controller was a military official, he could not be allowed to answer their questions.

Cameras and lights were switched off and the reporters turned back to the bar muttering darkly about the evasive Italians.

Sharlie's pictures had come out well. He had used the darkroom at the newspaper office, giving them in return, and as Citto had suggested, the first and free choice of pictures. Thirty of the best exposures had then been sent on the wires to Rome where an agency would sell them for Sharlie to newspapers and magazines all round the world. On the phone the agency had been disappointingly cool. After all the boy had never made much money for them before. "You're probably too late," they warned him. "Someone else is bound to have got something out."

Afterward, in the car, Sharlie tried to shrug it off. "Shit! I thought at least I'd get a pair of new jeans out of it." He pulled Citto's driving mirror round to look at himself. "The family's going to be surprised. I mean turning up looking like a tramp when I've been writing them how well I was doing."

Citto retrieved his driving mirror. "I'm sure they're not going to bother much about your clothes."

Sharlie's mother had not been home at her two-room tenement on the waterfront, and without a key the boy was stuck. Citto was driving him out to his grandmother's place in one of the fishing villages under the mountain.

"You didn't have to bring me all the way out here."

"What would you do? Sleep on the sidewalk?"

"My mother'll be back soon."

"She's gone off for the weekend."

"Where?"

"How should I know? It's *vendemmia*. She's probably picking grapes somewhere."

They drove on in silence past the lumps of the Cyclops standing forlorn in a yacht-pocked sea. Polyphemus and Odysseus—both would have chosen blindness in the face of this twentieth-century riviera ribboning unplanned and unbeautiful along the coast, Citto was thinking.

"I told her I was going to send her money," said Sharlie. He was still thinking about his mother. "I never had enough to send." He laughed. *"Paparazzi!* They're all Romans. Like a bloody Mafia. No room for new guys. And she thought I was going to make my fortune."

Sharlie's mother was a working woman. A tough little lady fighting for her life on a factory floor somewhere out near the city airport. A widow, Citto wondered? "My father was a sailor," Sharlie had told him long ago. But the "was" had never been explained.

This grandmother out in the fishing village came from the father's side. Nonna Lisa. She lived in an old fisherman's house on the black lava rocks a stone's throw from the sea: a pergola courtyard, one room for cooking and eating, and two rooms for sleeping. Washing was done behind a curtain in the courtyard. Her husband had been a fisherman and these few square yards of habitation had been her world for fifty years. Her only son had been Sharlie's sailor father, and her daughters were variously married in the fishing villages along the coast, or the farming villages higher on the mountain. The children of one of them were here now, a teen-age son and daughter and two younger kids, and when Sharlie walked in he was welcomed back with a great shouting and laughing, which Citto watched smiling from the car.

The boy needn't have been self-conscious about his clothes. They were all far too surprised to see him to worry about what he was wearing. But Sharlie was still worrying. When they were hauled off to admire a cousin's new motorcycle Citto could see the despair of desire and envy behind Sharlie's raptures. It was a 900 cc Desmo Ducati with drop bars and a fancy black and red paint job on the tank—the fastest beast on two wheels that ordinary money could buy. Even Citto felt a pang for it, but then Citto had long ago persuaded himself that he had the wrong physical shape . for motorcycles.

"Do you like motorcycles, too?"

Citto turned round. It was Sharlie's girl cousin who had spoken, taking him so much by surprise that he didn't even answer her question. She looked at the motorcycle with disapproval.

"It's a crazy way to spend money." The girl was very slim and serious with an El Greco face, and Citto watched her in amazement. Where had she come from? A couple of years ago he used to visit here but there'd only been kids running around. She smiled at him.

"You're Citto."

"I'm afraid I don't know you," he stammered in reply.

"I'm Laura. I remember you used to come out with Sharlie. You were on the mountain the time he took the pictures."

Sharlie interrupted, glad of an excuse to turn himself away from the motorcycle. "We were up on the mountain today. I'm working for a big magazine," he said flamboyantly. "They sent me down to cover the crash. I had to leave in a hurry. That's why I came without presents."

Why was he lying, the clown? There was no point.

The girl looked at Citto. "Have you seen the plane?"

"Yes."

"Is it terrible?"

"It is sad to see it—I mean if you think planes are beautiful it is sad to see one so smashed." He was still stammering like a fool.

"And the people?"

"I didn't see the people." Citto couldn't take his eyes off her. She was so grave.

She turned back to Sharlie. "Turi was up there."

"Who's Turi?" asked Citto.

"Our doctor at home. We live up on the mountain. He was called to help in the rescue."

"What's his full name?"

"Turi Pennisi."

"And which is your village?"

"Now don't go and see him and ask a lot of questions. He won't like that."

Sharlie interrupted. "It's the same village where your dirty black oil tanker came from."

"He won't help you," said the girl. "The doctor doesn't like newspapermen."

"Not many people do." Citto smiled and turned to go.

"Come on down to the harbor bar," said Sharlie. "I'll buy you a whiskey before you go. Come on," he added in a shout. "I'll buy you kids ice cream."

Sharlie pulled Citto outside and down the road before the others could organize themselves to follow.

"For Chrissakes," he said. "Can you lend me some money? Just until they pay me for the pictures."

The clown now needed to finance his lie: maintain his successful image, his *bella figura*. Citto fished out three tens for him. "Tell them the truth, you idiot. It's much easier in the end."

The others were behind them now and they all walked together down into the little piazza around the harbor. The children disappeared into their haunts and hideaways among the dirty concrete blocks that formed the seaward side of the harbor jetty, their shrieking unnoticed in the general hubbub. A three-wheel Vespa truck piled high with new mattresses was blaring pop songs at full volume through an amplifier while the driver drank coffee in the bar at the end of a fruitless day trying to sell bedding around the inland villages. He'd obviously left the music on as a public service for the village. No one seemed to mind. Citto wondered if they even noticed. We notice very little, he thought. We live with noise; with the ugliness of the new villas along the coast; with refuse piled on the shore as though trash cans and garbage trucks had never been invented. Even old Nonna Lisa would throw the fish bones and leftovers from supper into one of the gullies on the lava rocks and when challenged would reply: "The high sea in the winter will clean it all away." What are we, Citto wondered. Tired, lazy, uncivilized?

Two fishing boats came chugging into the harbor, cutting their engines and drifting onto the beach. Two families gathered round their tired men to help winch the boats up out of the water onto the gritty black sand. The fishermen heaved the baskets of fish onto the roadway and left them there, returning to straighten and stow their lines and nets. The grandfathers of the families, too old for the sea, took over the catch. It was their job to barter with the merchants waiting in their trucks. Sardines, *bonita, occhiata, sarago,* and some nasty-looking eels. One of the boats had landed a large dentice, steely blue and pink, with a flesh and taste as delicate as salmon. Not a prize to be wasted on the merchants. The old men laid it on a trestle table, sluicing its still-moving gills with sea water, shouting its qualities and its price over the cacophony of pop. Their shouts were ignored by the villagers for the price was too high, but the old men were angling for the Saturday evening cars out from the towns for the homemade ice cream in the harbor bar.

Citto and Sharlie drank their whiskies, Citto watching the fish auction, Sharlie watching Citto.

"You think something's going on, don't you?"

Citto didn't reply. He was listening to the old men with the fish.

*

"The plane. You think something happened and someone's doing a cover-up."

The fish sold at 25,000 lire, and Citto turned away with a smile. "I never said a word."

The mattress merchant drove his noisy Vespa truck away up the hill onto the plateau of citrus above the village, the blast of pop music fading into the evening scent of *zagara* from the lemon trees.

"Some things should be left alone," said Sharlie. "Especially around here."

13

Up on the mountain the investigators were lifted out by helicopter as darkness and cloud descended. They hadn't yet accomplished more than a general assessment: photographs; sketches; first impressions. The only "discovery" had been made by Raille when he dug through ashes and twisted metal to expose one end of the central number two engine. He had found the turbine blades intact, which virtually established that that particular engine had been shut down at the time of impact. It was too late now to carry the search any further. The investigators left the wreckage fading in mist and guarded by a none too wide awake platoon of carabinieri. Forty bodies were loaded with them into the two Vertols: the three crew members; the supposed hijacker; twenty of the burned bodies from the tail section; and sixteen torn victims from the tangle up front. Another fifteen bodies had already been evacuated. A hundred souls were left on the mountain in various states of disintegration and decay, appeased only by collective blessing from a local priest earlier in the day.

The helicopters landed after only ten minutes' flying,

one after the other at either end of a wide piazza in the highest of the mountain villages, the noisy intrusion bringing a crowd of inhabitants young and old from the bar and shuttered houses up and down the narrow hillside streets. The piazza protruded at the edge of the village, built out over the slope in a long scenic balcony, a promenade with stone benches, a straggly palm and oleanders, obliterated now in a hurricane of dust and scrap paper and old men's hats. The rotors turned in slow motion as Pherson supervised the unloading of his plastic sheeted bodies. Then the helicopters rose again leaving Mac alone with Sanju and the row of bodies, as a priest hurried from his church steps hands aloft to keep the villagers away from such an undignified and naked display of death.

The departing helicopters left a sudden silence as the village stood watching the bearded and coveralled giant who had so suddenly descended with his strange cargo and his turbaned companion. They watched from the edges of the piazza, silent and slightly aloof, as though they did not wish the newcomers to think that they were not used to unusual visitors. Only by the village bar was there conversation, for one of the huge Vertols had ripped off a dozen telephone lines on its way down and a local carabiniere was trying to figure out whose lines were damaged.

Mac squatted on his instrument case and wondered if anyone knew quite what they were waiting for. He roared across the square toward the bar holding up two fingers: *"Deux bières."* No one moved. *"Bière!"* He shouted again and raised a hand to his mouth in the gesture of drink, but his colonial approach cut no ice here. They'd seen them all coming and going since the time of Odysseus—Greeks, Italians, Spanish, French— with plenty of roaring bearded Macs and Jocks in occupation the last time war had passed them by. The quiet

Sanju walked to the bar and bartered for the beers with a one-pound note.

Two trucks were edging down one of the streets into the square, hooting furiously to move the crowd.

An elderly, much bowed little man climbed down from the first truck directing the driver toward the row of plastic shrouds in the middle of the square. Mac stood up to meet him.

"Dr. Turi Pennisi." The man announced himself and shook hands, looking up sideways at Mac from under bowed shoulders. "You wish to make autopsy." And he indicated the bodies.

Mac nodded and thanked providence for the man's English.

"Tonight?"

"It's important to look at four of them tonight."

"Tomorrow we find a better place to work, but tonight we can work at my surgery."

The backs of the two trucks were open—refrigerated meat trucks. The little doctor had improvised well.

"I represent the magistrato for the moment. You have papers for these bodies?"

Mac handed over a sheet of paper given him by the police up on the mountain. The little doctor counted the bodies and the numbers on the paper. Then the three of them stacked the plastic bundles inside the two trucks and squeezed themselves into the cabs with the drivers. The villagers watched them drive away up the narrow street on to the main road that joined these higher mountain villages with the outside world below.

Turi's house stood on a sloping street in the middle of a larger village where it seemed that the entire population was racing noisy miniature motorcycles and tiny Fiats. Impossible in such a place to be discreet, though the doctors tried to disguise their crude plastic bundles with blankets before carrying them from the trucks into the house. Turi's surgery was in the front of the house and through the shutters they could see the crowd sauntering from the bar in twos and threes to examine the strange meat trucks.

The four victims from the cockpit were laid out on Turi's tiled floor, and Mac began his preliminary examination. Two of the bodies were reasonably intact, only marred by an unpleasant flattening distortion to their skulls and faces: the two pilots held well by their seat harnesses but disfigured by the upper instrument panel telescoping down on top of them. One of them had an arm flung high over his head, an instinctive flinch as the plane had crashed; the older man was in a normal sitting posture but much damaged about the hands, forearms, and legs. Mac had made a sketch plan of the cockpit and the technical investigators would eventually work out which controls the captain had been operating to suffer such injuries. Left hand on the wheel, right hand on the fire levers, Mac thought. Passports in the men's jackets confirmed the names, and Mac entered them both on autopsy forms as positively identified: Captain Michael Duckham; First Officer Peter Nyren.

There was no evidence in either man's pockets to suggest illness or drug addiction. The older man had a box of aspirin tablets, which would have to be analyzed, but they were foil-sealed and Mac was quite sure they were genuine. He looked at a photograph in the captain's wallet: a pretty English face in a pretty English garden—Mrs. Duckham, Mac presumed, for there was a baby in her arms.

Sanju helped Mac as they separated the bodies from belongings, laying the two pilots aside for full autopsy when the preliminaries were over.

The flight engineer and the mysterious fourth victim were in more of a mess. The engineer seemed to have been torn from his wretched swivel chair, suffering multiple flailing injuries to his head and his limbs. In addition, his back had been snapped where the floor had buckled upward catching him trapped between his seat and that of the captain in front of him.

The cockpit intruder had a shattered forehead; her right arm was missing, torn off at the shoulder; the left forearm was impacted into her jaw where she had flung it up to protect her face; both her knees were fragmented, and most of the frontal area of her body was badly bruised. But for all her terrible injuries Mac had found her unentangled with the main cockpit damage, and depending on where they eventually located the missing arm, it was possible that she had arrived on the flight deck as a result of and after the crash impact. Such evidence, negative or positive, was obviously vital to any hijacking theory.

The flight engineer's documents tallied with Mac's crew list: George Raven, aged thirty-seven and unmarried. Next of kin was a brother in Australia. The intruder, however, had no jacket or handbag and therefore no documents to suggest identification. She was dark-skinned and what little remained of her features suggested Arabic, or certainly Mediterranean, origins. There would be trouble about identification here, thought Mac, and the possibility could not yet be excluded that this young woman had interfered in some way with procedure on the flight deck. Mac scribbled in his notebook: "F/E moving to keep intruder out of cockpit?"

Turi watched the huge bearded Englishman move dispassionately through his preliminary examinations, and remembered the battered bodies, some of them still alive, in the confusion of wreckage that morning. Turi had had his share of traffic accidents, increasingly so in recent years, but he had never experienced quite such grotesque disfigurements as he had seen on this occasion. Nor had he through thirty years of practice ever succeeded in distancing death. Death in his own villages had always meant the deaths of people he knew, often his own patients with connotations of loss and sometimes of failure or inadequacy on his part. But even the deaths of total strangers disturbed him more than he cared to admit. Especially this kind of ugly, violent, wholly indiscriminate, wholly fortuitous dying. He supposed the English pathologist had seen it often enough, but he still admired the man's absolute detachment.

The Indian assistant had covered the table with rubber sheeting, and Mac warned the Italian: "It's going to make a bloody mess of your surgery."

Turi shrugged.

"Just these four. That's all we need to do tonight." Mac grinned. "Just in case your magistrato pinches the bodies."

They lifted Captain Duckham onto the table.

Ralph Burden was thinking about Mike Duckham over his supper. "Dixie" to Burden, and even after thirty years Burden could still hear the dry impeccable-even-when-drunk, so wholly self-confident Harrovian arrogance of that voice. "Raffles Burden—survivor supreme," the voice had mocked one evening. "You know, chaps, it's extraordinary. Most bloody awful pilots got themselves killed pretty quick. Two sorts of chaps got killed—your gay young bloods swanning all over the sky, and your bloody awful pilots who couldn't hold their sticks straight. But this bloody awful pilot" —and here the voice raises tone as the eyes pick out Burden—"he came back every time. Plane all pulped ready for the paper mill, the bloody pilot still looking for his stick."

Duckham had been very drunk. VE-Day plus a week or so. Yes. He had been very drunk and the next morning he had not only apologized but had walked Ralph twice round the airport perimeter trying, it seemed, to find excuses for his behavior. In retrospect, many years too late, Burden recognized his despair. "Actually you see, none of the chaps I knew are around any more. I don't know what I said about you last night but what I can't work out is why *I* am still alive." He had laughed heartily, mocking himself for a change. Dixie Duckham. They were going to get to know each other well in the next few days.

Burden looked round the hotel dining room. The meal was over and the guests leaving in ones and twos. Burden wished the other members of his team were with him in the same hotel, but they were scattered all over the little town. Taormina, the Italians had told them, was in high season, hotel accommodations limited—though Burden noticed with not a little irritation that the Americans had managed to get themselves fixed up in a luxurious palace of a hotel, some old monastery on the other side of town.

He walked out afterward into the glow of the evening and the scatter of lights up and down the alleyways and narrow streets. It was a pretty touristy town, full of hotels and pensions and the odd discreet nightclub, down leafy stairways advertised with photographs equally discreet and unharmful. But Ralph Burden was not after entertainment. He tried in vain to find his way through the maze of steps, up the hillside to the even smaller pension where his engineers were billeted. Defeated, he sat at an outside table in the main piazza drinking expensive malt whiskey and watching the crowd grouped around a coin-operated telescope. They were training it on the mountain as though they could see through the darkness the glow of the crashed plane, or a cloud of flying souls ascending.

Later, back in his bedroom, Burden sat down at the table and opened the Hercules personnel file. "Michael Edward Duckham, born Rangoon, 1922." Rubber planters, Burden guessed. Ralph Sinclair Burden, he thought to himself as he started to make notes. Born Sanderstead, 1924, into a family of grocers.

Child of the empire, Michael Duckham had been: occasional voyager on the P and O, habitué of a half-dozen prep schools in Kent and Sussex. Why so many changes? Burden wondered. Did it denote a wild childhood? Overanxious absentee parents? Poverty? A wild childhood, Burden decided. Duckham had been removed from Harrow after only three years and had resurfaced in a London cram school, graduating with enough qualifications to have satisfied the bespectacled scrutineers at ACSC. Air Crew Selection Center, St. John's Wood, a kind of half-baked extension of boarding school with its curfew and communal rules. But then they all had been schoolboys. Except for the odd screwballs—the ones who had climbed out at night to chase the WAAF girls down Baker Street or the nurses up in Swiss Cottage. Was that where Duckham had learned his womanizing, or had it all been just a legend?

Michael Edward Duckham. Initial training wing in Newquay Grading School and Tiger Moths in Worcester. Classified as a pilot. Six weeks kicking heels in Heaton Park, Manchester, waiting for a ship, then flight training schools variously around Canada. Back across the Atlantic in one of those coldly comforting North Atlantic convoys. Operational training unit on Mosquitoes in Scotland. It was all very familiar. Burden had trod much the same trail eighteen months later. "Attached to 23 Squadron, December 2, 1942. Embarked for Malta, December 11. First active mission, January 1943. Shot down off the coast of Malta, February 1943. Missions recommenced, March 1943. Awarded DSO following low-level sorties during the Allied invasion of Sicily."

Sicily. Burden wondered how many times Duckham had been back on the island since the war.

"Crash-landed at Castelforte (Monte Cassino front),

April 1944. Invalided home. Rejoined the squadron,
July 1944, at Little Snoring, Norfolk."

Burden smiled to himself. He could remember the
very moment: the slightly raffish hero of whom so
many stories had been told, leaning on an unnecessary
stick, surveying them, the newcomers who had joined
the squadron during his absence. No, Burden hadn't
exactly liked Duckham, though the impression had in
no way affected a mild attack of hero worship.

"DFC March 1945. Transferred to 29 Squadron,
September 25, 1945. Transferred back to 23 Squadron,
September 1946." Of no significance those transfers;
the squadron had been disbanded for a year. Burden
instead had left it for good, moving to Transport Command and retraining first on Dakotas then on Hastings.
Burden looked again at the file photograph. Dixie's face
had filled out. It probably carried fewer lines than the
twenty-four-year-old fighter pilot's thirty years ago.
Burden wondered if that head had still ducked and
swooped over its shoulders. The temperament must
have changed or he would never have been appointed
fleet captain. He'd been a strangely uneven character in
those far-off days. Meet him outside, walking down the
lane, and he'd have a smile and a chat. But catch him
in a crowded officers' club or pub on a bad day and he
could turn the mob on you for no apparent reason.
You'd see him some evenings waiting for a night mission, eyes roaming the room searching out a victim, and
closing in for the kill. But it wasn't the best time to
judge a man, when he'd come back from a convales-
cence after injury. He had been shot down twice already and was living, as the squadron medic would
have said, somewhere along the razor's edge. One
winter's night he'd returned with a dead navigator beside him and a plane so shot to hell you couldn't even
make out its true silhouette. Everyone had thought that
that would finally tip him over. But oddly enough he'd

come the other way, as though the incident had focused
him again. It had been the successful combination of
his next three missions that had earned him his DFC.
He had even mellowed to his juniors—until that
drunken outburst in the early days of peace.

"Married July 1946, in Mereworth Parish Church,
Deborah Poynton-Stevens. Divorced 1951. Married
August 1952, Norwich Registry Office, Angela de
Waal. One daughter born 1958. Divorced 1967. Mar-
ried September 21, 1967, Guildford Registry Office,
Julia Ann Dutton. One son born 1969. One daughter
born 1971."

He'd had some bites at the apple. A screwball.

Ralph Burden. Married Mary Howard, 1957, Sels-
don Parish Church. Marriage petered out *sans* drama
sans everything over many years. Separation 1974.

Burden weighted down his papers with an ashtray
and put away his pens and pencils. Mary had gone to
live with a sister in Ibiza where, by all accounts, she
was busy making up for lost sex. Another screwball.

Ralph washed and undressed and carefully thought
of nothing in particular. But lying in bed later with the
darkness he dreamed old nightmares: pipe smoke from
the officers' club drifting on the evening air; Mosquitoes
lined up in rounded silhouettes against the open Norfolk sky ready to shadow the bombers on some long
night raid deep into Germany; the drone of twin Mer-
lins drumming through the wooden frame. Fear, continual fear, that drew youth from the mind and body
like sap from a wounded tree.

14

The elderly *magistrato* had returned home to
shower away the dirt and smells of the mountain and
the plane. He already felt better. He had left his

younger colleague in the office poring over reports and plans. Shared responsibility was more comfortable.

But his sense of satisfaction did not last long. The procuratore generale telephoned him at seven o'clock with a string of questions. He already seemed to know a great deal about the accident and the day's events.

"Tutto con calma si farà," he said. "We can't rush this kind of investigation."

He was not at all pleased to be told of the younger magistrato's participation.

"Too much technical knowledge is often a hindrance," he said after a long and rigid silence. "Our eager young colleague will be feeling sorry for the pilot."

The elderly magistrato, still damp from his shower, sensed pressures, local wheels, and whispers. He hated these oblique conversations, for he knew he would fall in with them. He was vulnerable to pressure.

"We are all on trial," said the procuratore. The procuratore generale who had too many friends, too many smiles, and too much protesting of his own incorruptibility. Though in a sense he was correct. There was never corruption as such; no open collusion; no crisp persuasions received under the table. It was far more ancient and sophisticated. More like a well-drilled soccer team: when the ball came to your feet in a given situation you sensed the play and you knew instinctively where to move and how to lay it off.

The Dino was traveling south along the old *Statale* 114 at speeds mostly in excess of 100 miles an hour. The young man in his now slightly soiled white suit did not believe in highways and his midnight rendezvous was well away from any main road. The afternoon had passed pleasantly if stickily on that hot beach with three of the four American women making a heavy play for him in their awful Italian. At dusk he'd offered to drive them back up the hill to Taormina, one at a time he explained, for the Dino was an impractical car. But his choice of first passenger had proved correct. The lady had opened his trousers while he was still maneuvering out of the darkened parking lot, and by the time they reached her hotel he was in no mood to think of the others. They were probably still on the beach waiting for him. Another day, he thought.

Tonight Flavio would play poker with friends and tell of his afternoon's adventures. He could stay out till dawn if he wanted, for his father had taken the afternoon flight to Rome and was not returning until Monday. His mother would not tell tales. She couldn't bear the noise they caused.

A blue Alfa waited in a darkened garage on the inside of a tight bend listening to the six-cylinder roar of a Ferrari Dino approaching down through its gearbox. The Dino snaked into the bend and accelerated past them in a haze of rubber and racing oil—100 mph, the police driver noted with grudging admiration. But both traffic cops had seen the license plate and the driver killed his engine with a shrug of resignation.

"Come on. Give him a scare," his partner said. "We can radio a car farther up the road."

"And all of us get docked two days' pay? He's more trouble than a gangster."

The Dino was an hour late for its rendezvous, and Capo Tomacchio in his van outside the cemetery muttered an unheard oath as the young man climbed without apology out of his low cockpit. Tomacchio watched in silence. He was playing the subordinate tonight, an unaccustomed role. But then he was a worried man; his trucks were at stake.

The young man pulled a dirty suede jacket from the trunk in the front of his car, walked across the road to the van, and dropped the keys of the oil tanker through the open window. He had an envelope of money in his hand.

"How much?"

"Five hundred for the fuel. We go halves." Capo Tomacchio had thick eyebrows in straight short lines; eyes on the small side watching for competition; his heavy face creased around the nose into a perpetual sneering challenge.

Flavio nodded, peeled off the money, and patted him a thank you on his arm.

"Any trouble?" the older man asked.

"No."

"You moved fast this morning."

"They called me from the airport as soon as the power failed. It wasn't the fuel. It was the valves all set wrong. The emergency tank ran itself dry."

"My fault last week, I suppose. I was in a hurry. I was running late." ·

The young man moved away.

"Is everything going to be all right?"

"Why shouldn't it be?"

"A whole damn airplane's come down, that's why. There's a hundred and fifty people dead. What did your father say?"

"He's got bigger problems than this. He's gone to Rome."

"Well, he's involved with us whatever happens." Tomacchio paused. "He is involved, isn't he?"

Flavio gestured impatiently and turned away without answering the question.

Tomacchio called after him: "If it was my mistake, I'm sorry."

The young man turned from his car with a lazy, limp smile. "If you want to make amends, you'd better talk to your daughter for me." The green and orange Dino screeched a U-turn on the road, completing it in a slide through the gravel by the cemetery gates.

Capo Tomacchio listened to the departing roar. One daughter he had—an only child, like Flavio Consoli. Giuseppina. The young couple would never be short of money. But that greedy young man had never explicitly talked about marriage, and if he'd ever suggested anything else Tomacchio would have taken his shotgun to him—influential father or not.

Citto Risarda was running about a day and a half ahead of the official investigators. He had covered fifteen villages in four hours. Fifteen village bars had given him most of the information he needed and in the early hours of Sunday morning he parked his old Giulia outside the perimeter fence at Taormina–Peloritana and waited for the last of the lights to die in the private aero club behind the control tower. He plotted last night's storm on a map, relying on the accounts, not always consistent, that he had picked up in the bars. Cloud and rain had covered most of the mountain but the storm itself had been restricted it seemed to a narrow triangle on the north and west of the mountain, between Linguaglossa, Bronte, and Randazzo. Heavy rain or lightning strikes had caused power failures in some villages at varying times during the night. By early morning the storm had apparently been centered somewhere around the Maletto on the southwest flank of the mountain.

Citto stared out through his dark windshield at another cloud-covered night. He had the basic facts, no more, and he wondered if his theory was really worth this amount of trouble. After all there were official investigators who were paid good money to unravel the mysteries of this Tango November. Still, the clocks had all stopped at 5.40. Could other systems have failed at the same time?

Lights went out and the airport slept with only one security guard prowling somewhere with his dog. Citto removed the bulb in the interior lamp to avoid showing light when he opened the car door, then slipped out, flashlight in hand, to take an investigative stroll. The night was close and still even at this altitude, the airlessness eerie and uncomfortable. There was nothing to feel on the skin, no sounds in the ear, and only the occasional pungency of a squashed centipede to bring any scent to the nose. Citto walked across the vast and empty parking lot past the façade of the aero club where he had first seen the dirty black oil tanker that morning. He turned once when he seemed to hear footsteps on the gravel; he even saw shadows move along a wall. But he had the innocence of inexperience; he didn't know when to retreat.

He found interconnected fuel tanks at the base of the control tower where the truck had been parked. The two feed pipes were labeled "Gasoline" and the two sheds next to the tanks labeled: "Generator—All Circuits"; "Generator—Emergency Circuits." Citto retired with a smile. Part one of his hunch had proved correct.

15

A group of intrepid sightseers, like hounds with their noses to the wind, sniffed out Tango November in the small hours of Sunday morning. Their discovery was entirely fortuitous for they had been wandering in the woods and on the lava, lost since night had come. Now they smelled stale fire smells, and, as they worked their way nearer, the more specific stink of burned plastics and kerosene.

There were seven of them in the group, three girls and four boys. They moved the last hundred yards in silence and the girls stood guard on the ground as the boys climbed the ladders into the unburnt front half of the fuselage. The carabinieri sentinels were fast asleep.

A quarter of an hour later the sightseers heard a helicopter approaching and saw searchlights descending slowly from the sky. The boys jumped down with their loot and the party scrambled away, still unseen, into the woods. They had collected a rucksack full of British and American passports, wallets and purses, wristwatches, assorted rings and cameras, and one packet of male contraceptives, which they shared out and used later in the morning when the sun had warmed the pine needle dust.

The nocturnal helicopters brought newcomers: efficient men in dark suits on a macabre mission. They moved quickly in the searchlights with their briefcases and their bags of equipment.

16

Day and night was all one long confusion in the hospitals, a vigil of waiting reporters in reception halls, a shuttered darkness in the wards, a floodlit nightmare in the operating theaters. Of the thirty-five survivors ferried off the mountain only fourteen were still alive. Of those fourteen six would die before morning, two from undiagnosed internal bleeding, one from an undiagnosed blood clot in the head, and three on the operating tables while tired and understaffed teams tried to keep them alive.

The five-year-old girl, her arm in a cast, wandered up and down a darkened hospital ward calling for her mother. In a smaller room nearby Stella Pritchard recognized the voice from the depths of a drugged sleep. "Trixie," they had called her. Yes, it was the voice of Trixie, who had somehow obscurely saved her life. Yet when Stella awoke she was aware only of a car accident, and terrified to know who had been in the car with her. Her parents in their Morris Traveller, or Mike in his white Volvo? Two Italian nuns listened to Stella's questions without understanding her alarm. Their strange soothing talk only increased her fear, driving reality even farther away. But late in the evening her pain returned and the nurses dispatched her once more with morphine, back into the limbo where Trixie's voice remained her only link with what had really happened.

Twenty miles northward in a small town hospital up the coast, Tino G. was lying in an operating room with a tune stuck obsessively in his mind, his body connected to a variety of artificial aids, tubes sticking in and out of him all over. He could see them quite clearly reflected in the glass of the huge lamp above him and he wondered why the doctors wasted so much time and energy. The clarity of mind he'd had when trapped in the wreckage had gone. It seemed to him that life was fading out of him like the color from a piece of coral taken from the water.

His liver had been stitched up, a damaged gut bypassed, and a tracheotomy performed to help his breathing. But when his condition continued to deteriorate the surgeon diagnosed kidney failure following the earlier and sudden loss of so much blood. In the absence of a kidney machine a continual process of peritoneal dialysis was theoretically cleansing his abdominal cavity and by that early Sunday morning the deterioration had been momentarily arrested. The old surgeon was snatching some sleep on a couch in the rest room. He had already described the boy's condition in a bulletin as "hopeless."

Guitar, harmonica, percussion, and a little piano. Tino G. hoped he wouldn't die with that tune lost in his head without words or title.

A small group of reporters waited in the lobby downstairs. Someone had wired from New York that this Tino G. played folksongs in Greenwich Village.

Part Two

1

Tango November hadn't moved. Broken-backed, she still sheltered her victims. But she looked unreal in this early morning light, as though a photographer had exaggerated each detail of disaster, as though the disaster itself, acceptable in yesterday's mist and cloud, was now somehow improbable and inexplicable.

A helicopter hung over the wreckage settling slowly to land—two Italian air force pilots, Mac, and the turbaned Sanju. Mac and Sanju had slept at Turi's house, the helicopter picking them off the village football field at first light. The four cockpit autopsies had taken half the night, without producing any spectacular evidence—no heart attacks—and Mac's preliminary tests indicated nothing abnormal in the contents of anyone's blood. Mac looked down at the crumpled 119 as they climbed out of the helicopter and wondered if that twisted mass of metal would ever reveal the secrets of its own death throes.

"Bloody soapbox," Mac said out loud, thinking of

the mess they had to face again inside the shattered fuselage. Floor, seats, and belts, all no doubt legally within minimum required specifications, and all totally inadequate in a crash that should have been 60 percent survivable. Gradual deceleration through the trees; energy absorbing factors during impact in the progressive collapse of landing gear and cargo hold; and finally a long slide to take off some more speed before the front impacted on the slope: it was possible, probable even, that maximum horizontal forces had been as low as 15 g and calculable in thousandths of seconds. The human body could survive milliseconds of up to thirty gravity but the seats, to comply with American and British safety standards, were only required to withstand 9 g. Mac hoped that the medical evidence might lead to one or two severe paragraphs in the accident report. Too often the results were ambiguous or inconclusive. It was difficult at the best of times to produce statistics strong enough to challenge the accepted norms of civil aviation safety. Perhaps this time. Perhaps Tango November, at such high cost, would save a few thousand future lives.

There were already small groups of men moving in and around the wreckage, the other investigators ferried from their hotels, Mac assumed. But the faces were all strange to him, a mixture of uniforms, dark suits, and dark glasses that suggested cops. Yesterday's carabinieri were still there, disheveled and unshaven after a night in tents. They tried to stop Mac and Sanju at their cordon but Mac brushed them aside, marching possessively toward the wreckage and his hundred unclaimed bodies. A couple of suits and dark glasses detached themselves to deal with him.

"Group Captain Pherson, Royal Air Force," Mac roared, instinctively spoiling for a fight. But he realized immediately that he should instead have smiled and taken them under their arms or clasped them over their shoulders. Another pair of dark glasses arrived, summoned by a call.

Mac glared down at him from his twelve-inch advantage. "We are helping your ministry in Rome to conduct an accident inquiry as is obligatory under international agreement. That includes the identification, examination, and proper disposal of bodies."

"Naturally. But the magistrato has also his responsibility. Death here"—the bodies, stiff, grotesque, and smelling, hardly needed his dramatic gesture—"that is our responsibility also."

"Is the magistrato here?"

The dark glasses turned and Mac followed him down a duckboard, past a half-buried engine and a scattering of burst suitcases and bags.

The magistrato had been changed since yesterday. This one was younger, more alert, detached, and inscrutable as Mac protested.

"I've been told I cannot continue to evacuate bodies."

"All evidence is subpoenaed."

"Another couple of hours," said Mac abandoning aggression, "and this place will be thick with American and English reporters. They're not going to be too happy to see bodies still lying around twenty-four hours after the accident."

"There will be no access for reporters."

"You can't keep them away for long. They'll question your motives if you do."

The magistrato watched Mac, a smile somewhere behind his inscrutability: "You are looking for something in particular?"

"These bodies are my responsibility. Another day out in this sun and they'll be crawling off the mountain by themselves."

"You have seen the body of the hijacker?"

"I have an autopsy report that is still incomplete."

"Because part of the body is missing."

"How would you know that?"

"These carabinieri were helping you yesterday. They tell me the hijacker was taken out with her right arm missing."

Mac nodded.

"Well—it seems someone has been here during the night. The arm has been found and taken away."

"With half a bloody regiment here meant to be guarding the place?"

"Someone arrived in a helicopter with an official warrant. There was nothing they could do to stop them."

"Did they see where the arm was found?"

The magistrato shook his head.

"If we don't find out, we'll never know what this woman was doing."

The young man handed Mac his card. "All my telephone numbers, official and unofficial. I hope you will get in touch if you make a discovery." He smiled. "I would be obliged if you could supervise the evacuation of bodies."

They shook hands before the magistrato returned to his helicopter, and Mac hoped he was on the way to making a local ally. This setup was beginning to look hairy.

2

Canon Ash Nyren pulled his Sunday newspaper from the mailbox. Even triple folded it was obvious which story dominated the front page. "170 Dead in British Charter Crash. Attempted Hijack Ends in Disaster."

Ash Nyren laid the paper open on the kitchen table.

"First Officer Peter Nyren, aged 29." There was even Peter's photograph on an inside page, a smiling, healthily tanned young man. Ash Nyren read the story he did not yet know, that Peter had flown as it were by accident, in place of a sick colleague. Somehow that made it even worse.

The canon looked up at the gray clouds above his rain-wet garden. Why not me, old and of no further use; a life so inconsequential that only the church could offer a framework? Too young for one war, too old for the next. Why not me? Why always the young men?

The church was almost crowded this morning. His average congregation might reach a half-dozen if the sky was blue, but today there were thirty or more dripping from the rain, gawping and murmuring to each other like Christmas or Easter tourists. They had come to see him. Had they come to share his grief? To remember Peter? Or merely to watch?

"I am weary of my crying: my throat is dried: mine eyes fail while I wait for my God." Ash Nyren read the text for his sermon. It was to be, it seemed, a sermon of texts.

"Thou turnest man to destruction; and sayest, return, ye children of men." The canon was quarreling with God, the culmination of a long and bitter feud.

"Why art thou so far from helping me, and from the words of my roaring?"

His church council met later over sherry in the rear-admiral's sitting-room across the village green. The rear-admiral called the rural dean and the diocesan secretary, and it was finally agreed that evensong should be conducted jointly with the neighboring parish, and that the canon should be flown out to Sicily as soon as possible.

All down the east coast of Sicily village priests that morning gave mass for the casualties of the air crash and offered special prayers for the survivors. Eight survivors were consciously alive: two American citizens, Tino G. and Trixie, the little five-year-old survivor; and six British subjects, Stella Pritchard, a retired army major and his wife from Malta, a young sales executive from Twickenham, a bachelor general practitioner from Weardale in county Durham, and a shopkeeper friend of his from over the Derwent in Northumberland. The investigators were not surprised to discover that apart from Stella Pritchard and the little girl, all survivors had been sitting in rear-facing seats, Tino G. in row 1 at the very front of the plane, and the other five of them in row 12 just forward of the main bulkhead and center fuselage toilets.

The sales executive and the major were the only ones coherent enough to help the investigators.

"Can't tell you very much, I'm afraid," the major was saying. "We seemed to be going down, then we were going up again, then down again. Then it started bumping and—bang! We went arse over head. That's what saved us. Always sit with my backside to the driver if I can. That's what the RAF transport command do. And if they do it, it's for a bloody good reason."

The Italians were having trouble understanding exactly what the Englishman was saying. The voice was too clipped, his mouth seeming hardly to move when he spoke.

The magistrato asked him about the woman hijacker. Had he noticed her at all?

"Good Lord. Didn't know about a hijacker. They all looked like stewardesses to me. Tell you the truth I was a bit pissed. Sleeping most of the time. I expect my wife'll be able to tell you more when she's feeling up to it."

"How long were you in the wreckage before you were rescued?"

"Felt like ten years. I don't know what it was really. Smashed my watch you see. So did Alec. He's in the room next door. We were the only two bodies *compos mentis*. Everyone else was upside down and broken, bones and all. We tried to break a way out, but then the fire started moving forward and we had to build a wall against that instead. Then there was first aid of course. Not much we could do really. Tear up some odds and ends and stop some bleeding."

"How many people were alive?"

"Difficult to say really. We could only move in the space where we were. A couple of rows backward and forward. I straightened out my wife and some other bloke. They had broken arms and legs and things."

Alec in the room next door was not in condition to help the investigators. "He doesn't seem coherent today," the major had warned them. "Quite all right yesterday. Worried about his friend I expect." The major didn't quite approve of the relationship he thought he had detected between doctor and shopkeeper.

The young magistrato left the hospital with the impression that witness statements were not going to help the investigation. They had already interviewed the sales executive from Twickenham whose account differed in almost every single detail from that of the major.

A young surgeon in the second hospital gave the investigators even less hope. Two of his survivors were on the operating tables and in critical condition. The young surgeon had diagnosed acute renal and hepatic failure respectively, but could find no obvious cause in either case. He had requested a second opinion but the machinery through which his request had to be

channeled was slow to react. A urologist was contacted
by radio on his racing yacht somewhere south of Syracuse becalmed and unable to help. The general physician spent his weekends in a hill resort halfway up the
mountain and it took him four hours to return to the
city and pronounce judgment. It was a forensic more
than a medical diagnosis. Both patients had had substantial transfusions of blood during the previous evening. The two transfusions, incompatible with one
another, must have been interchanged.

"What can I do?" the young surgeon asked in despair.

"Peritoneal dialysis—and make an official request
for a kidney machine," replied the physician. "When
they both die make sure the blood counts are kept off
the death certificate. Renal failure was due to severe
shock. Hepatic failure to hemorrhage from a lesion."
And having thus organized the affair the consultant
escaped back to his car in time to make the hills for
Sunday lunch.

The little girl was sitting on the bed when Stella woke
back into her pain and confusion. Drugged and only
partially conscious she had recognized the child's voice
and remembered her name, aware of some strong connection between her and whatever had happened. But
now, with her eyes open, even with the girl's face beside
her, Stella could remember nothing. The little face
somehow familiar, increased her dread about a car
accident. Was this a lone survivor from another car?
The accusing face of a child she had run over? The face
whispered.

"Where's Mama?"

They had been together, one way and another, for
twenty-four hours, Stella's face Trixie's only point of
reference. It had been a normal face at first, laughing as
it played a game, getting a little angry when the game

went on too long. Then it had been injured and blood-marked; now it was repaired, shiny, and dirty in patches all over. Trixie was conscious of what had happened, much more so than Stella, though her memory was equally dominated by dread. She was convinced that the crash had been all her fault, somehow a result of that game she had been playing up and down the airplane while everyone else was strapped into their seats. They had all been calling her; then this hostess had been chasing her; and finally her mother.

"Mama hurting," she whispered. She could still see the plane all smashed and burning and her mother somewhere there inside.

3

The Dino was parked with one foot in the fountain, its near end drunkenly wide across the courtyard: the lady's coupé was effectively boxed in but the *signora* in the dark gray dress merely shrugged and returned indoors. She didn't want to wake her son. She would go instead to evening mass.

The gods smiled on her this Sunday. Ten minutes later her husband telephoned from Rome, and she was able to explain that their son was out on an inspection in the orange groves, an insignificant untruth that neither of the maids would have dared to tell.

"Call him," was the order from Rome.

This time she had to waken the boy, explaining quickly what she had told his father. But the young man's voice when it appeared downstairs was still thick with sleep.

"And what were you looking at in the orange groves?" his father sneered. "The sky or a peasant girl's ass?"

Flavio Consoli laughed. It was his only defense. The avvocato loved his words to be appreciated. He told him now that he was to pay a call that morning on the procuratore, his wife, their daughter, and son. "You will pay special attention to the daughter and treat her with respect and admiration."

"She's just a fat little schoolgirl."

His father took no notice. "You will be invited to lunch and after making the correct gestures of reluctance you will join them and pay respectful attention to your host and make yourself useful in whatever way is possible."

"It's Sunday."

"When I come home tomorrow I want to hear word for word what has happened."

"I have to take a tape recorder?"

"Are you stupid?" And after a pause. "Yes, you are stupid, I know. A stupidity that comes with laziness and too much material comfort. And that is my fault." Another pause and a voice that seemed to regret those harsh words. "You have understood what to do?"

The young man nodded respectfully. Then remembered his father would not see the gesture over the telephone.

"Yes, sir."

Avvocato Consoli was installed in his usual hotel behind the Piazza Colonna, his room old-fashioned with heavy furniture and noisy with its dreadful plumbing, but otherwise discreet and unostentatious. He dialed another number. The airport had telexed that morning. Some reporter had been hanging around late last night. There were precautions to be taken.

The telephone was answered.

"You will not remember me," said the avvocato. "We met once or twice while you were sitting on an airport feasibility committee."

The man did remember. The heaviness in his voice recalled old debts and favors.

"There was a twelfth man on the committee," said Consoli. "A civil engineer. He didn't like our project. He resigned and I wanted to make sure his name had been cleared from all records."

"So far as possible it was done at the time." The heaviness of voice drooped even farther. "It was a public inquiry and difficult to close all references."

Consoli's voice was neither heavy nor threatening. Scarcely a murmur. "I rely on you."

The other man's affirmative grunt sounded more like a lamentation.

"Preuss was the name."

"I'm sorry?"

"The twelfth man. He lives in Venice."

Another affirmative grunt.

"Relying on you then." Consoli hung up. Relying hell, he thought. Reminding was the operative word: if anything goes wrong you are also implicated.

Consoli dialed another number. There were a lot of nervous voices answering this morning. Civil servants. The politicians had all left town.

Ingegnere Preuss watched with a shiver as color moved across the lagoon and the mist disappeared. Sunrise, belated or otherwise, through mist or over a horizon: he had never lost the sense of tremulous and total solitude that the moment provoked. He had felt it as a boy standing hand in hand with his mother. He felt it now, standing alone on the eastern edge of his decaying city, listening to a jet whistling over Jesolo as it circled to land.

Preuss had all but forgotten about that air crash. The news of it had worried him yesterday. It would return no doubt to worry him today. He didn't really want to be involved, not after all the previous heartache and wasted energy. There was an awful lot of mess to be dug up if someone looked hard enough.

He would go out to the Lido today, he thought. One last swim before the water cooled. He had tickets that afternoon for one of the films at the Festival. A couple of his young students were coming along with him.

4

Etnolio was a large courtyard of buildings and oil tanks in the same village where Turi and Laura lived. The establishment was set back from the village street and hidden by a high wall. Citto remembered the building as a distillery producing a good brandy from the local vineyards and indeed the chimney of the furnace still survived, with the tall copper retorts in the steam house that now seemed to serve for truck maintenance. The flat-roofed top of the storage buildings served as the terrace of the main house, and a girl was standing there, leaning over the railings in a bikini talking with someone out of sight. Voluptuous and unashamed, Citto thought as he watched her: big breasts, masses of brown hair, dark skin. Citto walked in at the yard gates. The girl saw him and turned away back to her sunbathing, shouting at her unseen companion.

"Renzo! Someone to see you."

A grimy mechanic crawled from under one of the trucks and Citto asked innocently and with his inevitable stammer about the distillery he remembered.

"Sold," said the young man in overalls. The family business it seemed had died with the originator, his sons too given to the soft life to apply themselves with the vigor and physical hard work necessary to keep such a business going. "Ten men thrown out of work," said the mechanic. "And forty acres of vineyard torn up. They're building holiday homes for the city people." The mechanic was young and sharp, and the energy of his disgust suggested a Communist or a Fascist. But Citto was not looking for a political discussion. He glanced round the yard: four tankers, all of them in middle age, the oldest of them black and oil-stained, dirty and smelling as it had been the previous day on that wide dirt pavement outside the town below the airport.

Citto nodded at the trucks. "Do you do contract work?"

"Maintenance you mean?"

"Delivery."

The boy nodded. "Naphtha, gas, and diesel."

"Are you the boss?"

"No."

"So who is?"

"Tomacchio. Capo Tomacchio." He was sardonic this young man, emphasizing the "capo."

"Is he inside?"

"The capo is out in the country."

"Do you know where?"

"Turn right halfway through the village and right again above the bridge. First left at the top of the hill, then stop the car and listen for shooting."

"Hunting?"

"You could call it that. The most he's ever shot is rats and snakes."

Renzo watched the tubby little man depart and wondered briefly if he could be a cop. Giuseppina reappeared on the terrace above. "What did he want?"

"Looking for your father."

Giuseppina was working on her hair with long lazy brush strokes. Renzo sat on the step of one of the trucks, lit the butt end of a cigarette, and watched her.

"Mother's gone to mass," the girl said after a while.
"So?"
"So you can come up if you want."
Renzo laughed. "Some trouble I can do without." He flicked away his cigarette and crawled back under the truck.

The countryside up on the hill was dry and scrubby, regimented into roads and building plots, with only two or three of the houses under construction and the rest of the site overgrown. It was easy to see how the terraced vineyard had been constructed, falling in a carefully interlocked pattern of walls and neatly built steps from the summit of the ridge down to the winter torrent by the bridge below. The carving up of building plots had ruined most of the walls, and only the bare outline was left of ten centuries or more of agricultural tradition.

Citto found Capo Tomacchio and his shotgun in a gorse thicket halfway up the hill, angry at the intrusion into his morning's duel with the three-legged hare that had been denying him since early summer.

Citto struggled through a stammered introduction. "They told me in the village where I would find you." He decided not to implicate the mechanic. He might turn out to be an ally.

"You have business with me?"

Citto was stammering a reply when the man cut in on him.

"It's Sunday you know."

Reactions to his stammer were often Citto's measure of an interviewee or opponent. This Tomacchio gave no quarter. When a man was vulnerable he attacked. He was a bludgeoner.

"I'm an investigative reporter," Citto said. "Dottor Risarda," and he named his newspaper. He was going to name everyone if he needed and all of them with their full titles—his editor, his MP, his cardinal, *professore, onorevole, eccellenza.* The bludgeoner had to be bludgeoned back in language he could understand.

"I'm writing an article about the new airport. I understand you do contract work for them."

Tomacchio had a very level stare and Citto only his spectacles to hide behind. He took them off and polished them on his shirt front.

"You are mistaken."

"One of your trucks was at the airport yesterday morning."

"Which truck?"

Citto read off the registration number from his notebook.

"The truck was rented out yesterday. I don't know where it went. It wasn't with one of my drivers."

"But you know who rented it?"

"If you think I'm coming all the way back into town with you just to fish a name out of a file—"

"It's a bit unusual, isn't it? Self-drive rental."

"Only way some of us can keep going."

"So you don't undertake regular work for the airport?"

"You think a two-bit outfit like mine can muscle in on airport fuel concessions? They fight about those things in Rome, and there's sure as Christ no one fighting there for me."

Capo Tomacchio broke his gun and reloaded. "And now if you don't mind I'd like to get on with my Sunday."

Citto slipped and stumbled his uncomfortable way out of the thicket and down through the thorny ex-vineyard, aware of the capo's level stare—and the shotgun—watching him go. He was a bludgeoner all right, though he didn't seem uneasy enough to be hiding anything. But then maybe a bludgeoner wouldn't be uneasy whatever he had to hide.

Citto stopped on his way back through the village. The mechanic was closing up to go off for his lunch.

"Did you find him?"

"Yes, thank you."

"Got a bag full of rabbits?"

"Not exactly."

The young mechanic laughed.

"He was telling me he sometimes rents out the tankers."

"Him rent them out? First I've heard of it. He must have liked your face. He even hates us driving his precious trucks."

"I must have misunderstood him. I thought he said he'd rented one yesterday."

"That old black monster? He lent it to a friend for the day—and it came back all messed up."

"Must be an influential friend to get a favor like that."

"Consoli." The young man glanced up at the terrace where the girl was watching them both. He spat into the grit under the wall. "Daddy's little boy with his racing car and his women. It's his father who bought the vineyard."

"Not a friend of yours?"

"I get told to clean his car sometimes."

"What does he drive—the son?"

"A Dino. You've probably seen it around. Luminous orange and green. And a horn that plays stupid tunes."

Giuseppina laughed from the terrace above them and Renzo scowled. "She loves it. She gets taken for rides in it."

The mechanic walked off to his lunch with a nod at Citto and nothing for the girl. A very severe young man. Not a severity of the right, Citto thought. Which must make him something of a black sheep in a village where, at a guess, 40 percent of the electorate voted for the neo-Fascists, and the remaining 60 percent for the

Christian Democrats. This Consoli was a Christian Democrat family way up the scale. Quite a different league from Capo Tomacchio. Citto couldn't see how the two got together.

He looked up at the terrace above the old distillery. The girl was playing with a large chained German shepherd, throwing him a bone, teasing it away from him before he could settle down with it. Citto had the feeling that her men suffered much the same kind of treatment.

Renzo was crossing the piazza when Citto caught up with him.

"Nice girl."

"A hell of a good beating is what she needs."

"From you?"

"From whoever decides to tame her."

Citto steered him aside into the village bar. "Why not you?"

"I'm just a mechanic."

"She kind of likes you though."

"She kind of likes a lot of guys."

"Do you like her?"

"What's it to you?"

Citto called to the barman for a couple of beers and they sat for a moment in silence.

"I'll pay for mine," said Renzo when the beers came. "That way I don't owe you anything."

"I'm trying to ask a favor."

"So ask it and quit stalling around."

"I'm a reporter. I want to ask you questions about your boss and the business he runs."

"How do I know you're a reporter?"

Citto pulled out his identity card and laid it on the table. "Call up the newspaper and ask them."

And to Citto's surprise that's exactly what Renzo did, tucking himself into the corner by the door with the telephone and Citto's card. Citto wondered why at his age the boy was so cautious, but he was pleased all the same. It should make his answers that much more reliable. He wasn't the type to elaborate or lie.

Renzo sat down again apparently satisfied and ready to talk, and by the time Citto left the village twenty minutes later he had a clear idea of how ETNOLIO operated and how the week's work was broken up into a timetable of collections and deliveries. One run in particular interested Citto: a midweek trip over the Peloritana mountains with an empty tanker and trailer to pick up gasoline at the oil refinery in Milazzo. According to Renzo that particular journey was always taken by the Capo himself, and always over the mountains instead of round the coast on the autostrada. The mountain road passed within shouting distance of the new airport.

Flavio Consoli had performed his duties well: the procuratore had been made a friend of; his fat daughter flirted with.

Lunchtime had been quite hard work as he concentrated on remembering the basics of good manners and charm. But his occasional lapses had been overlooked and after coffee the fat schoolgirl had offered compensations as they walked together through the procuratore's orange groves. A discreet kiss on the cheek had released a great energy of virginal passion in the girl. She had given him her mouth, offered her huge and satisfying breasts, and rubbed her crotch hard against his thighs. At which point, thankfully, her brother appeared through the trees and difficult sexual decisions had been deferred.

The brother had been given a ride in the Dino; the procuratore complimented on his orange trees; his daughter promised future satisfaction. Talk of the air crash was limited to careful generalities, though it seemed to Flavio that the many interruptions to the procuratore's Sunday, whether from the telephone or by visitors, had all been associated with some aspect or other of the disaster. One of the guests at lunch had been an elderly magistrato in charge of yesterday's rescue, and afterward, returning home in the car, Flavio used his pocket dictaphone to list the points he had picked up from conversation at the table—most important of them the name of the younger magistrato who had apparently taken over investigation at the crash site. "An overeager young man," the procuratore had called him, precisely the sort of detail Flavio's father would expect to be told when he returned from Rome.

Flavio flicked off his dictaphone and plunged a dashboard button for eight-track stereo, blazing a trail of six-cylinder megaphones and blared rock through sleepy afternoon villages. How would his father react to Tomacchio? he was wondering. Was it worth telling him? Just in case anything went wrong?

5

Undeterred by newspaper, radio, and television pronouncements on the inaccessibility of the crashed plane, cars had streamed up the narrow mountain roads all morning, funneling into a series of two-lane traffic jams. The hopeful sightseers had not come unprovided for. They had brought their food and drink with them and by lunchtime the woodland roadsides were ankle deep in empty Coke cans, paper, broken bottles, plastic plates, plastic cups, plastic knives and forks. Many of the families, as was their custom on weekend country outings, brought their household refuse with them in plastic bags and added these to the landscape.

The traffic jams were accompanied by a great deal of engine-revving and horn-blowing, and by midday the traffic police reported a large proportion of cars immobilized with overheating engines or dead batteries and unable to roll downhill and out of the way because of the crush of cars behind them. The combination of these stationary blocks finally froze the traffic jam solid.

When a cigarette end, or a broken bottle catching the sun's hot rays, set the woodland floor gently smoldering the car-encased spectators stared through their windows at the wisps of smoke as though it were another entertainment laid on for their benefit. Ten minutes later and with a gust of wind the smoldering woodland floor burst suddenly into a wall of flame.

The fire spread a steady 4,500 feet in a band 300 feet wide across the slope of the mountain, cutting the road in two places and isolating thirty cars in the curve of a long hairpin. Toward the end of the morning the wind freshened and veered from southeast to northwest, turning the fire toward the trapped cars like an angry, unpredictable, and suddenly noisy animal. Each gust of wind threw the blaze forward 150 feet with a sharp explosive roar, and as overfed citizens fled from its path their cars disappeared into a blanket of flame.

An air force helicopter pilot at the crash site had radioed notification of the fire when it first started and a couple of French-owned CL-215 water bombers had been sent from Taranto where they were stationed temporarily after combating a series of forest fires in the Gargano. By the time they arrived the front of the fire had broadened to 900 feet and a north wind was threatening to sweep the danger downhill toward the villages.

The sight of the smoke and flames on the mountain enticed another few thousand sightseers to the area and, two days too late, the carabinieri and the polizia stradale set up roadblocks to turn the cars back. The villagers on the mountain had seen the phenomenon before. They had watched the same faces gawking from cars as their woods and vineyards were burnt and buried during the last eruption. There had been resentment then against the sightseers and there was some grim amusement this time as news passed around of the burning cars and stranded city people.

The investigators at the crash site paused in their work to watch when the water bombers arrived, loaded from the sea, attacking the fire like Second World War bombers in their droning inexorability. They flew ten seconds apart, starting at one end of the fire with a practice run to judge the wind. Then the first plane dropped his artificial cloudburst, 1,200 gallons in less than a second on the forward-moving front of the fire. One hundred and fifty feet of flame snuffed for a moment, and the second plane arrived straddling its drop slightly forward of the same area. When the wind regathered the fire for another leap the heart was gone out of it and the ground ahead of it soaked. It survived only in pockets—small bonfires in the undergrowth.

They really need six planes, thought Raille as he watched the two tankers bank away toward the sea for a reload. The turnround would take at least twenty minutes and in that time the fire would recapture half of that lost one hundred and fifty feet. They would need ten round trips to break the blaze and he doubted that they had sufficient fuel left for five hours' flying.

Not that the fire was anything more than a distraction for the investigators. There was no apparent threat to the wreckage and their own helicopter transport would be unaffected by the long pall of smoke that was now reaching out southward toward the city.

Work in and around the wreckage had been exhausting in the full heat of the sun. Temperatures inside the forward section of fuselage had risen to over 140 degrees Fahrenheit and two investigators had already been evacuated with heat exhaustion.

In those conditions it was as well that death had at

last gone from Tango November. A final load of bodies had been lifted out with Mac in attendance and, before leaving, Mac had joined Larry Raille in the concertinaed cockpit to explain how the four bodies had been lying when he found them, describing from his autopsy the precise significance of the injuries to Duckham's hands and feet. The two men decided that the captain had been "landing" the plane at the moment of impact. The flaps were set in landing configuration, and the distribution of wreckage scattered back along the crash path through the trees made it clear that the landing gear was locked down. Only Duckham's right hand on the fire handle and the line of approach path broke the pattern of an apparently normal landing. As Burden had pointed out the day before, the path of wreckage through the trees described an unmistakable left-turning arc, and the plane itself had grounded in an attitude of left wing down, with the fuselage tilted. Duckham's shattered right foot braced on the rudder bar seemed to indicate an attempt to counteract the bank, and suggested that the plane was, for an as yet undiscovered reason, partially out of control.

"What about the hijacker?" Raille had asked.

"No comment. I'll need to see the evidence for myself." Mac's tone of voice had seemed like a warning.

He was an abrasive man, this pathologist, deeply critical about the aeromedical aspects of the crash. There'd be some sparks flying in his section of the report. "Are you a betting man?" he had asked earlier in the morning. "I'll lay ten dollars a head that a hundred and thirty of this lot were still alive after the crash." It wasn't going to make pretty reading.

And pretty reading was worrying a lot of people. They had waked Raille at four o'clock that morning with a call from Washington offering him a replacement investigator. "We heard about your wife's party," the

Washington voice had said. "We'll fly you home for it. Someone else can take over the investigation."

Raille could guess who the someone else would be. One of the Republican appointees who had arrived during the latter Nixon years. Someone who knew how to be discreet. Someone to take care of the "albatross" 119.

Raille had politely declined the offer. They couldn't actually extricate him unless he volunteered. It was too late. He was accredited representative here, constitutionally independent, answerable only to his board chairman. He had been sent out to reconstruct as exactly as possible the circumstances of disaster, whatever consequences they might have on jobs and votes. Make or break crash it might be for the 119, but if there was something wrong with the aircraft now was the time to find out.

The teams from Seattle and Burbank had arrived. The power-plant engineers were grouped with their clean tarpaulins pegged out around the engines. Already they'd discovered the generator on number one engine disengaged and since the 119 didn't carry an emergency wind-driven generator Tango November would have been down to single generator operation when the number two engine had been shut down.

There was even the suspicion now that the shutdown itself had been the result of an unnecessary fault—another false fire warning. The fire extinguishers in one and three engines had been found only partially discharged before impact damage, the antifire precaution taken by Captain Duckham seconds before the crash. But extinguishers in number two engine had been fully discharged some time prior to the crash, though without apparent signs of a precrash fire or overheat.

Everything would now need to be subjected to the microscope and to film and X-ray tests for a proper analysis. Eventually each part of the aircraft would be fitted together jigsaw fashion with the damage on impact and preimpact damage or deterioration carefully detailed. The mechanical and electrical systems would be reassembled and tested, and hopefully somewhere along the line they would discover why the sensing element had indicated a fire, why the number one generator had been disconnected, and what effects, if any, both failures had had on the operation of the aircraft.

The most difficult reassembly job had been tackled by two of the Italian investigators, joined now by four engineers from the aircraft manufacturers. They were piecing together the two shattered wings, with the ailerons and aileron mechanism. The left side wing had disintegrated back along the crash path and there was scarcely a piece of it larger than a car door. The Italians had found the two small ridges in the ground that provoked the breakup. None of the trees were resistant enough to have caused such damage. In fact they had been scythed off like stems in a wheat field. But when the wing tip had hit a protrusion of old lava the structure had given way ten feet from the fuselage. They were lucky the break had happened so spontaneously, thought Raille. Considering the angle of bank the plane might easily have cartwheeled. The pilot must have been flying it to the last hundredth of a second to put it down so flat, and not just flying it but fighting it. It was a pity his efforts had been rewarded with so few survivors.

Larry Raille turned back into the concertinaed mess of cockpit, which had yielded one cryptic piece of evidence that morning: a scribbled note on the flight engineer's pad found torn and bloodstained among the debris on the floor—"Battery high charge," the engineer had written, if handwriting comparisons proved conclusive.

Everything else was now to be worked out through a

painstaking dissection of electrical and hydraulic systems: bulbs to be examined for the stretching of filaments that would prove they had been lit at the time of impact; instruments to be photographed in ultraviolet to show up their original readings; wiring circuits to be tested and X-rayed for possible short circuits; manual controls fingerprinted to show which of the three men had been operating them and to establish whether the lady intruder had interfered in any way with the operation of the plane.

But dramatic solutions like hijacking were beginning to seem ridiculous. Already they'd discovered two technical failures, neither of them disastrous in themselves or even unusual, but potentially dangerous in combination, and combinations were what aircraft accidents were usually about. Raille had examined more than forty accidents in his time at the safety board, anything and everything from single-seat gliders to jumbos, from a steward's broken nose in a heavy landing to death in a major disaster. On every occasion where evidence was available the investigators had found themselves dealing with combinations of circumstances: bad design; inadequate maintenance; weather conditions; human error; technical failure; fatigue or stress, both mechanical and human; above all, bad luck in a game where luck theoretically should play no part. Raille pictured this Captain Duckham for the first time—in the middle of a storm, minus an engine, minus a generator, perhaps overtired, certainly overstressed.

Raille used to fly starfighters in the air force. More than once, with the combinations, it had scared him shitless.

Ralph Burden watched the conflagration through binoculars from his hotel balcony thirteen miles away. He thought at first that the smoke was Tango November, and he feared a repetition of an RAF accident in the tropics many years ago where wreckage had ignited spontaneously under the intense heat of direct sunlight. He took a compass bearing on the root of the smoke and plotted out the line on a map, but the line passed four or five miles clear of the crash site and Burden guessed with approximate accuracy that the fire was a result of picnicking sightseers.

He returned to his room and to a table that was slowly accumulating a weight of files, charts, and diagrams, together with his own notes. Hercules' safety officer had supplied him that morning with flight information covering Tango November: the payload of passengers, cargo, and luggage, fuel load and takeoff weights, and the records that brought Tango November's maintenance logbook up to date. Maintenance records would be passed on to the Americans when they returned to their hotel that evening, and Burden was checking quickly through them for any information relevant to his own investigation. He chronicled Tango November's delayed departure in his notes, tracing it back through Duckham's request for a recheck on the number two engine, the time taken to change cabin configuration from military charter back to normal requirements, and the initial delay and engine check in Germany. Until that trouble Tango November, in her seven months of service, had been relatively free of major faults and recent logbook entries were largely taken up with items of cabin furniture: loose seats, tables, and ashtrays; inoperative belts, a minor collapse in the overhead luggage rack. Burden made a brief note of them all. He had heard a tirade from Mac yesterday about conditions inside the cabin. A history of loose seats and belts could be relevant to his medical report, and it might not occur to the Americans to refer those sections of the log back to him.

Burden had sketched out the bare timetable of disaster on thirty sheets of otherwise blank foolscap; Friday evening to Saturday morning subdivided by vertical columns into half hours and further subdivided into one minute sections for the last half hour preceding the crash. Horizontal columns represented each member of the cockpit and cabin crew, the operations in progress, communications with air traffic control zones and airports, and, in case the flight recorders were found intact, entries for position, altitude, speed, and heading. Burden had set aside two additional columns at the foot of each page to cover "woman intruder" and "hijack indications."

A further four foolscap sheets dealt with biographical and professional summaries of the three cockpit crew members and any relevant details concerning the six hostesses. For the moment only one of these pages had come to life, and Burden had deliberately set that page aside. He had spent the evening and half the night renewing acquaintance with people, places, and sensations long forgotten. Dixie Duckham would have to wait. He was too distracting. Perhaps the Mrs. Duckham would supply the perspective, if and when she arrived.

The flight engineer's biography was a great deal simpler, deceptively simple, Burden thought as he checked Raven's RAF record. A single man with no known commitments, he had been in the service until three years ago, leaving at the age of thirty-six. And yet in eighteen years of service he had made very little progress in rank or status. His RAF career was recent enough for Mac to be able to find out something about him from assessment records and Burden laid his file to one side.

Copilot was Peter Nyren. Born 1947; father, Canon Ash Nyren; mother, Evelyn Mary, *née* Fawcett, died 1959; educated at the Dragon prep school in Oxford, and at Radley; entered Hamble Flying School 1965, graduated 1968 with average to good results. Entered

Court Line 1968 to fly 111s. Recruited eight months ago for Hercules and sent to the States for 119 training. Entered service with Hercules ten weeks later.

Burden scribbled down the relevant details: age 29; Hamble; flying hours as of September 5, 1,547; six years on 111s; eight months including training on 119s. There were two loose pages at the back of the file—a photocopy of a letter addressed to Captain Duckham, Fleet Captain Hercules Flight, and the carbon copy of a reply. Burden glanced over them quickly, caught the words "regret" and "complaint," and took both letters out to read them more closely.

Peter Nyren's letter to Duckham had been written in careful longhand and was the result, Burden guessed, of many rough drafts.

Dear Fleet Captain,

I am writing to you in your official capacity because I should like this letter and the nature of my complaint to be placed on record.

Strange, thought Burden, that these letters had been left in the file. No company liked to air its dirty linen, especially in the aftermath of a disaster.

At the time of my recruitment into the company I was given to understand that the seniority list would be as per normal practice based on length of service within the company. Indeed you yourself emphasized my early prospects of being appointed captain. It has since become known that you are now recruiting "senior" or older 119 pilots as captains, offering them entrance at three, four, or five increment levels. I feel that you have taken advantage of our friendship to foist this state of affairs on myself and the younger first officers whom I represent. It would not be an exaggeration of my feelings to describe your action as a betrayal. I must com-

municate to you the prevalent attitude among my fellow officers, for you have so undermined our confidence and trust that your continued office as fleet captain could seriously affect labor relations in the company.

I greatly regret having to write to you in this vein after your earlier kindness and hospitality. In this respect I hope my good wishes to your family are still acceptable.

The good wishes at the end of such a letter sounded more like a threat than a blessing. Duckham's typewritten reply merely acknowledged receipt without reciprocating regret, anger, or good wishes. The letters were both dated in the third week of July. Had the two men been in contact at all since then? On Friday night Nyren had been on standby. He had flown Tango November as it were by accident, substituting for another colleague on sick leave. Was that the first time Nyren and Duckham had flown together since the quarrel?

Dixie Duckham again. It was easy enough to imagine people quarreling with him, but Burden had to remind himself that his own memories of the man were thirty years old.

He was relieved when the hotel desk rang him to tell him that they were serving lunch in the dining room. He sat at his single table struggling with a plate of spaghetti and imagining in spite of himself how Dixie might have ridiculed him for his ineptitude.

6

Irrespective of technical opinion on site the office of the procuratore issued a press release that afternoon restating the scenario of hijack, this time without the usual reservations.

When the younger magistrato protested to his colleague about the release of ambiguous and unsubstantiated material he was told that the press release had been an unfortunate mistake too late to rectify.

Sharlie read the press release in midafternoon and rang Citto at the newspaper: "Looks like it's all over."

"We're just getting started," Citto told him. "Where have you been?"

"Looking for my mother."

"Or joyriding on your cousin's motorcycle."

"Maybe."

"Take it up on the mountain. There's a big fire burning. You might find some good pictures. I'll meet you at the doctor's house when it gets dark."

"What doctor?"

"Pick up your lovely cousin. Take her with you. She knows which doctor."

Sharlie's grunt was unenthusiastic.

I'm going to lose him, thought Citto as he hung up. Sharlie doesn't like being home. He'll be off back to Rome tomorrow.

Citto was shirt-sleeved and sweating, buried in the basement archives at his newspaper office. He had spent all afternoon with the card index, records, and back issues, tracing the respective histories of the Tomacchio and Consoli families.

Tomacchio was straightforward enough—country boy to small business owner in thirty years' labor. He'd been in trouble at the end of the war operating a black market in stolen drugs and equipment from a British army hospital on the far side of the mountain—sentenced to a year and a half inside and released on an amnesty after seven months. But he must have kept some of his money. He was running a small garage by 1950; driving his own trucks by 1955; advertising a transport business in 1959. A small-time hustler tough enough to look after his own limited interests. He'd bought that distillery three years ago, selling off the vineyards to a construction company. Which is doubtless where the Consoli *père et fils* had entered his life.

Avvocato Consoli was altogether more complex, the sort of man who traveled to and from his office in chauffeur-driven cars with a police escort to protect him from would-be kidnappers. The family went back generations as local lawyers, estate managers, and tax agents in the service of absentee landlords and rulers. The present head of family had established himself after the war with the Christian Democrats, a party organizer and local government dignitary. He had been rewarded ten years ago with a minor office in Rome and had afterward returned to Catania as what could politely be described the number one wheeler and dealer. Still a practicing lawyer he had been associated with all large-scale development on the east coast of the island—everything from the oil refineries at Augusta to the autostrada and the new airport. He had doubtless fostered his close links with politics and administration at local, regional, and national levels, and must have enjoyed unrivaled access to planning departments, not to speak of his professional participation in the distribution of official funds whether from Rome or from Brussels.

The newspaper had done a profile on him only a year ago on the occasion of some local party function. "A modest man," the reporter had written, "whose emotions are closer to the countryside than the city." The avvocato lived on his own farm somewhere out on the southern slopes of the mountain.

Citto checked the telephone number: 62-58991. The area code was somewhere out in the orange groves near Paterno. He dialed the number on an off-chance, listening to the ringing tone a long time before someone answered.

"Casa Consoli," announced a hesitant woman's voice.

"I'd like to speak with the avvocato, please."

"I am afraid he is out. He's been away since yesterday." The woman sounded genuinely apologetic.

"It's a matter of some importance. Do you think I would find him at home if I visited this evening?"

"Oh, no. I'm sorry. He's away until tomorrow."

"Is there any number where I can reach him?"

"I could pass on a message if he calls."

Citto tried guile. "I was asked to meet him. Tomorrow." His stammer made lying sound so innocent.

The lady believed him. "At the airport you mean?"

"Yes."

"Just a moment." There was a pause while she looked for something. "It's flight AZ 140. I'm afraid there's nothing written down here about when it arrives."

"Thank you, signora, I can find that out."

"Who shall I say called?" she asked, but the phone was already dead.

What a strange and illogical series of questions, the lady thought as she walked back upstairs. Better not tell her husband when he returned home. He would only yell at her. She remembered he had told her specifically to tell anybody that he was in Rome. AZ 140. She'd given away the flight number. Always intrigue, she thought to herself. Always things not to say and not to do. Signora Consoli retired to the shuttered silence of her room. The maids had their half day off and there were another two hours to live through before she could leave for mass.

Julia's hotel room was also shuttered and dark. She was lying on the bed, a jug of iced lemonade on the table beside her. She hadn't asked for it, but the proprietor's wife had brought it up to her soon after she arrived. The taxi had dropped her at the bottom of the long flight of steps off which the pensione was situated. She hadn't even been able to cope with paying him, handing over her purse as he was explaining the fare.

Julia Duckham had been scarcely conscious of effort at any stage of her journey from England. The children had been left with Pam; a car had driven her to Heathrow; an Alitalia hostess had met her at Rome and escorted her to the connecting flight for Catania; and at Catania the pilot himself had taken her from the plane to find her a waiting taxi. He had saluted her and stood back watching the taxi leave. The little freemasonry of airline pilots, thought Julia, helping each other or each other's families when things go wrong.

Reality was gone. At home it would be teatime: Pam calling the children in from the garden; bicycles and pedal cars to be wheeled into the garage; raspberries, apples, and spinach to be picked for the evening. Julia tried to think of the details but they were all broken. Little pieces of a nightmare that would soon reclaim her. She couldn't even bring herself to telephone and talk to the children as she had promised.

"Devo vedere il corpo di mio marito, il pilota." The phrase she had accumulated with the help of her patient cab driver. "I must see the body of my husband, the pilot."

Hospitals, morgues, police stations, she had tried them all up and down the coast without success. What had they done with Mike? Was there anything left of him at all? I must see him dead, she thought, or I shall never be able to accept it.

There were pots of geraniums on her balcony, a buzz of voices promenading in the square below, smells from a restaurant. It was the sort of place they'd always promised themselves to go when Mike retired.

"Come on, girl. It's an adventure." She heard him say it, saw his reassuring smile, felt his encouraging hand under her elbow.

Like the very first time they'd been out together, the evening her air-hostess sister had been stranded in a German fog. The two sisters had shared a flat near the hospital where Julia worked. Mike had arrived that evening to take Pam out and had seemed almost relieved not to find her.

"Come on," he said to Julia. "Let's you and me go out, and do just whatever the hell we please." And they had. They had been to Bentleys for oysters and smoked salmon; then to Rules for pheasant; and finally across the Strand for treacle pud and cream at Simpsons. Mike's expensive joke, of course. A bottle of wine at each establishment and a walk over Waterloo Bridge for their first very formalized kiss. A traditional seduction he had called it, though they were both too sloshed to do anything much more than giggle at each other by the time they got home.

"My God," he'd said, next morning, "but you're different from your sister." He had nicknamed poor Pam the "Prim and Trim," Pam who had been his mistress for six months and tormented by the fact that he was apparently inexorably married and with family. But that same first morning after he had proposed to Julia and they hadn't even made love properly together. "I offer you my life," he had said, "absolute and complete apart from my paternal affection and duties to my daughter." And he had carried out the whole operation on his own without apparent melodrama. He met Pam that day and told her what had happened; he had led his wife through the divorce and had made it seem to her inevitable; he had even won the affection of his daughter for Julia.

Nine years ago they had begun, courtesy of a Trident grounded at the Lohausen airport in Düsseldorf, only to end here, with another aircraft, in another country, and for reasons as yet unknown.

For the first time Julia wondered how the crash had happened. She remembered Mike's bitterness when a colleague had been killed: "You watch them, girl. You watch them make it pilot error. Dead pilots don't talk back."

The hotel room was dark, Julia sitting in a bowed slump on the edge of the bed. It was very late, well past the dinner hour on the notice behind the door. Yet the proprietor returned to escort Julia to the empty dining-room. He sat her in a window, poured wine, and left her alone with a cart of cold meats and salad. She ate and drank mechanically, watching the lights in the piazza, with Mike's voice and gestures jollying her along.

7

Mac's bodies were organized. Numbered, labeled, and bagged they had been stacked on make-shift shelves in four refrigerated Interfrigo freight cars parked on a railway siding next to the fruit market of a small town at the eastern foot of the mountain. Turi had organized the operation with the local carabinieri and he and Mac were now installed a mile away from the siding in a basement of the same small hospital where the elderly surgeon was still working, in apparent futility, over Tino G.

For the moment, and thankfully, no one else knew the whereabouts of the crash victims. Even the inhabitants of the town, crowding into the main piazza for their Sunday evening stroll, did not yet guess the function of the meat truck as it ferried its locked-up loads to and fro between the railway sidings and the discreet service door at the back of the hospital.

Mac and Sanju had been joined by an RAF dentist and two representatives from the London undertakers, and the process of official identification was under way, based in the majority of cases on the evidence of dental or medical records telexed from England. Direct identifications were impossible. Most passports and wallets had been stolen, and even the bodies that had escaped burning were in no condition to be shown to relatives. Mac had experienced the unwillingness of husbands, wives, mothers, or fathers to acknowledge the identity of a badly damaged body. They were better left out of the proceedings.

Mac's team had decided to complete the operation in two stages: identification first; autopsy only when relatives and authorities had been given official notification of death. The casualty lists published so far had relied on the names of passengers issued by the travel companies, and such evidence was not considered sufficient for any legal purpose. Mac reckoned that they had at the most two clear days before public opinion started to call for the burial or repatriation of bodies. He would have liked more time. He wanted full autopsies on each one of these victims, for only brute statistics in brutal detail would make any impression in the official report. He had limited himself so far to opening only three specimen bodies from the three different sections of fuselage and they had each confirmed his initial impressions on the survivability of the crash.

The body from the front section of the wreck had whiplashed over the seat belt. There was a tear in the mesentery of the small bowel, a common enough cause of death in commercial aircraft where lap belts are worn without shoulder harness. Any slackness in the belt would have provoked the injury and the passenger would have hemorrhaged to death long before the rescue teams arrived. It was clear that none of the bodies from the front of the plane had been affected by fire or fumes. The break in the fuselage would have acted as a ventilator.

The body from the wing section of the plane had suffered compound fractures of both lower legs where they had hit the row of seats in front. In addition he had bad bruising and swelling above his eyes where his head had hit the hard plastic lid of the recessed container in the headrest of the seat in front. The containers were designed to hold a pre-packed meal box— a way of economizing on cabin staff duties, but a way also of making the seats still more lethal in conditions of impact or turbulence. This passenger would have been immobilized after the impact, probably unconscious and certainly unable to escape from the ensuing fire. Apparent cause of death here was severe burning of tissue in the lung, but Mac was sure that blood tests would also reveal a high level of cyanide from burning plastic materials used in the 119 cabin.

A partially carbonized body from the central rear section had extensive fat and bone-marrow embolism in the lungs, again indicating major antemortem bone fracture probably of a serious enough nature to immobilize. Carbon in the trachea and bronchi established the fact that this passenger had still been breathing when the effects of the fire reached her. The burned remains of a watch on her wrist showed distinctly lighter patterns on the dial where the two hands had been pointing. The time indicated was 5:50. If the watch had been accurate it suggested that the fire had reached this passenger and finally stopped her watch as much as eighteen minutes after the supposed time of impact. It was clear enough to Mac that if passengers had not been immobilized by wreckage and injuries inside the cabin many of them would have had ample time to escape.

Later in the afternoon a police driver arrived with an up-to-date list of survivors and twenty-three bodies collected from hospital morgues. At least the figures now tallied. The only missing numbers among the living and dead were the four cockpit corpses, all of them in the hands of the local legal authority in Catania. But the autopsies on the pilots and flight engineer were at least complete, and only the fourth of the four, the mysterious lady intruder, presented any problem in that she had not yet been identified nor her missing arm located.

Two floors above Mac, Tino G. was watching the red secondhand of the theater clock. It moved slowly and spasmodically, jerking its way round, out of synch with whatever pulses now governed his consciousness. He felt he could have played one side of an LP in the time it took to make its full circle. He knew from the sweat-stained white-coated backs bent around his nether regions that no one present had realized that his eyes were open and his mind awake. He didn't want to trouble them. There was no point. He felt no pain and that thin red hand was moving far too slowly. He thought instead of his girl's face, oval through her long hair, eyes turned sideways, and grinning at him as they walked, her shoulders hunched into a heavy coat. Just whistle and I'll come, she'd told him. But who would pay her way 3,000 miles out here?

The plaintive notes of that tune came back into his mind: F sharp, E, D sharp, F sharp. C sharp, D sharp, E, D sharp, C sharp, B.

The simplest of melodies in dominant and tonic. A wandering traveling song: *jet plane, freight train,* and *early morning rain.*

8

The charred scar of forest fire was still blowing sparks in the breeze. Sharlie had arrived on the mountain road, passing the police roadblocks with the borrowed press documents he always kept in his pocket, Laura behind him on the rear hump of her brother's motorcycle, nursing the bag of cameras and film.

The mountain road was now empty. Apart from the piles of refuse there was nothing left to suggest the lines of cars that had blocked the road earlier in the day. The evidence was scattered high up on the hairpin where the fire had passed: two fire engines, groups of police, and a long littered line of burned cars. Sharlie parked the motorcycle and walked up the road to take his pictures: metal skeletons of cars still glowing in the fading light, ashfields of what had once been woodland and undergrowth. Sharlie walked through it, his shoes hot through cracked soles, scuffing clouds of dust and sparks. Then in a defile twenty yards from the main road he found wreckage that had survived the fire, mechanical capsules that must surely have been dropped by the crashing plane. Sharlie used a flash to photograph them in detail: two cylinders similar in shape to the self-inflating life rafts that lined the upper decks of ocean-going ships. For some reason they had survived the fire intact, only discolored by the heat and smoke.

Sharlie rejoined Laura on the road and they walked together back to the motorcycle as a helicopter passed low overhead: Larry Raille and his team of investigators returning from Tango November to their hotels in Taormina, and swooping, courtesy of the pilot, for a look at the remains of the forest fire. But from thirty feet up they couldn't make out any detail, and the two strange canisters remained undiscovered, but for Sharlie's camera, until the police retrieved them later that evening.

The two cousins freewheeled downhill in the chilly dusk and stopped at the first bar for a hot coffee.

The barman served them watching Sharlie: "You're a reporter."

"How do you know?"

The man shrugged. "You must be a reporter to get through the roadblock."

"They lost a lot of cars up there today."

"Serve them right. They shouldn't come gawping at other people's misfortunes."

Sharlie drank his coffee. "You think anyone heard the crash from the village?"

"People higher up might have heard."

"Who'd have been up in the woods at that time of the morning?"

One of the villagers joined in from behind his newspaper: *"Cantallaluna."*

The barman nodded. "That's possible."

The other man put down his newspaper. *"Cantallaluna.* He came down with a sackful yesterday. I saw him on his motorcycle on the top road."

"You didn't talk to him?"

"He didn't stop."

"Has anyone talked to him?" Sharlie turned to the other men in the room who were listening and watching.

"Who's seen him?" answered one old man. "I haven't."

Sharlie paid for their coffees and they returned to the motorcycle.

"How would we find *Cantallaluna?*" asked Sharlie.

Laura shrugged. "You'd have to choose the right sort

of day and catch him in the woods in the early morning."

Sing-to-the-moon. The origins of his name went back many generations. His family had been cart drivers, riding their loads at night and singing their way through the mountain villages. *Cantallaluna.* The name was still appropriate though he had no need to drive carts or trucks any more. He made a good living from the mushrooms in the woods high on the volcano, picking them in the early morning and putting them on the plane for Turin or Milan where they'd fetch around 5,000 lire a pound.

If he had been up on the mountain picking on Saturday morning he could have been very near to where the plane had come down.

"We'll find him one morning," Laura said.

Someone will, thought Sharlie. Not me. For he still believed he would return to Rome next morning.

The village slipped into evening as Mac and Turi came home: harvesters returning from the vineyards; young men calling for young girls and walking them to the little movie at the top of the street; children being yelled to bed, and the smell of someone's pasta and beans leaking out of a backyard and over the roofs to tease Mac's empty stomach.

Mac had sent Sanju with the day's report to Taormina. The monosyllabic Indian was well-enough equipped for the conference table, and Mac in his present state of exhaustion could not face one of those interminable multinational powwows. Not that he ever liked to attend the evening pooling of evidence until he had his own answers cut and dried. That missing arm was beginning to worry him.

The doctor's doors had not been barred tonight. There were two cars and a motorcycle parked outside;

a cabdriver in one of the cars, a lady in Turi's waiting room, Sharlie, Citto, and Laura on his terrace.

"Bloody journalists," said Mac. "I can't talk to them."

But it was Turi for whom Citto and Sharlie were waiting, and Turi who had to evade their questions by attending to his duties in the front of the house.

The lady in the surgery was no patient. *"Devo vedere il corpo di mio marito, il pilota."*

Both Turi and Mac recognized the pretty English face from the photograph in Captain Duckham's wallet. The pilot's wife. It was clear from her confused questions that she had not yet succeeded in tracking down her husband's body.

"I don't think there is anything for you to see," said Turi.

"I've seen bodies before."

"I examined the flight crew last night," Mac told her. "But the police took the bodies away this morning. I am afraid they have a legal right to their own medical examination."

"You make it sound as though they were criminals." The woman was angry and confused.

"You would expect the same after a car crash," said Mac.

"They told me you'd be able to help me. They said you would know where he is."

Turi was more accommodating. He knew where the police would keep their sensitive medical evidence: "It's an easy enough place to find. But I still say there is no point for you to see your husband's body."

"I didn't come here to sit in the sun," the lady said.

"If we did find him," suggested Mac, "we might find our hijacker's missing arm. Why don't we all go into town?"

Turi would have to come, thought Mac: the *medico*

condotto to give the escapade some spurious official validity. And Sharlie, too, for his cameras. Citto was less lucky.

"I only want photographs for my own purposes," Mac told him. "We'll be in bad enough trouble without turning the whole thing into a newspaper story."

9

Turi, Mac, and Julia left in the taxi and Sharlie met them an hour later at a prearranged rendezvous in the center of town. They walked into the building after only a perfunctory challenge from the policeman at the door. Turi was still carrying a pass issued to him yesterday by the carabinieri at the crash site and that, together with Mac's RAF ID card, seemed to satisfy the guard. Once inside there was no one in the corridors or on the stairs to question their movements.

They descended a flight of stone steps into a cold vaulted cellar, Julia suddenly afraid at what she might find. One of the rooms was lined in white tiles and furnished with a long refrigerator cabinet fitted with giant drawers. The bodies inside were oddly shaped and covered by plastic sheets.

Mac took Julia by the arm. "There is nothing for you to see. There is no point in looking." Death is ugly and irrelevant, he would have liked to explain.

"Captain M. E. Duckham"—a label in Mac's handwriting. He watched Julia raise one corner of the plastic sheet. She found a pair of feet cold and hard, one white, one bruised blue and ugly like part of a desecrated statue.

"Please," she said. "Please show me."

Mac took the sheet from her and folded it back. In that moment only pain and disgust kept Julia from collapse. The body was naked and broken, even further violated by a scalpel whose long incision had been sewn up with thick crude stitches. The face seemed masked. What was left of it was torn down in folds over the chin like soft red rubber. Even the shape of the skull had gone, flattened, grotesquely framed by unnaturally colored hair.

Mike. There wasn't much to identify. His stomach, hips, thighs, genitals. It was enough. She turned away to sit by herself while the two doctors pursued their own search.

Sharlie was watching Julia. He thought, I could have taken a terrible picture of her face in that moment with the body. An Italian woman would have shouted or screamed and demonstrated frenzy. This lady instead is sitting there frozen and composed as though posing for someone.

The doctors found the woman hijacker in a numbered drawer, her identification still unsolved. Her torn arm was lying grostesquely between her legs, but there was no mark or label on it to show where in the wreckage it had been found.

Turi was looking at the arm, remembering his cramped struggle to find the trapped American boy. The wrist was circled in rings of copper, silver, and gold, and Turi recalled the jangle of bracelets when an arm had fallen across him in the wreckage of the plane.

"I think I know where it lie," he said. "I was trying to reach that boy and it fall on me. I hear these rings—"

Mac picked up the arm and jangled the bracelets. Turi nodded with a grimace. "It was in the same mess where the boy was trapped."

"The American boy with the guitar?"

Turi nodded. Mac was studying his salvage plan. Tino G. had been found well behind the line of the front exit in the middle of a pile of loose wreckage that had accumulated against the galley wall. It was six or eight feet back from the flight-deck door.

"Was the arm loose or trapped in the wreckage?"

Turi thought for a moment before replying. "Trapped. I move something and then it falls."

Mac grunted. "Problem solved."

"How you mean?"

"No hijacker."

"Why?"

"She lost her arm when the plane crashed, right? So she was in the cabin when the plane hit the ground."

Mac was matching arm to body. There was no possible doubt that the two belonged together. Ligament and muscle damage were complementary and the skin pigmentation identical.

"I'd say she was out of her seat standing in the aisle—probably in a panic. When the plane hit the ground she was thrown forward at whatever speed they were traveling. A hundred and thirty miles an hour perhaps. She would have flung out an arm to stop herself and she lost it when it caught on the galley partition. She carried on minus arm and crashed through the door into the cockpit. The rest of the injuries are consistent with extreme frontal impact—splintered ribs and sternum, broken hips, both knees smashed, the other arm flung up to protect her face and jammed into her broken jaw."

Mac noted down what he could see of the woman's teeth. Many of them had been broken by the arm but there were two clear characteristics that might prove identification if related to dental records: a gold crown on a molar; and a gold cantilever bridge involving a canine, dislodged by the arm but still in one piece. The bridge looked like American handiwork.

Mac called Sharlie to take pictures of the body and the dental fragments.

Sharlie saw the body of a young woman terribly

disfigured, a severed arm lying loose between her legs, her jaws broken wide open, the trunk sewn together in clumsy stitches. No one would have recognized it, brother, mother, lover.

Mac held the flashgun for him. The boy was looking very green.

"I need a tripod for this," Sharlie told Turi. "I can't even hold the camera still. I never felt so goddamn sick in all my life."

Julia watched them as the repeating blue tinge of the flash lit up the cellar, and three silhouettes bowed like vampires or body snatchers over the corpses. When the giant Englishman was satisfied he slid the bodies back into the cabinet. Turi took Julia by one arm and the trespassers returned upstairs, down the empty corridors, and back to the taxi in the street.

Sharlie unloaded the film and handed it to Mac. Mac shook his head. "You get them developed and bring them to me. I've got no facilities." He shook hands with the boy and thanked him for his help.

Sharlie watched the taxi turn the corner and disappear. Those bodies had made him feel ill. He saw lights and cars and the bustle of people in the main street and walked down to find a bar on the Via Etnea. He needed a large whiskey and ice to dispel his nausea. But the drink only made him feel worse. He left it unfinished and wandered back into the obscurity of the side streets toward his motorcycle.

They caught him at the corner of Via San Francesco.

He didn't even hear the car behind him and only turned to look when the doors opened. He caught a glimpse of the rotating blue lamp as a strong arm twisted him face to the wall in the sunken alley beyond the pavement. They were in darkness, unseen by anyone, ignored from the main street for the flashing blue lamp that licensed the violence. He sensed two of them; faces he could not see, and voices that did not speak.

They frisked him; lifted a heavy boot into his balls when he tried to protest; and grabbed the camera case he had dropped surreptitiously in the angle of the wall. He heard them pull out the cameras and film; heard one of them mutter at his colleague; then heard the film reels break open under someone's foot on the pavement. He turned his head. They were unrolling the film through the slots of a drain cover. Finally one of them talked.

"Who were you with?"

The heavy foot came back when he failed to reply. Sharlie wondered how brave and obstinate he was meant to be in the face of such interrogation.

"Who was with you?"

"I was asked to do a job."

"Who asked you?"

"I thought it was official."

The interrogator turned to him with a sneer. "Come on, baby face. Don't give me shit." Soft and round this cop was. He had Sharlie's balls in one hand, squeezing them gently. It was obvious from his eyes he was enjoying it. "A smart boy like you always knows who he's working for." He had pushed Sharlie back to the wall and was leaning close to him, tobacco and garlic breathing into his face. Sharlie felt the man's hand pull down his zipper and move inside his trousers fondling his cock. He hit out at him instinctively, saw the man weave his head aside, smile, and look to his colleague.

The colleague nodded. "He's assaulting you."

The soft round cop flicked his fist twice into Sharlie's face, back and forth so fast that the boy didn't even see it. But he felt the pain, blood warm in his mouth, and his tongue deep in a pit where one of his teeth used to live.

"What car were they in?" The man patted Sharlie's cheek where the tooth had broken. "You want to lose all of them, pretty boy?"

The pain had made Sharlie cry. He didn't want to show himself crying. He mumbled a reply.

"You make it sound like a love scene if you whisper."

"A taxi."

The man's hand was back inside his trousers churning around for a reaction. "What sort of taxi?"

"From Taormina."

"What sort of a car?"

"A Lancia."

"Color?"

"Dark blue."

No more was said or done. The hand was withdrawn, disappointed, and the two men vanished in their car while Sharlie groped around on the cobbles retrieving his cameras and the broken pieces of film cartridge. He spat blood and the broken tooth into his hand and wondered whether it was anger he was shaking with, or just fear. He also wondered what trouble there would be for the others in the taxi.

But the two cops were not in luck. Their mission was not official enough to call out more cars, and the taxi had taken the inland roads to drop Turi in his village. The cops, burning rubber along the autostrada, found no Lancia and it was only much later in the evening that they were able to trace the cabdriver and ask him questions about his passengers and their itinerary.

Citto and Sharlie met at the newspaper, the boy's face bruised and swollen, his voice thick and stumbling like that of a beat-up boxer after a bad fight. He told Citto of the bodies in the morgue and the cops nailing him afterward. He was still shaking, his mouth bloodied and his face bruised.

Citto went over the details of both stories making Sharlie repeat the sequence of events.

"Where did you go afterward?"

"I came right here."

"You didn't go to your mother's place?"

"Looking like this? She'd be out with a gun shooting cops."

"Did the English doctor leave an address?"

Sharlie took out a piece of paper with the name and telephone number of Mac's hotel in Taormina. Citto copied it into his notebook.

"Better go back to your Nonna Lisa. Get yourself patched up by your beautiful cousin."

"I'll scare hell out of them." Sharlie pulled what he could of a grin. "Will the paper print the story?"

"Half of it. The bodies in the morgue. They'll blow the hijack theory but they won't print anything about the cops."

"No. They never do." Sharlie turned at the door. "If you want my help you know where to come."

Citto grinned. "I thought you were going back to Rome."

Sharlie fingered his face. "After this? I want those bastards. They wouldn't have done this if somebody wasn't hiding something. You want anything done you come and tell me."

Citto followed him down the corridor and waved good-bye at the stairs. He telephoned a message for the English doctor explaining the fate of Sharlie's photographs, then called on his news editor and repeated Sharlie's stories. At least Sharlie's earlier pictures had survived, the strange capsules on the mountain.

"Flight recorders from the plane," said Citto. "People think someone's been trying to hide them."

"Why should they do that?"

"Frightened of the story they might tell."

"So what do we print?"

"The truth about the hijack body and pictures of the flight recorders."

"Everything out in the open."

"Almost everything. I'd like to keep going at it."

"What's stopping you?"

"I'd have to go to Messina and Rome. Maybe even farther."

The news editor waved his arm and laughed. "Draw expenses and go. At least if you're not here no one can have you taken off the story."

Citto left the office but without drawing expenses. He didn't want any written record of where he was going or what he intended to do.

He would have to catch the early train to Messina, and, if he finished there in good time, the midmorning flight to Rome from Reggio Calabria. Time for five hours' sleep he reckoned, before he packed his bags.

10

Julia Duckham felt the darkness closing in again. The woman in the cockpit had been a myth. The bearded doctor had told her that a hijacking was now excluded as a possible cause of the accident. It seemed to Julia that Mike would now be heading the list of suspects, with "pilot error" the most probable result of any investigation. How unfair if his life were to end with such a lie.

Mac had guessed at one half of her anguish. He, too, believed that the odds were shortening against Captain Duckham. He would have liked to tell this pretty woman to go back home and forget all about the circumstances of the crash and the inquiry. She had a young family. He knew that from Duckham's file. She ought to find another man. Death was not to be lingered over, except as a medical equation.

He stared from the taxi window. They were high on lava cliffs above the coast, the whole sea covered it seemed with bobbing lights, like a procession of lanterns. The lady was also watching them.

"Fishermen," Mac told her. "The fish come up to the lamps, then they pull the nets in."

She looked at him and nodded, and her eyes in the dark looked so sad and so lost that Mac wanted suddenly to take her hand and offer her some comfort.

When they arrived in Taormina he paid off the taxi and walked her up the flight of steps to her hotel.

"You've been a great help," he said. "I wish there were some way I could help you."

"He was a good man," she answered in a low voice. "He really was a good man."

Mac watched her cross the lobby of the little pensione, a forlorn, unhappy figure. He wondered for the first time what this Captain Duckham had really been like.

A few hundred yards away in a different pensione Ralph Burden was asking himself much the same question. He had been interviewing the Hercules safety officer about those strange letters in Peter Nyren's file. The American did not deny that the two letters were left there deliberately.

"Within the company it was a very public quarrel. Sooner or later someone would have found out. Much better for you to have the precise evidence, not hearsay and gossip."

Burden nodded. "That's a very commendable attitude to take. Some companies might have tried to cover it up."

"You will find, Mr. Burden, that our company will cover up nothing in its efforts to get at the truth."

Burden turned to his notes. "We will have to know whether Duckham and Nyren had flown together since the exchange of letters."

The American shook his head. "There was a tacit

agreement to keep the two men apart until the quarrel was resolved. They flew together on Friday night because someone called in sick. Nyren was on standby."

Burden nodded. "In your opinion was it a bad enough quarrel to have affected their mutual efficiency on the flight deck?"

"I am quite sure a captain of Duckham's experience would not allow personal animosity to get in the way of good flying procedure. In fact I imagine when you listen to the voice recordings you will find they had already patched up the quarrel."

Burden referred back to his notes again. "Was there any particular reason why you recruited Duckham as your fleet captain?"

"Experience. Excellent safety record. Very safety conscious. And he'd had twenty years' flying on the European routes we were trying to set up."

"He was responsible for most of your recruitment?"

"Yes."

"Were there any problems with recruitment?"

"It was almost complete. He wanted one or two older 119 pilots. They couldn't very well come in at the bottom of the ladder. That's what caused the quarrel."

"Nyren claimed in his letter to be speaking for the younger pilots in the company."

"I don't think they shared his vehemence."

"So there was something personal about the quarrel?"

"They had been close friends. I don't know." The American paused and grinned. "He was quite a guy for the girls of course."

"Nyren?"

"Duckham."

Dixie Duckham, hard-drinking womanizing crown prince of Little Snoring. The young fighter pilot was like a ghost walking round them in the hotel bedroom. Burden stood up.

"That'll be all for now, thank you. We might have to go over some of it again."

The American turned to the door. "Mrs. Duckham has arrived. I expect you will want to ask her one or two questions. She's staying at the Pensione Albert."

Burden wrote down the name. The American paused at the open door.

"There is just one more thing. Again it's something I'd rather not say, but it's one of those things some smart reporter is going to dig up. I don't suppose it has any relevance at all, but it seems Duckham had something going with one of the stewardesses on this flight."

Burden stared at the American, deciding suddenly that he did not much like him.

"Company gossip I'm afraid. Probably nothing in it. It was the girl who survived. She's in one of the hospitals. Stella Pritchard."

The American closed the door and Burden heard the squeak of his soft rubber soles receding down the corridor.

11

A sequence of chords and one line of melody had held the thread of a boy's life. If someone had suggested that to the masked man in the white coat he might almost have believed it. The tired surgeon was ready to believe anything. He'd been working over the broken body on and off for nearly two days, by now almost willing death on its way. For until the boy finally died he could not bring himself to wash up and go home.

Then sometime in the dawn of Monday the surgeon changed sides again. Sometime during that night he had stopped anticipating silence from the monitor and started instead to listen for the rhythm of that pulse. To fight so long. Even the tired old man suddenly wanted this mess of shattered bones and body to defy the shadows in the corner of the theater.

see the silver bird on high

The boy's mind smiled. Tino G. had found a verse of words for that lost tune in his head.

Hear the mighty engines roar
  see the silver bird on high
She's away and westward bound
  far above the clouds she'll fly
Where the morning rain don't fall
  and the sun always shine
She'll be flying over my home
  in about three hours' time.

Part Three

1

The storms had returned, a frenzy of impenetrable rain that flooded the roads and erased all apparent movement from the sea. Families began to move out of their summer homes along the coast returning to the city, or the towns and villages in the hills. The gathering of grapes stopped in the vineyards, and on the mountain where the forest fire had destroyed the trees a slope of earth and loose lava slipped a hundred feet and buried the road.

In the wreckage of Tango November the investigators, partially sheltered under tarpaulins and wrapped in heavy oilskins, continued to search for their evidence. Plastic sheeting had been taped over the left side remains of fuselage and tail, and the reassembled left wing had been laid out under canvas on a suitably flat and cleared area of scrub nearby. Engineers had found traces of fuel and hydraulic fluid that had leaked, it seemed, from damage in the wing. The fluid stains, too substantial to have been caused by accidental spillage, were found on the insides of buckled sections and complementary on both sides of fractured wreckage, establishing that the fluids had been leaking before the plane broke up. The outside ten feet of left wing and ailerons were missing from reassembly and a search party of two Italians and two of the aircraft manufacturer's engineers were equipping themselves for a long and uncomfortable hike. Aerial search had discovered no wreckage and until the missing wing section was found no one would be able to pronounce on the possibilities of a midair collision, or earlier impact with the mountain.

Raille laid out the large-scale maps and plotted Tango November's left-turning bank, projecting it in a consistent arc from the pattern of damage in the splintered trees on the crash path. The search party would have to follow the likely path of that arc back across the mountainside in the hope of finding the missing pieces of wing. Whatever they found or failed to find, it seemed likely now that the doomed plane had already lost half its maneuverability some time prior to impact.

At least the flight recorders had been found and the younger magistrato had already arranged to send them back to England for readout and analysis. They had turned up rather mysteriously lower down the mountain, and the local authorities had handed them over that morning after Sharlie's photographs of them had been published in the newspapers. Without those pictures they might have disappeared altogether, for it was clear that someone in the local hierarchy was doing his damnedest to hide or obscure evidence. Even a transcript had disappeared—testimony given to an Italian investigator by the air traffic controller at Taormina–Peloritana. "Nothing of importance," the Italian investigator had said, but Raille decided he would request a second interrogation.

He watched the four men move off heavy under the rain with their packs and bivouac tents. They had an uncomfortable time ahead of them, whether in the wet or in the heat and humidity that seemed likely to return afterward. The arc they were following swept across the eastern flank of the mountain, through dry scrub and over fields of lava as wild, featureless and inhospitable as a moonscape.

There were only five investigators left now in the actual wreckage—Raille and one of the Englishmen, with the engineers from Burbank and Seattle and an analyst—three of them buried waist-deep in the blackened tail wreckage salvaging the engines. Raille could hear them at odd times during the day cursing the rain, the occasional blasphemy exchanged between the two Americans, or the Englishman's dry-toned scolding as they overlooked his careful rules of procedure.

Raille and the systems analyst were bent up double in the floodlit cockpit, oil-skinned surgeons with their tangles of wiring and disembodied instruments.

Number one generator unserviceable, number two engine shut down. The instruments were beginning to reveal part of the nightmare: weather radar, one HF radio set, galley power and two booster pumps all apparently switched off, and cabin heating and lighting reduced. The flight engineer must have been shedding electrical load to protect that one surviving generator, though it seemed a lot of load to shed. Galley power and pumps were usually sufficient on a 119. A single generator could cope with the remaining equipment. Unless there'd been trouble on the number three as well. That would have been stretching bad luck to absurd limits. Even safety regulations had to depend on some law of probability.

Raille turned his attention back to the number two engine. Only six weeks ago, after the Nairobi crash, the safety board had sent a recommendation to the Federal Aviation Authority for further tests and development work to be carried out by the manufacturers on the

119's number two power-plant. In twelve months there had been over thirty reported cases of fire warnings necessitating in-flight shutdown. No one had yet come up with any answers though it was thought that lack of exterior cooling due to the position of the engine under the tail was causing distortion giving rise to hot gas leaks.

The FAA had passed on the recommendation but without any mandatory conditions, content to leave further research to the initiative of the power-plant manufacturers. A Washington solution for a corporation already in financial difficulty.

A whistle blew lunchtime from the helicopter higher up the slope. It was half past twelve. Sun up in Washington. In fifteen hours, thought Raille, his wife would be opening their front door to the first guests, her eyes carefully sparkling, her makeup superb, her New England manner impeccable, his booze flowing freely. She gave very good, and very expensive, parties.

2

The rain marked the end of summer, however brilliantly the sun would afterward return. It was time to think on serious things.

The young magistrato returned to his office that morning to find a corridor full of waiting counsel. The judicial timetable had been altered and three prosecutions brought forward, unexpectedly and without warning. Why and how he could not find out. A week's work, he calculated, and at the end of the week no doubt another three cases would appear. His participation in the air crash inquiry had been effectively curtailed without obvious interference or collusion.

The procuratore generale seemed surprised when his young colleague complained.

"Your involvement with the air disaster was only advisory. Merely to help settle some of the technical problems."

"So far as I know I haven't solved a single technical problem."

"These crash inquiries take years to sort out. We cannot allow our timetable to congest as a result."

"My own timetable was very uncongested—until this morning."

"I expect some lawyers have been complaining about delays." The procuratore referred to papers on his desk. "Two of your prosecutions involve men who have been waiting trial in prison for nearly a year."

"Then statistically they should count themselves among the more fortunate."

The two men eyed each other in distant half smiles.

"You feel you have something to contribute to the investigation?" asked the procuratore.

"I feel it is too much for one man to cope with, however able and experienced."

"There is really very little to do at the moment. We have to cooperate with the technical investigation and wait for their results."

The young man nodded. "We have to be sure that they have access to all the evidence. Someone tried very hard to hide the flight recorders."

"We're making inquiries into that. It seems more likely they fell from the plane during the crash. There is some confusion about their exact location."

The young magistrato could imagine what kind of confusion. He tried again.

"Will the hijack theory be officially abandoned?"

"It is not our job to officially abandon any theory. Everything must remain a possibility."

"Including the malfunction of the airport or airport instruments?"

"Good heavens!" For the first time the procuratore looked almost alarmed. "Who's suggesting that?"

"It is another area for investigation."

"Of course." The procuratore turned away. "You can rest assured that our own side of the inquiry will be thorough. If there is fault to be found we will find it."

The young magistrato returned to his office. He had as it were staked his claim. If nothing else, they would at least be more careful with their evidence. He bound up his share of the Tango November files and referred them back down the corridor to his elderly and still reluctant colleague.

A mile away across the city a Christian Democrat delegate of the city council was speaking eloquently of the distress caused by the disaster. He suggested a series of three charity concerts in Taormina, Catania, and Syracuse to raise money for the bereaved relatives and injured survivors. A Dutch orchestra due to play at the opera house in Catania agreed to postpone its departure to perform at the three concerts, and a Japanese pianist who had given a recital of Ravel and Poulenc in the Greek theater at Taormina offered a concerto from his repertoire.

On the far side of the mountain shopkeepers and businessmen in a village near to the airport met with their administrative authority and decided to offer facilities for the burial of the victims. A representative was sent directly to the prefetto in Catania and to the travel agency officials in Taormina and a plan for a mass grave was accepted.

Unfortunately for the village authority the villagers themselves reacted against the idea of mass interment, which seemed to them to offend the dignity of death.

There was no room in the cemetery for anything else, they were told, but the administrators had not reckoned with the community's sense of outrage. Two reluctant families owning land adjoining the cemetery were approached by their own peasants. Language and threats were used that had certainly never been heard in quarrels over wage claims or conditions of work. The two families relented: a chestnut, a row of olives, and half a dozen lemon trees were sacrificed; a high stone wall was demolished and rebuilt by voluntary labor; the cemetery gained a half acre of ground, and the municipality, at more expense than it had bargained for, was obliged to lay out dignified lines of headstones, gravel paths, and ornamental shrubs.

Outside Sicily the crash had dominated headlines for only one day. When the hijack theory had been blown and the blood and tears washed away the accident lost its box-office potential.

The reporters and film crews began to disappear and in their place arrived the insurance men with Monday morning briefs from London and New York, anxious to settle damages and compensation before sentiment or anger escalated. There were a few million dollars at stake between airplane and passengers, and the odd hundred thousand or two to be saved by asking the right questions in the right quarters.

Mac was one of the prime targets for their polite but insistent requests for medico-legal information. Had husbands died before their wives? Was there evidence of natural disease in the corpses that might have shortened life expectancy? Had there really been suffering associated with death?

There were a dozen such queries already waiting for Mac and Sanju that morning, five of them relating to the same two victims—Mr. and Mrs. Janius, the "honeymoon couple." Mac remembered the name.

Julius Janius had been one of the whizz kids of the sixties rebuilding the nation's essential industry. What angle of the market was it he had cornered?

Sanju had read the newspapers. "Velvet linings for parakeet cages. Diversified into luxury dog and cat foods; then into boutiques and discos; finally into land and property."

Enterprising Janius. What an expense of energy; what wastes of productivity.

Who, the insurance companies were asking, had died first, Janius or his newly wedded wife? In the event of her surviving his death five companies would be obliged to pay out £50,000 each to the widow. It didn't matter whether she had died four seconds after him, or forty years. If she had survived him, Mrs. Janius or her estate collected a quarter of a million pounds.

Insurance men and Interpol were working hard on that one, tracing the origins of those unusual policies. Many of Janius's subsidiary companies were having a lean time and with that kind of money at stake someone might have tried to sabotage the plane.

3

Cloud had covered Taormina for the first time since spring. Torrential rain turned the hillside alleys into rivers and waterfalls, washing earth from the flower boxes, the lizards from their walls, and a summer's dust from the roofs and terraces.

Ralph Burden watched it from his hotel room, the windows thrown open to let in the sudden freshness of scent from the gardens next to the pensione. He was waiting for Mrs. Duckham, trying to imagine what Dixie's third wife could be like, trying to make up his mind about the questions he should ask.

Statistics and a photograph in a file; two strange letters in the first officer's file; secondhand and unreliable gossip; his own bad memories: it seemed to Burden the more he learned of Dixie Duckham the more confused his picture grew. Dakotas, Ambassadors, Viscounts, Comets, Tridents, and 119s—Duckham had seen and participated in each phase of airline growth since the early 1950s, and after twenty-two years of commercial flying still had a clean and uncomplicated record. Burden wondered if that in itself might not be relevant. If his flying had always been easy he might no longer have had the reflexes for an emergency. Ralph Burden had never found his flying easy.

The reception desk called him to say that Mrs. Duckham had arrived and he told them to send her upstairs.

A young boy had shown Julia the way to Burden's pensione, padding uncovered and unconcerned through the downpour while she tried in vain to keep herself dry under an umbrella. When she walked into Burden's room her thin dress was blotchy with rain, her legs splashed and dirty, her shoes flooded. She knew as he looked at her that he had thought, my God, what a mess.

She's so young, Burden was thinking instead. She seemed almost as young as the birds Duckham was picking up thirty years ago. "Quite a one for the girls," the American safety officer had told him. Dixie had been known to lay them anywhere in those far-off days—under hedgerows on the airport perimeter, in the long grass of roadside verges, standing up against the wall behind a village pub. "Raffles" Burden had preferred not to believe such stories. He didn't even get to kiss a girl until VE-Day.

He apologized to this Mrs. Duckham for asking her to come on such a day and sat himself down at his table. There was only the bed for Julia to perch on. He

apologized again, feeling awkward and ill at ease, then
led her, rather brusque and cold, through the timetable
of events on the day preceding the crash: when had her
husband eaten; when had he slept; when had he left
home for the airport.

It was the first time Julia had relived the scene: little
Clara with her singsong dirge of good-byes; the white
car disappearing down the drive; Mike's hand waving.
When had she last touched him, she asked herself. He
had kissed her in the hallway outside their bedroom.
When had she last heard his voice? What were his last
words to me? She remembered that red rubber face in
the morgue.

"How much did he drink that day?" the man was
asking her.

Burden saw the woman tighten up. "You don't have
to answer that question. There are medical tests to
establish blood levels of alcohol or drugs."

Julia was incredulous. "You make it sound as though
he's a criminal. You talk of him as the guilty party. He
is guilty, isn't he? Unless something actually happens to
prove him innocent."

The outburst quite frightened Burden. "I only meant
to ask did he have anything to drink during Friday."

"He had a glass of wine with his lunch. He always
does when he has to sleep in the afternoon."

"One glass of wine."

"One normal glass of normal wine." She was eyeing
the whiskey bottle on Burden's bedside table.

The rain outside stopped as suddenly as though a tap
had been closed and Burden looked round at the open
window. Out over the sea forked lightning ran slowly
zigzag parallel with the horizon.

Burden stared back at his papers. "There was a
storm on Saturday. Not as bad as this. But they were
very bad conditions."

He had offered it as a possible and innocuous explanation but Julia was fighting on reflex now.

"That would be nothing new for him. He's been flying thirty-five years. He was in the war. He's done every possible sort of flying."

"He must have had a good temperament."

Julia did not reply. She was trying to tell herself to calm down.

"If one took a poll of airline pilots in the major companies your husband would have been considered among the very top pilots on safety and experience."

Julia stared at her wet shoes. She could feel the damp creeping up her legs.

"It must have been a wrench for him when he left his old company. Twenty years, wasn't it, he's been with them?"

"We've only been married eight years."

"Have you any idea why he changed companies?"

"He was offered a better job."

"Did he need the extra money?"

"I don't know anything about the money."

"His job with Hercules doubled his salary. You must have known that."

Julia stared at him. It's not only drink, she thought. It's going to be his salary. Three children. Two divorces.

"He had heavy commitments, I believe."

"I don't know what you mean."

"Two ex-wives," said Burden. "Three families to support."

"What's that got to do with the crash?"

"Everything is relevant that concerns the state of mind of a pilot. He might have been worried or depressed about something. Distracted."

There was a silence, and when Julia spoke it was in a whisper. "We were very happy. He liked me to keep house for him. He liked the way I cooked for him. He liked everything. We were very happy. There's nothing to hide." She was crying, talking head down.

Burden felt inexplicable hostility. "Then you must have been aware that he was having an affair. He was sleeping with one of the hostesses involved in the crash."

She stared across the room at him and Burden looked away. He didn't even know why he'd said it. It was nothing more than an unsubstantiated piece of gossip thrown out by a company man preparing scapegoats. I can't apologize, he thought. It would make me seem absurd.

"The girl in question is the surviving hostess in the hospital in Catania," he said. "Her picture has been in the newspapers."

Julia replied in a calm voice. "I haven't seen any papers." Why has he told me? she was asking herself. Such a story was nonsense. Why is he pretending things? To make me talk? About what? What tales do I have to tell on Mike? We were happy. I was happy. Was Mike happy? Who is this girl?

Burden sifted the papers on his table. He started again. "So far as you know he had no particular anxieties?"

She shook her head.

"His health was good?"

She nodded.

Could he still take a girl standing up, Burden wanted to ask her. How many times a week? How long could he keep it up? Did he have this hostess in the airplane restroom? When Burden's Mary had left him ten months ago they hadn't had sex in ten years. Now he had heard she was having good times with the young men of Ibiza. A nympho. Burden used to imagine that ordinary women only suffered sex. Favors bestowed.

The tap had been turned on again outside, a wall of rain obliterating sight and sound. He was staring at it, the woman still perched, uncomfortable and bowed, on the edge of his bed. How long was it since he had asked her a question?

"Did your husband's responsibilities as fleet captain cause him any additional worry?"

"I don't know."

"Was his behavior different in any way after he changed jobs?"

"Obviously he had more to think about." About what? she wondered suddenly. About air hostesses?

Her interrogator was staring at his papers. "A long time ago he was a very wild young man."

"I don't know what you mean."

Burden looked up at her. "Did you know he was called 'Dixie'?"

She nodded.

"Did you get to meet any of his friends from the RAF?"

" 'Dodo' Griffin."

Griffin had joined the squadron a few months before Burden in 1944. Another wild young man. Another screwball. Dixie, Dodo, Raffles: what an absurd collection of names. Perhaps all flying men were mad.

"Did he get on well with his colleagues?"

"He had a lot of friends."

"You met them?"

"He liked to have people around."

"Did you ever meet a young first officer called Peter Nyren?"

Julia nodded.

"You knew him?"

"He was a regular visitor a few months ago. He and Mike were flying together a lot."

"They were friends, were they?"

She paused before answering. It was a trick question, she thought. He wouldn't have asked that if he didn't already know something. "They quarreled."

"Do you have any idea why?"

"Something about recruitment."

"Was it a bad quarrel?"

"Peter was very bitter. They'd been good friends."

"They stopped flying together after the quarrel, did they?"

"It all went back to normal crewing procedure. Friday was the first time."

"Do you think it might have made things difficult?"

"Mike wouldn't have let it. He'd have made friends again before they even started. He was going to invite Peter round for breakfast when they got back." Julia remembered the sunlit kitchen on that Sunday morning; the food ready on the table; a bottle of wine; the bed made up in the dark room; the children upstairs. She felt her heart falter, her whole body weaken.

"There was nothing more personal about the quarrel?" Burden asked the question but she didn't appear to have heard him. "Was there a quarrel over the girl?"

"Girl?"

"The hostess."

Julia shook her head in despair. "I don't know anything about a girl or a hostess. I don't want to know." She stood up. Her dress was sticking to her in patches where the rain had wet it. "You're going to blame him, aren't you? You're inventing stories about him. And I don't want to hear them."

She walked out of the room. The man had been testing her. Mike was so quietly and totally in love with her. That is what he told her time and again. "You have made sense of my life," he would say.

Dejected tourists sitting in the reception lounge with their foreign newspapers watched Julia appear from upstairs and march defiantly out of the pensione into the rain, leaving them to guess at her pain and her anger.

It was with the freshness and noise of the rain that Stella Pritchard returned to the conscious world. She woke in gloom listening to the water cascading out of broken gutters, and when the nurses wheeled a telephone to her bedside she was able to speak coherently to her aged father and mother far away in Harrogate.

Both parents were sternly stiff-upper-lip, anxious to explain why it had been impossible for them to travel out to her bedside. Stella did not need explanations; she would not have expected them to come. In fact she would have been very alarmed to see them at all. She would have believed herself to be dying, for her father only undertook dramatic, unscheduled gestures *in extremis*.

It was he who replied calmly and factually to her questions when she asked him what had happened. Stella, equally calm and objective under the influence of her father's voice, accepted his account of the air crash and her miraculous survival. He told her of the little girl who had survived with her; of the large casualty list: of the other crew members all of whom had died. She realized in that moment that Mike was dead. And Peter. She could not for the moment remember who else had been flying with them.

The nightmare of the car accident receded, still a suspicion, to the edge of her subconscious. She remembered instead chasing the little girl up the aisle of the airplane and the sudden thump of uncontrollable movement when they hit the turbulence. She began to remember other things: Mike picking her up in the evening on the way to Gatwick; the honeymoon couple, self-conscious and self-important as the plane loaded two hours late; the American boy with the green eyes and the guitar and the soft smile. She remembered clearing coffee cups from the cockpit and realizing that Mike and Peter were still silent with each other. She remembered thinking that's the fault of Peter sulking, the silly kid. But now the silly kid was dead.

Was the American boy also dead?

When the telephone call was over the little girl came into the room shy and afraid, her hand held tight in one of the nurse's. Stella remembered her name.

"Hello, Trixie."

Trixie sat next to her on the bed, Stella's face still her only link with past events in her life. All other faces were strange and the language they spoke associated with her mother and grandfather, both of whom had disappeared. She was in fact the only survivor from a Brooklyn family party of twelve passengers.

When Stella took her hand Trixie lay on the bed with her head on the pillow and refused to move.

Tino G. was alive, and the old surgeon had returned home.

Tino G. was now to be considered a probable survivor. He was wheeled from the theater and slid off rubber sheets on to clean white linen in a bed. His body was still perforated with rubber and plastic tubing, his every function monitored. But these functions now presented a coherent pattern. The specialists who had at last arrived from sailing boats and mountain retreats confirmed the obvious and wisely slipped away.

The nurses who had suffered with him arranged the room with flowers cabled from "Corinna" in New York. Two patient reporters still waiting in the lobby were led upstairs and a photographer allowed one picture of a sleeping boy.

4

Flight AZ 140 landed with a prayer through a curtain of rain and in a cloud of spray. Disaster was vivid in people's minds, not least those of the pilot and the air traffic controller in the tower at Catania Fontanarossa Airport. But the DC-9 pulled up on the short wet runway with—well, a few yards to spare. The pilot, clammy and thankful, taxied right up to the reception buildings to save his passengers a long walk in the rain.

Sharlie was waiting under a Coca-Cola umbrella on the terrace outside the bar, well protected in his cousin's motorcycle waterproofs and armed with his Nikon and a telephoto lens. Citto had been very precise on the telephone from Messina. He wanted photographs of every face that left the airplane, with particular attention paid to any passengers associated with Avvocato Consoli. Sharlie knew Consoli well enough as a local VIP, and he picked him out as he appeared on the steps of the aircraft. But the scamper through the rain from the airplane to building broke up the groupings. Only afterward as the arrivals waited for their baggage, did Sharlie notice the two faces accompanying the lawyer and the young man meeting them in his orange and green Dino. It was Sharlie's bad luck that the weather made his job so difficult. His inquisitive camera, inconspicuous outside on the terrace, was seen by more than one vigilant pair of eyes as he circulated inside the reception buildings. His face, his clothes, and later his motorcycle were carefully remembered.

Canon Ash Nyren had also landed on AZ 140. He had transferred planes in Rome but had omitted to check that his baggage changed planes with him. They had assured him at Heathrow that his suitcase was labeled through to Catania and that consequently he had no need to concern himself about it. He now watched luggage rolling down the conveyor belt and being stacked up on the baggage counter, which was situated for some extraordinary reason on the exterior of the building exposed to the rain. His fellow passengers claimed their pieces and hurried away through the downpour to their cars and buses, until he was left alone still waiting by the conveyor belt for his angular and old-fashioned suitcase.

Sharlie saw him there: a sunken face, a hook nose, a mop of graying blond hair, a priest's collar standing alone against the rain and the empty counter. It was a good picture and Sharlie did not miss the opportunity. But having secured his picture he went up to the man to ask him if he could help in any way.

Ash Nyren spoke no Italian, but he had traveled over most of Europe in his time and always succeeded in some form of communication through his Latin. Now with this boy he spoke slow Latin trying to soften the vowels to approach an Italian sound. "My baggage is lost," he told him.

Sharlie picked up the gist of what the old fellow was saying. "I'll help you," he told him. "I'll fix it all for you." He registered the old man's loss with the Alitalia desk, then took him out to the Taormina bus, promising he would be in touch about the lost case by letter, *poste restante* at Taormina, for the old priest had no accommodation yet fixed and therefore no address or telephone number.

One good deed done, Sharlie returned to his motorcycle. Good deed number two was to stop off at the nearby factory where his mother spent her days. He left a message to say he'd be coming to see her that evening, then rode carefully back into town on the flooded roads and spent the rest of the afternoon shut up in the darkroom at the newspaper.

Consoli had been closeted with his son for three hours asking the same questions a dozen times before he was satisfied he had the full answers.

Signora Consoli sat on the covered verandah trying unsuccessfully to hear the conversation over the noise of the rain. She was afraid her boy might be in some kind of trouble. He had been silent over breakfast with her that morning and had most unusually driven to the airport to meet his father. Fruitlessly it seemed, for Consoli had arrived with two colleagues and the Dino could carry only one passenger.

The signora walked into the house on the pretext of ordering a cold tea from the kitchen. To reach the kitchen she could legitimately pass, and linger, outside the study. She heard talk as usual of the airport, that monstrous undertaking that had dominated their lives for so long. She had been told countless times how that strip of asphalt and concrete had secured their family future, and she had decided that given the choice, which she never was, she would have preferred to risk any future rather than live with such an obsession. But then Signora Consoli had never lacked for money. Her life had always been easy. She did not, as her husband often told her, understand or appreciate money.

She ordered the tea and retired upstairs to her bedroom where she could watch the two men whenever they approached the study windows.

Flavio Consoli had reported to his father the events of the previous day: holding hands with the fat schoolgirl; obsequious lunch with the procuratore; the gossip exchanged around the table.

What, asked the father, appeared to be the prevalent attitude toward the disaster?

"Fear of scandal," the son replied. "Sicily must not suffer," was a phrase he remembered.

The avvocato laughed. "In Rome they were saying, 'Italy must not suffer.' "

The son dared a question of his own. "Were you successful in Rome?"

"Do you know why I went to Rome?"

"No, sir."

"Well then—you can have no interest in my success or lack of success." The father concluded with firm advice: "Act normally," the avvocato said. "We must all act normally. Everything must go on as before. That is most important. After all, we have nothing to hide, have we?"

"No, sir." Flavio hesitated before replying, but his father did not notice. Flavio was thinking about Capo Tomacchio and their little sideshow. He'd meant to tell his father. But goddamn it, he didn't want his head yelled off. "No, sir, nothing to hide."

It was a tragic exchange: bad advice and a fatally evaded opportunity to confess.

Act normally. Flavio had intended to cancel the truck for this particular week. That reporter had been poking around ETNOLIO and Tomacchio was uneasy. But the avvocato had been adamant and Flavio, obedient and unintelligent, resolved to act as normally as he knew how—apart from an unusually attentive walk later that afternoon around the orange groves with his father to assess the effect of a day's rain.

That evening Flavio telephoned Tomacchio and told him to do the week's run as usual.

"We might attract attention to ourselves by not doing it," he explained.

"What crap," replied the voice at the other end. "What we ought to do is lie low right now."

"My father said quite expressly we must act normally. Everything must go on as before."

"He said that?" There was a silence and a grunt. "Still sounds like a lot of crap to me."

Stupid ape, thought Flavio. He would go somewhere else for his trucks when this business blew over. In fact he'd have gone elsewhere long ago if it hadn't been for Tomacchio's delectable daughter.

5

In Rome there had been no sign of rain, not even a cloud. Summer prolonged itself lazily, the city center still occupied by tourists, the boulevards and gardens of EUR empty, the fountains playing to themselves, halls of government departments silent, corridors deserted.

Yet Citto had found a few pockets of activity: two separate offices on the Quirinale with a flurry of official cars; hidden pandemonium behind a glass façade out in the Piazzale del Grande Archivio. Citto had been at work since midday, rebuffed not always politely or calmly at his every destination. But there was certain information that could not be refused him. The administrative and legal history of Taormina-Peloritana was available to anyone prepared to sit down and search through documents and reports. Citto was able to trace the airport from conception to ceremonial opening, and by careful cross-checking of the names and addresses associated with the undertaking he had mapped out the darker areas of confusion that seemed to link the corners of the spider's web.

In Messina he had discovered the consortium formed three years previously to promote the planning and building of the new airport. The names in the consortium were not unfamiliar: a pair of distinguished figureheads from Catania and Palermo; and an otherwise unholy alliance of construction and finance companies, most of them publicly respectable, but some of them known to Citto for their connections with Mafia families or Mafia money. That in itself was no surprise. Any sizeable undertaking south of Rome, be it autostrada, industrial complex, or airport, would be influenced to some extent by Mafia finance or Mafia interests in local planning.

Once the airport plans had been submitted they were examined and authorized by a government appointed committee in Rome. It was this committee that now gave Citto his first tenuous lead. Documented at its inception as a committee of twelve, the final report was only signed by eleven names. The twelfth name had been carefully erased from all lists of attendance. It was obvious that the name had been there and any death or illness would have been recorded in the minutes. One possible explanation was that the man's evidence had been deleted from the report, and certain gaps in continuity within the final document seemed to support such a theory.

Citto showed the first page of the committee's proceedings to a ministry clerk in the archives. "There's a name missing. An omission. Could you look up records to correct the mistake?" I'd be very grateful, Citto implied—100,000 lire grateful.

The young clerk nodded. "I expect it will be possible. I'll meet you tomorrow after lunch." And he named the time and place: a parking lot in the Piazza Enrico Mattei at two-thirty in the afternoon.

That evening Citto found a cheap hotel near the railway station and shut himself into a dingy little bedroom with a bag of rolls, a carton of milk, and a day's laboriously accumulated notes.

The ministry clerk, home with his family in the sprawl of new housing beyond Monte Sacro, was having second thoughts about the favor he had negotiated with the stuttering little Sicilian. He telephoned a colleague and told him of the rendezvous he had made for the next day but decided that if he heard nothing more about it he would proceed as agreed. One hundred thousand tax-free lire would mean that he could take the family back south for Christmas.

Colleague rang colleague rang colleague. There were those who knew about that one-time committee, those who did not know. But eventually the one-time secretary of that one-time committee was given the news of Citto's unwelcome inquiry.

"I'm relying on you," Consoli had told this civil servant. The poor man did not now know where to turn for advice. He should have ignored his fears and telephoned direct to Consoli.

He resorted instead to amateurs.

6

Sharlie spent that evening playing good son for his mother, inventing success stories about Rome for her neighbors in the old tenement block down by the waterfront. He'd bought her chocolates and flowers, and, when they had appeared to him inadequate, a silk scarf from a boutique on the Via Etnea that had taken the last of his borrowed tens. If his agency didn't come up with some fees for the Tango November pictures he wouldn't even have money for the train ticket back to Rome. Unless there was some more money to be made from selling pictures on the side. There had been a message waiting for him at home—another reporter wanted to see him. He had left a telephone number. Maybe he wanted to buy pictures.

And if he didn't buy? Well, there was Citto to help him out again. He had a bad conscience about Sharlie's broken tooth.

When the neighbors all had gone Sharlie and his mother looked at each other across the kitchen table. Sharlie had told them he'd cut his face falling off the motorcycle, but mother and son didn't really fool each other.

"You working for that madman again?" She meant Citto.

"I'm freelance."

"But he's telling you where to go and what to do."

"He's a good reporter."

"You're the only living thing I got in this world," the mother cried. "I don't want to be left with the priests and candles for the rest of my life."

"I told you, I fell off the motorcycle."

"I live on this waterfront thirty years. You think I don't know the marks of a fight?"

Sharlie grinned at her and poured them both wine. She'd been picking grapes for pocket money over the weekend and the padrone had given her a couple of last year's bottles.

"One day soon," he promised, "you'll have enough money so you won't ever have to go out and work again." And he took her hand across the table and made her believe again in the dream.

7

Mac climbed the steps to the Pensione Albert past windows flickering in candlelight. A power failure was the only evidence left of the day's rain. The streets and alleys were already dry, the sky over Taormina was clear, and the moon out over the sea as sharp and white as a winter moon back home.

"Can we investigate the possibility of power failure at the airport on Saturday," Larry Raille had asked round a candlelit table earlier in the evening. But the

Italians had already thought of that possibility and they were able to report that Taormina–Peloritana had been supplied by generator power during the storms on Friday night and Saturday morning. Witness statements taken from staff at the airport confirmed that there had been no lighting failure at any time during that night. Attempts had been made to recall the air traffic controller for further questioning, but he was said to be on sick leave and incommunicado.

All groups of investigators had met to exchange evidence together over supper in a private room at the San Domenico. Only the search party on the mountain was missing, encamped somewhere high and cold on the lava. Burden had taken the chair tonight and the meeting had been consequently swift and economical of words. Amazing, thought Mac, how fifteen years in the British Civil Service can concentrate a man's mind on the essentials—though he did also suspect that Ralph's thoughts had been focused elsewhere for most of the time tonight. Dixie Duckham, Mac had guessed. He knew himself how hard it could be to meet old friends among the dead.

The Pensione Albert seemed well prepared for power failure with gas lamps in its small reception lounge. Mac asked for Julia Duckham and wrote down his name for the manager to carry upstairs. Signora Duckham, he was told, had spent most of the day in her room.

But she didn't keep him waiting, following the manager downstairs without a pause for patting up her hair or adjusting her face. She came into the lobby, two large anxious eyes in that soft gaslight, a face without makeup that seemed even younger than the night before; a crumpled skirt and blouse, and hair flat and matted on one side where she had been lying on her bed. The force of her emotion left Mac quite without words. She was anticipating God knows what: perhaps that her husband had somehow returned from the dead? Officially consigned to the dead would be nearer the truth. Duckham's Knightsbridge dentist had been out of town Saturday and Sunday, and the captain's dental records had only just arrived. Not that there had been any doubt about his identification.

"We have the final results of some of the tests," Mac said. "I mean the blood tests and that sort of thing."

She was watching him, her eyes suddenly vacant as though she wasn't even listening.

"I just wanted to tell you that there's nothing wrong with any of them. Your husband was quite all right. There was nothing wrong with him medically or in any other way."

She nodded. Mac was convinced she had not heard him. But she thanked him.

"You are very kind," she said. "You are very kind to take the trouble to come and tell me."

They were standing in the middle of the lobby facing each other like soldiers on parade. It was the hotel manager who rescued Mac, leading them over to a table and two armchairs set into a white wall alcove.

"Everyone's trying to blame him," said Julia. "I don't understand what's going on."

"They've been asking a lot of questions, have they?"

"Drinking; money; divorce. It's like they were adding things up against him."

"I'm afraid it always happens. They have to ask. It doesn't necessarily mean anything bad."

"He said things he couldn't have known anything about."

Ralph Burden, thought Mac.

"He even made out that Mike had been having an affair with one of the hostesses." She looked up at Mac. "Do you know anything about that?"

"Good Lord, no. I'm only the medicine man." Mac

did know. Burden had mentioned it at the evening meeting: two dozen words under the heading "possible flight deck tension." Some talk of a quarrel between Duckham and Nyren, and the possibility of the surviving air hostess being somehow involved.

"He even told me who the girl was," said Julia. "I can't stop thinking about it. All day I've been thinking, could he have done that? And why? Her picture's in all the papers." She looked around the lobby as though there might be newspapers on the table. "I even met her once. At a cricket match."

Stella Pritchard. Mac had seen her medical report that morning. She was recovering at a hospital in Catania from head injuries, abrasions, and shock. Condition satisfactory.

The lady was watching him as though waiting for confirmation, denial, or advice. "You see," she said, "we were very happily married. I don't understand."

"Well, then," said Mac, "if you were happy it doesn't really matter, does it? Whether he did or he didn't." But it was not quite the moment, Mac realized, to deliver a lecture on the differing natures of love and sex.

"It matters to me," she said. "Perhaps it shouldn't. But I can't stop thinking about it because I don't know whether or not it's true." Those large anxious eyes of hers were all over the place now, up and down the walls, all round the lobby, out of the windows.

"Why don't you come for a walk?" said Mac. Fresh air and exercise were his antidote to all trouble physical or mental. "The rain's stopped."

She stood up with him and followed him outside. He had the sort of voice and bearing that made suggestions appear commands.

They walked down the steps along a main street now lit by a scattering of oil flares. Apart from the occasional taxi the center of the little town was free from traffic and the street silent but for the distant shouting of some kids and the slipslop of sandals as tourists wandered up and down. Mac bought brandies standing up at one of the bars. He was telling Julia about the repercussions from last night's adventure at the city morgue: the flurries of angry cops jabbering away in Italian. He even coaxed a smile out of her when he mimed their agitation.

They walked on down the narrow steeper streets below the main road past faces they could not see, and mysterious shops and houses flickering in candlelight. He asked her about her home; where she lived; the names of her children; who was looking after them.

She answered him with something of the outside of her life—bits and pieces, but none of the secrets or the dramas: the house and garden in Virginia Water; Andrew and Clara; her one-time air-hostess sister.

They came out on the edge of the hill overlooking the narrow exit road that circled the lower part of the town. A car horn was blaring and headlights picked out the erring pedestrian, an elderly man with a mop of light-colored hair and a stooping plunging stride— Groucho Marx or an earnest horseman who'd lost his mount: Canon Ash Nyren, searching as he had been all afternoon for somewhere to sleep that night.

"Peter's father," said Julia as she saw him.

"Peter?"

"Peter Nyren. The first officer."

"You know him?"

"He's very old. I should go and see him and make sure he's all right."

But the canon had passed on out of sight.

"You'll find him tomorrow," Mac told her. "I expect Hercules are looking after him."

"We went down to his village one day," Julia explained. "To play a cricket match. Everyone was playing except me. Mike, Peter, the canon." Julia paused. "She was there."

"Stella Pritchard?"

"It was a charity match. Men and women, and everyone called by what they did. Pilot. Doctor. Vet. There was a writer and a film star. She was the air hostess."

"She's in a hospital in Catania," said Mac. "Maybe you ought to go and see her."

"Why would he do it?" she asked in a whisper. She was looking at the moonlight over the sea 700 feet below them. She was trying to live the dream again where she and Mike were together in places they had always promised themselves to visit. But now there were too many questions in her mind.

"Why would he do it?"

"I didn't know your husband," said Mac. "Why don't you tell me about him?"

Julia looked at Mac. There seemed no threat in that question. Not from him. She opened her mouth to talk about Mike, but started suddenly and without warning to cry.

"Another time," said Mac. "You tell me another time."

"You've been very kind. I'm sorry," she whispered.

Mac took her arm. "Let it all go. You go ahead and cry. You cry out loud if you feel like it."

And with her head against his arm she did so, her whole body sobbing violently until emotion was exhausted.

Mac walked her back to the pensione then, his own feelings toward this distressed young woman suddenly guilty and uncomfortable. He wanted to protect her, yet he would have to play the spy instead, telling Ralph Burden what she had been saying.

Power was back, street lights, and music from a radio or a jukebox filling the silence.

Canon Ash Nyren watched the lights and sounds return. He was sitting on a hillside above the town. The evening was strangely warm, the ground almost dry, and the canon tired of his plodding inn to inn. Without suitcase or money he had been treated with suspicion by hotel clerks. No room, they had told him, and *"bacauda perdita est"* had not persuaded them.

Late in the evening he had seen a group of young American students climbing from an alley up a stone wall and under a fence on to a hillside of cactus. He had followed them, laying out his mackintosh some way from their rucksacks and sleeping bags. For the moment he was neither cold nor hungry.

"A cricket match?" Burden frowned. "How very odd."

Mac had caught Burden in his pyjamas and the older man was rather embarrassed.

"She's a very hysterical woman, of course."

Mac shrugged. "I don't think so. She's obviously still in shock. I think she's coping rather well."

"I suppose she complained about my questions this morning." It irritated Burden that Mac had been gallivanting around with that woman all evening.

"No. She had no complaint. She's defensive about her husband, that's all." Mac grinned. "She's a pretty girl, isn't she?"

"For God's sake, Mac! There are occasions when such observations are tasteless."

Burden heard Mac laughing all the way back to the lift. Mrs. Duckham pretty? Burden had been thinking all day about the transparency of those wet blotches on her dress.

8

Far away in Washington Priscilla Raille's party had been a great success: the amount of drink generously calculated; the food visually sensational; the guests gossiping, joking, and flirting with each other and with Priscilla.

Her choice of pander was limited. She needed someone influential enough to make or sway decisions and since the eldest and most senior of the colonels had been paying her obvious attentions she made sure he stayed on after the other guests had gone home. They sat side by side on the couch talking rather drunkenly of the necessity of human understanding. She took his hand to emphasize a point, and he left the hand with her. They talked of health and of keeping fit, and Priscilla, in describing her palpitations, placed the colonel's horny hand over her left breast. Thus encouraged he caressed her, and thus committed he kissed her. When he finally pulled her head roughly down into his lap she understood what task she had to perform. At least, she thought, being a military man he will be clean.

She was mistaken, and when he was finally through his spasms she was quietly but comprehensively sick in the kitchen sink while she freshened his drink.

Next morning he telephoned to thank her for the party. "You can rest assured," he said, "that we have our eye on your husband. I'm told he is an outstanding engineer." He arranged to drop in on Priscilla again that evening—"just in case I have any news."

The colonel had found the favor unexpectedly easy. Inner administrative circles had been trying for two days to find some way of shifting Raille off the Tango November investigation. It hadn't occurred to them until the party that Raille might be tempted with a transfer to a job with NASA.

9

Sharlie left his mother in the early hours of Tuesday, collecting Laura from the fishing village at three o'clock. The rain had passed and the sky was clearing. It would be a good morning for *Cantallaluna*. They rode uphill fast and noisily through darkened sleeping villages, and when they reached the mountain road they stopped to wait in the damp silence. After ten minutes or so they heard another distant motorcycle and saw a headlight zigzagging up the hillside toward them. Laura waved it down, and *Cantallaluna*, not overjoyed to have company, killed his engine to listen to Sharlie's questions.

"You'll lose me too much time," he grumbled, looking over his shoulder at the lightening sky. "If you want to talk you'll have to come with me."

So they drove on behind him until they reached the earth slide beyond which Sharlie dared not pass with his cousin's precious Ducati. They followed *Cantallaluna* on foot, tailing the sound of his old-fashioned motorcycle as it bounced and roared its way over the boulders and up the hillside into the woods.

When they caught up with him he was already at work, bent double and running in quick scampers from one likely spot to another. Even in the half light he could see enough to pick out the small humps of earth where the mushrooms were pushing their way up. He used one hand to hold the sack, the other to excavate round the hump, and when the two cousins joined him he handed Laura the sack to streamline the operation. It was comic opera: *Cantallaluna*, small and stocky, hurling out snatches of operatic aria, moving with extraordinary speed; Laura high-stepping fastidiously through the undergrowth behind him; Sharlie circling their darting movements as closely as he could, persisting with his questions.

The answers came in bits and pieces as the rhythm of the hunt allowed. Saturday morning? Yes—now where had he been?—over the ridge. He'd been able to move farther from the road that morning because he wasn't hurrying to catch the plane. The day's pickings had all been ordered by local restaurants. Saturday and Sunday lunches. He'd set out at half past three; started picking at maybe half past four.

The darting movements of the hunt took over for a while, the sack already beginning to bulge. He seemed to be finding them not in ones or twos but in half dozens. "It brings whole families of them out, a little rain," he told Laura.

Saturday morning—yes. He'd heard the plane. "Seemed like an earthquake at first. Then more like an eruption from the top. Not really a noise. The whooshing of air. The speed it all happened. It really scared me, I can tell you."

Cantallaluna paused, swooping for another family of mushrooms.

"I didn't know what it was until I looked up. And even then. An eagle? It blotted my sky out and then it was gone. The real noise came afterward. A terrible noise. The jet noise. But I can't say I heard the crash. What was it? Two miles away."

The light was widening all the time, filtering from a pale sky into the trees. Sharlie started taking pictures. After all, *Cantallaluna* was the last man to have seen Tango November in the sky. Some paper or magazine might want to publish his picture. *Sing-to-the-moon*. He was worth an article in his own right, part of the folklore of Sharlie's mountain. *Cantallaluna* grumbled at them both for slowing up his progress. "Seven o'clock the flight leaves. I have to be gone at six."

Sharlie looked at his watch, then up at the sky. "What time was it on Saturday morning?"

"When the plane passed? A half minute or so to five thirty-five."

Citto had told Sharlie about the stopped clocks on the airport. 05:40, he'd said. The two times didn't seem to correspond. "How can you be so sure about the time?"

"I always carry a watch because of catching the flights." *Cantallaluna* was grunting, bending low to massacre another family.

"But you weren't flying them out on Saturday."

"It's habit, though. Knowing what the time is. The watch on my wrist is only a check. My real clock's up here." He tapped his head behind one ear.

Sharlie panted along in his wake as he darted away, scrambling up a bank. "What clock did you use on Saturday?"

Cantallaluna seemed to have disappeared into scrub, but he reemerged both hands full of goodies like a bunch of fat fingers. "Always check with the watch, like I told you."

The light grew from flat gray monotone to a depth of layers as the sun hit the tops of the ridges above them. *Cantallaluna* glanced at his watch and tied up his sack.

"I suppose you want some for your lunch?"

"Don't worry," said Laura. "We'll stay on and pick our own."

"You know which ones are good and which ones are dangerous?"

"Well—if we make a mistake my grandmother will know. She's the one who'll be cooking them."

"Your Nonna Lisa," said *Cantallaluna* over his

shoulder as he hurried away. "How is she? She's a good woman. Tell her I'll come and see her one day and she can cook me a nice *sarago*." The voice was fading through the trees as *Sing-to-the-moon* hurried for his motorcycle and the early morning flight. He shouted again, almost out of earshot. "She's a good woman. You tell her I said so. You tell her if she's tired of the sea I have a fire in my hut for long winter evenings."

They heard the motorcycle push start somewhere below them. Laura was laughing. "He used to pay court to Nonna Lisa when grandfather died. But the sound of the sea drives him mad, and Nonna Lisa wouldn't leave the house."

The four members of the search party woke that morning to what they thought was the sound of voices and laughter. But when they unsheathed themselves from sleeping bags and pup tents they found themselves alone. In fact they had heard Sharlie and Laura, for the two parties were, at that moment, only 900 horizontal and 150 vertical feet apart from each other.

The four men set to work with the tiny Gaz fire, a can of water and powdered coffee. They'd had to call off the search as soon as the light went the night before, and after struggling with the tents and their soaking wet clothes none of them had felt like socializing very long over their cold meat and biscuits. They'd been fast asleep by nine o'clock. At least they would get their clothes dried today. It was a long slow game this search. The span of the 119 was 119 feet and they had to double that measurement on both sides of their line to allow for error. It had taken most of the previous day plodding under the rain to cover a mile, and to-day's ground looked even worse: thick scrub to start off with, and beyond it a maze of lava ridges rising up from the woods.

They decided to leave the tents set up where they

were, and yesterday's clothes hanging to dry. They could then come back at lunch and strike camp for a longer trek in the afternoon.

10

Ash Nyren had awakened with the sun on the horizon already hurting the skin with its glare and heat. He felt untidy and dirty and physically uncomfortable. He didn't understand why he was here. Yesterday on the bus from the airport he had been asked whether he wished to see the body of his son. He thought the idea grotesque and he had told them so.

What would happen now? Peter would be buried and the canon would return home. Someone had wasted a lot of money sending him out here. White stones in a wilderness.

In 1920 his father had taken him to a military cemetery in France. They had found his brother's grave on a warm summer's evening and his father had cried for the first and last time in his adult life. In 1946 Ash Nyren, alone, had tried to find the grave of his own eldest son. But there was no grave. The boy had just disappeared, his manner of dying unrecorded. Like Peter, he had fallen out of the sky.

Ash Nyren left the American students still asleep in their bags. He climbed off the hillside under the fence down the wall into the alley. The town was quiet below him, only the cats prowling the backyards before the garbage men came. How easy for cats, he thought. They can even make scavenging seem dignified.

The old canon could not quite make up his mind about his retreat to the hillside last night. Had that been dignified? Should he not have made a fuss about his predicament?

He walked for an hour while the town awoke around him, and until he discovered a public convenience tucked away down some steps in the main square. When he reemerged twenty minutes later he imagined himself albeit unshaven quite clean and tidy. He visited the *poste restante*—in vain, for that young man had not yet communicated about his lost luggage. Then back in the street a policeman approached him. When Ash Nyren verified his identity he was led across town to a comfortable looking hotel. But the canon's hopes were not fulfilled. He had been brought here only to answer questions.

"Accident Investigation Branch, Department of Trade and Industry," an Englishman said at a bedroom door.

Strange place for an interview, the canon thought. It felt even stranger when the man asked him of all things about a cricket game played earlier that summer.

"It is my fortune or misfortune to run the village cricket team," Ash Nyren explained over coffee and buns. "We had an invitation match for charity." The old canon corrected himself. "Well, not really charity, I'm afraid. Our church steeple. Yes. Somehow there are more important things than church steeples, aren't there? It was the Women's Institute's idea. They call it "what's my line." The invitation team is named by profession. Doctor, farmer, solicitor—that kind of thing. Duckham was our airline pilot."

"And Miss Pritchard—?"

"Yes. Air hostess I believe they're called."

"Do you remember when this match was played?" Burden's notes required precision.

"Early June. The last week of the rhododendrons I would think. They're a feature in the churchyard and the vicarage."

"Did Mr. Duckham come down with his family?"

"Yes. His wife and children."

"They stayed with you?"

"They had supper in the vicarage and then drove home. It's difficult for me to have guests overnight."

The old canon was pinched and frail, an odd fuzz of white stubble on his face where he had not shaved. His clothes were crumpled. His shirt seemed dirty. Burden wondered where he had been sleeping.

"Did you form any impressions of Duckham?"

"He seemed very nice. Very pleasant. He brought a dozen bottles of wine I remember. That was very generous. I don't keep a cellar myself. Not since the war."

"Good cricketer was he?"

"Oh—he made quite a knock. Twenty or thirty or something. He had great style. Peter said the only cricket he played was on the lawn with his children so that made his achievement even more impressive."

"And Miss Pritchard?"

"Well—she was very elegant. She was wearing, I seem to remember, a particularly becoming short white skirt."

"And she came down because she was a friend of Peter's?"

"I imagine so. She did not appear to know Mr. Duckham very well. I had the impression she was quite shy with him."

"She was at supper at your house with them all?"

"Yes. And she stayed for the night I believe. I left her talking with my son that evening and she seemed to reappear for breakfast."

"You have other sons or daughters?"

"One son who died in the war. It was after his death that Peter was born. It has meant, I'm afraid, that he has an old father."

"Your wife—?"

"Died ten years ago." The old man interrupted before Burden could begin his next question. "I think

Peter saw Duckham as something of a substitute father. More the right age. Able to give him proper advice. That sort of thing."

"Did you see Duckham again after the cricket match?"

"No."

"He didn't return the invitation?"

"Yes. I was invited to their house one Saturday. Then there was some sort of a quarrel between Duckham and my son and I made some excuse not to go."

"You didn't want to see him?"

"It was very silly of me. I think I could have helped them forget all about it. Instead of that, of course, it just made things worse. Very stupid." There was a sudden vehemence in the old man's voice as he castigated himself. "A stupidness. It is hard to forgive one's real mistakes."

"Your son told you about the quarrel?"

"In a way. Not directly of course. We don't—we didn't talk directly about things like that. He was upset about something. He came down one weekend for a game of cricket. He was drinking afterward in the pub. That's when he talked about it. With some of the others. I was there because of the cricket." The canon seemed very briefly and invisibly to smile. "One half of bitter every Saturday evening as president of the club."

"Peter was upset?"

"Oh, yes. And angry."

"Did he easily get upset about things?" Ash Nyren looked up at the face interviewing him and saw it clearly for the first time: a closed face; a thin mouth; careful eyes—sitting in judgment on his son.

Burden rephrased the question. "Had you ever seen him upset like this before?"

"When his previous company went bankrupt and he lost his job."

"He must have been very worried."

Nyren paused before answering. He began to see traps in front of him. "Anyone is worried if he is unemployed." Was Peter an anxious type, he wondered? He was certainly a brooder. They'd called him that at school. Even written it on some of his reports.

"Did you ever visit him in London?"

"No. His flat was very small. Just two rooms I believe."

"Miss Pritchard was his girl friend?"

Again Nyren paused. Yes and no both sounded dangerous.

"They were not engaged."

Burden stood up from his desk. "You've been very kind to cooperate at such a distressing time."

Nyren stood up from his chair and Burden noticed again how scruffy he appeared.

"I hope you are being looked after properly?"

"My luggage was mislaid. A young man at the airport said he was sorting it out for me but I haven't heard from him yet."

"You should tell Hercules about it."

"I don't like to fuss about little details."

Burden opened the door for him. "Do you think the quarrel between Duckham and your son could have upset their concentration?"

The question took Ash Nyren off balance. It was a question that had been haunting him, and he did not know the answer. "I am sure they were too experienced to let that happen," he told Burden. But he was thinking to himself, Duckham was too experienced to let it happen, not Peter. Peter did get worked up about things, and he did lose concentration. And in such a mood he did make mistakes. Ash Nyren knew that from watching him at cricket or chess, driving a car, playing a piano. He remembered him thumping the piano once in rage when he had played a succession of wrong notes.

Stella Pritchard opened her eyes briefly in the silence of siesta, the ever attendant Trixie at her bedside.

"There is someone waiting to see you," the little girl told her. "She's been waiting all day. Do you want to see her?" The child was suspicious. She didn't want to lose proprietary rights.

Stella smiled and took her hand. But by the time a nurse had called Julia Duckham, Stella's eyes were closed once more and she was sleeping.

"It's all right," said Julia. "I'll stay with her."

The nurse disappeared, the door closing Julia and the little girl into shuttered halflight. "Hello," Julia whispered to the little girl. But the girl put a finger to her lips to hush her. The small room was filled with rasping open-mouthed breathing that sounded like death's door. There was no resemblance here to those newspaper photographs of a pretty young girl. Stella Pritchard's head was half-shaved and bandaged, her remaining hair matted with dry blood. The face hung loose, like that of a drunken woman, the flesh vibrating with each irregular breath. Once she paused so long between breaths that Julia thought she had surely passed away. But then the rasp recommenced, and Julia and the little girl breathed again with her.

Julia drew up a chair, took off her jacket, and prepared herself for a vigil. Through the shutters she could see a thin strip of sunlight at one end of a shaded courtyard, and later, as afternoon grew into early evening, siesta faded with that sunlight and the city sounds returned: cars and noisy motorcycles; a traffic cop's whistle; songs from a jukebox in a bar; the laughing of young voices.

11

"Time me fifty seconds. Gear down and landing checks."

"Spoiler switches."

"Armed."

"No Smoking signs."

"On."

Three monotones like a dirge swapping the responses of the check list: Captain Duckham, First Officer Nyren, and Flight Engineer Raven.

Three engineers, two Englishmen, and an Italian, feed the voice-recorder tape through special playback equipment in a soundproof lab at the Royal Aircraft Establishment in Farnborough. They have been playing the final few minutes of the thirty-minute loop over and over again without reaching any conclusions.

"Established on the ILS. Four thousand feet." Nyren calling up Taormina–Peloritana.

Air traffic control replies from the airport: *"Roger Tango November. Call me on outer marker."*

On the flight deck Nyren confirms instrument landing system: "Glide slope alive."

A lower voice interrupts in an amused mutter: "Miracle number two!"

"Shut up, George!" Duckham.

There is a pause of about four seconds, then the sound of a bleeper.

"Outer marker." Another short pause, and Nyren's voice again: "We're two hundred feet too high."

"Hell!" A silence. "It checks out on my side. I'd say it looks good. Confirm glide slope your side."

"Check on the glide slope."

The lower voice, again a mutter and barely distinguishable: "Bloody marvelous. I bet they changed the slope and forgot to tell anyone."

"OK. Let's have a bit of quiet."

Nyren calls the airport. *"Tango November over outer marker."*

"Roger. Tango November you are clear to land."

A pause. Then Duckham's voice: "Disengaging auto pilot. Full flap."

"Full flap."

"Fifty. Fifty. Two greens."

"Check list complete up here. Let's hope they've got it together downstairs." Another joke from the flight engineer.

"Let's have quiet again. Eyes up for contact, Peter. I'm staying right on the instruments. George, you better give me an altitude check over the middle marker."

"Roger." A laugh. "Now we'll see what his runway visibility is really like."

A pause, then the bleeper again: "We're fifty foot high I'd say."

"As near as dammit then."

Almost immediately Nyren's voice calling: "I have approach lights. Half right. Twenty right."

A pause. Then voices suddenly overlapping.

"Shit!"

"Whoops! Sorry skipper." That was Peter Nyren.

"Overshoot!"

"Flaps two five."

"Positive climb. Gear up." A pause. "We're lifting like a whale. Give us full power, George. Let's get back in the sky. Peter—tune in to Oscar Echo on both."

"Roger."

"Speed OK. Flaps to one four."

"Where's that beacon, Peter?"

"Beacon's tuned in. Identing Oscar Echo."

A pause. Then an exclamation.

"Judas!"

"Air speed and rate of climb all over." Peter Nyren's voice alarmed and jerky. Interference and noise on the tape.

"Losing air speed and altitude." The thumping of the aircraft is clearly audible on the tape. Turbulence or a systems failure?

"Fly attitude, Peter." Duckham's voice reimposing calm.

A warning bell shrills, scaring even the three engineers listening to the tape in the lab.

"Engine fire number two." The warning bell stops as someone cancels it.

"Another false alarm. It has to be."

"Probably." Duckham still calm. A short pause of decision. "Carry out fire drill on number two."

"For Christ's sake! It's a false alarm!" Whose voice that?

"Fire drill, George." Duckham again.

"Essential power to number three." The flight engineer. "Close number two throttle."

A pause. Then Duckham terse and loud: "Peter!"

"Yes, sorry." Peter Nyren in a shaky voice. "Closing number two throttle."

Flight engineer: "Shutting start lever."

Nyren: "Pulling fire handle."

A pause. The flight engineer calls: "We're on battery. Number three's tripped on overload."

"Shed some load and get us back on generator." Duckham.

A pause—of what—two seconds? Then Duckham in a sudden shout: "Fucking Christ Jesus!"

The sounds die away to a moan on Duckham's blasphemy and the tape stops.

Three engineers look at each other across the lab. The loop of tape is designed to hold thirty minutes of conversation, canceling as it rerecords. On Tango November something had stopped the tape dead before the crash ever happened. Preliminary examination indicated the same stoppage on the "Black Box" flight recorder. The last four, five, or six minutes of Tango November are silence.

The Italian has a list of words to look up in his dictionary. None of them will prove to solve any problems for him: *whale, whoops, shut up, dammit, skipper, shit, fucking Christ Jesus, Judas,* and *miracle.*

12

Sharlie was early for his appointment with the other reporter. Quarter to one, the voice had said; under the elephant in the Piazza del Duomo. Sharlie came into the square from the arch, crossing the road behind a bus. The man was waiting, gesticulating a message to some car parked in front of the cathedral. He didn't look the part with his heavy mouth and jaw. His lips were so swollen it was like he had a bee sting.

He hadn't yet seen Sharlie. Maybe he's just noticed a friend passing, Sharlie was thinking. Then "bee sting" saw him, nodded, and turned nonchalantly to meet him. Was there something in his face; something in the way he moved? Sharlie slowed up trying to think. You don't ambush people in broad daylight in the middle of the Piazza del Duomo, even in Catania. Anyway, he was another newspaperman. Wasn't he?

The square was scattered with people; the sun was shining; the city full of the smells of lunch. Innocuous. Sharlie was five paces from "bee sting" when he noticed the phalanx: three men from that car heading across the square to cut him off. Sharlie had already had one tooth broken. He wasn't walking wide-eyed into any more trouble. Nor was it time to linger over questions.

He dodged "bee sting" and ran for the corner of the square, looking back once. All four men were after him. He turned down the steps into the fish market, slipped on the wet paving, and cannoned into a stall of shellfish—mussels, oysters, limpets, and sea snails in an avalanche. He was up and running again, the four men close behind, the yells of the shellfish trader filling the market. Two merchants went for him under the arcade, all three of them sprawling into a cart of seafood. Fish this time—octopus, a pail of live eels, and the severed trunk of a large tuna slithered with Sharlie on the pavement. There was a cleaver in a wooden board where he stood up again and he ran now, cleaver in hand, the crowd scattering in front of him. He burst out into the open under the railway and headed back toward the waterfront where he alone knew how to hide and seek.

He was stinking with fish, bruised from the falls, but laughing at himself for the hell of it all. Quite like old times. A pity he didn't have a number to call Citto in Rome. Citto would have liked the cartloads of fish. And I bet they really were reporters, Sharlie was thinking. Four customers for my photographs I've lost. "Bee sting" must think I'm nuts.

Citto walked from the metro station toward the Piazzale Enrico Mattei and his last Roman appointment. He seemed to be the only living creature in the whole expanse of EUR, surrounded and dwarfed by empty boulevards, gardens, lake, and palaces sleeping in the hot afternoon.

In restrospect Citto would blame himself. A day and a half of open questions and search had been too long. He had become conspicuous and though he was not yet conscious of a pursuer or a tail his movements had in fact been under close observation since early that morning. At least he had finished his researches, and so far as the spider's web was concerned he had joined up the two remaining corners. Notwithstanding the quasi-military status of Taormina–Peloritana as a NATO emergency field, it seemed from documents in the two departments concerned that concessions for the ancillary services at the airport—fuel, catering, and maintenance—had been made over to three private companies: Servizi TP for the fuel; Panetellana for catering; Air Mecanico for the maintenance. Telephone calls to Messina and Palermo had connected the names: secretary of Servizi TP was the young Flavio Consoli; Panetellana turned out to be the maiden name of Flavio's mother; and the chief executive of Air Mecanico was the *paterfamilias* himself, Avvocato Consoli. The remaining names on the boards were connected with the other members of the initial consortium that had dreamed up the airport in the first place.

Nothing illegal about it, of course—unless negligence or corrupt practice had contributed in any way to the crash of Tango November. But it was the fear of such criminal responsibility that was feeding panic in Rome.

Citto reached the top of the Piazzale. The parking lot sloped away from him down toward the twenty green-glassed stories of Mattei's skyscraper. Citto turned to look across the deserted wastes of lake and lawns. No one following him. No one walking in the streets or gardens.

The ministry clerk was waiting, as promised, sitting in the shade of a pine tree at the edge of the parking lot. They exchanged money and message without preamble: 100,000 lire from Citto to the young man; and a name in return, but no address.

"Preuss. He lives in Venice," said the clerk.

"Teaches at the university. He'll be in the book. There's no address on the papers. I only worked out who he is from the initials."

Citto wrote down the name, watched the young clerk depart across the road and round a corner and out of sight, then retraced his own steps downhill to the metro station. That was nice and easy, he was thinking.

The car must have been coasting for he only heard it at the last moment, as the driver banged in the clutch to fire the engine. Even then Citto was still unaware of danger, turning only in surprise for the parking lot had seemed uninhabited. It was a battered-looking BMW, ten yards away and heading straight for him. He could see two faces in the front seats screwed up in concentration or fear. Nothing more than kids they seemed. No one had ever taught Citto how to run away from car assassins, but whatever instinct made him react was entirely correct. He ran at the car, like a *bandillero* at the bull, jumping away when it was too late for the driver to turn. Citto lay sprawled on the tarmac. He picked himself up, his mind a total blank, silent and blind. Kids having a game, he thought to himself. And they nearly killed me. He felt an oppressive panic: strange aggressive faces in a strange empty city, with home so far away.

Then he heard the car turning behind him and he ran. The parking lot was divided into wide avenues by lines of low hedge. Sharp hedge, Citto found when he tried to jump one. He waded out knee-deep in thorns as the car turned yet again at the top of the slope. At the bottom end of the lot were the lawns and the lake, and a chain across the avenue to prevent cars passing. But the chain had been left unpadlocked for a gardener's cart. Citto reached it a few yards ahead of his pursuer, and took to the grass. The car ploughed through the chain, thumped onto the lawn, churning up grass as it tried to follow Citto's zigzag flight. Citto kept to the line of the lake heading toward the road bridge, tubby and awkward, scuttling like a fat hen, his briefcase banging against his body. He was at the end of his limited energy. It came into his mind that he could stop running and let whatever happened happen. He wanted to stop. He wanted to give up. Then he saw the lake beside and below him, and he rolled down the bank into the water. The car skidded behind him, swerving away from the lake back onto the lawn. It waltzed around a tree, turned hard on two wheels tearing over the grass through a bush, and away.

Citto pulled himself out of the water. He stood on the bank and wiped his spectacles, peering around at the emptiness. EUR, deserted as a city after the holocaust, had absorbed the little drama without a reaction. Three hundred yards away up on the hill across the lake a couple were standing, seemingly watching him, but without gesture or movement.

Citto listened as the roar of that car faded in the distance. They hadn't tried to kill him for a game, and to be here waiting for him they must have known where he was coming. Did that mean the young ministry clerk had set him up? Was the name he'd given just a fiction, this Preuss? Citto crossed the gardens to the metro station, noisily wet, leaving a trail of water drying fast on the hot asphalt path behind him.

A mile away toward San Paolo two frightened youths abandoned the BMW and any intentions they might have had of picking up their money. The man had offered them 200,000 lire. "Doesn't matter what happens," he told them. "Just hit him hard with a car."

The metro platform was as deserted as the world outside, and Citto, standing in a shaft of sun, pulled off his jacket and squeezed water from his trousers. By the time a train arrived he was halfway dry, and when he climbed back into inhabited streets he looked quite normally crumpled, like a tourist back from a swim out at Ostia. Even the center of the city looked thin in the early afternoon—a straggle of German tourists drooping to a bus; a postcard stall; a couple of *carrozze,* horses sleeping in their nose bags.

Citto's hotel was a little flea joint a hundred yards from the station. He paid his bill, collected his pajamas and shaving kit, and left by the narrow alley at the back of the building. Then realized he should have operated in reverse, paying his bill at the last possible minute in case the shirt-sleeved *padrone* had been primed to brief anyone on his departure. The man had asked: "Leaving town?"

"Going home," Citto had told him with a nod. Now, as he walked two blocks to the station he was sure he had a tail.

There was a through train for Venice at four o'clock. Citto had ten minutes to check this Preuss's address and number in the Venice phone book. He dialed an *interurbano* in the praying hope he was at home. When the man answered Citto had neither time nor energy left for planned dialogue. He wanted to know if the man was real and if he would talk. All he could cope with was statement and direct question. It came out more like a telegram. *"Ingegnere*—I am a reporter. I believe you gave evidence to the feasibility study on Taormina–Peloritana and that your evidence was suppressed. I am arriving in Venice at midnight tonight by train from Rome. If you can talk to me I will be in the bar at the station."

There was a long pause at the other end, then an amused voice replied in lilting Veneto dialect: "You work fast. I had expected maybe a week or two before someone traced it all back. What is your paper?" And when Citto told him—"All right. I'll be there. How shall I know you?"

Citto described himself: "I'm fat. I wear round steel glasses, and a light gray suit—very crumpled."

"And I shall be in a red sweater, drinking Grappa."

The *gettoni* ran out and the line cut off. The young ministry clerk hadn't been bluffing after all. Citto wondered if he would suffer any consequences.

It was four minutes to train time. Citto had bought no ticket. His tail would discover too easily where he was going. He sauntered the length of the concourse as carefully as he could. Three, two, and one. The train jerked into motion a half minute late and Citto ran from an adjoining platform. He looked back as he climbed aboard, but there was no movement in the crowd. No one running to catch the train with him.

Why should they bother, he thought as the train threaded its way out of the city. A fast car on the autostrada would catch them at Bologna. Or they'd have a friend to call in Florence with his description. If they were really following him it would be very difficult to stay hidden.

He passed and repassed over the events of the last two hours in wonderment and disbelief. Most things he could have invented, but not that car and its squealing, tire-thumping pursuit. One near-hit might have been a prank or a mistake. But turning around to come again, that was deliberate, premeditated, nasty. Young frightened faces those two kids had had. Citto wondered how much money they'd been offered.

The train was in two sections, bound for Venice and Munich. Citto chose the German half of the train and sat himself in a compartment otherwise full with Bavarian nuns on their way back from the Eternal City. Their low guttural chattering had him sleeping before they'd left the city limits, and he woke only twice in five hours, at Florence to buy a drink, and at Bologna to change into the Venice half of the train.

The platform at Bologna was dark and cool. One could feel the change in latitude, and the presence of mountains to the north and south. Citto bought himself a cardboard plate of hot lasagne and a bottle of wine from one of the food carts, and stood eating in a corridor crowded with a party of tired and jaded children returning from a *colonia*. When the kids left the train at Ferrara Citto found an empty compartment and watched the scattered lights across the flatlands of the Po delta, wondering whether he would ever bring himself to come north and work out of his *ambiente* with people he did not understand. His brother had done it far away in Germany. But then his brother was a realist. He didn't imagine things like hostility and alienation. Citto had always been a dreamer. A bad-dream dreamer. Until he was ten years old he had spent more time alone in the hills with sheep and goats than with lessons or other children in a classroom. It was the village priest who had told his mother to encourage books and learning. What would his priests say now if Citto wrote to tell them where that learning had brought him: to near death from a car in the middle of a wide and empty Roman park.

Citto smiled through the window at a moonlit sheet of water. There was church money in the airport. One of the names in the consortium handled holy money on the island, investment moved around the markets as discreetly and anonymously as Mafia capital. Citto wondered, not for the first time, whether he should think of such things with amusement or a prayer. His faith and his gratitude were not always comfortable to live with.

The red sweater was waiting in the bar at the station, a bottle of Grappa and two glasses in front of him, and the self-mocking smile of a lonely man when he turned to greet Citto.

After the Grappa they walked out of the station, across the piazza, over a vast hump of bridge into a maze of narrow alleys and passages. Citto tried hard not to look around with too much interest but all in vain.

"Your first time in Venice," Preuss observed. "See it while you have the chance. Your grandchildren won't have that privilege. Socialism came too late."

Citto smiled. The red sweater was watching him.

"You found my name very quickly."

"With some help," said Citto.

"Do we know how this crash happened?"

Citto shrugged. "I have my ideas."

"About the airport?"

"The plane was trying to land there."

"Don't worry. I hold no brief for it. The brief I held was for objective rational analysis. And you know how highly that is praised in our poor country."

"They removed your name from the report."

"Not just my name. They removed my name because of everything else they had removed."

"Your case was against the airport then?"

"You have seen the airport and you have seen the crash. You have drawn your own conclusions."

"Taormina–Peloritana is no nearer to the mountain than the airport at Catania."

"Which proves what? I know Fontanarossa is your local airport. But you can't tell me it is either safe or well sited."

Citto gestured vaguely toward unseen Alps. "There are airports in Austria and Switzerland built in the very middle of mountains."

"Not volcanoes, dear boy. Volcanoes have very special characteristics. So far as you Sicilians are concerned the characteristics are fire and earthquake. So far as planes are concerned the characteristic is turbulence."

"Was that what you wrote in the report?"

"I made two general points against the existence of the airport and detailed points against the actual plans. If you are interested in minutiae," he said.

"That is why I came. I have been studying minutiae for two days."

Red sweater touched his arm in apology. "I am sorry. Arrogance is unforgivable and I am always guilty." He smiled his lopsided smile.

They were crossing a humped bridge over a canal, black empty water, narrow black empty alleys in front and behind them, and but for the slapping of water silence everywhere.

"Another airport was unnecessary unless it had been sited to replace and improve on Fontanarossa. That would have meant taking it south of Catania and away from the mountain."

"So the case you made in the report was that the airport should never have been built?"

"There was no social or economic justification. And it was sited in just about the worst possible place."

"So why do you think it was built?"

"You don't need me to tell you that. A lot of people made a lot of money out of it. There was land to buy, runways to lay, buildings to put up, roads to improve, an industrial estate to develop. And generous grants to help it all along."

"Why didn't the other members of the committee share your opinions?"

Preuss shrugged. "Various reasons. Some genuine, some not so genuine. There were only five technical experts. Everyone else was political."

"Was the committee rigged?"

"Not blatantly, no. That is—not until I made my own opinion clear."

"They were worried about your opinion even though it was a minority opinion?"

"The report was published. My criticism could have attracted a lot of attention. There was opposition to the whole idea. Especially locally."

"Conservationists in Taormina?"

Preuss smiled. "That sort of thing. Hopeless, isn't it?"

Preuss stopped on a bridge. The moon was framed down a narrow canal, the world momentarily pure black and white. A clock chimed somewhere. Five minutes fast, Citto hoped with a glance at his watch.

"When you were—dismissed—you made no public statement?"

"I am not possessed of that kind of courage."

"They threatened you?"

"Not violence or anything crude like that."

"Blackmail?"

"I suppose so."

"There is no need to tell me. But the question will be asked if you present your evidence to the American and English investigators."

Again that smile, brief, contorted and sad. They walked on leaving the moon and the water, losing even the sky in a narrow alley between two palaces.

"What were the detailed criticisms in your report?"

"A plea for good instrumentation. An airport in a position like that needs all the visual and radar aids available. ILS, VASI, and precision approach radar. They're not really very expensive. It would all have cost less than the money they spent on promotion and presentation. You might say it's an unpopular part of the budget."

"They have ILS."

"ADF beacons. Very unreliable." Preuss turned to Citto. "There were storms that night, I believe."

Citto nodded.

"In bad weather an ADF beacon is like a dead leaf in a storm, blowing around all over the place."

There were more bells ringing in the city. Citto looked at his watch again. His return train left in half an hour from across the lagoon.

Preuss took his arm, a gesture, it seemed, of restraint. "You are welcome to stay. Tomorrow I could show you our doomed and beautiful city." That self-mocking smile was back in his face. Agony from somewhere. Citto could recognize agony, though he wasn't much good at analyzing it.

"You have evidence that ought to be given to the crash investigation. Why not travel back with me?"

"Now? Good Lord, one cannot travel quite that abruptly."

"I'm sure the investigation will pay your expenses."

"It's not a question of expense, dear boy. I have to prepare myself psychologically."

"But you will come?"

"I don't know. Tomorrow. The day after tomorrow. The investigators will be there for a long time."

Preuss led him now at a somewhat increased pace, turning back through a succession of alleys, crossing a succession of bridges. "You know your train leaves from Mestre. We must find you a taxi."

"There were points of detail you were going to tell me about."

"Ah. The airport again. Yes. There's an industrial development on the access road with a lot of modern street lighting."

"I know it."

"There was a danger in certain conditions that some of those lights could be mistaken for the runway approach."

"What conditions?"

"Coming out of low cloud when the pilot has to see everything at the last minute. Especially if the roads were wet and the light reflected. It only takes a split second to make a wrong decision and sometimes a split second is all a pilot has."

Citto smiled. "I think you were a pilot yourself."

"A long time ago. Little planes with guns. Since then I've never had the nerve to fly again."

They skirted a garden and crossed a last bridge, in front of them the tall block of the garage at the end of the causeway. There were a couple of late-night taxis by the bus station.

"You didn't see much of Venice."

"I think you should come with me," Citto said again. He wondered later whether he had said it to ease the pain of that lopsided smile; or whether it was premonition. A lot of things he wondered later.

"I'll see you in a few days' time. I will come down with my offerings. They silenced me too easily last time, didn't they? I should have made a little scandal." Preuss tapped Citto on the arm as they shook hands. "One needs company to find one's courage." And the red sweater smiled, one corner of his mouth turned down in self-mockery.

The taxi ran the length of the causeway, a spit of flame from an oil refinery on the mainland reflected in the lagoon. The train was waiting in the station at Mestre. Citto read the destination boards as he walked up the platform. Vienna, some of the carriages had come from. Trieste. Tarvisio. All roads wending south to Rome. He used his spare cash to buy himself a berth for the night, hoping he would lose in sleep the menace he had felt growing in all things around him that day. Peasants we were born and peasants we should have stayed, his Stuttgart brother would have told him.

13

"I am Julia Duckham."

Stella looked at the face staring at her in the darkness. She couldn't see the expression in the eyes nor determine the inflection in the voice. But she understood the name.

Julia had been sitting by the bedside for nearly twelve hours, dozing off regularly through the evening, and awaking each time from a frightened dream. Never of Mike but always of despair. She began to fear that semiconscious state of mind. Sleep was no blessed oblivion. She had watched the little girl falling away reluctantly on Stella's pillow. And when Trixie was asleep Julia laid her in the cot. Some time later a nurse had brought supper, and told Julia there was a free bed in the next room whenever she felt tired. They were glad enough of some English-speaking help.

Stella had waked in the early hours, without a sound, her eyes opening suddenly and trying to focus.

"How are you feeling?"

Stella was watching her.

"Do you want the light?"

The bandaged head moved in a gesture that could have been either yes or no. Julia decided on darkness.

"I am Julia."

No response.

"And you are Stella. We met at the cricket match."

Stella couldn't think what to say. She decided the face and voice seemed kind.

"You are the only one of the crew left alive. The hospital has let me help look after you."

"Why?" Stella asked. "Why should you want to look after me?"

"It seems the only thing I can do. There's nothing else. Except waiting for the funeral. The town is full of people waiting like that."

"Where's Trixie?"

"Sleeping."

"What happened to her?"

"She has a broken arm. And she is in shock."

"There is no one with her?"

"They are all dead. A whole family."

Stella closed her eyes. "How many of us are dead?" She meant Tango November and all who had flown in her.

"There are only six survivors."

"It wasn't his fault." Stella's eyes were still closed.

"How do you know?"

"But you know it wasn't, don't you? It couldn't have been."

Julia took her hand. Neither of them had found it necessary to mention him by name. She wondered if that implied anything: I know; and you know that I know. She couldn't be sure. She would never be sure unless she was told exactly how and when it had happened; and where, and how often, and why, and with whom else. How many girls? Did she want to know? Isn't that why she was here, sitting on the girl's bed, waiting for her secrets?

"Do you know what happened?" Julia was referring to the crash.

Stella shook her head. "It was all chaos. Confusion. It seemed to go on for a long time." She paused. "We saw the sunrise. We thought we were safe then."

"Was there something wrong with the plane?"

"I think so. I don't know."

"They will be asking you."

"Who?"

"The people investigating the crash. They're trying to blame him."

"What do they say?"

"Just about everything they can think of. That he drank too much. That he was after money because he changed jobs. That he was quarreling with Peter Nyren"—Julia plunged on while she still had the courage—"that he was having an affair with you."

Stella turned her head looking for Julia's face. Julia continued quickly: "They'll say anything and everything if they want to blame him." She was still holding Stella's hand. "I'm glad you said it wasn't his fault. I mean—I'm glad you believe it wasn't."

Stella closed her eyes trying to concentrate. She couldn't follow what the woman was saying.

"You're the most important person really. What you say. You're the only member of the crew. The only one who might have known what was happening. They'll have to listen to you."

"I need to drink," Stella whispered.

"I'm sorry." Julia stood up. "I'm talking too much." She turned on the bedside lamp, angling it into the wall to dim the light. Stella saw her clearly for the first time: her eyes wide with shock and her face hollowed out with distress. Stella wondered how long she had been sitting there with her.

"What is the time?"

"It's one o'clock in the morning."

"Monday?"

"Wednesday."

"Wednesday? When did it happen?"

"Saturday morning."

"I've been here all that time?"

Stella remembered talking with her father. She had thought then it was Sunday. "How long have you been here?"

"Only this afternoon." Julia pressed the bell on the wall. "There's nothing here for you to drink."

Two nurses came and Julia backed away to the door

as they set to work stripping and changing Stella. She saw wounds down the girl's side, raw and scraped like burns.

Stella watched her leaving. "Are you going?"

"Not if you want me to stay."

Stella's head moved again with the gesture that was neither yes nor no.

Tino G. had left the world of lost songs and pictures in his mind. His body was hurting and the music had gone. If anyone had told him that the pain meant life for him he would have found it difficult to summon either laughter or anger. For the moment he had forgotten everything. Corinna; the airplane; the red sunrise; the advance and retreat of death. All he had now was the pain in his body, different pains he was beginning to identify and place—abdominal pain, pain when he breathed, and strange sensations like exaggerated hunger and thirst and a bladder that seemed to be bursting and about which he could apparently do nothing. None of it was really unbearable and the nurses would not give him drugs for they relied now on his consciousness of pain to tell them if anything else was going wrong.

Late in the evening he woke to find a visitor. An old man leaning on a stick, watching him from under bowed head and shoulders. It was only when the man talked that Tino G. recognized the voice of the doctor who had kept him company for half a day inside the broken plane.

"Do you mind me coming?" the voice asked. "Maybe I remind you of bad things?"

Tino G. shook his head.

"They say you are all right now." The old man smiled. "Just hurting all over."

Tino G. nodded.

"I am glad to see you recover."

"You saved my life."

"I do not think so. You saved your own life. You decided you would live. That's what is important. The will to survive."

Tino G. shook his head. "I thought I was dying. I knew I was dying. I was expecting to die."

Turi looked at flowers on the table, newspaper cuttings, telegrams. The boy spoke behind him on the bed.

"Crazy, isn't it? A week ago no one knew me. Today I get offers for a contract with two recording companies. You know what one of them's for? For writing songs about planes. Flying and falling."

"The newspapers say you come from Sicily?"

"My mother. She wanted me to come. And now I'm here and my feet haven't even touched ground." The boy paused, his face drawn and tired. "I'll come back again. To walk around."

"Then you must promise to visit me."

"Yes."

"I have a nice house. A vineyard. A lemon grove. A terrace where to sit and drink in the evenings."

Tino G. smiled at the picture. He felt himself falling away into sleep again. Blessed sleep. "Do you have any children?" he asked the doctor, but his eyes closed before the old man answered.

Turi watched the boy sleep. I had a son, Turi was thinking. For three days I had a son.

That evening in Taormina the investigators had listened to a recording of the voice tape flown back to them from England. The voices confirmed that Tango November had had trouble making visual contact on the approach; that the landing attempt had been aborted; that during the first minute of overshoot the crew had had to face turbulence and a fire-warning on the number two engine.

In climb out, thought Raille, like all the other number two engine fire-warnings on the 119. There was no conclusive proof that the warning had been false. The engine had been too badly burned in the crash to give any immediate clues.

Raille and the systems analyst from California sat half the night in a hotel bedroom studying a full-size plan of the flight engineer's panel, trying to guess the sequence of events that would have followed the engine shutdown. What had caused the flight recorders to pack up at that very moment? It was clear from the voice tape that number three generator overloaded as soon as the number two engine had been shut down. They would have gone on to battery temporarily while the engineer shed some of the power load: galley power; one of the HF sets; a reduction in cabin heating and lighting; weather radar; booster pumps—in that order according to the company manual. Raille looked at the panel. The engineer would have been in a hurry, he thought, in the middle of a fire drill. The galley power switch was on the top corner of the panel, easy enough to find. Selecting one of the HF sets would have been more difficult. He'd have had to look for it. Supposing he went left hand and eyes to the HF set and right hand by feel to the galley switch? There were two switches together in that top corner, at different heights but very close: battery and galley. He was moving fast, in a bit of a flap: he could have hit the wrong one. He could have turned off the battery instead of the galley. Without battery or generator they'd have been flying blind without lighting or instruments, and the flight recorders would certainly have packed up. Raille propped up the panel plan and tried the movement, mistaking the battery switch for the galley.

The Burbank analyst shook his head. "Not possible—the switches are different shapes and colors."

Only if you look at them, thought Raille. The battery

switch was square and red; the galley power a black tadpole. They could feel much the same if you were in a hurry. Unlikely perhaps, but certainly possible. An interpretation of Murphy's Law—if a mistake is allowed to be possible then sooner or later someone will make it.

Whose bright idea to put those two switches so close together?

"Looks to me more like the battery failed," said the Burbank analyst. "It had been charging high, remember." The flight engineer's note on that bloodstained pad. "It could have died under load."

Needless to say the ultimate proof, the battery itself, had been totally destroyed in the crash. Another of the unknown quantities.

But what if the flight engineer had made that mistake? He also would have assumed it was the battery gone. With no lights on his panel he couldn't have spotted his error. What would have happened? They'd have had the flashlights out, and eventually the engineer would have got them back on to generator. Presumably at that stage he had forgotten to reconnect the flight recorders.

How long would they have been flying blind? A minute? A couple of minutes? Quite enough to lose their way.

14

One member of the search party crawled from his pup tent into another dawn to seek out a secluded, downwind, and out-of-earshot spot for his morning voidings. He picked a patch of ground where he could see and evade the attentions of ants. He crouched, squatting, hanging on to a bush with one hand, staring up at the blue sky and coming to the slow realization that this clearing on the hillside was no natural open space. The scrub had been torn, the ground marked as though something had been dragged across it with force.

His evacuations complete, the engineer followed the marks down the slope and saw, half-buried in the soil, the lumps of torn aluminum missing from Tango November's left-side wing.

An hour later his team found the point of original impact high on the ridge above the camp site—an outcrop of lava breaking the even slope of the ridge. It was even possible to match the damaged fragment with marks on the rock, and calculate the angle of collision—a steep angle suggested by the fact that impact had occurred halfway across the width of the underside of the wing. The plane must have been climbing to clear the ridge in some desperate last-minute maneuver.

Whatever the scenario the margin of disaster was not much more than ten feet and the final downfall of Tango November a hillock of lava haphazardly formed in some eruption three or four hundred years ago.

Isolated pieces of the jigsaw were beginning to drop into place. Some guides from the volcano had been interviewed. Yes, they had been up on the mountain Saturday morning, and it had been very cold and wet. Snow, sleet, hail, everything.

Yes, they had heard a plane. Very close, and very low. They'd heard it twice, they thought. Once to the north and vaguely overhead, once to the east, when the sound of the engines seemed to be coming from somewhere down in the valley below them. But then that could have been an impression caused by atmospheric conditions.

The storm? All to the north and west of the mountain at the time they heard the plane. Everything was clear to the east because they'd seen the dawn and the sun breaking out of the sea.

The lower slopes of the mountain? Patches of cloud all over it—like looking at a frozen lake with little islands where the ground showed through. Only the top few hundred feet of the mountain had been completely clear of cloud.

The sunrise? Blood red and dramatic. Quite frightening really. Violent.

15

Taormina–Peloritana was slumbering in the warmth, apparently oblivious of the dramas unfolding on its behalf up and down the length of Italy. Civil operation was still forbidden, though word had it that the airport was about to reopen. A skeleton staff was keeping buildings swept and the traffic controllers took turns in the tower, fulfilling their military duties. The airport administration with Servizi TP and Pantellana were manning their combined offices anticipating the resumption of traffic, and helping to feed the day's cancellations into Fontanarossa or Reggio Calabria.

Somewhere beyond the Aero Club an oil tanker and trailer arrived along the avenue of knee-high oleanders. But there was, to anyone sitting on the terrace of the club bar, no more than a buzz of insect in the air and a faint and inconspicuous drone of machinery as the tanker maneuvered into position.

Fifty-four cubic inches of Ducati exploded into that tranquility with the effect of a dozen machine guns. Every inhabitant of the field walked to a window or a door, and one vigilant pair of eyes recognized both motorcycle and boy, and telephoned the recognition to a private number in an orange grove thirty miles away under the southern slopes of the volcano.

Sharlie was only belatedly aware of the noise he had made. He had been following Tomacchio's oil tanker since early morning through the villages under the volcano, across the valleys to the north, and up into the Peloritani hills. He'd had to stop in the last town for gas and had then momentarily lost track of the truck, only guessing at its destination. He killed his engine now and coasted across the empty airport parking lot trying to appear uninterested in his surroundings. But behind his visor he was quartering the ground for that elusive tanker, and when he spotted it behind the Aero Club building his hurried sequence of action was neither disinterested nor inconspicuous. He had to work his way as close as possible to the truck and its operation. Citto had briefed him and Sharlie knew that the essential evidence was the positioning of those long black hoses unreeled from the tanker. He moved as casually as was possible and without showing himself to the driver, running off a dozen exposures from various positions to describe the tanker's operation. He couldn't make sense of it himself without knowing the location and functions of all the taps and attachments, but by the time he returned to the bike he was confident he had enough evidence for Citto to work on.

He rode as quietly as the beast would allow out of the parking lot and down the approach road, pulling the bike into a sidetrack to wait for the truck.

Flavio Consoli was unlucky with the telephone that morning. His mother was on the line gossiping with one of her ten sisters and by the time Taormina–Peloritana got through to him Capo Tomacchio and his truck had already left the airport.

Flavio listened to the narrative of crisis: a photographer who had been seen recording the arrival of

Avvocato Consoli at the Fontanarossa airport two days ago was now photographing the activities of a fuel truck at Taormina–Peloritana.

Flavio had neither the experience nor the natural "cool" to cope with so immediate a situation. He had reacted successfully on Saturday morning by soliciting Tomacchio's help and advice. But now the capo was on the spot and there was no way of talking with him. The man who had telephoned was one of the catering managers. At least Flavio knew enough about the secret deals he made to be able to rely on his discretion.

"Do you know the villages farther up the hill?"

"The empty ones?"

"Yes. Number three as you come to them. Above the road off a hairpin. The truck stops there for a job. Take your car and catch up with him."

"What do I tell him?"

"Tell him he's being followed. Tell him about the boy on the motorcycle."

"Anything else?"

"Tell him to do everything as usual. Tell him to carry on as though nothing had happened. And tell him I'm on my way. I'll watch the motorcycle. Tell him whoever the boy is I'll buy him off."

Two minutes later the Dino was tearing up dust and gravel along the track between the orange trees, and Flavio was thanking God for having sent his father away on business that morning into the city.

The empty village was tucked away in a fold of ground near the top of the pass: a piazza; a church, ugly and modern, marked with rusty ironwork; deserted houses in rows up the hillside, their doors and shutters broken; cracked streets and brick steps growing dry burned grass—desolation without a sheep or a goat or a dog or a madman to break the silence. A misconceived attempt to resettle peasants on an arid hillside; or more probably just another excuse for the buying and selling of land, and the pocketing of government grants.

Sharlie had smiled when the truck turned off the main road, for he now guessed the story his camera would record. He drove the cycle into the long grass and pulled it up on its center stand. He took three quick pictures of the track from the main road to place the location, then changed the half-finished film in case he ran out of exposures at a more critical moment. After all Citto was paying for these rolls. He slipped the half-finished film into the inside front pocket of his leather coat.

He heard the truck stop where the track was closed by a pole barrier; he heard the rattle of chain and padlock, then the truck straining again up the hillside. Sharlie climbed straight up the slope and cut off the corner, scrambling fast on banks of thistle and twisted thorn. He was already at the far end of the village when the tanker backed alongside the church. He watched as the driver unrolled a length of hose from the truck into a side entrance at the rear of the building. Sharlie needed to be nearer. He worked his way up a concrete drainage channel into the main street, the Madonna and Child in colored enamel watching him from above each gaping door—icons spared by God-fearing vandals. A broken shutter creaked, and a thin black snake whipped away angrily in the grass under his feet. He could see the shimmer of fumes around the church door where fuel was leaking from the pipe and evaporating in the sun. He wondered what size storage tank there could be inside that shell of church.

The tanker engine was throttled up for pumping and the noise prevented Sharlie from hearing the arrival of a car in the piazza. Nor was he particularly alarmed or uneasy that he could no longer see the driver of the truck. He assumed the man was in the church waiting for the pump to complete its work.

But Capo Tomacchio had walked out as the car appeared. He recognized the blue Audi and the catering manager from the airport. He'd been expecting trouble ever since he started out that morning. This of all weeks the Consoli could have relinquished their run. Greedy bastards.

"Have you seen the motorcycle anywhere?" he asked when he heard the story.

"Down on the main road. In the grass."

Tomacchio glanced at the tanker still pumping away at the side of the church. That boy with the camera was somewhere around, hiding in the houses. He pulled the car door open. "Drive me down there. Then get on back to the airport."

Slow the little bastard up, thought the capo. Give Flavio Consoli time to catch up with him. Immobilize him. But not right here on the doorstep. Delayed action he wanted. The Audi dropped him by the motorcycle where the track joined the main road, and when the car had gone Tomacchio grabbed a handful of gravel and tried to open the gas tank. There was a flip lid across the cap, but a lock underneath. Tomacchio squatted instead to unscrew the sump filler. He funneled his dirt into the hot oil and ran in two extra handfuls for good measure. He was back up the hill and into the village three minutes later to turn off his pumps and roll up his pipes.

Sharlie had his pictures, two dozen of them: fuel siphoned out from tanks at the airport, driven uphill to the deserted village and stored here presumably for resale. That appeared to be the operation. He now watched the truck pull away across the cracked paving of the piazza, down the track back to the main road. Airport and village had taken forty minutes out of the day's run, and no one any the wiser. The capo would be down in Milazzo by lunchtime and back home with his load of gasoline by supper. There seemed no point in cataloguing the rest of the day's journey and there was, anyhow, a risk of being spotted on that lonely road over the top. Sharlie decided to turn back with his pictures. It was not a happy decision. If he had been following the tanker, he'd have spent the next few hours driving slowly.

Sharlie rode back down the pass through the town in the valley with only a vague sensation that the cycle was misbehaving. Running a bit sluggish. On the far side of town he noticed a flamboyant green and orange Dino passing in the opposite direction and he wondered briefly if it was the same car that had met the avvocato Consoli at the airport yesterday. If he'd had a mirror on the motorcycle he might have seen the Dino turning in the road and starting to follow a hundred yards or so behind him.

I'll stop him out in the country, Flavio was thinking, and either buy him off or frighten him off.

Sharlie was happy. He'd done the job well and now the road was wide, straight, and open beyond the town. He dropped down a gear to accelerate the cobwebs out of the engine. The oil pressure warning light was on, and the engine straining, but Sharlie hadn't noticed the light and the bike ran on, building up to 105 mph before the boy finally realized that something was really wrong. By then it was too late. His left-hand fingers went groping out for the clutch about a tenth of a second too late. The engine had jammed, and the back wheel had locked. He was out of control, broadside and falling. He felt his leg break as it hit the road under the full weight of the cycle. His levis shredded along the asphalt. He shut his eyes with the pain. Christ, he was thinking, I've ruined the bike.

From the car behind Flavio watched in disbelief. It seemed to him afterward that he had witnessed the whole incident in slow motion; the sudden trail of smoke; the cycle starting to skid; the back wheel drawing out a thick black line on the road. Then the fall, motorcycle and rider spinning around each other down the road still traveling at something over 60 mph.

An approaching truck pulled across the road to avoid them, and the Dino braked to a standstill behind. The motorcycle bounced with a cloud of dust into an orange orchard. Sharlie instead spun on down the asphalt head first into the concrete divider. His body flipped over, rolling into burnt grass and dust, coming to a stop slumped between two oak trees.

The truck driver ran toward him kneeling in the dirt over the crumpled heap of road-torn denim and leather.

Flavio moved the Dino toward them, stopped and climbed out.

"You'll have to take him," the truck driver shouted. "He needs a hospital very bad."

Flavio had no choice. It was law in Italy where public ambulances were few and far between. They carried the boy to the Dino and folded him into the low and awkward passenger seat. Flavio noticed beyond his sense of shock the broken camera bag lying at the side of the road.

"I'll take it," he said. "There might be his papers in there."

"It just happened, didn't it?" said the truck driver. "No one touched him."

"A blowout maybe," said Flavio. "I'll tell the cops in town. They'll want to pick up the bike themselves."

"You'd better write down my name," said the truck driver. "Don't want them to think it was anyone's fault."

Flavio turned the Dino back toward town. There had to be a first-aid post somewhere. He turned up his lights, held a white handkerchief from the window, and leaned on the horn—the conventional signs for a private car doubling as an ambulance.

He looked at the boy slumped in the seat beside him:

the visor of his helmet was broken, the face below it pale, almost blue, and blood running in streams from underneath. Flavio had placed the camera bag on the boy's lap. There were rolls of film inside and a camera damaged in the fall. It wasn't difficult to pry the camera apart and extract the film. Flavio pocketed the cassettes, then let the bag fall on the floor at the boy's feet.

The Dino must have been visible or audible to everyone in town as it came blasting up the road, and sure enough a police car met them, drawing alongside to have a look, then preceding them with its siren wailing to clear the traffic as they made for the *pronto soccorso*. But all they could do when they arrived was lay the boy on a stretcher and wait. Another ten minutes passed before a doctor was located, and the boy's breathing grew shallower and his pulse weaker. Sharlie's heart stopped beating just two minutes after the doctor's arrival and when they cut the helmet off his head they found the skull visibly and irrevocably broken.

It was half past eleven on Wednesday morning. Stella Pritchard, Trixie, the retired army major, his wife, the Twickenham sales executive, and the Durham GP were alive; Tino G. and the Northumberland shopkeeper more or less alive.

In Rome Citto was waiting for the bus out to Fiumicino and the lunchtime flight back home to Catania. In Venice Ingegnere Preuss had been reading pages of an old report deleted three years previously by the personal intervention of a minister. In Taormina Larry Raille had received a sixty-word cable offering him transfer and promotion into NASA. On the mountain the search party was on its way back to civilization, and in the wreckage of Tango November engineers were unraveling the last structural and mechanical evidence.

Sharlie's mother was told of her son's death when she came home for lunch from her dirty workbench in a dirty factory. Her yell of despair was heard right across the city harbor, above the hooting of a ship, the noise of cranes, the screech of wagons shunting on rusty rails.

Part Four

1

"You joined Hercules in March of this year?"
Stella Pritchard nodded from her bed and Burden, eyes down on his clipboard, made the necessary note. He was interviewing for the first time outside his pensione room and he felt a little disoriented. After the tranquility of Taormina the bustle and noise of the city had given him a headache.

"Can I ask you when you first met Peter Nyren?"

"I think in May some time."

"You flew together?"

"Yes."

"I don't wish to intrude on your private life. If there are questions you would rather not answer—"

"It doesn't matter, does it? Everyone's dead."

"You went out with Nyren—?"

Stella cut him off again: "He took me out some evenings. There was nothing more to it than that. He was very shy."

"Would other people in the company, your friends

and his friends, would they have considered that you
were his girl friend?"

"I expect they imagined we were sleeping together."

Burden stared uncomfortably at his clipboard trying
to phrase his next question. The girl, lying in bed and
watching the fan on the ceiling, asked and answered it
for him.

"He used to hold my hand and kiss me good night.
Otherwise he never touched me."

Burden was still silent. The interrogation seemed to
have escalated out of his control. He couldn't even see
the girl's face. She was lying flat on a high bed, and he
was to one side in an uncomfortably low armchair.

The girl spoke again. "If you're wondering what my
feelings were you can write down that I liked him. I
wouldn't have objected if he had touched me or se-
duced me or whatever."

Burden coughed to clear his throat. "Did you ever
visit his home in the country?"

"He asked me down for a weekend. There was a sort
of charity cricket match on the village green. Something
to do with his father. He's the local vicar."

"Was that the Saturday when Captain Duckham
came with his family?"

"Yes."

"You must have known Duckham as fleet captain."

"In the distance. We had never flown together."

"So this cricket match was the first time you met
him?"

"Yes."

"And you were playing as well?"

"We used to play cricket at school."

"Did you meet his wife there?"

"Just to say hello."

"And his children?"

"I suppose so. There were a lot of children. I don't

really remember. I expect I was nervous about meeting Duckham."

"Like meeting the boss?"

"Sort of."

"But you made friends during this cricket game?"

"We ended up batting together. It was more comedy than cricket. I was at one end and he was at the other and we used to meet in the middle and talk between overs. He was flirting with me if that's what you're asking. But it was all a joke. I mean we had everyone laughing at us."

"Was Peter Nyren playing?"

"He was playing for the village."

"He didn't object to this—this flirting?"

"Why should he? We had everyone laughing and clapping. He thought we were a great success."

"You stayed down there for the weekend?"

"I stayed until Sunday. I wasn't really invited. I mean Peter's father didn't really know. He was quite surprised to see me next morning."

"And the relationship was still the same between you and Nyren?"

"We didn't even kiss good night."

"You mean you quarreled?"

"No. I mean what I said. We didn't say good night to each other. If you want to know why, I thought he was going to come and spend the night with me."

Another nympho, Burden was thinking.

"Sunday afternoon he drove me home. He could have stayed the night at my place but all the other girls were there. He was shy about that sort of thing."

"You shared a flat?"

"A house."

Burden referred to his notes. "In Redhill."

"We all worked out of Gatwick."

"Are you all air hostesses?"

Stella nodded.

"All with Hercules?"

"There's one girl from British Caledonian."

"And Nyren I believe lived in London?"

"He had a room somewhere off the Finchley Road."

Burden sifted through his notes again. "Frognal."

"He used to work out of Luton. Before he came to Hercules."

"Can I ask you what your feelings were toward Nyren?"

"I don't know. How would I know? We didn't even sleep together."

Burden was silenced again. He fitted a new sheet of paper onto his clipboard, then began again, as carefully as he knew how. "A certain rumor has been made known to me concerning yourself and Captain Duckham"—

The voice from the pillow cut in, soft and expressionless. "We slept together a few times."

Burden was lost for words or a question. Dixie Duckham strikes again, he was thinking. "Can I ask over what period this happened?"

"From June onward."

"All the time?"

"Once a week, once every two weeks. Just as it happened."

"Was this when you were flying together?"

"Only the first time. We didn't do it on the plane if that's what you're thinking."

She was reading him without even looking at him. If Stella had been able to see him now she would have found him blushing furiously. Pretty hostesses straddled on his lap in a plane restroom. The thought had occurred to him not a few times.

She went on. "It was a stopover. Casablanca from Monday morning to Friday evening."

"This was after the cricket match I take it?"

"Two weeks after."

"Do you think Duckham arranged it that way?"

"It's not possible. Casablanca is the trip everyone wants to do and there are only two a week. Mondays and Fridays. It's on strict rotation."

"How often did you fly with Duckham after that?"

"Two or three times."

"And with Nyren?"

"About the same."

"Were you ever in Casablanca with Nyren?"

"No."

"I take it Duckham came to your house a few times?"

"No. Never. Not with the place full of other Hercules girls."

Burden was again at a loss for words. He wasn't even sure that the questions he wanted to ask were relevant to the investigation. Again the girl seemed to read his thoughts.

"We used to do it in his car."

How and in which particular ways? Burden wanted to know, but he dared ask no more.

"Were you in love with him?"

"I enjoyed making love with him, if that's what you mean."

"I imagine you would have preferred a more lasting relationship."

"What does that mean?"

"You never talked together about the possibility of a divorce?"

"Good heavens, no." Stella closed her eyes. The man was beginning to exhaust her. "I wouldn't have wanted anything like that. Anyway he was very much in love with his wife. He wouldn't have dreamed of leaving her." Her head moved as though she was trying to look around the room. "She's here."

"Mrs. Duckham?"

"She's looking after me."

Burden also glanced round as though he expected to find her behind a curtain.

"They're very short-staffed. She's a trained nurse."

Extraordinary, thought Burden. Extraordinary how women behave. He couldn't conceive how people lived in such a way. It was all so untidy. He looked at his sheets of notes. He'd completely lost his way. Dixie Duckham, fifty-three years old and knocking off twenty-year-olds in his car. The man was more than a womanizer. He was some kind of freak. And his women along with him.

"Did Peter Nyren know what was happening between you and Duckham?"

"Yes."

"Did you ever talk about it?"

"Yes."

"Was he upset?"

"I don't know. I suppose so. He was just a kid really."

"Did you quarrel about it?"

"No."

"Did he quarrel with Duckham?"

"They were already quarreling. About something else."

"How did Nyren find out about it?"

"One of the crew out in Casablanca spreading the good word." Her head moved again. "Have we finished?" Her voice was very thin and tired.

"I have to ask you about Friday night. The flight. The crash."

"Not now," she whispered.

"I'll come and see you again."

Burden stood up, and they looked at each other for the first time since he had sat down. He was embarrassed at the way they had talked, and he tried to rationalize it.

"I'm sorry the questions are so personal," he said. "It's the fact of you and Duckham and Nyren all being together on the same flight."

"Personal feelings wouldn't have made any difference to anything."

"I'm not saying they did."

"When they're in the cockpit they're just pros doing a job."

Burden nodded.

"He was the best pilot of all."

"Duckham?"

"Yes." Stella closed her eyes again. "You can tell the good ones. There's never any fuss. It's always quiet. Taking off, landing. Even when things go wrong they never fuss."

Her eyes stayed closed and Burden stood watching her awkwardly for a moment before backing away to the door.

There was a woman outside waiting in the corridor. Julia Duckham, less bedraggled than when Burden had interviewed her three days ago, apparently calm, her face made up, her hair brushed into a bun.

"I was trying to listen outside the door. I couldn't hear anything." She stood in front of Burden as he tried to turn away. "Can I ask you what she said?"

"All information required by the investigation is considered confidential unless ultimately published in the report."

"He was my husband. You have no right to conceal anything from me."

"You must talk with her yourself if you want to find out what happened."

"There was something. That's what you're saying, isn't it?"

"I'm not saying anything."

"You can't do that." Her voice was no longer calm. She cornered him against the wall by the elevator.

"You said a lot of things the other day when you didn't even know whether they were true or not. And now that you do know you're suddenly not saying anything."

Person-to-person, full-frontal anger scared Burden. He hadn't had to face it many times in his life. It made him quite weak at the knees. And of course it was true what she said. He had tossed things at her the other day that were at the time nothing more than second- or third-hand gossip.

"It would appear that your husband had been having sexual relations with Miss Pritchard."

Burden saw her composure deflate. That well-adjusted face began to fray at the edges. Her alarm or dismay or whatever emotion it was gave him an un-wanted but uncontrollable feeling of satisfaction. He tried to frown it out of his head and tried to mitigate what he had said.

"It seems to have been a very casual and insignificant relationship. A self-indulgence," he could not help adding.

The elevator arrived and he stepped quickly inside to leave Julia staring at the closing doors.

Eight years. Eight years without a real quarrel, eight years without tears. Eight years being happy and only the illness of children or an occasional overdue airplane to worry about. Fool's paradise.

Julia walked into Stella's room. The girl waiting for her, eyes on the door.

"I had to tell him things."

"I know."

"I must tell you."

Julia nodded.

"It was nothing. It was just nice making love with him."

"Jesus Christ. You think I don't know that."

"That was all it was. It was nothing. Like having a cigarette or a drink. It didn't mean anything."

Julia sat on the bed: "The first time he took me out he told me he felt like making love to every pretty girl he passed in the street. That was warning enough, wasn't it?"

There was a long silence.

"He told me—he said—'one day my life is all going to blow open and reveal itself for what it really is.' "

2

Sharlie was dead. A traffic accident statistic. A broken naked boy. A pile of clothes with identity card, driver's license, a single thousand lire note, a penknife, a battered plastic bag of broken camera and lenses. One roll of film had been found still intact inside the leather jacket by the hospital staff and it was enclosed with the rest of his belongings in a large plastic bag to await the next of kin.

Identification of the body was made that afternoon by Sharlie's mother. She had been driven forty miles to the hospital in a police car. Apart from the professional solace offered by the police driver and a nurse at the hospital, her only comfort was from members of the family: Nonna Lisa, Laura, and Laura's brother Pietro. They sat together in a waiting room, the two older women hand in hand crying together, the young brother and sister side by side on a wooden bench staring at the floor. Laura was thinking of Sharlie yesterday, high on his mountain picking mushrooms with *Cantallaluna,* happy, laughing, all that tightness from Rome disappearing from his face. Pietro, it had to be admitted, was thinking of his motorcycle.

Citto joined them late in the afternoon, blundering into the waiting room at the hospital, peering through a pair of steamed-up glasses as though unwilling to be-

lieve the news he had been given. The news editor from
the paper had met him when his plane landed from
Rome. Even at this stage in the proceedings neither of
them believed the death to be an accident.

He will blame himself, Laura thought, when she saw
Citto. He'll be saying to himself, I sent Sharlie after
that truck; I am responsible for his death.

Laura watched him sit with the mother and take her
hand, trying to comfort her. Sharlie was a good boy,
Citto was telling her. Honest, brave, hard-working. *Un
bravo ragazzo.*

A courageous boy, Citto would have liked to say. He
would have liked to tell this mother that her boy had
discovered anger and courage before he died. But Citto
didn't want those mother's eyes turned accusingly on
him. You again, they would say. Always leading him
into trouble. And now into death.

A nurse brought the plastic bag with Sharlie's clothes
and effects. There was a form to sign, a list to check.
The mother did not want to see it, and Citto took the
bag to check its contents. It was just as well that he did
so, for some unthinking fool in the nether regions of
hospital or morgue had packed the split and bloody
remains of the boy's crash helmet. Citto asked the
nurse to wrap the torn jeans, leather jacket and the
helmet separately. The mother could be spared those
details. Citto would take them himself together with
that roll of film. He was thinking about forensic examination and evidence.

He visited the local traffic police as reporter and
friend, and asked his questions. They listened politely
to his theories; made notes on the possible culpability
of the man with the green and orange Dino. Citto asked
them about the motorcycle.

"Examined: found defective; engine jammed at very
high speed. No signs of a collision."

Can the cycle be photographed?

"It was taken away by a garage pending instructions from the next of kin or the insurance company."

The name of the garage?

"Autoboom." It was a wrecker's yard on the coast in Giardini.

Citto returned to the hospital, picked up Pietro, and drove fast and furious in the fading light down the valley toward Taormina.

Giardini liked to call itself the lido of Taormina, sited as it was on the strip of land between the sea and the rock on which Taormina stood. In reality it was nothing much more than a railway station, a jumble of pensioni and a long straggle of small specialist garages: body works, car electricians, tire dealers, mechanics.

Citto and Pietro found the cycle under a tarpaulin in the wrecker's yard along the road toward Naxos, a couple of men already at work by lamplight, separating the engine from the frame.

Who had told them to break it up?

"We're just taking out the engine that's all."

On whose authority?

"I don't need any authority to work in my own yard."

But Pietro had the cycle's documents with him, and when Citto threatened to walk round the corner to call up the carabinieri the two men stopped their work and faded away.

Vandals? Or saboteurs?

The cycle was badly bent, worn and almost molten down the one side where it had slid on the road. The front wheel was twisted, and the whole machine impregnated with tufts of dry grass and earth.

Citto left Pietro mourning over that grim wreckage, guarding it against further desecration. Citto was thinking, there were a dozen men up in Taormina equipped and trained to examine mechanical wreckage. He drove up the hill and around the town to the hotel where the investigators had set up their center of operations.

But Citto's only link with the air crash investigators was not yet back from his day's work. The English doctor, they told him, would return at nine o'clock. Two hours to wait.

Citto wandered into the narrow hillside streets, his frantic movement running down, his mind beginning to fill with Sharlie. How many times they had haunted these steps and alleyways together lying in wait after a tip-off about some celebrity staying in the San Domenico, Sharlie prowling, camera tucked into one hand as though it were a knife or a gun. He never missed exposure or focus shooting on the turn. It was pleasing just to watch him at work.

What had happened this morning? Sharlie must have got his pictures for he was on his way back when he crashed. Citto still had that cartridge in his pocket. Had it been used? Citto had searched for more film in that black hospital bag and in the remains of Sharlie's cameras and camera bag. The boy would have traveled with at least half a dozen rolls, but there were no signs of them. They couldn't all have been lost in the spill.

Citto found a studio up one of the alleyways off the main street, the photographer an elderly man of doubtful nationality. He was closing up for the evening but agreed to develop the cartridge for an exorbitant fee. He mistook Citto's urgency for furtiveness. Citto waited in a purple-draped studio, wondering at the portraits displayed on the walls—elderly Teutonic gentlemen and the traditionally beautiful local boys posed semi-naked by the sea, or framed in the pillars of the Greek theatre. The old photographer would be disappointed if he thought he could steal some porno prints from Sharlie's roll of film.

Capo Tomacchio was tired. Tired, dirty, hungry, and thirsty. He drove the heavy tanker and trailer through his yard gates, parked, locked up, and climbed the iron steps up to his terrace above the old boiler house. Unloading could wait until the morning. A black shape leapt at him at the top of the stairs in a frenzy of barking, mad green eyes pulled up short and head high at the end of a chain. The capo muttered affection and a curse and the German shepherd subsided. He had no nose, that dog. You had to talk to him before he recognized you. Tomacchio glanced across the terrace at the house: lights in the kitchen and the sitting room. His wife in the kitchen, his daughter in the sitting room with the stereo or the TV or some boy friend. Young Renzo no doubt: aggressive and political, useless except as a mechanic.

Renzo must have heard him coming. He was on his way out as Tomacchio entered and they exchanged casual good nights passing each other in the kitchen.

The capo called after him across the terrace: "She's dropping oil from somewhere." Renzo could be fixing that when he came in next morning. It would give Tomacchio an extra twenty minutes in bed.

"Oh, get off my back," thought Renzo down in the yard. He took the flashlight from his bicycle and squatted down by the truck. Better find the leak while it was still warm and dripping. It'd take all morning tomorrow for the yard was pock-marked with oil stains old and new. The leak was on the differential and he pushed a dry tray under it. By the morning he'd have an idea how much it had been losing.

It was as Renzo returned to his bike that he heard the Dino climbing the hill into the far side of the village. It had to be Consoli. There was only one young blood in this part of the world who drove six cylinders with quite so much throttle blipping, air-horn blowing, and tire-squealing. Renzo stood listening to it. Was he coming to take Giuseppina out for the evening? Was that why she'd told him he'd better leave? Renzo's bicycle was in the old distillery office just under the yard gates. He waited there as the Dino turned into the street and parked outside. Little bastard, Renzo thought. I'll murder him if he takes her out.

He heard Flavio ring the bell on the outside of the gate, and pictured him pushing his face up to the wall to talk into the speaker grille. The flabby lazy voice was trying hard to sound urgent: "I've got to see you," Renzo heard it say. "I'll wait in the yard for you."

See who? The remote-control door lock buzzed and clicked and Renzo smelled aftershave as Flavio pushed his way into the yard not two feet from where he was standing. He's not going upstairs, Renzo thought, because he's scared of the dog. Flavio was the one human that old German shepherd always recognized. Flavio had kicked him once, hard in the head and the body, and like elephants old shepherds bide their time and never forget.

It was not Giuseppina but Tomacchio himself who appeared in silhouette along the terrace and down the iron steps.

Renzo thought he should go now, but it would look a little funny if he appeared suddenly out of the darkness. He waited as the two men met, wondering what kind of conspiracy they were cooking up. Their first words froze him.

"He's dead." That was Flavio in a low voice.

"Who's dead?"

"The kid on the motorcycle."

"So? He had an accident."

"Did you have anything to do with it?"

"What happened to him?"

"I was right behind him."

"You didn't time that very well then."

"Did you have anything to do with it?"

"I wasn't there, was I?"

"*I* was there, you idiot. And if there's anything the

cops are going to find out about it I've got to know."

"Don't you idiot me, young man."

There was a pause as they seemed to move farther from the house and even nearer to Renzo. Tomacchio spoke again.

"You haven't told me what happened yet."

"His back wheel locked up. He must have been doing 110 miles per hour."

There was a short pause and Renzo sweated in the silence and the darkness. Eavesdropping on this kind of secret carried a death sentence. Who in God's name were they talking about?

"I put gravel in his oil. His engine must have jammed."

"Holy Jesus." There was another, longer silence.

Tomacchio spoke: "Seems to me you'll have to tell your father. He can hold the cops off."

"Tell him? Are you crazy? He'd kill me. He would literally tear me to pieces."

"It's his business, isn't it? Just because you're running it for him and part of it goes wrong, he can't chew you up for that."

Another silence. Tomacchio tried again. "I'll go and see him myself if you're scared of him."

"He doesn't know what we're doing." From Flavio's tone of voice that was a major confession.

The longest silence of all now. Renzo couldn't see where they were, nor what they were doing.

The capo's voice was angry and hard. Renzo knew that tone. It meant what it said: "If anything goes wrong for me I'll drag you down with me. I'll hurt you and him so damn hard you won't know what hit you. Do you think I'd get myself involved in this two-bit swindle if I'd known your old man wasn't in on it? I thought I was doing him a favor. I sure as hell don't need to do you any favors."

There were sounds of movement, then Flavio's voice

uneasy through its lazy slur. "Where are you going?"

"To get my coat." Renzo could see Tomacchio climbing the steps back up to the terrace.

"What for?"

"We're going to drain that goddamn storage tank."

"Tonight?"

"And you're going to drive me there."

Two minutes later the capo reappeared along the terrace and down the steps, carrying not only his coat but a hunting gun.

"What's the gun for?" Flavio was sounding queasy.

"Get in the car and drive."

The two men passed by Renzo and out into the street. Flavio's aftershave and the older man's sweat.

When the roar of the Dino had faded out of the village Renzo eased his bicycle quietly out the side door and cycled home. You're involved, he was telling himself. You talked to that reporter. Today's the day they were following the tanker. He thought of the tubby little man with the stammer, hoping he was not the victim and then spent the rest of the evening wondering if he shouldn't tell someone what he had overheard. But native caution prevailed. Communist or not this was still Sicily where eyes and ears had learned instinctively to keep their secrets.

There was music in Taormina that night, piano and orchestra drifting from the columns and amphitheater on the edge of town high above the sea: a Japanese pianist, a Dutch orchestra, a German conductor, ignorant of each other's languages, uninvolved personally in the tragedy, but gathered under the moon to play a Mozart piano concerto in an open-air theater excavated three centuries before the birth of Christ. Of such complexity and compassion, thought Ash Nyren, is the kingdom of man.

The old canon was perched high in the auditorium,

hunched up, one elbow on one knee, listening to the music. Yesterday his stubble had been shaved and he'd been dressed in someone's baggy clothes. People had been looking for him and those American students had told them where to find him. He had been lodged in a room under a roof where the sun punished him from morning to evening and where he looked out on a burnt hillside of cactus.

He listened to the cadenza below him losing itself in the darkness. God's strength, he was thinking, is based solely on the arbitrary nature of death. Man against God.

Citto found the English doctor as the investigators dispersed from their evening meeting. They were scattered in groups around a small interior cloister in the San Domenico at the opposite end of town from the Greek theater. No music filtered in here, only the sound of a fountain and the pattering of rubber-soled waiters carrying drinks.

Mac was in a fighting mood that night. He'd been held up all day sorting the remains of five carbonized and fragmented bodies and trying to establish some method of identification. He was falling behind on his detailed autopsies and he had asked for a postponement of interment and repatriation. To no avail. He was told that the funeral arrangements had been finalized for Saturday, which left Mac with at the most two days to complete his evidence.

"If seats, seat belts, and cabin fittings had been 15 percent more resistant," he had announced at that evening's meeting, "we would have found a 1,000 percent improvement in the casualty figures. I believe it is of the utmost importance to collect specific data to support this aspect of the investigation so that public pressure in England and America can be brought to bear for revision of minimum safety regulations."

Boy, that had gone down like a stone. How they hated that phrase "public pressure." He had a very quizzical look from Ralph Burden over their coffee. Only Larry Raille had supported him with anything approaching wholeheartedness, but then he'd had his own differences of opinion at the meeting. The air traffic controller at Taormina–Peloritana had been contacted and questioned about power cuts on the night of the crash. He had admitted, under pressure, that there had been a temporary loss of control tower lighting some five minutes after contact had been lost with Tango November. The control tower was wired into the same emergency circuit as the instrument landing aids and runway lighting, and both Raille and Mac had demanded evidence as to the timing of that power cut. The two of them were still talking together in the cloister when Citto arrived to interrupt them.

The little Italian, blinking, stammering, struggling with his English, was no champion advocate. But he had facts, and even evidence of a sort. Burden was called to join the little group and Citto told his story from the beginning: the stopped clocks and the fuel truck at the airport on the morning of the crash, and the lines of inquiry he had followed both on the island and in Rome. He told them of Ingegnere Preuss with his own controversial evidence on the siting of the airport. And he told them finally of the events of that day and the death of the young photographer on his motorcycle. The evidence was the film from the half-finished roll found in Sharlie's pocket, for Sharlie had worked well that morning. He had covered the truck at the airport to show up the positioning of pipes and taps, and his last three exposures identified that derelict and uninhabited village high in the hills. Even without the missing film there was a clear enough indication of malpractice.

"Why should they be interested in that particular fuel?" asked Raille.

"It's paid for by the military," Citto replied. "Part of the agreement to have the field available as a NATO standby. The Italian air ministry pays all the bills for emergency equipment."

Mac interrupted him: "You really think the photographer was killed?" Mac remembered Sharlie taking pictures for him in the city morgue. He had felt badly enough about the boy's subsequent scuffle with the police. Now he was dead, and the idea that the death might not have been accidental worried Mac as much as it worried Citto. The reporter didn't have to request their participation. They were all alarmed.

"Better have a look at this motorcycle," Raille suggested. "If you know where it is."

They sat in the wrecker's yard at Autoboom for forty minutes watching Raille work with a flashlight and wrenches on the cycle: Mac, Burden, Citto, and Pietro. Ralph Burden had his misgivings. He could see the impetuous Mac leading the investigation into all kinds of trouble with the local authorities. This talk of dark and dirty deeds had no place in Burden's well-ordered routine. Even Larry Raille had felt a twinge of that same misgiving, but he was glad enough to be offered diversionary activity. He had cabled polite refusal of the offered transfer and promotion, and had as a result already suffered one heated call from his wife in Washington. The further away he stayed from the telephone the easier he felt. And a motorcycle did make a change.

He worked his way backward through the sequence of disaster: the wheel locked solid, the bottom of the rear tire worn to the cover from friction on the road, the final drive chain immovable, the gearbox distorted and jammed. Finally when he'd dismantled the forward of the V-angled cylinders, the piston and cylinder wall could be seen fused together, the original point of the jam. He unbolted the oil pump and filters. They were buried in grit and small stones. Oil flow had been effectively cut off from the engine.

At which point Burden insisted that the cycle with all its attendant parts be handed over to the police. "It would seem right," he said in his best department manner, "to adjourn for the night. We have opened many new complications."

"It's a long time until tomorrow," said Citto. "Evidence in our country has a habit of disappearing."

Mac looked at the reporter: "Officially we can adjourn. Unofficially we can have an informal look around—" Mac's blood was up. If someone had really killed the photographer he wanted to see what the boy had been photographing in that odd-looking village up in the hills. "How about it, Ralph?"

Burden shook his head. "I'll stay here with the motorcycle and talk with the police. I think it is advisable to allow them to make the next move."

Mac turned to the American. "You coming, Larry?"

Raille was cleaning his hands with gasoline and a rag. He had visions of his hotel room and an insistent transatlantic telephone. "Why the hell not. We're only tourists."

3

For six miles of the climb the headlights behind them had been normal enough: something to keep an eye on; nothing in particular to get alarmed about. Flavio had been watching them in the mirror; Capo Tomacchio, slumped in the low passenger seat, from the window beside him.

"Cut the lights before you turn off."

It was the elder man's first comment in twenty miles. Flavio had felt the capo's anger as heavy in the air as the sweat and oil from his driving overalls. If my surname wasn't Consoli, he thought, this ape would have had me rolled up in a ditch by now with a broken head.

Flavio turned off the lights as they approached the side road for the deserted village, then used the handbrake to stop the car at the barrier. The capo hauled himself out to swing the pole skyward. Flavio could hear cicadas in the grass and far away the oscillating drone of another car lower down the pass, changing tone as it turned in sweeps through the hairpins.

The Dino climbed the track in moonlight and rounded the shoulder of hill into the piazza. They stopped by the church.

"What happens to the gasoline when we open the taps?" Flavio was talking in an undertone as though the ghost village might come suddenly to life.

"It'll seep away. The paving is cracked. There'll be nothing left of it by tomorrow." The vestry door was stiff on its hinges and the capo kicked it open. "You wait here and keep listening."

Tomacchio disappeared inside, the glimmer of his flashlight fading from sight. Flavio waited in the black silence. It was like a kid's game all this excitement, though he could think of better companions than Capo Tomacchio to share it with. There'd be trouble with him when this fuss had all blown over. Maybe I ought to run off with his daughter, thought Flavio. What a sensational pair of tits—and enough money to make life forever comfortable.

He saw the lights of the other car still weaving through the bends. Probably a traveling salesman on his way home to Milazzo. But then the sound of the engine suddenly changed, slowing up somewhere near the turn off for the village. It seemed to stop for a moment, then reverse. Flavio watched the headlights swing out into the valley, and turn uphill on the track toward them. He banged on the door to warn Tomacchio.

"That car's coming up here."

"Goddamn!" The capo was outside before Flavio had finished speaking.

"Did you find the tap?"

"Damn thing's rusted. It's only half open. Running out like a kid peeing. Take all night to empty."

Flavio saw him reach into the car for the shotgun.

"You're not going to use that, are you?"

"Keep out of sight. Stay here with your car, ready to move."

"We can't use guns—" But Tomacchio was gone. Even the sluggish Flavio felt suddenly alarmed.

The track to the village was barred with a pole. Citto parked the car and the men moved off on foot three abreast to cover the width of the track, their flashlights picking out the unmistakable double tire treads of a heavy truck in the gravel.

The three men felt no presence of danger. There was a low moon and a distant moonlit sea on a long white horizon. There were sweet smells left over from Monday's storm and a buzz of crickets. They were not to know that their three wavering flashlights were being held in a gun sight.

Tomacchio had thought he would be dealing with one man. One corpse was possible, three impractical. He'd seen the dark crimson of a battered Giulia and knew that these three were no policemen. He squeezed the trigger and the night exploded. Voluntarily or involuntarily the three spots of light disappeared.

Lying in the dirt by the roadside Citto decided that the shot had been fired from the bank above them. He'd been aware only of the noise and a stinging sensation in his face. He thought his glasses were broken and there was warm blood coming from somewhere. He looked round. The other two were lying across the road from him. Dead?

Then he heard the American swearing. Was the English doctor hurt?

"Are you all right?" That was Raille calling over the road to him.

"He is hurt?"

Citto saw the American prodding his colleague. "You all right, Mac?"

The English voice was muffled and outraged. "I've torn my bloody trousers."

There was a silence; maybe a few seconds, though it felt much longer to the three men on the ground.

"I'm not sleeping here tonight," said Mac.

"So what do we do?" That was the American.

Turn round and go home, thought Citto. He hadn't counted on guns.

"Anyone for kamikaze?" That crazy Englishman was getting up, flashing his torch on to the bank above the road. The gun roared again, into the road in front of them as before, and this time Citto saw flame from the barrel maybe ten yards from where he was lying. Mac was down again, in more of a crouch than a sprawl. They heard the gun break for the reload.

"Next time he does that—" said Mac. "Two barrels. We have to make him fire twice, then charge him."

Idiot, thought Raille. He's seen too much television. There's only one rule with guns: get out of their way and stay out of their way. "I'd say," he said over his shoulder, "that whoever it is doesn't want us up in that village. If we turned around and went away he'd probably let us go."

"What? Let him scare us off with that noise?"

Raille called out loud in stentorian tone: "Whoever you are, we're moving back to our car." He looked across at Citto.

Citto repeated the words in Italian, stuttering dreadfully as he tried to communicate determination.

Capo Tomacchio recognized the voice and the impediment—the tubby little reporter who had tried to interview him on Sunday. His companions were presumably foreign newsmen. He saw shapes moving on the road. They seemed to be crawling back down the hill on their hands and knees. Would they go away? They'd call the police. How long would it take the police to arrive? Half an hour to get up here? That goddamn fuel would still be draining. Better get rid of the whole mess. Lay a fuse to the tank and blow it up. But immobilize their car first. He needed time.

He moved along the bank, not caring about the noise he made, for he was sure they were not carrying guns. Stocky though he was, he could move fast, a great deal faster than Citto and Larry Raille on their hands and knees. The capo found their car parked on the slope below the barricade, unlocked, but without the ignition key. He didn't have time to fiddle with wires. The wheels were set at an angle and he released the handbrake, letting the car run back gently into the ditch by the side of the road. It would take them all night to dig it out.

Tomacchio doubled back, still on the bank and off the road. Two minutes later he had rejoined Flavio in the weed-grown piazza. They had to devise a delayed fuse that would not blow them both up in the process of igniting those storage tanks in the church.

Mac had not moved back down the road with Citto and Larry Raille. He had seen the gunman moving uphill again into the village, and he followed, keeping to the edges of the road, his silhouette below the cover of the banks. He was a degree more apprehensive than before. He knew nothing about the layout of the village, nor how many men were there and with how many guns.

Flavio and Capo Tomacchio were both out of sight behind the church when Mac paced carefully into the piazza. The tall Englishman kept to the iron railing at the side of that strange open space. The dead village lay under a low and waning moon, the weeds in the square throwing long exaggerated shadows, the door and two windows of each house like the mouth and eye sockets of skulls. Twice men moved at the far end of the piazza and twice Mac froze, naked against the moonlit façade of the church. It was at the far corner of that façade that he first smelled the fuel, an overpowering cloud of vapor.

He moved back along the wall to the main door of the church. It was not locked and he edged it carefully open, each crack of warped wood or rusted hinge echoing like so many gunshots round the village.

The inside of the church was bare; no altar, no pews, incense, or candle to suggest the presence of Christ and his angels. The moon slanted in at three windows, low angles of light to show a vaulted ceiling, some artisan's forgotten masterpiece, admired by no one except the birds and the bats. One black doorway led to what would have been a vestry. He could smell the gasoline so strongly now that a cigarette would have blown the roof off. He inched his way into the darkness, obliged now to use his flashlight. The paving was cracked where the ground had settled. Mac could hear the trickling of fuel and the sound led him to the large storage tanks at the far end of the building—15,000 gallons or more in each he estimated.

Outside the village Tomacchio's fuse was ready—a line of dry grass and sticks soaked with gasoline and running from the vestry door across the corner of the piazza to where the Dino was parked. But it was a night

of unending problems for Tomacchio. Neither he nor
Flavio were smokers, and neither of them possessed a
lighter or box of matches. Tomacchio rolled up a page
of newspaper and soaked it in gasoline. They uncovered
the engine of the Dino and disconnected one of the plug
leads. Flavio started the engine and after a few blank
moments and some nasty shocks up Tomacchio's arm
the loose spark ignited the newspaper.

Mac heard the car but could see nothing. It wasn't
until the car actually moved that he found a low ventilator grille to give him some visibility outside. He saw
then the narrow snake of fire approaching the church
across the piazza. The car disappeared from his view in
a wheel-spinning frenzy leaving him staring at the advancing flame. His brain froze. The burning trail was
some five yards short of the church, spluttering and
crackling, accelerating in a whoosh each time it reached
a pool of gasoline. Some of the tall dry weeds in the
piazza were burning, like trees in a forest fire from
where Mac was watching on ground level. Then his
brain moved again and he turned and ran for the
church door. I'm not going to make it, he thought. I
stood there like an idiot staring at it and now I can't get
out. He slipped on the broken paving into a pool of
petrol, lost his flashlight, then could no longer find the
dark arch into the nave of the church. He was soaked in
fuel, his mind and body anticipating explosion. He
scrabbled a way round the wall until he found the gap,
then ran for his life up the empty shell of that would-be
temple. The main church door was closed. He had shut
it carefully himself when he'd entered and couldn't now
find the latch to open it. He threw himself at it and fell
out onto the steps back into the moonlight and a quiet
night. It seemed from this side of the church that nothing had happened. Only the sound of the sports car far
away racing down the hill.

Mac was halfway across the piazza and running

when it blew. There were two explosions, the first when the flame hit the gasoline on the floor. Mac threw himself flat, turning his head to watch as the tank blew up. He saw a window grille disappear, arcing somewhere high over his head; the inside of the church lit up. The explosion must have blown through the walls for the flame was already inside the main body of the building and reaching for the roof.

Citto and Larry Raille were struggling with the ditched Giulia when they heard the six-cylinder roar of the Dino and the explosions of the fuel in the cellar. The Ferrari reached the barricade before the two men had time to react, its blazing headlights bucking up on to the bank to avoid the obstruction of road pole and ditched Alfa. Even through his cracked lens Citto could pick out the lines of that low-slung sports car. He didn't need to see the driver's flushed and fleshy face to know who it was. But the second man was hidden, ducked down below the level of the window and out of sight. Citto watched the lights recede and disappear.

The American was already gone, running back uphill toward the village, yelling anxiously for his colleague.

Explosion and flame high in the Peloritani hills passed unnoticed, and it was two o'clock on Thursday morning before the three men had walked down the pass and up the new connecting road to the nearest telephone—the airport pay phone at Taormina–Peloritana.

Another four hours passed while the police gathered them and their evidence, and inspected the burnt-out church in the hills. The decision to arrest Flavio Consoli and his unknown companion was not made until Mac himself telephoned the young magistrato at his home in the early morning, but by then too much had already happened.

4

Flavio dropped Tomacchio outside the gate of his yard at shortly after midnight. Flavio himself was blissfully unconcerned with the realities of the situation. The explosions and the fire had greatly excited him and Tomacchio had some difficulty in making him realize that the newspapermen, if that is what they were, would have seen and identified his car.

"You need a lot of help," the capo said. He tapped his forehead. "And someone to think for you."

Not that Capo Tomacchio had the slightest intention of leaving the matter to chance or to Flavio's doubtful initiative. As soon as the Dino had gone he called up the Consoli household, using the telephone down in the workshop so as not to alarm his wife and daughter.

"If anything goes wrong for me," he told old man Consoli, "I'll land you all in it, you and your son and everyone else in that Godforsaken consortium."

It was an unwise threat to make to someone of Consoli's stature and influence.

"I'll meet you in an hour's time," Avvocato Consoli told him, calm and quiet. "At my office in town."

Avvocato Consoli sat brooding in his study formulating strategy and waiting for his son. Flavio could see light in the study as he drove down the long approach road through the orange trees. He knew there would be trouble, but what still escaped him was the overall blackness of his own situation.

There would be no pulled punches tonight. The avvocato had had a full account of events from Tomacchio. He didn't have to wait for confession. He beat his son in fury with a pair of drumming fists all the way from the courtyard back to his study.

"Everything and everyone endangered for the sake of a few hundred thousand lire a week—"

It was the insignificance of the money involved that pained the old man most of all. "Insanity," he kept shouting. It wasn't even pocket money. Flavio was pushed into an armchair and told the course of action he would follow. Phone calls were made: to the wife of a cousin's cousin in Reggio Calabria; her Neapolitan brother who owned a luxury car business; another distant relative of that same cousin who taught at a small village school in the Swiss Ticino; finally the cleanup men, two heavies roused from their beds and given a rendezvous.

Upstairs in bed, Signora Consoli listened to the continual pinging of the phone on her table. She resisted the temptation to listen in, but the yells of her outraged husband told her that her precious boy was in bad trouble. When Flavio came hurrying upstairs she heard closets and drawers opening and closing. By the time she had plucked up enough courage to move it was almost too late. Flavio was on his way down to the courtyard with two suitcases. The mother clung to him in desperation: Flavio, the only focus to her life, leaving home. The avvocato pushed his wife to one side. Time tonight was counted in minutes; seconds even.

The poor signora would spend all night and all next day on her knees and in despair seeking miracles from her God.

Capo Tomacchio had left soon after midnight for his meeting with the avvocato. He wasn't looking forward to the confrontation. There'd be hard talking, and a lot of recriminations, but the tough truckdriver reckoned he held enough of the consortium's secrets to guarantee his own protection. It never occurred to him —until an hour too late—that the meeting might never take place, and that the arrangement had been made to get him away from his home and family. The realization came when he returned from Consoli's deserted office to his parked car and found it slumped in the gutter with all four tires slashed.

Tomacchio's wife climbed out of bed when the front doorbell rang some time before one o'clock in the morning. She assumed her husband had mislaid his keys, and the gruff voice on the door speaker certainly sounded like him. "It's me," the voice said, and she pressed the button to unlock the yard gate. Her first signal of alarm was the dog's continued frenzy of barking on the terrace outside. Why hadn't her husband called up as he always did to hush it? And when the dog did stop, it was with a sudden snarl, a yelp and a choking whimper.

The door on to the terrace was always unlocked, and she hurried now into the kitchen to bolt it. The kitchen was in darkness, and two men already inside. When she screamed Giuseppina woke up and ran for the telephone, but the wires had been cut. There was a third man in the bathroom and a trail of blood drops on the floor. The dog it seemed had taken someone's ounce of flesh.

Giuseppina knew neither of the two men but their message was very clear. Get dressed and pack a suitcase, or your mother will be hurt. She did as she was told. She even swallowed the pills they gave her. "Sleeping pills," they told her. "They won't do you no harm." Kidnap and ransom, she was thinking, and that idea terrified her. When they took her outside she asked what would happen to her mother. "The same pills that you have swallowed," she was told. "We will stay with her until she sleeps, and make sure she's quite comfortable."

The third man had slipped out of the house again but neither mother nor daughter had seen him. Only when they brought Giuseppina down into the yard and she saw the Dino waiting in the street did she begin to realize what was really happening. Flavio, sweaty-faced and puffy—with a torn and bloodstained trouser leg. She knew then that she was being abducted, in time-honored fashion, but did not realize the added complications to her state of kidnap. She was only relieved in that moment to see a face she recognized.

"I won't hurt you," Flavio told her as he accelerated away.

They were the last words she heard for twelve hours. By the time they reached Messina—and her first opportunity to protest to the outside world—she was fast asleep. The Dino drove onto the 1:40 ferry unchallenged and with five minutes to spare. By half past two they were on to the southern tip of the Autostrada del Sole and traveling north at 130 miles an hour. The car was changed at five o'clock on a forlorn piece of waste ground beside a factory on the edge of Naples. The brother of a cousin's wife's cousin was waiting there for Flavio on the old connecting road between the two autostradas. He helped him move the sleeping girl from the Dino into a Porsche. The two men exchanged cars and documents, and Flavio drove on northward, rejoining the autostrada and passing Rome soon after six. The Porsche Carrera was cruising at 145 mph and only four times on the journey had to slow for construction or congestion in the Apennine tunnels: Florence disappeared at half past seven; Bologna at a quarter past eight; Milan soon after nine.

The police had started their search for the young Consoli at seven o'clock, unaware that they were also looking for a kidnapped girl. More than an hour passed before confirmation was obtained that an orange and green Ferrari Dino had crossed on the ferry in the middle of the night. By then the young magistrato had arrived to take charge of the inquiry and police departments up and down the length of the peninsula were given details of the fugitive Dino. Airports as far north as Pisa were circulated with Flavio's name and passport number. No one believed it possible that he could arrive at any other border crossing before midday.

The young Consoli, tired, almost inebriated with driving, crossed the Swiss border on the autostrada checkpoint above Chiasso at ten o'clock that morning. Since changing cars outside Naples he had driven 530 miles in five hours with only one stop for gas. The girl beside him was still fast asleep.

5

Scandal and outrage unrolled like a long slow wave through that Thursday. A death; an abduction; a fuel racket: Tango November was back in the headlines and TV cameras and reporters returned to the narrow picturesque streets of Taormina.

The three-nation team of investigators held a press conference that same morning in an attempt to reimpose objectivity on their proceedings. All in vain. Reporters were only interested in Mac and Larry Raille as protagonists in last night's drama, and the result of the drama was a generally accepted assumption that Tango November had lost her way after the blackout of all lights and landing aids at the airport, which was in turn caused by the combination of a power cut and the lack of fuel for the emergency generators.

But, even if true, that was, as the investigators knew, only one small piece of the jigsaw. It did not explain how the plane had come to crash on the opposite side of the mountain. It did not analyze the effect of a bad generator and an inoperative engine. It did not interpret the partial failures of voice and flight recorders. Nor did it take into consideration the possibility of error or miscalculation on the part of the crew, which now seemed to Burden on the personal evidence available to him an inescapable factor in this accident.

The search party had found the missing piece of wing, and the mountain guides had heard the plane somewhere below the crater. The two pieces of evidence tied in with Tino G.'s red sunrise. It seemed that Tango November had circled the mountain counterclockwise and had flown clear of the storm clouds before hitting the lava ridge and losing control. So why had Duckham flown around the mountain at so dangerous an altitude, and why hadn't he turned eastward for the open sea when he came out of the cloud?

"Hell," Raille said to Mac after the press conference, "I wish you'd left us with a hijacker in the cockpit."

Sharlie's surviving photographs had linked Tomacchio and his fuel truck with the fuel racket at Taormina–Peloritana, and it did not take the young magistrato long to connect the abduction of Giuseppina Tomacchio with the disappearance of Flavio Consoli.

Not that Capo Tomacchio was giving anything away. He feigned bewilderment and ignorance as he sipped coffee on his terrace that morning. "The Consoli boy was infatuated," he supposed.

The young Torinese magistrato was unconvinced. "Consoli was busy evading arrest and yet you say he took time off to organize a complicated abduction? He must have had some very strong motive for taking your daughter."

"Love or lust." Tomacchio shrugged. "He was a very arrogant young man."

"You had business arrangements with him."

"Not with him. With Servizi TP. A contract to service generators and fuel installations at the new airport."

"One of your tankers was at the airport yesterday."

"Yes. I was there myself."

"Photographic evidence suggests you were drawing off fuel from the tanks supplying the emergency generators."

The capo nodded. "There was a fault to be checked. I knew the airport was out of service. It seemed a good time to work on it."

"I believe fuel for the emergency circuits is paid for by the military."

"I wouldn't know about such things."

"It might explain why someone thought it worthwhile to siphon off regular weekly amounts."

"I wouldn't know. Like I said I was only checking a fault."

"And what was it, this so-called fault?"

"Fuel flow. That's why the tank had to be drained."

"But it wasn't drained completely—"

"The level had to be lowered below the point of interchange between the two tanks." The capo explained patiently. "There are two separate electrical circuits, two generators, and two tanks. One system for nonessentials like internal lighting and heating, the second circuit for emergency instruments, clocks, and runway lighting. The two tanks are connected in such a way that if fuel starts to run low priority goes to the emergency generator."

"But last Saturday it was apparently the emergency generator that failed."

"Exactly. That's why I was checking for a fault."

The young magistrato could not help but smile. How many times in his short period of office on the island had his interrogations been led in these elegant and intricate Byzantine circles. There was enough evidence, or coincidence, to hold this Tomacchio for further questioning, even to construct a charge. But better to slacken the rope for a day or two and watch just where this stocky, tough old truckdriver would lead them. He'd surely go chasing after his daughter.

The signora woke from her barbiturate sleep well but weeping, and once the police had taken her confused statement they left the premises, the young magistrato returning to his office with a new file of evidence for the Tango November inquiry.

Mechanics and truckdrivers resumed that day's work, and at midday the boss sent for Renzo.

"You know what has happened?"

Renzo nodded.

"You care for Giuseppina?"

Renzo did not reply. The capo took an envelope from his pocket.

"There's money in there. You spend what you have to and find her. You follow that young puppy's trail and bring my daughter back home and I'll make things good for you."

Renzo said nothing. But he took the money. He telephoned Citto's newspaper from the bar down the street, returned home to pack a small suitcase, and left the village on the afternoon bus.

Six miles down the road Mac had returned to his basement room in the small hospital where Sanju and Turi met him with a different kind of drama. "A black comedy," the Indian told him, for their meat truck and carabinieri had disappeared. When Turi drove Mac down to the produce market they found truckdriver and carabinieri contemplating an empty railway siding. The four cars full of refrigerated bodies had vanished, "shunted in error" during the night, attached to a fruit train, and now lost somewhere in the vast complexity of the Italian state railways.

Turi led Mac away from the huddle of railway and police officials before the wild Englishman could commit some act of irrevocable violence. He walked him instead through the market, stopping at each merchant to ask about the loads they had dispatched by rail the day before. There was not one of them who did not know Turi and they were all ready to help him, where with anyone else they might have been reticent. Even in these rich lands on the east coast wholesale fruit and vegetables was monopoly country, reflecting the shadow of the Mafia if not its actual presence. Turi pieced together something of a picture: freight cars had departed last night for Switzerland and Germany, and a whole train in the early morning for Milan and Turin.

Mac watched the little old doctor nosing out the information, head bent over his stick as he dutifully admired the box of grapes or a basket of tomatoes. He could have walked off with enough produce to stock a shop from the offers he had—*"pighiasse, Dutturi, pighiasse."* It was a colorful mess of a market, mountains of green, red and yellow peppers, melons and watermelons of all colors, and sizes, purple eggplant in baskets, the last of the summer's peaches, the first of the autumn apples. And above it all, as nowhere up or down the coast, hung the mountain. Etna rose out of this town without gentle slope or easy contours, smoke from the central crater lying over them as it was carried by the wind, a perpetual omen in the sky. Mac had been a lot closer to the mountain, nearer to the crater, higher on its slopes. But he had never felt its threat so strongly.

The omens were for him, he thought. He was now responsible for the disappearance of 180 bodies and he'd lost the evidence he needed for his report. In this atmosphere of intrigue he could be forgiven his instinctive suspicion of conspiracy.

6

It was midday before Burden arrived back at the hospital in Catania. After his previous confrontation with Julia Duckham he was not surprised to find her waiting for him when he stepped out of the elevator. They walked in silence up the corridor and into Stella Pritchard's room.

Stella was lying, as yesterday, flat on her back staring into the ceiling. She glanced only briefly at Burden and Julia as they came in. There was a little girl sitting with her on the side of the bed and Burden recognized Trixie from the photographs and stories in the newspapers.

Julia closed the door, leaning against it like a sentinel or a bodyguard. Today's interview it seemed was to be conducted with an audience and Burden, remembering yesterday's unpleasantness, chose to raise no objections. He busied himself instead with his briefcase and clipboard.

"I should like to go through the events of last Friday so far as you remember them."

Stella's head moved on her pillow. A nod. Stella could see Julia by the door watching her. The two women hadn't talked any more. Truce or peace or neutrality—neither of them really knew what had been established.

Burden cleared his throat and spoke again from his chair. "You had a couple of days off, I believe?"

"Wednesday and Thursday," Stella replied. "I went up to Harrogate to see my parents."

"And you arrived back on Friday?"

"After lunch. I caught the Yorkshire Pullman. I was home about three o'clock and I went to bed."

"Your duty began at ten-thirty in the evening. I take it you used the train between Redhill and Gatwick?"

Stella didn't reply for a moment. She turned her face away from Julia. "Captain Duckham had arranged to give me a lift."

Burden flipped over his pages of notes. He couldn't remember whether he had an exact time for Duckham's own departure from home. Stella answered the question.

"We met at eight o'clock. We thought we would stop on the way." She did not say why or what for.

Julia was motionless and composed, still leaning against the door. She remembered Mike's words that Friday lunchtime: "I'll leave early, love. Get some paperwork done."

"And did you stop on the way?" That was Burden, clearing his throat again.

There was another long pause. "We used to meet by the station, then drive up the hill. We had a place to pull off the road in a country lane. Somewhere behind Nutfield."

Probably a nice big car, thought Burden. Reclining seats. A radio. Well—there was an eight-hour no-drink-before-flying regulation, but no laws on sex. Mac would probably claim it increased concentration and efficiency.

"We sat and talked," said Stella. "Not for very long." She was remembering how tired Mike had looked. She didn't want to tell that to the investigator. "We didn't feel like—doing anything else."

Julia heard Mike calling her into that black-painted dressing room after lunch. "Come and help me sleep," he had shouted, and they had made love while Clara was playing next door. The last time they had ever made love, but now Julia could hardly remember what they'd done or how it had happened. Was she telling the truth, the girl, about not doing anything that evening?

"You then drove on to Gatwick?" asked Burden.

"Yes."

"You must have arrived early."

"No. Not particularly."

"So you had been talking in the car for quite a long time."

"I don't know. We were listening to the radio. And I was telling him about what one of the girls had been saying that evening at the house. Something about her boyfriend. I just used to prattle on about things like that. He seemed to like listening."

Stella was remembering exactly what Mike had said: "I don't feel like flying tonight. I feel like a tired old man." Again they were not words she wanted to repeat to this inquisitor. "How about breaking rules and having a drink?" Mike had suggested. The Plough in Smallfield. But in the pub he had just grinned and ordered two tonics and ice. No gin. No vodka.

"Do you remember when you arrived at the airport?" Burden asked.

"Ten o'clock."

"You arrived together?"

"He used to drop me off in the tunnel under the terminal. Then he'd go and park the car and we'd arrive separately."

"And that's what happened on Friday?"

"Yes." Stella pictured the crew room. It had been crowded when she arrived. There were two crews preparing for flights and their own plane still to arrive. Two crews signing off, three crews signing on. That's when she saw Peter.

Burden was thinking in the same direction. "When was it you found out that Peter Nyren was flying with you?"

"When I signed on."

"Had you seen him recently?"

"About two weeks ago."

"You went out together?"

"We'd arranged to go to a concert. I mean we had arranged it a long time ago. There didn't seem much point in canceling it."

"In London?"

"Yes. Peter used to go to a lot of them."

"Was it a nice evening?"

The insinuation did not escape Stella. "The music was very good and we had a nice meal."

And afterward? Burden wanted to ask.

Poor, confused Peter, Stella was thinking. "What would you say if I asked you to come home with me?" he had asked. "I don't know," she had replied. "Are you asking me?" And when Peter had shrugged in moody fashion she had told him to drive her to Victoria for her train home.

Burden shifted on his chair. "Did you talk to each other in the crew room on Friday evening?"

"We said hello."

"That's all?"

"There was quite a crowd, and I was saying hello to the other girls as well." Stella remembered the expression on Peter's face when Duckham walked in a couple of minutes after her. He had sunk himself back into a magazine, his face set in the brooding pout that Stella had come to know.

"Did Duckham talk to Nyren in the crew room?"

"He came over and said hello."

"You were with Nyren, were you?"

"No. I was watching. I knew about the quarrel. I wondered if they were going to make it up because of flying together."

"Did they?"

"Peter said hello back. That's all."

"And Duckham?"

"He said something about the delay and the cutoff time. You know—when it gets too late and they have to call up another crew."

"I suppose you were all hoping that would happen."

"One or two people said we might get an early night. Mike told us the cutoff time was two hours fifty from then."

"When did he say that?"

"He came and said hello to all of us. The cabin crew I mean. He always did that."

"Did he say anything in particular to you?"

"No. Just that there would be some short-tempered passengers around tonight, and to be careful with them."

Burden turned a page of his notes. Duckham had come within five or ten minutes of his cutoff time. If he had known what the weather was going to be like he'd probably have packed it in. He had had no indication in his briefing about bad weather in Sicily. But then that, unfortunately, was only to be expected. One more of the shortcomings of lesser-known and lesser-used air-fields. Ralph Burden could suddenly feel himself in Dixie's place that evening, praying silently for the delay to extend so he could go back home and sleep. How often Ralph himself had prayed that way on Norfolk evenings as the clouds rolled up from the southwest to blot out an evening's mission.

He looked up. Mrs. Duckham was watching him, waiting for his next question. Had Duckham screwed this Stella Pritchard that Friday evening? And was it important? Burden wondered. It would surely have made him more tired. And what about postcoital guilt; anxiety; depression; self-disgust. Perhaps Dixie Duckham didn't suffer those reactions. Burden turned back to his questions.

"Did the crew all wait together during the delay?"

"For the first quarter of an hour or so. We didn't know what was happening really. About the delay I mean. Then it was confirmed—and Mike went off to work in his office."

"And you all stayed on in the crew room?"

"Yes. With George telling his jokes."

"George?"

"George Raven. The flight engineer."

"Did you know him well?"

"I don't think anyone did. I mean everyone knew him enough to say hello. But no one really was a close friend or anything like that. Not that I know of anyhow."

Burden turned up his relevant notes. "He lived in Brighton, didn't he?"

"I don't know." Stella did know. She'd seen him there once in a club, holding hands with a younger man. But that was no business of the inquisitor.

"He had some strange hobbies."

"I wouldn't know."

Burden read from his notes. "Hang-gliding, sky-diving, scuba-diving."

"And motorcycles." Stella remembered George arriving or departing in strange bulky waterproof outfits.

The George Raven file had been passed back to Burden by Mac, and Mac had left one queried comment scribbled in the margin: "Compensatory personality—doubtful reaction under extreme pressure?" This Raven was the one crew member Burden could not successfully picture. He turned back to Stella. "Would you say he was an unpopular man?"

"I don't know. He probably thought he was quite popular. I suppose other people quite liked him—in small doses."

"You don't know what Duckham thought about him?"

Julia saw Stella smile suddenly, a brief illumination

of eyes and mouth that faded quickly as though it seemed to hurt her. "He once said that being shut up in the cockpit with him telling stories was like the Chinese water torture."

Burden looked at the photograph in Raven's file—a tight-skinned, fit-looking face with thinning hair. Like any old British face staring from a newspaper after winning the George Cross or having murdered little girls.

Burden pulled out his time chart with its neat columns and predictable information. "Can you remember when you first made contact with the passengers?"

"We were sent over to the departure lounge after about an hour and a half. Just to calm things down a bit."

"Were there any troublemakers?"

"Not really. Just people getting fed up and drinking too much."

"So you didn't see the flight crew again until you were on the plane?"

"No."

"Did you get to see them on the plane?"

"Captain Duckham came into the cabin soon after takeoff to talk to one of the passengers."

"Because of some trouble?"

"Oh, no. Just some bigwig on his honeymoon or something. They're always worse on charter flights. As though they've got to let everyone know that they're really superior beings."

"I take it the plane was divided up so far as your duties were concerned?"

"Yes. I was in charge of the forward galley. They were mostly Americans in the front section. They were really tired." Stella paused. "I remember there was a boy with a guitar. He was from New York. I got him to play some songs to cheer everyone up."

"Tino G.," said Burden.

"Who?"

"That's his name. He's still alive."

Julia saw Stella's brief smile once more.

"But he was right up front."

Burden nodded. "Yes. He was very lucky."

"Is he going to be all right?"

"They think so."

Stella smiled again. It really was a lovely smile if you could imagine it without the scars, and framed in a proper head of hair.

"If you were in the forward galley you must have had some contact with the crew?"

"There were four of us in the front."

"Did you go into the cockpit at all?"

"Only at the end—to clear their coffee cups."

"Can you remember when that was?"

"We were preparing to land."

"At Taormina?"

"Yes."

"Was there ever any suggestion you weren't going to land at Taormina?"

"Not that I know of."

"Can you remember any conversation in the cockpit?"

"Not when I was in there. They were reading the descent checklists."

"Did you have the feeling that anything was wrong at all?"

Stella remembered Peter Nyren's moody-looking face. But that was surely not relevant. "Everything seemed normal."

"So you took the cups and left?"

"Yes."

"And then?"

"I cleaned up the galley and stowed everything. Then I went into the cabin to help check safety belts."

"Were there any problems?"

"In the cabin?"

"Anywhere."

"There was a loose cupboard in the galley. It had to be tied up with a piece of string."

"You tied it up?"

"One of the other girls had to sit underneath it. I didn't want everything falling out over her head."

"There were two hostess seats in the front galley?"

"Yes. And two by the front entrance but they weren't being used on Friday night."

"Why?"

"Company policy. If there are spare seats in the cabin the folding seats are not to be used."

"Any particular reason?"

"No one likes them. They're dangerous."

"So you were sitting in the cabin?"

"After everything was checked, yes."

"Whereabouts?"

"Halfway down the front section. A rear-facing seat. Where the partition goes when they make up a first class."

Burden referred to the 119 plans. "Row 6."

"We keep that seat free if there's room because it means there's a hostess next to the emergency exit."

"Company policy again?"

"Sort of. The front window exits are very stiff to operate. They get jammed very easily."

"And the fourth hostess was with you?"

"Yes. On the other side. We were both on the aisle."

"And both in rear-facing seats?"

"Always. Yes."

"Because they're safer?"

"Yes."

Burden looked again at the Hercules 119 plans. The maximum commercial seating plan called for rear-facing seats to be grouped around the emergency exits where facing seats on either side of the exit increased access room from the central aisle. But like all the seating it was on quick-change mountings. Tango November had been flying military charters in Germany on Thursday and Friday, and the military contracts specified rear-facing configuration with a minimum leg room between the seats four inches longer than the maximum pitch allowed in commercial aviation. The seating had been changed at Gatwick before the doomed flight. Remembering the mess of twisted seats in the wrecked cabin, Burden wondered how much of the death and injury had been caused by the inadequacy of those quick-change mountings.

He looked back to his time chart. "Do you know at what stage of letdown you actually sat in your seat and strapped in?"

"No. I have no idea."

"What was the sequence of events from then on as you remember them?"

"Everything seemed to happen together. I think the first thing was the sound of the engines changing and the plane pulling up into a climb."

"Did you have any impression of the plane banking at all?"

Stella paused. She was trying to think herself back into that cabin. "I can't remember. I don't think so."

"You didn't see anything from the window?"

"No—it was dark cloud all the way down."

"You must have been conscious of the movements of the plane after you started climbing again."

"Not really. It was almost straightaway that I saw Trixie here in the gangway."

The little girl looked up for the first time.

Burden smiled at her. "Out of your seat were you, Trixie?"

She did not reply. Burden saw her take Stella's hand. Then Stella spoke again.

"She undid her belt. She was having a game, weren't you, Trixie?"

The little girl nodded.

"I undid my belt and got up to take her back to her seat. So she started playing the game with me. I chased her most of the way up the aisle."

"Toward the back or the front?"

"The back. I caught her once but she slipped away." Stella's voice altered. "I think I got a bit cross with you then, didn't I, Trixie?"

The girl nodded again.

"It was just about then that the lights went out."

"The cabin lights?"

"Yes."

"All of them?"

"Except for the emergency light."

"How long?"

"I don't know. It must have been quite a time because I know I was getting scared then. We were bumping all over the place and I'd never seen all the lights go like that."

"But they came back on?"

"Only the emergency ones."

"Where were you placed at that moment?"

"About halfway down."

"And Trixie?"

"She got frightened by the dark and stopped running and I managed to grab her. I was taking her back to her seat when we seemed to get into a bad rough patch. Everyone was scared by then."

"What did you do?"

"I was by the toilets in the middle of the plane. I pulled Trixie down and we both sat on the floor. I jammed us in with my legs and my back against the walls. That's where we stayed. I don't really remember any more."

There was a long silence, then the little girl spoke for the first time. "There was the sun."

Stella remembered. "Oh, yes." She paused. "A red sun. Yes." Julia saw the outline of that smile again. "It seemed to fill the whole plane. I suppose we came out of the clouds and the sun was coming up and with all the lights off it filled the whole plane with a red glow." She was remembering more. "Yes. People were clapping. That's right. Everyone was happy. Everyone thought we were all right. They applauded the sunrise. I began to get up and that's when the plane went diving down again. Down and then up. And down more gently in a long slow circle."

"Mama was coming," said Trixie.

"Yes." Stella seemed to nod.

"Her mother?" asked Burden.

"She got out of her seat to come and fetch Trixie."

The "hijack" lady who had lost her arm: Maria-Grazia Ragonese, Fifty-fifth Street, New York City.

"People started screaming." Stella shut her eyes. "I suppose they could see the mountain out of the windows."

There was a long silence.

"You don't remember any more?"

"No."

Burden stood up with his papers and his briefcase. "The fuselage broke just where you were sitting. You were both very lucky."

Stella turned her face to him. She was crying. "It's not fair," she whispered. "All those others. They could see what was happening. They were trying to hold hands, some of them. It's not fair, is it, to die like that?"

7

On the lunchtime news television cameras had shown a predictable jam of reporters and photographers by the locked gates outside the Consoli orange groves. A few intrepids had climbed the stone walls and dodged the dogs to approach the house. But they had found it barred and shuttered, more than probably empty.

Citto instead spent a more fruitful hour and a half in the newspaper archives. Marriages, births, social gossip, and telephone directories: he was tracing Flavio's relatives through the mother's side of the family. A solid, wealthy shopkeeping dynasty that had split off the island into Calabria and north to Naples earlier in the century.

Citto chose a secretary from upstairs, one of the innocents with a soft innocuous voice. The signora had heard his stutter once on the telephone and it was not, as Citto knew, a voice easy to disguise. He coached the girl in a little speech: "It is essential I speak with Signora Consoli. I have news of her son, and he has a message for her."

Citto had a list of thirty-five relatives to call and by the fifteenth repetition the secretary was beginning to get the giggles. They got lucky on number seventeen. Signora Consoli was called to the phone, her voice palpitating with anxiety. Citto, listening in on an extension, recognized the self-effacement and innate apology in her tone. He gave the girl a thumbs-up, and the secretary, overcoming the giggles, read out the second part of her speech: "My brother will call on you at five o'clock, signora. Will you be there?"

"Oh, yes. Yes, of course."

"It is important not to say anything about this. Your son is in great danger—"

"Oh, my God!"

And down went the phone on Signora Consoli's sob of anxious despair.

"That's awful," giggled the young secretary. "That's an awful thing to do."

Citto dismissed the girl and wandered out on to the *Circumvallazione* to find his car. Not for the first time in the five days he had failed to spot two radio cars keeping watch on his movements.

Half an hour later Citto met Renzo off his village bus in Acireale. The little town, usually so crowded, was lost in siesta and the two young men sat at a table in the piazza, Citto lunching belatedly on Costarelli's renowned and extraordinary ice cream while Renzo drank a nervous succession of coffees and brandies and told Citto what Tomacchio had asked him to do.

"How much money did he give you?"

"Two hundred thousand."

"That won't get you far if you have to start bribing people."

"It is not my intention to bribe anyone," said the young Communist. "If people don't tell me what I want to know there are other ways of making them talk."

"You can't take gangsters on at their own game. That's the way to get killed."

"I'm not carrying a gun."

"Going to fight them with your bare fists? And you expect them to play by the rules?"

Renzo laughed. "Is that how you broke your glasses?"

Citto fingered the cuts on his face. "That, my friend, was your capo's shotgun."

Renzo nodded, still grinning. "I told you he wasn't much of a shot."

"Then you knew it was him, up on the mountain last night?"

"Maybe."

"And yet you're prepared to take his money to go looking for his daughter."

"I have my own reasons for looking."

Citto stood up. "Time to start earning it then."

"I thought you told her five o'clock?"

"And give her time to set up watchdogs?"

Citto paid the bill and the two men walked up the hill into a narrow street of eighteenth-century palaces. It was a town of palaces; a town of impoverished aristocrats still trying to live on tithes, still puzzled by the collapse of their once so comfortable feudal economy.

The signora's cousin lived in one of the larger palaces near the top of the hill, an echoing covered courtyard behind doors large enough to admit two tanks in line abreast. Living quarters were on the second floor and an apprehensive maid was waiting for them on the wide stone stairway. Citto had announced himself in the door speaker as *"polizia."*

"There's no one in," said the maid.

"Signora Consoli is in," Citto replied. "Tell her a girl called up about an hour and a half ago. We have a message about her son."

"You're not the police then?"

"No, my love."

They were shown into a drawing room of great elegance and formality—frayed carpets, tapestries, peeling frescoes, and spindly-looking furniture, a museum that surely no one used for living. Neither Citto nor Renzo trusted themselves to the chairs and they waited standing in the middle of the room gazing at the naked cherubs on the ceiling.

Signora Consoli arrived, peering at them as though

she had emerged from a very dark room. Praying in a chapel, Renzo thought. He smelled priests in this house.

"Your sister said five o'clock." Signora Consoli looked at them both in turn not knowing whom to address.

"The sooner we start," replied Renzo, "the sooner we find your son."

Alarm or fear came creeping into the lady's face, taking up their accustomed place in the creases around her eyes. "What has happened to him?"

"He's been kidnapped."

The signora sat down, one hand to her mouth. "I don't understand. I thought he had done the kidnapping."

Renzo nodded. "Yes—he took the girl. Now someone else has kidnapped him."

The giggling secretary would have disapproved of this second lie. But it was working.

"Does my husband know?"

It was Citto's stuttering turn to draw the lady on. "You probably realize that your husband has too many other worries to spend very much time on your son."

"I don't understand who you are." The lady remembered that soft stutter on the telephone some days ago.

"The girl has been kidnapped along with your son. We're only interested in her. We have to know where to start looking for them."

"But what happens to my son?"

"If we find them we set them both free. I've told you, we're not interested in him."

"But he—abducted the girl."

"It's the girl's safety we're concerned with. Not her virginity."

The signora shook her head. "I don't understand what you want from me."

"We think you might know where Flavio would have gone."

"How could I know? They don't tell me anything."

"Were there any telephone calls this morning?" Citto asked.

"I don't know. I don't know anything." The signora was distraught. "We left very early. My husband sent me here. He was going to the airport."

"Was your son driving his car last night?"

The signora nodded.

"The Dino?"

She nodded again.

"It's a very obvious car. He would have tried to change it."

"How do you mean?"

"An orange and green sports car. The police would have picked him up right away. He'd have been looking for another car."

The signora seemed to see light, or glimmers of it. "I know where he would have gone for a car. My cousin in Reggio Calabria, his wife has a cousin in Naples who sells sports cars. It was he who sold the Dino to us— you know, at cost. If Flavio wanted another car that's where he'd have gone."

"And his name?"

"I don't know his family name. His business is called Highway. There was a sticker in the car." She pronounced it *higvay*, and Citto asked her to write it down.

The signora was thinking onward, remembering the ramifications of that Reggio half of the family. Wasn't there an even more distant cousin teaching somewhere in Switzerland? She thought suddenly, and aloud: "That's where I would have sent him."

Citto and Renzo left the palace a few minutes later with a list of half-remembered names but no addresses. "It's a good start," said Citto. "And if you're lucky it'll be enough."

The signora watched them leave from an upstairs

window. I've done wrong, she thought. If they're
friends of the girl they are not Flavio's friends. But if
my boy is in trouble what else can I do? At least they
will find out where he is. That man with the stammer
was right about one thing. Flavio's father would do no
more to help his son. She had heard him last night after
the Dino had gone telephoning Rome. "I've got him
away," he had said. "If we can find a country without
extradition he can take the rap for the whole thing.
With a big enough noise no one will think to look any
further."

The signora turned away from the window back to
her prayers in a shuttered room.

The town was coming to life again: conversation in
the streets, lights in the twilight, the inevitable smells of
coffee and cigars, lines of lethargic traffic in the piazza
below. Citto and Renzo cut across the slope of the hill,
zigzagging down through narrow alleys to where the car
was parked. Renzo was silent as they walked.

"You don't have to follow this through, you
know—." Citto stuttered like a broken record.

"It's you who sound scared," said Renzo.

Sharlie, Citto was thinking of. The two pieces of
bloodstained crash helmet.

Citto drove fast back toward the city. An ATI flight
left for Naples at half past six and they made Fontanarossa with half an hour to spare. There were seats
available and the first two tens of Tomacchio's money
disappeared for Renzo's ticket.

Citto bought newspapers at the bar: the evening
edition from town, and the afternoon's from Rome.
"Our National Shame," read one of the headlines, and
the picture underneath was a by now familiar silhouette, the half-burned, broken-backed shell of Tango
November.

"I'm going to shit in my pants," Renzo said as Citto

took him to the gate. "This is the first time I've ever been up in one of these things."

Ingegnere Preuss had been under observation at his home on the Calle del Paradiso since Citto's visit to Venice on Tuesday night. Preuss would have laughed at the melodrama of such an idea had someone openly suggested it to him. But within himself he was afraid. He was a loose end; a controversial and exorcised chapter in draft copies of a report; initials in the footnotes; a name that could, as the Sicilian journalist had demonstrated, be dug out of files. If I were they, thought Preuss—whoever "they" may be—I wouldn't leave me or my copies of that expurgated chapter lying around. Taormina–Peloritana had been a very large project. He had seen the budgets and could guess at the kickbacks. Bribes and payoffs all the way up the line to the highest possible levels. When reputations on that scale were endangered one not very distinguished bachelor academic was surely expendable.

So his thoughts had run since Citto's visit, sapping his zeal for public honesty and voluntary heroics. But when he heard the radio news that Thursday his courage returned. The smell of scandal was now out in the open. As a potential witness he could surely consider himself immune. Interference with him would be tantamount to an admission of guilt.

He walked almost jauntily to the travel agents over the Rialto and bought himself a railway ticket south. When Citto phoned him in the early evening Preuss was able to say with honest bravado, "It's all right, dear boy, I'm on my way."

Citto was tired, hungry, grubby and unshaven. He hadn't been home now in four days. His shirt was black and his suit stiff with sweat and dirt from last night's adventures in the hillside village. He drove through the evening rush hour wondering, as was his gloomy habit, what everyone did in this city to be able to run such sleek and expensive cars. On any level of consciousness his mind was too distracted to notice the two radio cars, blue and red, interchanging with each other as they kept tabs on him.

Laura had telephoned him at the newspaper. Sharlie's funeral was on Saturday and the family had asked him to be there. Citto wondered whether the mother had seen the papers these last two days, and if so how much she might have read between the lines. The coroner's verdict had been postponed, though Citto had a feeling they would never pronounce finally on the accident. That silted-up oil pump was only half a story. The police were already suggesting that it had been caused by an accumulation of dirt over a period of months; at worst a prank by young kids who knew no better.

So was it fair to plant a doubt in the mother's mind? Would she want to live the rest of her life wondering if someone had killed her son? Citto had seen those sad relatives in the streets of Taormina. They would certainly live with doubts, and the anger and grief of suspecting that Tango November need never have crashed.

Citto raised both hands off the wheel in supplication to the windshield, or to God up there somewhere in the sky.

God does not exist, Citto's mother had told the priest when her husband's body had been found two days dead on a hillside, their precious flock of sheep irrevocably lost. Citto had been nine years old, his father thirty-five. Heart attack, the doctor had said. Poverty, worry, and the fear of failure, Citto had later decided.

Citto found himself near enough home to park and walk. There was never room for the car in his own narrow street. As he turned the corner and out of sight the two radio cars settled down like chickens to roost five and ten yards away from the Giulia.

The concierge called from her basement kitchen as Citto unlocked the street door. He waited as she waddled up from her quarters in a haze of frying oil holding a bunch of bills and periodicals.

"Your cleaning lady came twice and couldn't get in," she complained. "She's coming again tomorrow so I hope you're going to be home."

Citto's cleaning lady came twice a week in the early morning, usually well before he ever left for work. But who knows when he would start tomorrow. He slipped the spare key off his ring and gave it to the concierge.

"We were wondering where you'd got to," she said eyeing his disheveled and dirty clothes, the cuts on his face, his cracked lens.

"Working hard," he told her and nodded good night knowing he had left her curiosity unsatisfied. She'll read about it in tomorrow's paper, he thought, and in an article under my name. She'll be carrying it under her arm all day showing it to everyone. One of my tenants, she'd be telling them all.

Citto climbed the stairs past the smells of a half-dozen suppers without provoking any feelings of hunger. He wasn't looking forward to his empty flat and the thoughts that would pursue him there. It was difficult to believe that Sharlie was already thirty hours dead.

Citto stopped suddenly a half flight below his landing. There was one simple and routine precaution he had always adopted: a thin rectangle of cardboard pinned out of sight on the top of the door. Set with its short face outward it would lever on the door post and turn itself when the door was opened. If it was not reset one corner of the cardboard remained protruding, visible to the practiced eye. The cardboard telltale was pointing warning from his door tonight. Maybe he had forgotten to reset it. Or had they been there to search through his papers? Was someone waiting for him now, watching him through the peephole?

He stood for a long time gazing at his front door, then turned and walked back slowly downstairs. He waited a moment before unlocking the street door. The concierge had returned to her cooking. There wasn't a sound on the stairs above him. Coward, he told himself as he returned toward his car. Even the battered old Giulia looked suddenly dangerous to him. It was illegally parked, but he left it, veering away across the road and back toward the city center. That bloody shotgun last night, he thought; that's what unnerved me. Or the two pieces of Sharlie's blood-soaked crash helmet.

He took a taxi back to the office and told the news editor that his car had broken down. He didn't want to sound quite the fool he felt himself to be. He was given the keys to the only staff car available and he drove out of the city, north along the coast with an idea of visiting Mac and Larry Raille in Taormina.

"The three musketeers," they had called themselves last night walking down the pass from that deserted village. The two Anglo-Saxons had spent half of that long trek talking and speculating about Tango November, and the other half shouting obscene songs or hurling curses at the taillights of the two cars that swept past their waving thumbs and arms. Not that I blame the cars, thought Citto. I wouldn't stop on that lonely road for three wild-looking men in the middle of the night. Citto had walked in silence most of the time, his mind half-conscious, on the edge of exhaustion. Once or twice he had found himself asleep as he walked; at other times faces had come to him: an old shepherd who used to follow and frighten him in the hills when he was a boy; a professor who had befriended him at the university, a man, Citto realized, with the same lopsided smile as Preuss far away in Venice; then Sharlie's face as Citto had first known it, the bright-eyed waterfront delinquent, sharp and laughing and full of life. Sharlie, who had been his pupil, at times even his only friend. Poor Sharlie, poor Sharlie's mother, poor Sharlie's Nonna Lisa; poor whole damn world of dead and dying.

Citto gave up the idea of Taormina. What could he talk about with an Englishman or an American? He turned aside down the narrow walled lane into the fishing village and the harbor piazza crowded with scooters and scooter trucks. The man with the mattresses was back. They were piled behind his blasting pop-song loudspeaker, plastic-covered, as many as there had been however many days ago it was that Sharlie had bought them whiskey and ice cream in the bar. With my money, remembered Citto. The last three tens of Sharlie's lifetime's spending.

There was a light on Nonna Lisa's terrace; the old lady, Laura and her brother sitting there? Citto didn't see them. Even them he couldn't face. He turned the car on the rough track and drove back out of the village stopping only to buy himself a bottle from the harbor bar. A mile or so into the country he pulled the car into a gravel parking area, locked the doors from the inside, climbed on to the back seat, and folded himself up for the night with the bottle by his side.

8

Information had been relayed earlier in the evening to an unlisted number in Naples, and the ATI flight from Catania was consequently met at the Campodichino Airport by two men—one on a small motorcycle and one in a car, both supplied with a

rather vague description of Renzo. The description
seemed to fit at least two of the passengers and the car
and motorcycle split up to cover both possibilities.

Renzo had permitted himself the luxury of a taxi for
the first time in his life. A few minutes with a telephone
directory had given him the address of Highway Con-
cessionaires and he wanted to be sure of reaching their
showroom before they shut up for the night. But as the
taxi crossed the city in a crawl of rush-hour traffic
Renzo became slowly aware of the high-pitched persis-
tent buzz of a *motorino* somewhere behind them. There
seemed no good reason why the motorcycle wasn't
joining its two-wheeled companions overtaking the
snarl of cars and buses. When the high-pitched buzzing
stayed with them through the traffic lanes on the sea-
front Renzo decided the motorcycle was tailing his taxi.
He waited till the traffic flow halted again in the one-
way tunnel under the headland, then paid off the taxi
driver and walked back toward the tunnel entrance,
disappearing into the darkness in search of a second
taxi, and leaving the motorcyclist struggling unsuccessfully to extricate himself.

Renzo stopped his second taxi round the corner from
his destination. He paid the driver but asked him to
wait.

Highway was still open, a luxury showroom for luxury cars; Ferraris, Porsches, and Jaguars displayed
under multicolored lighting, their wheels deep into thick
pile carpet. The manager looked up through a one-way
window in the office wall as Renzo walked into the
shop. A drooler, the manager decided when he saw
Renzo's cut of clothes. They usually came in this time
of the evening on their way home from work, gazing
with impotent passion at the objects of their fantasies.
They'd be tolerated for a few moments if they were
clean; sometimes even allowed to sit in the driver's seat.
But eventually they would need to be shamed to the

door, handled, as it were, by remote control. It was
company policy not to waste time or brochures on such
people.

"Can I help you?"

Renzo looked round. The voice, disembodied, had
come from one of the walls. Renzo rocked one of the
cars on its suspension and banged hard on the roof as
though to test its thickness of steel. A new XJS Jaguar.
He swung open the door and climbed inside.

Trouble, the manager was thinking—a *lazzarone*
with too much drink inside him. But you could never be
absolutely sure. They'd once chased away a ragged man
in jeans, and the guy had walked thirty yards up the
road and spent ten million on a Mercedes.

"Can I ask you your price range, sir?"

The silly damn fool leaves the ignition key in the
cars, Renzo was thinking as he climbed back out. "I
was wondering about a secondhand Dino," he said to
the wall. "Do you have any in stock?"

"There would certainly be nothing under seven million, sir."

Renzo had decided the voice was coming from the
mirror-wall behind him. He turned toward the door
beside it as he spoke. "To be more exact I was thinking
of a secondhand Dino with a fancy paint job. Orange
and green. Something like that."

The manager had three "security" buttons on his
desk: one to lock the office door, one to lock the
showroom doors, and one alert plugged into the nearest
police station. He locked the doors but left the police
button alone. He had picked up an orange and green
Dino in the middle of last night—a direct swap for a
high-mileage Porsche. A family favor carried out in
secrecy. He'd been told to keep the Dino hidden away
for a few weeks. He had no idea why, but he didn't
want trouble with the law.

The young man in the showroom had tried the office

door and found it locked. He was walking back toward the cars.

"If you would like to call in the morning our used car manager will be able to help you."

Renzo climbed back into the Jaguar and started the engine.

"Nice and quiet, isn't it?" he said to the mirror.

"You will have to leave, sir. We're closing. If you come back in the morning—"

"Secondhand Ferrari Dino, green and orange, and Catania license plates. I'm quite sure you have one."

The manager was still at his desk, one hand on the telephone, wondering who on earth he could call up for help. The Jaguar was moving, creeping forward toward a half-million lire's worth of special plate glass. The manager shut his eyes. But there was no crash of glass or crunch of steel. He heard the young man's voice again.

"What did you do? Lend him another car?"

Do a little favor for the family and see where it lands you, thought the manager. The Jaguar was creeping back on to its carpet.

"You'd better start talking, it's getting late."

There was a silence. What the hell, the manager was thinking. We didn't break any laws. Why shouldn't I tell this guy about it? Except that the family might find out.

There was a sudden roar of engine from the showroom. The Jaguar, front wheels off the carpet, back wheels on and spinning, gyrated slowly around through 180 degrees until it was pointing at the mirror wall and door.

"Whoever you are you'd better believe I'm going to start smashing this place up if you don't talk."

"I don't know what you want."

"I want to know what kind of car you gave him. The registration, the license plate number, the whole thing."

The Jaguar moved again, toward the mirror and the office door. This time there was no gentle creeping. The car accelerated hard through a row of rubber plants and into the mirror. The whole wall cascaded in over the manager's desk, the desk itself shunted by the car and pinned him, still in his chair, into the opposite corner of the room.

For the first time they looked at each other face to face across a glass-strewn desk and crumpled hood. Renzo stayed where he was, in the driver's seat.

"Did he come here?"

The manager was staring in catatonic silence. Renzo revved the engine and eased off the brake to pin him even tighter to the wall. The chair began to splinter.

"Did he come here?"

The manager shook his head. He was pale and his voice tremulous. "Out of town."

"Who made the arrangement?"

"His father telephoned."

"Was there a girl with him?"

The manager nodded.

"Did she say anything?"

"She was asleep. I had to help carry her."

"Where?"

"To the other car."

"She was sleeping?"

The manager nodded. The girl, he was thinking. That's where this boy fits in. An abduction.

"What car did you bring for him?"

"A Porsche Carrera."

"Color?"

"White."

"Registration?"

"I don't know, not without looking it up."

"So look it up." Renzo backed the car off and the manager fell forward out of his chair. He picked himself up and walked to a filing cabinet. It was the first time he had moved since the young man came in. He felt his trousers and shirt wet with perspiration, his knees sore where the desk had hit him.

"What else did the old man say when he rang up?"

"Just to fill her up with gas. Yes—and have all the documents for going abroad. Insurance and everything."

"For what country?"

"Switzerland."

The manager found the registration number in his files and read it out.

"Where were they going in Switzerland?"

"I don't know." The manager was alarmed, sheltering by his filing cabinet. "I really don't know."

"You have relatives in Switzerland."

The man paused before answering. "There is someone. He teaches. Some little village in the Ticino." The manager named the village.

"And his address?"

"I don't know. Honest to God, I don't know."

Renzo climbed out of the Jaguar. "If you were more polite with people you wouldn't get your walls knocked down."

Walls, thought the manager. He was looking at twenty million lire of bent Jaguar.

Around the corner the taxi was still waiting for Renzo, and forty minutes later he was back at the airport checking in for the late evening flight to Milan. Linate by 11:20 P.M. was, it seemed, as near and as fast as he could get to the Swiss border.

9

Preuss left home at ten o'clock that evening carrying a small valise and dressed immaculately in a lightweight charcoal suit. He was, after all, making his first appearance on a public stage. He was a witness. Eventually there would be reporters and photographers; even television cameras. He patted good-bye to his front door, little finger and first finger on the wood, the horns of superstition, as though he were off to the mountains for a weekend's climbing.

He walked to the station through empty narrow alleyways, up and over the even narrower and darker canals. His jauntiness of the afternoon had passed away and the natural caution of a secretive life crept back into Preuss's blood with the damp of the night. He even convinced himself for a while that he was being followed: footsteps on the paving behind him or shadows on the walls, and always someone to observe his progress at each intersection of alley or canal. He looked at them carefully as he passed, but they appeared quite normal. No baroque little dwarfs with knives; no men in shabby trenchcoats or lodens. In fact some of the faces were quite familiar. By the time he emerged from the maze onto the canal front by the station he was laughing at himself once more, despising his cowardice.

The train was late and the platform already crowded with a party of student tourists who had failed to find seats in the carriages that started from Venice. There would be a scrimmage for the pickings on the Trieste half of the train and Preuss resigned himself to an uncomfortable night. Couchettes and berths had all been booked.

He was instead the beneficiary of a double coincidence that should have prolonged his life. One of the art historians from the university was just vacating a sleeping car when the second half of the train finally arrived. Preuss met him on the platform exchanging pleasantries. The art historian had been to Moscow for a month of research.

"I'm going south," said Preuss. "I change at Rome in the morning if we get there in time. The train is late."

"Late," hooted the art historian. "My sleeping car is a whole day and a half late. We were eighteen hours standing still in Cop. You have a seat, Ingegnere?"

No, he had no seat.

"I tell you what, then. I've made friends with the Russian car attendant. You can't help making friends if you have to travel together for four whole days. He will let you sleep in my berth. You'll have it to yourself. The carriage goes on to Rome."

Introductions were made and favors happily offered. Preuss was installed in a berth of inegalitarian opulence where he might happily have stayed, sleeping to Rome and the comparative safety of daylight.

But after an hour or so of travel and quiet reading he set out to explore the length of corridor outside. The Russian conductor had already retired to his bunk and the carriage seemed empty—a long, carpeted hallway where the usual noises of a train were inaudible. There was a strange mixture of smells, something like coal fires and sauerkraut. He wondered who could be traveling behind all these locked doors—spies, diplomats, escapees. Tractor salesmen more like.

He paid a visit to the toilet at the end of the coach. Even here the sounds of the outside world were muffled, insulated presumably against the Russian winter. How strange, thought Preuss, to wash one's hands with Russian soap and dry them on Russian towels on a simple journey down to Rome.

Then he heard the sounds of the train suddenly more clear as though a window or a door had been opened somewhere letting in the noise. He stepped back into the corridor.

Preuss hardly saw the two men. He felt himself seized, thumped hard somewhere in his midriff and propelled through the doors into the adjoining carriage. They held him in the recess by the exit, his arms twisted behind him as they searched his pockets. Preuss was doubled up with pain staring at the open door in front of him where the noise and the wind were rushing in a black void.

They seemed to hold him there for an eternity and he was thinking all the time, why am I not fighting them? Because, he rationalized to himself, I do not believe that these men are foolish or evil enough to harm me. Citto would have recognized the slight downturn of mouth, the ghost of self-mockery. And ghosts were all that remained to Preuss.

As he tried to straighten up one of the men propelled him with a foot in the small of his back. Preuss saw lights scattered over a flat landscape as he tipped head-first through the open door and into the gale. He had two distinct thoughts as he fell: an angry regret that he had not sent a copy of his chapter to that reporter in Sicily; and an impression that somehow his body would catapult across the Polesine into the estuary of the Po to die embraced by the sea that was trying so hard to destroy his beloved city.

He bounced instead at eighty miles an hour on hard metal tracks, a body bursting open like a sack of stained *vinaccia* as it ricocheted into the reeds of a drainage ditch.

10

The death of Preuss, strategically mistimed, tactically ill-planned and clumsy, was by any criterion an unlikely "accident." In Italy it was no longer publicly acceptable that people fall unaided from buildings or from trains.

Avvocato Consoli was a realist. Until now a coverup had been possible. Someone instead had overreacted, a colleague in the consortium or some exposed official or politician. No hope this time of sitting tight and letting

the scandal fade away like countless others into the
Italian tapestry. Tango November was a foreign plane
with foreign deaths—Anglo-Saxon investigators, Anglo-
Saxon reporters, Anglo-Saxon insurance assessors and
opinion. The other men involved would protect themselves with the influence or immunity of office. They
would certainly not endanger themselves to shield a
mere upstart lawyer from Catania. But they might, at
such an anxious moment, be prepared to speed the exile
of a voluntary scapegoat.

Flavio and Giuseppina were asleep on separate floors
of the one-time farmhouse that Flavio's distant cousin
had rented for them outside the small Swiss village
where he worked. Flavio was sleeping on cushions in
the living room, disappointed by the girl but with, he
imagined, time on his side. Giuseppina had successfully
prolonged the effects of the barbiturate until the evening and when Flavio had arrived to claim the ultimate
fruits of abduction she had peered at his naked body
through very sleepy eyes. "My God," she'd mumbled,
"what a tiny cock." Thus challenged, Flavio had found
his mind incapable of mastering his matter. Under
cover of her feigned sleep he had retired, limp and
puzzled, to the distant cousin's gift of whiskey and the
pine log fire in the living room.

The farmhouse, Giuseppina had noticed, was lost in
trees above a wide valley. In the daylight she had seen a
village a mile away across the fields below them, high
mountains all around, terraces of vineyard on the hillside. She imagined she was somewhere in northern
Italy. Not that it greatly mattered. Her bedroom door
was locked and her clothes had been taken away. There
was nothing she could do about escaping and even if
she shouted there was no one to hear her. The distant
cousin she had not seen.

Giuseppina lay awake most of that night trying to

analyze her feelings toward Flavio and his fleshy face: boring, boorish, stupid. He was certainly rich. But then she wasn't exactly poor and, with or without lovers, she did not fancy passing the rest of her life's nights pinned under his heavy body. She hadn't known many men: an uncle had once tried to deflower her on a drunken picnic; village boys had kissed and pawed her; a schoolmaster had nuzzled her. Only Renzo's hard and grimy hands had held her with any authority—but what was Renzo? A mechanic. An honest mechanic, who'd never taken a bribe or argued himself into a bonus in all his working days. Why else would her father employ him? She had got to know him at school, holding hands at the back of the bus on the way home from Acireale each afternoon. He had given up school a year before anyone else. No one knew why, though people said he'd quarreled with one of the teachers. His politics were certainly very unfashionable.

Giuseppina heard the fast mechanical rattle of a train down in the valley. All day and all night they'd been passing, and each time they passed she would hear the bell at a crossing or a station ringing away like a priest at mass. This time the bell made her feel sleepy and as light began to silhouette the mountains she fell asleep with all her thinking still unresolved.

At about the same time Renzo of the hard and grimy hands arrived in the village a mile away across the fields, climbing off the early morning train from Bellinzona. He left his suitcase in the station and set out on foot as the world awoke, pacing each street and courtyard of the village in search of a white Porsche Carrera with a Naples license plate.

A fourth protagonist was closing in on the village, also from the south and at a speed at times in excess of 900 miles an hour. The avvocato Consoli was traveling in the rear seat of an MRCA prototype, an "observer" on a routine test flight. Less than an hour after takeoff at Ciampino the plane landed at an airfield some thirty miles from the Swiss border. A chauffeur-driven Mercedes complete with bodyguard was waiting for the plane, and the car with its three occupants crossed the Swiss border unchallenged at Ponte Tresa shortly after six o'clock.

Except for the wood smoke from chimneys the little Swiss village came to life much as Renzo's own village did back home in Sicily: men with carts or tractors riding to the fields across the valley, or to their pastures higher up the hillsides; the cars of dark-suited men scurrying off down the valley to their work in the towns; the smell of baking bread as the long shadow of mountains gave way to the sun.

Renzo had found no white Porsche, and when the gas station opened below the village he walked down the road to ask the attendant whether he had seen such a car around yesterday.

The elderly man laughed at him. "You think I got time to look at cars? I have to run this place on my own. Gas, servicing, repairs. You tell me if I got time to remember individual cars."

The village doctor, sweeping leaves in his patch of garden, was more helpful. Renzo made out he was looking for a friend; a friend who'd been bitten by a dog and who might have requested treatment.

"Yes," replied the doctor. "He's on vaccine. A tourist. He's out on one of the farms across the valley."

There were half a dozen farms dotted about the slopes on the far side of the valley. They were connected to the village by a track over the railway and the fields, but Renzo took a longer way round, climbing the main road for a mile above the village, crossing railway and river where the valley narrowed and where he was well out of sight from village and farms. He walked back through the larch woods high on the hillside and eventually spotted the Porsche tucked away behind some outbuildings on one of the smaller farms.

Renzo would have moved faster had he known how little time was left to him, for as he slipped out of the woods and into the deserted farmyard the avvocato's chauffeur-driven Mercedes was entering the village a mile away.

The farm kitchen was tidy and empty, undisturbed by the new tenants except for two half-empty boxes of crackers and a carton of milk on the table. Renzo found the Consoli boy in the shuttered living room, asleep on the floor in a roll of cushions and blankets, the fire long dead, the room reeking of stale cigar smoke and surgical alcohol. An elaborate collection of bottles and bandages littered the only table. Renzo smiled. Capo Tomacchio had been right. The old German shepherd had had his retributive pound of flesh.

There were two suitcases on the floor and what looked like Giuseppina's clothes draped over a chair. But no sign of the girl. Renzo climbed a creaking wooden staircase and found an upstairs bedroom locked, with the key in the door. He opened it. The girl was sleeping curled up in the quilt, her long hair spread all over the bed.

Not that Renzo had time to linger or to daydream. As he bent down to claim Giuseppina with a kiss he glanced out through the low window and saw a large car on the track crossing the floor of the valley toward them. The limousine looked too clean and hurried for any farmer and Renzo obeyed his intuition. He left the girl asleep, ran downstairs and out of the house, and scrambled in and out of the yard buildings until he had found a suitable weapon. The Mercedes was crossing the river forty yards below him as he hurried back into the farmhouse shouting and prodding Flavio awake with the business end of a pitchfork. The young Consoli, weak from his vaccine and doped with whiskey and sleep, was in no mood for argument. He preceded the pitchfork upstairs and into Giuseppina's bedroom. The girl woke up to find both Flavio and Renzo barricaded into the room with her.

"Come on you lovebirds," they heard the avvocato shout from downstairs. "It's time to move again."

Avvocato Consoli was not expecting trouble at this stage of his journey. The bodyguard, friend of a friend, had been brought along merely to subdue the girl if that proved necessary. It took five minutes of confused shouting through the door to establish that Flavio was being held prisoner by a determined young man armed with a pitchfork. The avvocato would have felt in that moment like disowning and relinquishing his contemptible son if Flavio did not have a specific role still to play. Time was short. There were funds to draw from a bank in Zurich. A plane to catch. A further connection to make in Lisbon. Flavio was to "disappear," leaving a rather dirty and obvious trail behind him. He did not know it, but he was, besides his other crimes, in the process of absconding with airport funds. Avvocato Consoli was preparing himself for the role of outraged father.

He bargained through the door. He wasn't carrying much money, he explained. He offered 10,000 Swiss francs. Too bad, he was thinking, if the girl gets left behind. He would have to find some other means of silencing Capo Tomacchio.

Renzo was equally unprepared for such a situation. It had been his intention to drive Flavio back to the frontier and hand him over to the Italian police. That was the bargain he had made with Citto. But he wasn't going to get the boy back into Italy with the avvocato waiting outside the door. He accepted the money, not for himself but on behalf of the girl who had suffered the indignity and shame of abduction.

The notes were passed under the bedroom door and Flavio allowed, with the help of the bed quilt, to climb down from the bedroom window. Only Giuseppina had reservations, for when she surrendered the quilt she was left with nothing to cover herself. Flavio disappeared through the window and out of her life with even stronger regrets about his loss and last night's failure.

The quilt gave way when he was still halfway from window to ground. He fell painfully on his dog-bitten leg and had to be carried to his father's car. The Porsche was entrusted to the bodyguard and two minutes later Renzo, watching from the bedroom, saw both cars rejoin the main road and disappear at high speed, northward toward the Gotthard Pass and Zurich.

Renzo stayed on in the bedroom with the naked though now no longer protesting girl. He did not need the pitchfork to complete the scenario of hijacked abduction and by the time they came downstairs hand in hand to look for breakfast Giuseppina had been irrevocably "dishonored."

Later that morning Renzo walked over the fields to call Capo Tomacchio from the village and tell him that his daughter was safe.

"Good boy," Tomacchio shouted up the telephone from Sicily. "But don't waste any more money on airplanes. You can both take the train home."

"Maybe for Christmas," Renzo replied. "We're staying here to get ourselves married."

Renzo put the phone down on his prospective father-in-law's yell of anger. He walked out into the village street to buy food for lunch, then strolled downhill to chat with the old man in the garage. It seemed to Renzo by the time he rejoined Giuseppina at the farmhouse that he had already found himself a new home and a new job.

Tomacchio's apoplectic rage proved to be his last free speech for many years. He was arrested by direct order of the procuratore later that day.

11

Earlier that morning the middle-aged woman who acted as Citto's cleaning lady had left her home by the old port. She walked to the two blocks of apartments and offices where she did most of her work and collected Citto's front-door key from the concierge at seven o'clock.

A few minutes later an explosion destroyed the third-floor landing. The cleaning lady had been shielded from the blast by the half-open door and miraculously escaped injury. The interior of the flat was destroyed by the explosion and the fire that followed.

The concierge downstairs told the police that Citto had been home the evening before. She described his manner and appearance as "strange and secretive."

Half an hour later traffic police attempted to move an old and battered Giulia parked illegally in a side road a quarter of a mile away.

Duplicate keys were used to open the door and start the engine, but as soon as the wheels turned an explosive charge was detonated. The police driver inside the car was killed and five onlookers in the street injured badly enough to be taken to hospital.

Citto had been uncomfortably asleep and hungover on the backseat of an office car in a quiet country lane. He was awakened by banging on the windows, and when he climbed out of the car he found himself surrounded by two jeep loads of police.

Unshaven and dirty, smelling of whiskey and unsteady on his feet, he was treated like some kind of dangerous fanatic. Police later announced that he had been found in "suspicious circumstances" and detained for questioning. After cross-examination he was said to be suffering from persecution-mania, and later that same day was charged with leaving explosive booby traps at his home and on his car.

A day of black comedy was completed by Swiss border officials at Chiasso when they examined four apparently misdirected Interfrigo freight cars. Instead of the expected crates of fruit and vegetables they found mutilated human bodies labeled and wrapped in plastic bags. For some hours the Swiss police believed they had uncovered some grotesque atrocity. Luckily for the Italian authorities the four cars were still in the no-man's-land of the Chiasso marshaling yards and the bodies were successfully reclaimed after embarrassing explanations at the highest levels of government in Berne and Rome.

Military teams worked through the night to lay the bodies in coffins and five Italian Air Force G-222s flew the remnants of Tango November's payload into Taormina–Peloritana exactly a week after their originally scheduled arrival.

12

The funeral procession descended from the airport at midmorning, crossing the valley to climb another hillside toward the chosen cemetery. The army trucks carrying the coffins had been draped in black and peasants in the lemon groves and vineyards stood up from their work to bare their heads as the bodies passed. A band and a church bell played the trucks through a crowded village street where women stood crying on the pavements. Even the boys and girls on their motorized bicycles were silent and watching.

Relatives of the dead were waiting along the new gravel paths at the far end of the cemetery. They stood in small groups by each grave while loudspeakers relayed a short service, the appropriate prayers being read alternately by a Catholic and an Anglican priest. Canon Ash Nyren had been asked by Hercules flight to conduct the Anglican half of the service but had refused, saying simply to the puzzled American who had sought him out, "I am no longer a man of God." He watched a woman, one arm around her husband, trying to comfort him. She was oblivious to them all, kissing the collar of his jacket, touching his cheek as though his frozen face was about to break apart, breathing on his hands. And when she lost him later in the crowd he stood quite still looking, it seemed, at people's knees until he was reclaimed.

I can't help you, thought the old canon. I cannot help any of you. There is nothing to say. There are no answers. You just spit at the sky; shake a fist.

The plots in the cemetery annex had been laid out in alphabetical order and there was no one near him that he knew. He had noticed Julia Duckham somewhere far away. There seemed quite a crowd around her and Ash Nyren felt a momentary resentment that his son should have so little to show for his twenty-nine years. One aged and confused father. The Nyren line was dying in solitude at one end of this hot white-stone cemetery. Three centuries of priests and soldiers and the only event left to record, his own death.

And though after my skin worms destroy this body,
Yet in my flesh shall I see God.

He wanted none of that drunken poetry said on his behalf.

There was chaos for some minutes as the coffins were unloaded from the trucks. Groups of soldiers, sailors, and airmen were carrying them to the named and numbered graves. Inevitably mistakes were made which distraught relatives were trying to sort out as photographers and cameramen moved in to record their distress.

Julia watched it all in a blank haze, her children on either hand, her sister behind, her stepdaughter to one side. Other people had joined them, she knew not from where: some of Mike's old colleagues who had flown out from London with Pam and the children; the bearded English doctor who had come to shake her hand; even that investigator who had asked all those unpleasant questions. It was Mac who told her that this "Raffles" Burden had been with Mike flying Mosquitoes in the war. Why hadn't Burden told her? She didn't want his deviousness here hovering over Mike's graveside. Perhaps he had come to spy on Pam and the children; perhaps he thought they were also relevant to his investigation.

But Burden's motives were quite genuine. He felt he owed a final salute to his old fellow combatant, and he stood stiffly to attention when the final prayers were read.

Man that is born of a woman hath but a short time to live, and is full of misery . . .

The bodies were blessed and lowered in batches of ten as the priests and military teams moved along the gravel paths. But Ash Nyren said his own farewell and slipped away before they reached him. Peter's coffin was lowered by four Italian airmen and with no one in attendance.

Mac too was leaving the ceremony, angry and troubled to see his bodies—his evidence—placed so finally out of reach. It was he who saw the old canon leave, plunging away behind the crowds, his arms and legs swinging as the previous time he'd seen him, left with left and right with right, just like Groucho Marx.

That same afternoon on the far side of the city Sharlie Barzizza was buried, a mother, a grandmother, an aunt, an uncle, and two cousins accompanying him from a midtown church to the cemetery.

Citto's request to be allowed to join them had been turned down by a local prison governor, for Citto was not, within the meaning of the law, a member of Sharlie's family. He spent the afternoon instead under further interrogation trying to answer questions so absurd and farfetched that he was tempted at times almost to laugh. He peered and blinked at his accusers through thick lenses and stammered his replies, but they were neither moved by his vulnerability nor convinced by his protested innocence. It was as well for Citto that he did not yet know of the Ingegnere's death. He could cope with the privations of a fetid crowded cell, drawing on the stoicism accumulated from twenty generations of disease, drought and earthquake. But to feel a direct responsibility for two men's deaths would hurt him, weaken him irreparably for the rest of his life.

Autumn descended upon the Veneto and the Polesine in wild gray squalls. On the Monday after his death, and after elaborate but inconclusive forensic examination, Preuss's body was carried, bucking and tossing, in a black gold-scrolled launch across the lagoon to the cemetery island of San Michele. He was buried in a circle of umbrellas—colleagues and pupils from the university. To them his death still seemed an inexplicable and tragic accident.

A story leaked to a newspaper had tried to suggest that the Ingegnere had been inebriated when he fell from the train—vodka drinking with the Russian car conductor. But the level of alcohol in autopsy was minimal.

Subsequently and more strangely a suicide note had been discovered, a typewritten confession from the Ingegnere that he was being blackmailed for reasons of his homosexuality and had thus decided to take his life. But police in Venice found evidence of a break-in at the Ingegnere's apartment and the "confession" was destroyed without its contents being made public. As with Sharlie, the coroner's verdict had been postponed.

13

Four months passed. Tango November had been picked clean, a half-buried carcass in the winter snow, her wings and engines crated and lifted out by Skycranes, her instruments and systems packed in polyurethane and flown to laboratories far away. The broken-backed fuselage remained, appearing and disappearing as the snow fell and melted and fell again.

Lanterns on adjoining lemon trees threw wild shadows where the two men were working. The incessant sound of water flowing and falling governed the urgency of their movements as they pulled loose earth into channels with long right-angled shovels guiding the flow from the aqueduct. Old Turi and his even older *massaro* had one hour's water left and thirty trees still to irrigate.

Mac would have liked to join in but he knew any

attempt to help would only interfere with a routine perfected by years of practice. He moved away not to disturb them, ducking his six and a half feet through the trees, placing his feet with care in the darkness. It was midwinter and though the orchard was full of lemon scent Mac felt frost not so far above. He climbed steps in the wall and saw the mountain rising over the trees, a white moonlit cone in the black sky. Old Smokey covered with snow. Mac could pick out the ridge where Tango November had lost her left wing, and the dark shadow of dead ground beyond it where the plane had finally fallen.

Landing was aborted when interruption of power supply at the airport caused failure of all ground instruments and runway lighting.

The senior members of the three-nation investigation had reconvened in Taormina to discuss the first draft of the Italian government report—Burden, Mac, and Larry Raille, who had arrived complete with strident wife on what she told them was a second honeymoon, a celebration.

There was nothing much to celebrate within the investigation. The outline draft of the report was too full of reservation and qualification. *One minute into a missed approach the flight crew were led to shut down number two engine after a fire warning. The single remaining generator overloaded and a subsequent battery failure probably affected all essential flight-deck instrumentation. It is impossible to establish the duration of the failure but the combination of incidents seems to have caused the pilots to lose their position.*

Thus the bare outlines. There were countless pages of analysis discussing each of the technical failures in detail. But they only told half a story. It was the general scenario that had escaped them, Mac thought, the human element that could not be read out on instruments, X-rayed or photographed in ultraviolet.

Even the timing was wrong. The journalist had seen the airport clocks stopped at 05:40. But two of the crew's watches on the crashed plane had stopped at 05:37, and the mushroom man had heard the plane over his head high on the mountain at 05:35. Prognosis: ground instrument and lighting failure occurred, as the air traffic controller had insisted, *after* the crash and in no way contributed to the emergency.

But the melodrama of corruption and intrigue had fogged that issue. The world, even Italy herself, preferred to believe in traditional villains. Capo Tomacchio was in prison; Flavio Consoli had fled to South America: they were the culprits, and the scenario was accordingly fitted around them. It seemed that nothing would be learned from the disaster.

The failure of components in number two engine was almost certainly provoked by the suddenness of the lighting and systems failure at the airport, which caused the crew to adopt a last-minute emergency climbout procedure, which in turn ignored stress limits on the power plants that might otherwise have been observed.

Not a word about previous fire warnings in 119's on that notorious number two engine. Not a word about the generators, for surely the time had come to stipulate a fail-safe emergency wind-driven generator for all civil aircraft. Not a word about the nitrogen fuel-inerting system, which blankets the fuel tanks with a foam and would have prevented the outbreak of fire. Not a word about the ADF beacons, so dangerously inaccurate in dirty weather. Not a word about the lack of emergency breathing apparatus in the cabin. Stronger seats and smoke hoods would have saved 150 lives.

The 119 still flew unmodified; landing aids and lighting layout at Taormina–Peloritana had not been improved; minimum cabin safety regulations laid down by the American FAA and British CAA had not been challenged.

Hercules' own company report had paradoxically blamed their own flight crew. Administration, safety standards, aircraft, and aircraft maintenance had all been exonerated.

Ninety percent of the time, thought Mac, even 99 percent, flying the big jets could be less frightening and less taxing than driving a London bus. It was during that other one to ten percent of the time that pilots earned their money: when flying aids failed to give them adequate information; when turbulence pulled them out of the sky; when their machinery started to act up; when they had to come down at night or in cloud to land at primitive airports in the middle of mountains; when they were overtired, frightened or lost.

"Tango November, you are clear to land . . ."

They had heard the tape again that morning in the conference room. Listening to three dead men approaching their moment of truth had sobered up the esoterics of investigation. Not surprising that Duckham's last recorded expression was a despairing blasphemy.

"Fucking Christ Jesus!"

Mac shivered in the darkness. The two lanterns were moving far away through the lemon trees, the water still cascading. Mac climbed down on the far side of the wall and followed the rough path across the dry bed of a river. The village was outlined on the other side, a scattering of lights along the line of the village street, and on this side of the houses the glow of a charcoal brazier on Turi's terrace where supper was cooking. Mac smelled sausages and chestnuts. He could hear the stuttering staccato of the tubby little reporter, and the slight shy laugh of the pretty girl with him.

Julia Duckham was up there somewhere, probably in the house talking with Turi's wife. Julia had been studying Italian ever since September. Mac couldn't quite figure out why. Something to do with her husband being buried here. A sort of obligation she felt.

Mac had visited her a month or so after their return to England. A courtesy call, or so he had kidded himself, though he was the last person to make gestures of that sort. A week later he had driven down again, this time to build the bonfire and let off the fireworks he had promised the kids on his first visit. After that he had become a more or less regular visitor. Not that there had been an iota of intimacy between them, not even soft talk. In fact Mac was convinced he would never bring himself to make a move. His whirlwind seductions had no place in her setup, not with kids and a dead husband. If there was a decision to be made she would have to make it herself. She had only traveled out with him now to visit the grave. Mac picked his way through boulders in the riverbed and scrambled up the far bank. He looked back at the mountain and saw a brief glow of explosion on the crater.

Citto heard the rusted hinges of the iron gate at the bottom of the garden and saw the tall English doctor appear along the path under Turi's fig trees. This Mac had changed since September—less exuberant; care or trouble in his eyes. Everyone had changed, Citto thought: old Turi, tired and talking of retirement; Nonna Lisa, sad and silent, staring at the sea all day; Laura, buried in her books and her studying.

And Citto himself had changed. Five weeks in an Italian prison were enough to change anyone. God help those, he thought, who spent half their lives inside. The newspaper had supplied good lawyers—but no publicity. The whole affair had been low key and muted, silent and invisible to the point of nightmare. It was little Laura who had kept him sane, visiting him once a week with her serious smile.

Citto had been saved the delays and inconsistencies

of Italian law by the vigilance of the young Torinese
magistrato and with the help of an attempted bomb
outrage at a Communist party office in Brescia. Forensic evidence, spotted by the magistrato in a law journal,
linked the unusual type of friction detonator used in
Brescia with the explosions at Citto's apartment and in
his car. All three incidents were subsequently attributed
to one of the militant right-wing groups, the vendetta
against Citto having been doubtless suggested to them
by persons unknown in Rome.

Citto had been released without charges. But he'd
nevertheless found his status at the newspaper subtly
changed, as though the period of imprisonment had
somehow sullied him. Perhaps his own attitudes had
changed. Maybe he had lost his fervor and the mildly
crusading zeal he had previously displayed. Certainly
he had lost all sense of purpose and direction. His
Tango November involvement had started as something
of a crusade. Somehow somewhere it had gone wrong
and Citto felt himself to be at fault. Preuss had told him
about the deceptive lighting layout round the factories
to one side of the airport. His theory had been passed
on to the investigators, but the weather conditions—the
wet roads of that September morning—had never been
repeated. In the four months since that storm it hadn't
rained once. Diabolical, thought Citto, if young Flavio
Consoli and Capo Tomacchio had been innocent of any
involvement in the crash. Poetic justice was no substitute for the truth, and Citto knew that the whole truth
had eluded them all. The real culprits had escaped.

He stood over the brazier turning the sausages,
watching Laura's face across the glow as she fanned the
charcoal. If she would come with him, he thought, he
would apply for another job somewhere on the mainland. Follow the rainbow north like Sharlie had tried
to do.

Mac joined them over the heat, and the women came

out from the house wrapped in shawls. They had thought they would eat indoors, but somehow no one moved and they stayed on the terrace facing the mountain, the moon high behind them over the village. The two lanterns returned across the river, Turi and his old retainer with their tools and their boots, the job completed. Old Turi washed under the pump and climbed the steps from the garden with two jugs of wine drawn off from a barrel in the cellar below the terrace.

They ate and drank, and Turi brought up more jugs of wine. They turned the charcoal out onto the stones and made a fire with old prunings from the lemon trees. And in the darkness where they couldn't see or be seen too clearly they talked of many different things: of grapes and lemons and harvests; of children; of Renzo and Giuseppina, married and living in Switzerland; of the $5,000 Sharlie had posthumously made on his pictures of Tango November. They talked in the end and inevitably of death and dying—Turi who had watched it happen too many times; Julia trying to cope with it as a calamitous violation of her own and her children's lives; Citto who remembered his father and mother and Sharlie and Preuss's sad lopsided smile; Turi's wife who long ago had lost her only child.

Mac did not join in. Death was his profession. Too late now to become like Turi and concern himself only with the living. Each time Mac looked up away from the fire he saw the outline of the mountain, and each time he saw it he waited for that glow on the crater to explode and die away. Once every forty seconds, he reckoned, like a slow mammoth heartbeat.

The next day over a hotel lunch the investigation disbanded, the evidence now left to the Italians for their ministerial and legal reports, to be published after two or three or four years, by which time memories and the risk of legal complications would have faded.

The Italians thanked their British and American collaborators, and Priscilla Raille, uninvited guest, toasted her husband's last investigation. The other men dutifully raised glasses to wish him luck in outer space: NASA's troubleshooter designate for the manned space labs of the future, solving technical jigsaw puzzles in solitary splendor fifty miles into the sky.

Here's to the 119, thought Raille as he raised his own glass. Let's hope the "albatross" gets lucky. Almost unnoticed the FAA had issued a service bulletin suggesting the repositioning of sensing elements in the number two fire-warning system. But a service bulletin was a long way short of a mandatory air-worthiness directive, and as for those battery and galley power switches, they remained in close proximity, red square, and black tadpole, inviting Murphy's Law and another "unlikely" disaster.

Raille's successor was smiling at him across the table. A board member of reasonable disposition who would probably ask no difficult questions. Apart from Burden he was the only man around the table not conscious of failure. And even Burden felt some regret, for he knew that Duckham would not escape criticism in the final analysis. Notwithstanding pages of mitigating circumstances and notwithstanding their efforts not to apportion blame, the crash would be classified in most minds as "pilot error."

That afternoon two taxis drove them all to the airport, and on the way both cars made a detour to a small cemetery high above a village.

The hillside was cool in the afternoon sun, the crowded jumble of mausoleums, headstones and wall tombs white as the almond blossom in the gardens below. Larry and Priscilla Raille, Ralph Burden and Mac Pherson were standing by the brass plaque that recorded the facts of the crash in English and Italian.

Julia Duckham, walking away down the gravel path toward her husband's grave, heard the American woman reading the words in her hard brittle voice.

"In memory of one hundred and eighty-seven passengers and crew in Golf Foxtrot Echo Tango November who died on our mountain."

The cemetery annex was well kept with flowers and shrubs—courtesy of the Tango November Disaster Fund. Dutch orchestra, Japanese pianist, Beethoven, Mozart, and Rachmaninoff: $1,000 for the cemetery; $2,000 for Trixie in New York; $15,000 for a private numbered bank account in Lugano—"administrative expenses" incurred by a local politician.

Julia laid her flowers on Mike's grave. There was only his name on the stone, no inlaid photograph like the Italians used. She would have preferred that. Something to keep his reality alive—his smile here in the sunlight.

The valley filled with sound, the slow whistling roar of giant turbofans, a black shadow floating over the hills. Two hundred tons of shining silver and 300 lives hanging in the air as a DC-10 settled on runway two nine Taormina–Peloritana. In the daylight; in the sunshine; without problems. The pilot could have done it standing on his head.

sleek and expensive cars. On any level of consciousness his mind was too distracted to notice the two radio cars, blue and red, interchanging with each other as they kept tabs on him.

Laura had telephoned him at the newspaper. Shirlie's funeral was on Saturday and the family had asked

Epilogue

"Tango November, you are clear to land."

Duckham felt the first shudder of turbulence, the outside edge of the storm that according to the weather radar was centered somewhere on the flank of the mountain to their left and beyond the airport. It was time to get the feel of the plane before landing.

"Disengaging auto pilot."

She tried to snatch forward as the auto pilot un-coupled and Duckham eased back on the wheel to catch it. The flat tiredness of the last few hours was lifting as adrenalin took over: sweat on the palms; heartbeat accelerating; his brain reviewing the unknown factors, the permutations of possible difficulties—doubtful ground visibility, a storm, and a mountain.

"Full flap."

Peter acknowledged with a grunt. Duckham glanced over at him. He was still brooding like a sulky kid, and not, it seemed, in the least perturbed by the landing approach. After all he had been here before and in the daylight. He could visualize it all.

"Full flap."

"Fifty. Fifty. Two greens."

"Check list complete up here," said George. "Let's hope they've got it together downstairs."

"Let's have quiet again." Duckham didn't want his crew distracted in any way. "Eyes up for contact, Peter. I'm staying right on the instruments. George, you better give me an altitude check over the middle marker."

"Roger." The flight engineer laughed. "Now we'll see what his runway visibility is really like."

The amber light and bleep signaled the middle marker beacon. George Raven took the third bleep as center. "We're fifty foot high I'd say."

"As near as dammit then."

Peter Nyren called out contact. "I have approach lights in sight. Half right. Twenty right."

Duckham looked up from his instruments for the first time and saw the comforting glow and pattern of a double line of orange lights twenty degrees or so to starboard. He peeled the plane over, watching and straining for the runway lights beyond, then was suddenly uneasy about those orange lines.

Both he and Peter saw it simultaneously, a factory emerging from the cloud, a factory yard, four simple orange street lamps reflecting deceptively into double lines on the wet asphalt.

"Shit!"

"Whoops," said Peter. "Sorry, skipper."

The real runway lights appeared, ten degrees left. But they couldn't get back anywhere near them. Bloody half-assed airport. It was even worse than the street-lighting layout at Basel.

"Overshoot!"

The three men reacted simultaneously. Duckham pulled back to rotate; George Raven applied power; Peter operated the flap controls.

Sorry, skipper, Peter had said. The first nonbroody remark since they'd met in the crew room, Duckham thought. It had taken a mistake to shake him out of it.

"Flaps two five."

"Positive climb. Gear up."

Peter acknowledged and raised the landing gear lever.

Duckham could feel the plane lifting sluggishly, beginning once more to thump in turbulence. His mind's eye was full of storm and mountain. "We're lifting like a whale. Give us the lot, George. Let's get back in the sky. Peter—tune in to Oscar Echo on both."

"Roger." They were aiming now for the outer marker on the opposite approach path, the ADF beacon Oscar Echo. Over the beacon they would turn north on a two-minute timed leg. Only then would they be definitely clear of high ground.

Peter was tidying up flaps. "Speed OK. Flaps to one four."

Duckham nodded. "Where's that beacon, Peter?"

"Beacon's tuned in. Identing Oscar Echo."

They hit the bad rough quite suddenly, with a thump that took Duckham right out of his seat and up against his straps.

"Judas!" That was George. His seat didn't hold him too well in turbulence, especially when he was swiveled frontward to monitor.

"Air speed and rate of climb all over."—Peter, watching the instruments and beginning to sound jumpy. They were bumping hard enough now to throw their loose gear to and fro on the floor. "Losing air speed and altitude."

"Fly attitude," Duckham told Peter. Take it easy and keep your eye on the one instrument, he meant. When it starts to get bad most of the instruments go berserk. Only the artificial horizon stays clean and gives you any idea of what the plane is actually doing.

A warning bell shrilled.

Not now, thought Duckham. Please God, not now.

Raven reached up to cancel the bell: "Engine fire number two." Even George's voice momentarily lost its professional cool.

"Another false alarm. It has to be." Peter looked across to Duckham.

"Probably." Duckham shrugged. "Carry out fire drill on number two."

"For Christ's sake!—It's a false alarm!"

Duckham ignored Peter and repeated the order. "Fire drill, George."

George Raven carried out item one of the fire drill, diverting power demand away from the fire-affected engine and generator: "Essential power to number three." Down to one generator, he was thinking. Just for a false fire warning. "Close number two thrust lever."

There was a pause, then Duckham terse and loud: "Peter!"

"Yes, sorry." Peter took it up in a shaky voice, both hands over to the central console as he buffeted in his seat. "Closing number two thrust lever."

George cut off fuel. "Shutting start lever."

Peter reached for the fire controls. "Pulling fire handle."

The number two engine was running down. Then warning lights flickered on the panel as the one remaining generator overloaded and switched itself out of circuit.

"We're on battery," called George. "Number three's tripped on overload."

"Shed some load and get us back on generator." Duckham remembered the engineer's earlier misgivings about the state of the battery.

Get rid of galley power and one of the HF sets, thought George, and he reached simultaneously for the two switches. But as he turned them the lights died.

"Fucking Christ Jesus!" Duckham turned with a shout to look back over his shoulder. Apart from a small emergency light in the ceiling the flight deck was in total blackout.

"The battery must have gone. The bloody battery—I can't see to do anything—" George Raven was staring at where his panel had been. He could see nothing; illumination, warning lights, indicators, everything had gone.

"Get some flashlights out!" Duckham faced front again. The quick turning of his head had made him dizzy and in the dark he could hardly see the instruments. The ones that were visible seemed to be inoperative. "Chrissakes, George, I've lost everything. Get a light on the artificial horizon. I can't see bugger all."

Duckham could no longer "feel" what the plane was doing. The dizziness was still with him, and he felt vaguely nauseated. The turbulence was thumping them now like a wild horse trying to throw a rider. Duckham had to keep the plane flying straight and climbing. It felt to him as though they were banking right. But that could be his head. "What are we doing Peter? I can't feel it. Are we turning right?"

"Feels straight to me."

"Are we climbing?"

"I think so."

"Get a flashlight on the altimeter and air speed."

George Raven was out of his seat on hands and knees, bracing himself against the turbulence, looking for the flashlights. He had a pair of them in his bag, but the bag had been turned inside out in the buffeting. He was trying to think what could have failed. He knew he hadn't made a mistake. He had never made an operating mistake in his whole career. It must be the battery. It had been charging high all the way out. Nickel cadmium. Those bloody things could catch fire under high

charge. And what about that warning on number two?
They hadn't completed the fire drill yet. The whole
back of the plane could be ablaze for all they knew.
Closed-circuit TV you needed with engines at the back,
at least so you could see what was going on.

Peter had pulled out one of the emergency battery
lamps and was using it as a hand-held light, pinpointing
what was left of the instruments. "Looks like we're
climbing."

Duckham was trying to fly the plane "seat of his
pants" and on the standby horizon midway between the
two pilots. He still had his pressure instruments, air
speed, vertical speed, and pressure altimeter, with the
old-fashioned liquid compass on the ceiling. But the
plane was hammering like a pneumatic drill in the
turbulence and he still felt giddy and sick. "George, get
me some more light on the instruments. Altitude and
air speed."

"They're up and down like yo-yos. I think we're
climbing through six five. And it looks like two-fifty
knots."

"What in fuck's happened to the electrical system?"

"Overload. Then the battery went. I'll try and get
back on generator."

"Keep your flashlights on what we're doing for the
moment."

George was back in his seat facing forward, one
hand out to keep a flashlight on the instruments and
controls.

"What are we steering, Peter?"

Peter shifted his flashlight on to the standby compass
in the ceiling. "Can't tell. It's spinning all over the
place."

"I'd say we've kept it more or less straight."

"I think so."

"We should be somewhere over Oscar Echo by now

if we had our ADFs. I think we'll keep straight on and make height. I've had enough here. If we can get power back and a radio working we'll try and get clearance for Malta."

"Roger."

"George. Try and get us some power back."

Duckham sounded calm and matter-of-fact, but he didn't fool himself. The storm was throwing them around like a Ping-Pong ball on a fountain. They couldn't really tell what attitudes they'd been flying during the last few minutes. He still felt the plane right wing low and was trying to stop himself from over-correcting. They were disoriented and lost, and given the chronic instability of ADF beacons in storm conditions even their original fix on Oscar Echo might have been wildly inaccurate. In which case they could be quite literally anywhere. They might break from cloud straight into the side of the mountain at any moment. Duckham had to force himself to keep his eyes down on the little instrumentation left to him. You could get hypnotized anticipating disaster through the windshield —like speeding down a highway in fog faster and faster, waiting for the taillights of a truck to come up and hit you.

George turned the flashlight back on his panel. He had to shed power and try to reactivate the number three generator. Cabin lights and heat, the weather radar, two booster pumps; he switched them off one after the other. He'd already disconnected galley power and one of the HF sets. He moved the flashlight to check them; HF set off; galley power on. But he'd turned it off. He checked the switch; the spring was all right. Then he saw the heavy red switch next to and below it. The battery was off. Even then he didn't realize what had happened. The battery switch has bust, he thought. No, it was OK. He flicked it on and lights and instruments came back to life. What the hell had happened to it?

"Good boy!" Duckham's eyes were over the instruments checking each reading.

Peter turned, grinning at George in relief.

Good boy? I'm fucked if I didn't hit the wrong bloody switch, George was thinking. Battery for galley, so help me. He tried the number three generator again and this time, with the load shed, it reconnected without trouble.

"Check on that fire," called Duckham.

"Number two fire lever—light's out. Fire extinguished."

"If there ever bloody well was one."

"Altitude check, Peter."

"Climbing through eight five."

"Two more lovely thousand and we're clear." George meant the height of the mountain at 10,800 or 10,900.

Peter remembered the sight of its smoking cone clear of the clouds just eight or nine minutes ago. It already felt like a hundred years. How the hell do we know where we are, he was thinking. Why is Duckham so damned unperturbed?

There was suddenly more light coming from outside, and the turbulence was easing. Duckham felt the plane lift lighter. An upcurrent, he thought. We're somewhere near that damn mountain. "Altitude?"

"Nine eight."

"Heading one nine five." Peter's voice, abrupt and censorious. "I don't think we know where the fuck we are."

You're late, thought Duckham. You should have picked up the heading as soon as the juice came back. That's your job. But he said nothing for the moment. The boy was nervous enough.

"Heading one nine five," Peter repeated.

Duckham acknowledged. "I know, I've seen it. No point in turning now. We need height. We'll keep climbing in a straight line."

They were flying more or less southwest instead of northwest, into the mountain instead of away from it depending on their original position and attitudes over the last two or three minutes. The drift would have been gradual: a storm-affected reading on Oscar Echo beacon that could have been as much as twenty to thirty degrees out; then flying blind when Duckham had imagined they were right wing low. He must have over-corrected. Something like a gentle but continuous ten degree turn. Four to five minutes—even on two engines and full climb they could have made twenty to twenty-five ground miles. We're bang over the mountain, he thought, and we need another 500 feet.

"Jesus Christ!"

The red flash and thump were simultaneous. Number two engine blown up, thought Duckham; or else we've hit the volcano. But they were still flying. Still climbing. Two fifty knots. All instruments OK. He looked up.

The cloud had broken, like flying out of the end of a wall. A blood-red sun was halfway out of the sea on the horizon, its glow filling the whole cockpit with lurid crimson light. The thump must have been an air pocket on the edge of the clouds.

They were over the lower northern peaks of the mountain with about 200 feet clearance if they kept climbing straight. The main ridge of crater was a mile or so to starboard and above them. They were going to make it. The sky ahead was clear forever.

"Hallelujah!" That was Peter beside him. He was smiling, almost laughing.

Duckham eased himself forward out of the seat cushion. He was soaking wet, as though he'd been standing under a shower, his arms and legs suddenly weak as muscle and mind relaxed. It was the most beautiful sunrise he had ever seen.

"Shepherd's warning," said George looking at the sky. It was my balls up, he was thinking. I'll have to tell them when we're down. I switched battery for galley. There'll be a fucking report to write. A fucking great black mark against my name. Better keep the flight recorders tripped out, he thought. That way no one'll be able to check up too closely.

Clearance for Malta, Duckham reckoned. That sun will get rid of the cloud by the time we get back. Bugger the schedules. Hercules will survive.

He watched the mountain floating below them, the crater still to starboard and spewing smoke. The ground in front of them fell away almost perpendicular. Another two seconds and they'd be clear.

That bloody smoke, Duckham thought suddenly. It disappears, down over the edge. Leeward side. We're flying with the wind and we haven't got height. What if the gale that was helping lift them over the mountain pulled down on the other side with equal force?

Anxiety started pumping through his arteries again, tired mind and tired body calling "enough." He had anticipated it by a second or two, the plane by rather less. It started to shudder. Duckham's brain seemed to be moving in slow motion as though working its way through paragraphs in a textbook. Clear-air turbulence around a volcano that could snap off wings and engines —the 707 over Mount Fuji, he thought. Fly attitude, he told himself.

They hit the downdraught beyond the edge of the ridge like falling into a hole in the ground. The initial drop was about 500 feet straight down. George Raven, unstrapped, was thrown up on the ceiling. Then the plane bounced steady and level at 9,500 feet, ninety tons deadweight shuddering through the frame and the wings. There was a deep wide valley below them, and ridges coming up on the far side.

Ride it, you bastard, thought Duckham. His eye was now on the altimeter, his whole body waiting for the airflow to lift them again. The highest ridge in front of us is at six five or six six, he thought. We've still got room to fly.

The altimeter was holding at nine five—but holding like an ironic smile. Duckham could feel the pull, gentle, inexorable. Then the digits started spinning—quite slowly, like the indicator in an old-fashioned elevator: nine four, nine three, nine two, one, nine, eight, seven, six, five . . . they seemed to be flying straight and normal. Only the altimeter and the vertical speed indicator told them they were sinking, slow and gentle and terrifying, like falling in a nightmare. All they could do was wait for the bottom of the downdraught. It would lift them before the floor of the valley, but would it lift before they fell below the level of the ridges beyond?

"You all right, George?"

George Raven was on the floor, dazed and trying to pull himself back onto his seat. Peter was transfixed, eyes staring through the windshield, watching the lower slopes of the mountain with their cappings of cloud floating up toward them.

Eight two, eight one, eight, seven nine . . .

The valley lay tangential to the mountain, running left and northward. We could try to turn with it, thought Duckham, but there was barely room and if they banked hard they would lose too much air speed. They were condemned to that ridge in front of them, two miles away and closing fast as the elevator went on down and down.

"Christ! Do something!" Peter blowing his cool in a mutter.

Duckham knew what he was thinking. Nose down,

turn, and fly out of it down the valley. But if the spiral kept on down they would never pull out of a dive, not before they hit that green valley floor 2,000 feet below. It has to lift, thought Duckham. The air has to lift over that ridge and pull us with it. Law of nature. Law of life and death.

The downdraught stopped at five thousand nine, the top of that ridge perhaps 300 feet above them—pine trees and lava in a jumble of skyline just above the cloud. They were lifting again. Two sixty knots at an angle of climb. Six thousand, six thousand one, six thousand two. Tango November seemed to move like a tired heron flapping across the sky.

Duckham could see where they were going to hit. A protrusion of rock above the trees as small as a small truck.

Right rudder.

"We're going to hit," Peter yelled.

It was the sort of easy-shaped lump of rock a kid would scramble up on a Sunday walk and it took the underside of the left wing with a thump and an explosion, turning the whole plane through thirty degrees like a car broadsiding in a corner.

"You've killed us!" Peter yelling again.

Duckham pushed the wheel right forward. The ground beyond the ridge fell away steeply—treetops and a gentle slope twenty miles down to the sea. Clear sky forever.

They were left wing low but still flying. Duckham used right rudder and ailerons. Tango November was yawing, hanging in the air, an acrobat swaying off-balance on the tightrope.

Duckham looked back through his side window as he dragged on the wheel. Ten feet of the left wing had been sheared off like a torn arm, fuel and hydraulics spewing from the arteries. The ailerons had gone and there was no lift from that left side. They were slipping left wing down in a long arc that was turning them back into the high ground and the mountain.

Air speed dropping. Nose down for speed and some semblance of control. Full right rudder to counteract the drag on the left. Ease back on the wheel as they made air speed.

There was nowhere to go. Clear sky and sea were passing to starboard and out of sight.

"I can't get her out of the turn. We're going down." Duckham heard his voice ridiculously calm and measured.

In and out of wisps of cloud now, still seeming to float above the world a thousand feet clear of reality.

"Landing gear down. We want somewhere to put down. Somewhere flat."

Going through the motions, thought Duckham. There's no field on this mountain. They were heading back at it now, the ground rising to meet them.

"Landing gear checks. Peter."

Peter's voice was barely audible: "Three greens."

Oh, Christ Jesus, it can't be happening to us. This is when life is meant to come flooding back through the mind. All those years in a split second. Tell me something, Duckham was thinking. Tell me what it was all about. But he couldn't get his mind to move. Born Rangoon, 1922.

Peter was stuck like a kid on a roller coaster, mouth open, staring at the wind. George was doing something with his seat. God help the passengers who can see it all happening. Is there time to tell them? He didn't even have one hand free. Come on, cloud, close us in and make it decently unexpected.

Right rudder and trim. Nose up to flatten out. Two hundred feet. One fifty. One. Fifty. They were floating no more. The world was hurling itself past them in a violence of trees and rocks.

Peter was making some noise like a moan, his hands

and feet stuck out in front of him like a baby in a high
chair. George was frantically screwing down the safety
bar on his swivel chair.

Keep your eyes down, Duckham told himself, or
you'll freeze. He had picked a few hundred yards of
somewhere that looked flat. There were lives to be
saved if he could take off some of their speed. Spoilers,
reverse thrust, and turn the fire levers at the last possible moment. Three jobs to do. Think about them.
One, two, and reach forward for the fire levers.

Peter's moan had turned into something else. George
had lost his safety bar. His hands were scrabbling for it.

Duckham felt the landing gear hit the trees. He had
to keep flying it or the left wing would dip and they'd
cartwheel. His right foot was hard down on the rudder.
Three jobs; five moves. Pull for spoilers; select reverse
thrust; wait for the reverse operating light; then pull
back throttles and reach forward for the fire levers.

Mike Duckham reached with both hands, his mind
clear: only one and three; number two was already shut
down.

George was screaming, his chair swinging loose.
They were on the ground, the fuselage tearing and
jumping under them. Slow down. Please, dear Lord,
slow this bugger down.

Duckham pulled and turned the fire levers. The three
jobs were done.

The light darkened outside. He looked up and saw
death on a black lava slope one hundredth of a second
away.

WHAT IF . . .

Fires, floods, air disasters, political intrigue. Event
that could happen . . . and do in these exciting best
sellers. Guaranteed to keep you on the edge of your
seat.

☐ 12245	AIRPORT *Arthur Hailey*	$2.2
☐ 10940	BLACK SUNDAY *Thomas Harris*	$2.2
☐ 11708	JAWS 2 *Hank Searls*	$2.2
☐ 12600	JAWS *Peter Benchley*	$2.5
☐ 12513	RAISE THE TITANIC! *Clive Cussler*	$2.5
☐ 11766	DELUGE *Richard Doyle*	$2.2
☐ 11767	IMPERIAL 109 *Richard Doyle*	$2.5
☐ 12679	RUNWAY ZERO-EIGHT *Arthur Hailey*	$2.2
☐ 10048	SEVEN DAYS IN MAY *Knebel & Bailey*	$1.9
☐ 11631	22 FIRES *Agel & Boe*	$1.9
☐ 12520	ICEBERG *Clive Cussler*	$2.2
☐ 12151	ICE! *Arnold Federbush*	$2.2

Buy them at your local bookstore or use this handy coupon for ordering

---

Bantam Books, Inc., Dept. DI, 414 East Golf Road, Des Plaines, Ill. 60016

Please send me the books I have checked above. I am enclosing $_____
(please add 75¢ to cover postage and handling). Send check or money order
—no cash or C.O.D.'s please.

Mr/Mrs/Miss_____

Address_____

City_____State/Zip_____

DI—4/79

Please allow four weeks for delivery. This offer expires 10/79.